K H Blake
November 1922

PSYCHOANALYSIS
and
CONTEMPORARY SCIENCE

PSYCHOANALYSIS
and
CONTEMPORARY SCIENCE

An Annual of Integrative
and Interdisciplinary Studies
VOLUME I, 1972

editors
ROBERT R. HOLT
and
EMANUEL PETERFREUND

The Macmillan Company
New York
Collier-Macmillan Limited
London

Library of Congress Catalog Card Number: 72–84741

The Macmillan Company
866 Third Avenue, New York, New York 10022

Collier-Macmillan Canada Limited, Toronto, Ontario

printing number
1 2 3 4 5 6 7 8 9 10

In Memory of George S. Klein

Acknowledgments

The editors wish to thank the following publishers for permission to use certain materials included in this volume.

"The Nature of Individual Psychological Change and Its Relation to Cultural Change," by Lawrence S. Kubie, M.D., was revised and expanded from "The Nature of Psychological Change and Its Relation to Cultural Change," which appeared in *Changing Perspectives on Man,* edited by Ben Rothblatt and published by the University of Chicago Press in 1968.

"On Psychohistory," by Robert Jay Lifton, M.D., is a longer version of an essay that appeared in both *The Partisan Review* (Vol. 35, No. 1, 1970, pp. 11–32) and *The State of American History,* edited by Herbert Bass and published by Quadrangle Books in 1970. Reprinted by permission of the author through the International Famous Agency. Copyright © 1970 by Robert Jay Lifton.

Figures 1A and 1B in the selection titled "On Hearing, Oral Language, and Psychic Structure," by David A. Freedman, M.D., are reprinted by permission from "Some Determinants of Individual Differences," from *Transactions* of the New York Academy of Sciences, Vol. 27, No. 7, Fig. 2, p. 805, S. K. Escalona. Copyright 1965 by The New York Academy of Sciences. Figures 1C and 2 in the same selection are reprinted by permission from David A. Freedman, M.D., "Congenital and Perinatal Sensory Deprivation: Some Studies in Early Development," *The American Journal of Psychiatry,* Vol. 127, No. 11, 1971, pp. 1539–1545. Copyright © 1971, by The American Psychiatric Association.

The quotations from John Benjamin in "The Stimulus Barrier in Early Infancy," by Katherine Tennes *et al.,* are reprinted by permission from John Benjamin, "Developmental Biology and Psychoanalysis," in Norman S. Greenfield and William C. Lewis, editors, *Psychoanalysis and Current Biological Thought* (Madison: The University of Wisconsin Press), Chap. 4, pp. 60–68. Copyright © 1965 by the Regents of the University of Wisconsin.

Figure 9 in the selection titled "Cognitive Response to Stress: Experimental Studies of a 'Compulsion to Repeat Trauma,'" by Mardi J. Horowitz and Stephanie Scharf Becker, is reprinted by permission from the same authors' "Cognitive Response to Stressful Stimuli," *Archives of General Psychiatry,* Vol. 25, 1971, pp. 419–28, Fig. 4. Copyright 1971 by the American Medical Association.

Regarding the poetry excerpts in "On Metaphor and Related Phenomena," by Benjamin Rubinstein: "The Manifestation" (p. 79), by Theodore Roethke, is reprinted from *The Collected Poems of Theodore Roethke* by permission of Doubleday & Company, Inc. and Faber & Faber Ltd. Copyright © 1959 by Beatrice Roethke, Administratrix of the estate of Theodore Roethke; "The Monkey Puzzle" (p. 79), by Marianne Moore, is reprinted from *Collected Poems* by Marianne Moore by permission of The Macmillan Company and Faber and Faber

Ltd. Copyright 1951 by The Macmillan Company; "a salesman is an it" (p. 79) and "anyone lived in a pretty how town" (p. 84), by e. e. cummings, are reprinted from *Poems 1923–1954* by e. e. cummings by permission of Harcourt Brace Jovanovich, Inc. and MacGibbon & Kee, Ltd; "The Love Song of J. Alfred Prufrock" (p. 80) and "Morning at the Window" (p. 83), by T. S. Eliot, are reprinted from *Collected Poems 1909–1962* by T. S. Eliot by permission of Harcourt Brace Jovanovich, Inc., and Faber & Faber Ltd; four words from p. 17 of *Exile* (p. 84), by St.-John Perse, translated by Denis Devlin, are reprinted by permission of Princeton University Press (Bollingen Series XV, copyright 1949 by Bollingen Foundation).

Contents

5 PSYCHOHISTORICAL AND PSYCHOBIOGRAPHICAL

List of Contributors

Stephanie Scharf Becker, M.A., Department of Psychiatric Research (Psychology), Mount Zion Hospital and Medical Center, San Francisco, Cal.

Hartvig Dahl, M.D., Senior Research Scientist, Research Center for Mental Health, New York University, New York, N.Y.

Robert Emde, M.D., Associate Professor of Psychiatry, University of Colorado Medical Center, Denver, Colo.

David A. Freedman, M.D., Professor of Psychiatry, Baylor Medical College, Houston, Texas; Training and Supervising Analyst, New Orleans Psychoanalytic Institute, New Orleans, La.

Norbert Freedman, Ph.D., Professor, Department of Psychiatry (Psychology), Downstate Medical Center, State University of New York, Brooklyn, N.Y.

Robert R. Holt, Ph.D., Professor of Psychology, New York University, New York, N.Y.

Mardi J. Horowitz, M.D., Assistant Director, Department of Psychiatry, Mount Zion Hospital and Medical Center, San Francisco, Cal.; Assistant Clinical Professor of Psychiatry, University of California Medical School, San Francisco, Cal.

Anthony Kisley, M.D., Assistant Clinical Professor of Psychiatry, University of Colorado Medical Center, Denver, Colo.

*George S. Klein, Ph.D., Professor of Psychology; Director, Research Center for Mental Health, New York University, New York, N.Y.

Lawrence S. Kubie, M.D., Consultant on Research and Training, The Sheppard and Enoch Pratt Hospital, Towson, Maryland; Clinical Professor of Psychiatry, University of Maryland School of Medicine, Baltimore, Md.

Robert Jay Lifton, M.D., Foundations' Fund Research Professor of Psychiatry, Yale University School of Medicine, New Haven, Conn.

Marta Lugo, *Licenciada en Quimica,* Research Assistant, Research Center for Mental Health, New York University, New York, N.Y.

David Metcalf, M.D., Associate Professor (Encephalography), University of Colorado Medical School, Denver, Colo.

Bernard C. Meyer, M.D., Clinical Professor of Psychiatry, Mount Sinai School of Medicine, New York, N.Y.

Benjamin B. Rubinstein, M.D., Psychoanalyst, New York, N.Y.

Arthur H. Schmale, M.D., Associate Professor of Psychiatry and Medicine, University of Rochester School of Medicine and Dentistry, Rochester, N.Y.

Lloyd H. Silverman, Ph.D., Research Psychologist, Manhattan Veterans Administration Hospital; Adjunct Associate Professor, Graduate Department of Psychology, New York University, N.Y.

Donald P. Spence, Ph.D., Professor of Psychology, New York University, New York, N.Y.

Irving Steingart, Ph.D., Assistant Professor, Department of Psychiatry (Psychology), Downstate Medical Center, State University of New York, Brooklyn, N.Y.

Katherine Tennes, M.A., Developmental Psychology, University of Colorado Medical School, Denver, Colo.

Frederic G. Worden, M.D., Professor of Psychiatry; Executive Director, Neurosciences Research Program, Massachusetts Institute of Technology, Cambridge, Mass.

* Deceased.

Introduction

The aims of this new series of publications grew out of the thinking of the editors concerning the conditions necessary for the further growth of psychoanalysis as a science. The editors believe that psychoanalysis needs, first, an atmosphere that encourages innovation. *Psychoanalysis and Contemporary Science* will therefore be open to any original clinical or theoretical contribution to psychoanalysis. Second, psychoanalysis needs rigorous standards of historical scholarship, for new advances presuppose a thorough knowledge of the development and present status of psychoanalytic method and theory. This Annual will therefore be open to scholarly surveys and historical reviews of important psychoanalytic concepts. Third, psychoanalysis needs the clarity about the nature and meaning of scientific theory and, more generally, about underlying premises and their implications that is given by philosophical analysis. Papers on philosophy of science will be particularly welcome, but other branches of philosophy can help deepen and broaden our understanding as well. Fourth, psychoanalysis needs continual contact with its original source—the intensive naturalistic observation that is possible only in the psychoanalytic treatment situation. The Annual therefore seeks to include clinical contributions that contain new observations and clearly distinguish these observations from theoretical elaborations. Fifth, psychoanalysis needs a thorough understanding of the nature of the psychoanalytic process itself; it needs basic clarity about the nature of clinical inference and the nature of psychoanalytic evidence. Papers that deal with these issues will be most welcome. Sixth, psychoanalysis needs stimulating ideas from other sciences, such as psychology, ethology, genetics, neurophysiology, psychiatry, psychopharmacology, philosophy, linguistics, anthropology, history, sociology, and the information and systems sciences. The editors particularly invite critical surveys reviewing the status of theory or empirical knowledge in any relevant discipline, and pointing out its significance for psychoanalysis; or attempts to apply models from other sciences to the reshaping of psychoanalytic theory; or applications of methods developed in other fields to psychoanalytic data. In general, the editors are eager to stimulate the development of new investigative methods, and will be particularly happy to present examples of innovations in research method applied to psychoanalytic problems or data. The Annual will be hospitable to the full range of investigative methods used in the biological and behavioral sciences, including (for example) phenomenological and behavioral observation, cross-cultural comparisons, computer simulation, formal experiments, and statistical studies.

Manuscripts (three copies) and all editorial correspondence should be sent to The Board of Editors, Psychoanalysis and Contemporary Science, Research Center for Mental Health, 4 Washington Place, New York, N.Y. 10003.

1

GENERAL THEORETICAL

FREUD'S MECHANISTIC AND HUMANISTIC IMAGES OF MAN

Robert R. Holt, Ph.D.[1]

The modern reader of Freud may expect a mixture of delights and difficulties. Despite the lapse of generations, Freud remains enjoyably and absorbingly readable even in translation, plainly a master writer of prose. Yet anyone who is not thoroughly versed in his works repeatedly encounters baffling difficulties in grasping his meaning in any but a general sense.

To some degree, the problems are those to be expected in reading works that are anywhere from 30 to 80 years old: some terminology is bound to be outdated; some references to scientific or literary works that Freud could assume his contemporary readers were familiar with convey nothing any longer (or little to an American reader who does not know his continental classics). To a large extent but not completely, the devoted editorship of Strachey anticipates these problems and his footnotes provide helpful explanations. Other problems arise from Freud's habit of occasionally assuming that the reader knew his previous works, even his unpublished ones. Thus, a great deal that was baffling about the seventh chapter of the *Interpretation of Dreams* (Freud, 1900)—e.g., his reference to ψ-systems—became intelligible only after the belated publication of the Project (Freud, 1895). A corollary of this point is the widely conceded necessity to read Freud sequentially; his thought cannot be understood if his developing ideas are taken out of context. Even so, much remains obscure if one has no conception of the contemporary scientific status of the issues he was discussing. Fortunately, contemporary historical scholarship is supplying a good deal of this needed background (e.g., Amacher, 1965; Andersson, 1962; Bernfeld, 1944; Ellenberger, 1970; Jackson, 1969; Spehlmann, 1953; see also Holt, 1965a, 1968).

The modern reader may have special difficulty in getting a sense that he knows what Freud was trying to say in a number of the speculative, far-ranging works of his later years (e.g., Freud, 1913, 1920, 1921, 1927, 1930, 1939). As I

[1] Preparation of this paper was supported by a United States Public Health Service Research Career Award, No. K6-MH-12,455, from the National Institute of Mental Health.

3

have argued elsewhere (Holt, 1963), the loose and literary rather than scientific texture of these works seems to grow out of *Naturphilosophie,* emerging as a kind of return of the suppressed.

Certain methodological errors became habitual with Freud, and they often get in the way of our effort to grasp a precise meaning. He often reified concepts, even personified them, for he was fond of slipping into metaphorical, almost poetic usage. He did not always make clear distinctions between what he observed and what he assumed; in fact, conceptual innovations were often treated like empirical discoveries, and facts were confusingly mingled with theory.

These last considerations verge on the realm of what might be called Freud's cognitive style, his personal way of thinking and writing, which had a number of more or less unique and unexpected features that may perturb or mislead the modern American reader. I have surveyed and documented a number of these stylistic features elsewhere (Holt, 1965b); here, let me briefly recapitulate some of the salient points of that analysis.

First, there is a great deal of inconsistency in Freud (partly apparent, partly real). Of course, a good deal of it is not stylistic but an inevitable consequence of his long scientific life and his willingness to change his mind when new clinical observations presented themselves; it would not be fair to look for consistency across many years of his intellectual growth. But there was a second source of inconsistency, in Freud's cognitive style. He once wrote a friend, "I so rarely feel the need for synthesis. . . . I am evidently an analyst and believe that synthesis offers no obstacles once analysis has been achieved" (1960, p. 310). He did in fact have great gifts in synthesizing vast amounts of data, but he disliked that kind of work; so it was simply not his way to re-read his own work critically and try to pull it all together. When he revised one of his books, he added new material but rarely omitted the old, even if it clashed directly with the new formulations.

Here is another bit of self-description: "I work, step by step, without the inner need for completion, continually under the pressure of the problems immediately on hand . . ." (1960, p. 319). This strategy of working might be called *piecemeal empiricism.* To follow one's nose empirically, adding to the theory whatever bits and pieces accrued along the way, was the procedure Freud preferred, with his faith that ultimately the truth would prevail. Consistent with this viewpoint, he considered it a mistake to begin by defining concepts clearly and unambiguously; such a procedure he thought typical of barren, speculative, philosophical systems, as opposed to science, which struggled along with approximations that became clarified by the attempt to use them. "It is true," he would admit, "that notions such as that of an ego-libido, an energy of the ego-instincts, and so on, are neither particularly easy to grasp, nor sufficiently rich in content." Nevertheless, psychoanalysis would "gladly content itself with nebulous, scarcely imaginable basic concepts, which it hopes to apprehend more clearly in the course of its development, or which it is even prepared to replace by others" (1914, p. 77).

In spite of this flexibility, Freud had the habit of stating things "as it were, dogmatically—in the most concise form and in the most positive terms" (1940, p. 9), which makes it easy to misread him as a rigid systematist. He was so eager to discover basic laws that he often stated his observations with sweeping generality. He was also fond of extending concepts to the limit of their possible applicability, as if stretching the realm of phenomena spanned by a concept was a way to make it more abstract and useful. These propensities exposed him constantly to the dangers of oversimplification, which he tried to overcome by following one flat statement with another that qualified it by partial contradiction. Therefore, he was well aware that one statement undid another, and used such sequences in the effort to cause a richly complicated conception to grow in the reader's mind, as he introduced considerations one at a time.

Thus, if you catch on to these peculiarities of Freud's cognitive style and learn to read him properly, you will not be nonplussed by much that seems contradictory. I have tried to bring together what I have learned about his cognitive style in the form of the following 10 rules for reading Freud:

1. Beware of lifting statements out of context. This practice is particularly tempting to research-minded clinical psychologists, who are generally more eager to get right to the testing of propositions than to undertake the slow study of a large corpus of theory. There is no substitute for reading enough of Freud to get his full meaning, which is almost never fully expressed in a single paragraph, no matter how specific the point.

2. Don't take Freud's extreme formulations literally. Treat them as his way of calling your attention to a point. When he says "never," "invariable," "conclusively" and the like, read on for the qualifying and softening statements.

3. Look out for inconsistencies; don't either trip over them or seize on them with malicious glee, but take them as incomplete dialectic formulations, awaiting the synthesis that Freud's cognitive style made him consistently draw back from.

4. Be on the watch for figurative language, personification in particular. Remember that it is there primarily for color, even though it did at times lead Freud himself astray, and that it is fairest to him to rely primarily on those of his statements of issues that are least poetic and dramatic.

5. Don't expect rigorous definitions; look rather for the meanings of his terms in the ways they are used over a period of time. And don't be dismayed if you find a word being used now in its ordinary, literary meaning, now in a special technical sense which changes with the developmental status of the theory.

6. Be benignly skeptical about Freud's assertions of proof, his statements that something has been established beyond doubt. Remember that he had different standards of proof from those we have today, that he rejected experiment partly from a too-narrow conception of it and partly because he had found it stylistically incompatible with his outlook.

7. Freud was overfond of dichotomies, even when his data were better con-

ceptualized as continuous variables; in general, don't assume that the
theory is invalidated by being stated much of the time in this form.
8. Be wary of Freud's persuasiveness. Keep in mind that he was a powerful
rhetorician in areas where his scientific footing was uncertain. Though he
was often right, it was not always for the reasons he gave, which are almost
never truly sufficient to prove it, and not always to the extent that he hoped.
   Finally, be particularly cautious not to gravitate toward either of two
extreme and equally untenable positions: that is,
9. Don't take Freud's every sentence as a profound truth, which may present
difficulties but only because of our own inadequacies. Don't assume that
our difficulty is that of a pedestrian plodder trying to keep up with the
soaring mind of a genius who did not always bother to explicate steps that
were obvious to him, but which we must supply by laborious exegetical
scholarship. This is the temptation of the scholars working from within the
psychoanalytic institutes, those earnest Freudians who, to Freud's annoyance, had begun to emerge already during his lifetime. For most of us in
the universities, the corresponding temptation is the more dangerous one:
10. Don't let yourself get so offended by Freud's lapses from methodological
purity that you dismiss him altogether. Almost any psychologist can learn
an enormous lot from Freud, if he will listen to him carefully and sympa-
thetically, and not take his pronouncements too seriously!

   Considerations of style aside, there remains a pervasive, unresolved conflict within all of Freud's writings between two antithetical images of man, which
is responsible for a good many of the contradictions that his cognitive makeup
allowed him to tolerate. Quite a number of writers have noticed this duality and
have formulated it in various ways. Rapaport (1959) distinguished the general
theory from the special or clinical theory of psychoanalysis; Klein (in press) cuts
the cake a little differently, speaking of metapsychology and the clinical theory;
Yankelovich and Barrett (1970) talk about the two worlds or two truths of science, and of intuitive existentialism in Freud's thought. We all agree that the
main thrust of Freud's theoretical effort was to construct what he himself called
a metapsychology, modeled on a simplified, mid-nineteenth-century grasp of
physics and chemistry; partly embodied in this and partly lying behind it is what
I will call his *mechanistic image* of man. The opposing view, so much less prominent that many students are not aware that Freud held it, I like to call a *humanistic image* of man. It may be seen in his clinical works and in the broad, speculative, quasi-philosophical writings of Freud's later years, but it is clearest in
Freud's own life and interactions with others, best verbalized for us perhaps in
his letters. Unlike the mechanistic image, the humanistic conception of man was
never differentiated and stated explicitly enough to be called a model; yet it
comprises a fairly rich and cohesive body of assumptions about the nature of
human beings, which functioned in Freud's mind as a corrective antagonist of
his mechanistic leanings.
   There is little evidence after 1900 that Freud was conscious of harboring

incompatible images of man, neither of which he could give up. Nevertheless, many otherwise puzzling aspects of psychoanalysis become intelligible if we assume that both images were there, and not just as static assemblages of information; we must assume further, I believe, that they functioned in many ways like conflicting motive systems. Indeed, one can even formulate some plausible guesses about personal motives that were probably bound up with them, though I shall not indulge in any such psychologizing now.

Let me emphasize again that what I am going to present is not an epitome of various theories specifically proposed by Freud. Rather, the two images are inferred complexes of ideas, extracted from Freud's life and writings and reconstructed in much the same way as he taught us to use in understanding neurotic people: by studying dreams, symptoms, and "associations," we infer unconscious fantasies, complexes, or early memories that never become fully conscious, but which enable us to make sense out of the patient's productions, which seem on the surface so bewilderingly diverse. Such an endeavor is fraught with a certain amount of risk. Even the mechanistic image was made fully explicit as a theoretical model only in the Project, the unpublished attempt at a neuropsychology that Freud sent to Fliess in 1895, tinkered with for a few months afterward, and finally abandoned. Thereafter, this model seems to have been largely forgotten, suppressed, or at least allowed to remain preconscious, along with its dialectical antithesis, the humanistic image.

FREUD'S HUMANISTIC IMAGE OF MAN

Neither of Freud's images was especially original with him; each was his personal synthesis of a body of ideas with a long cultural history, expressed and transmitted to him in considerable part through books we know he read. Long before and long after Freud decided to become a scientist, he was an avid reader of the belletristic classics that are often considered the core of Western man's humanistic heritage. He had an excellent liberal and classical education, which gave him a thorough grounding in the great works of Greek, Latin, German, and English authors, as well as the Bible, Cervantes, Molière, and other major writers in other languages, which he read in translation. He was a man of deep culture, with a lifelong passion for reading poetry, novels, essays, and the like, and for learning about classical antiquity in particular but the arts generally, through travel, collecting, and personal communication with artists, writers, and close friends who had similar tastes and education.[2]

Very few of the many nonphysicians who were drawn to psychoanalysis and who became part of Freud's circle were trained in the "harder" or natural sciences. Mainly, they came from the arts and humanities: for every Waelder (a physicist) there were at least a couple like Sachs and Kris (students primarily

---

[2] Ellenberger (1970, p. 460) tells us that Freud showed the playwright Lenormand "the works of Shakespeare and of the Greek tragedians on his [office] shelves and said: 'Here are my masters.' He maintained that the essential themes of his theories were based on the intuition of the poets."

of literature and art). Surely this tells us something not only about influences on Freud but also about the kind of man he was, and the conception of man by which he lived and which he conveyed in subtle ways to his co-workers.

In his Autobiographical Study (1925) Freud described himself at about the time he was finishing his secondary education:

> *Neither at that time, nor indeed in my later life, did I feel any particular predilection for the career of a doctor. I was moved, rather, by a sort of curiosity, which was, however, directed more towards human concerns than towards natural objects; nor had I grasped the importance of observation as one of the best means of gratifying it. My deep engrossment in the bible story (almost as soon as I had learnt the art of reading) had, as I recognized much later, an enduring effect upon the direction of my interest. Under the powerful influence of a school friendship with a boy rather my senior who grew up to be a well-known politician, I developed a wish to study law like him and to engage in social activities. At the same time, the theories of Darwin, which were then of topical interest, strongly attracted me, for they held out hope of an extraordinary advance in our understanding of the world; and it was hearing Goethe's beautiful essay on nature read aloud at a popular lecture by Professor Carl Brühl just before I left school that decided me to become a medical student (p. 8).*

This passage makes it clear, I believe, how strongly humanistic Freud's interests were during the early, formative years of his education.

In various ways, then, Freud came under the influence of the prevailing image of man conveyed by the important sector of Western culture we call the humanities. Let me now outline some of the major propositions that compose this image of man, which can be discerned in Freud.

1. Man is both an animal and something more, a creature with aspirations to divinity. Thus, he has a *dual nature*—carnal passions, vegetative functions, greed and lust for power, destructiveness, selfish concern with maximizing pleasure and minimizing pain; but also a capacity to develop art, literature, religion, science, and philosophy—the abstract realms of theoretical and esthetic values—and to be unselfish, altruistic, and nurturant. It is a complex view of man from the outset, as a creature who cares deeply about higher as well as lower matters.

2. Each human being is *unique, yet all men are akin,* one species, each being as human as any other. As the classicist Freud preferred to put it, *Nihil humanum mihi alienum est* ("nothing human is alien to me"). This assumption carries a strong value commitment as well, to the proposition that each person is worthy to be respected and to be helped, if in trouble, to live up to the extent of his capacities, however limited these may be. Freud was one of the main contributors to an important extension of this assumption, through his discovery that there was indeed method in madness (as Shakespeare knew intuitively), that the insane or mentally ill could be understood

and in fact were actuated by the same basic desires as other men. Thus, in the tradition of such men as Pinel, he did a great deal to reassert the humanity of the mentally and emotionally abnormal and their continuity with the normal.

3. Man is a creature of longings, a striver after goals and values—fantasies and images of gratification and of danger. That is, he is capable of imagining possible future states of pleasure, sensual joy or spiritual fulfillment, and of pain, humiliation, guilt, destruction, etc.; and his behavior is guided and impelled by wishes to obtain the positive goals and to avoid or nullify the negative ones, principally anxiety.

4. Man is a producer and processor of subjective meanings, by which he defines himself; and one of his strongest needs is to make his life meaningful. It is implicit in the humanistic image that meanings are primary, irreducible, causally efficacious, and of complete dignity as a subject of systematic interest. Pathology, accordingly, is conceived of in terms of maladaptive complexes or configurations of ideas, wishes, concepts, percepts, etc.

5. There is much more to man than he would usually want us to think: more than is present in his consciousness, more than is presented to the social world in public, and this secret side is extraordinarily important. The meanings that concern a person most, including fantasies and wishes, are constantly being processed without his awareness, and it is difficult for him to become aware of many of them. To understand a person truly, it is necessary therefore to know his subjective, inner life—his dreams, fantasies, longings, preoccupations, anxieties, and the special coloring with which he sees the outer world. By comparison, his easily observed, overt behavior is much less interesting and less important.

6. Man's nature makes inner conflict inevitable, because of his dualities—higher and lower natures, conscious and unconscious; moreover, many of his wishes are mutually incompatible or bring him into conflict with demands and pressures from other people.

7. Of these wishes perhaps the most important ones make up the complex instinct of love, of which sexual lust is a major (and itself complicated) part. Man's urge for sexual pleasure is almost always strong, persistent, and polymorphous, even when it seems thoroughly inhibited or blocked, and it may be detached from love. At the same time, Freud was always sensitive to the many different forms of anger, hate, and destructiveness, long before he formulated the dual instinct theory.

8. Man is an intensely social creature, whose life is distorted and abnormal if it is not enmeshed in a web of relationships to other people—some of these relationships formal and institutionalized, others informal but conscious and deliberate, and many of them having important unconscious components. Most human motive systems are interpersonal in character, too: we love and hate other people. Thus, the important reality for man is social and cultural. These Sullivanian-sounding propositions are clearly implicit in Freud's case histories.

9. A central feature of this image of man is that he is not static but is always changing: developing and declining, evolving and devolving. His most important unconscious motives derive from experiences in childhood: the child is father to the man. Man is part of an evolutionary universe, and thus in principle almost infinitely perfectible, although in practice he is always subject to setbacks, fixations, and regressions.

10. Man is both the active master of his own fate and the plaything of his passions: he is capable of choosing among alternatives, of resisting temptations and of governing his own urges, even though at times he is a passive pawn of external pressures and inner impulses. It therefore makes sense to try to deal with him in a rational way, to hope to influence his behavior by discussing things and even urging him to exert his will. Thus, man has both an id and an autonomous ego.

Being extracted from a body of work in which it has no systematic place, this humanistic image, as presented, is somewhat vague and poorly organized. Nevertheless, I see no intrinsic reason why it could not be explicated and developed in a more systematic way.

THE MECHANISTIC IMAGE OF MAN

The humanistically educated and philosophically inclined young Freud, fired by a romantic and vitalistic conception of the biology he wanted to study, went to the University of Vienna medical school, where he found himself surrounded by men of great prestige and intellectual substance, who taught exciting scientific doctrines of a very different kind. Here he underwent a hasty conversion, first to a radical materialism, and then to physicalistic physiology, a discipline that had grown up in reaction against vitalism. A frankly reductionistic program had brought it into being in the group surrounding Helmholtz, including du Bois-Reymond, Ludwig, and Freud's teacher Bruecke, the head of the Physiological Institute in Vienna. Physicalistic physiology was a principal heir of the mechanistic tradition that had started with Galileo and which now sought to explain everything in the universe in terms of Newtonian physics.

Freud was for years under the spell of Bruecke, whom he considered the greatest authority he had ever met. Several other teachers and colleagues of his were also enthusiastic members of the mechanistic school of Helmholtz, notably Meynert, Breuer, Exner, and Fliess. The outlook of this narrow but rigorous doctrine was forever after to shape Freud's scientific ideals, lingering behind the scenes of his theorizing, almost in the role of a scientific superego. In this sense, I believe that the mechanistic image of man underlies and may be discerned in Freud's metapsychological writings, even when the latter seem to contradict certain aspects of the image.

In many details, the mechanistic image is sharply antithetical to the humanistic one. I have attempted to bring out this contrast in the following catalogue of assumptions.

1. Man is a proper subject of natural science, and as such is no different from any other object in the universe. All of his behavior is completely deterministic, even including reports of dreams and fantasies—that is, all human phenomena are lawful and, in principle, possible to explain by natural-scientific, quantitative laws. From this vantage point there is no meaning to subdividing his behavior or considering his nature to be dual—he is simply an animal, best understood as a machine or *apparatus,* composed of ingenious *mechanisms,* operating according to Newton's laws of motion, and understandable without residue in terms of physics and chemistry. One need not postulate a soul or vital principle to make the apparatus run, though *energy* is an essential concept. All the cultural achievements of which man is so proud, all his spiritual values and the like, are merely sublimations of basic instinctual drives, to which they may be reduced.

2. The differences among men are scientifically negligible; from the mechanistic standpoint, all human beings are basically the same, being subject to the same universal laws, and the emphasis is put upon discovering these laws, not understanding particular individuals. Accordingly, metapsychology takes no note of individual differences and does not seem to be a theory of personality.

3. Man is motivated fundamentally by the automatic tendency of his nervous system to keep itself in an unstimulated state, or at least to keep its tensions at a constant level. The basic model is the *reflex arc:* external or internal stimulus leads to activity of the CNS, which then leads to response. All needs and longings must, for scientific purposes, be conceptualized as forces, tensions that must be reduced, or energies seeking discharge.

4. There is no place for meanings or value in science: it deals with quantities, not qualities, and must be thoroughly objective. Phenomena such as thoughts, wishes, or fears are epiphenomenal; they exist and must be explained, but they have no explanatory power themselves. Energies largely take their place in the mechanical model.

5. There is no clear antithesis to the fifth humanistic assumption, the one dealing with the importance of the unconscious and the secret, inner side of man. Perhaps a corresponding reformulation of the same point in mechanistic terms might be: consciousness too is an epiphenomenon, and what happens in a person's awareness is of trivial interest by comparison with the multifarious activities in the nervous system, most of which go on without any corresponding consciousness.

6. The many forces operating in the apparatus that is man often collide, giving rise to the subjective report of *conflict.*

7. The processes sentimentally known as love are nothing more than disguises and transformations of the sexual instinct, or, more precisely, its energy (*libido*). Even disinterested or platonic affection is merely aim-inhibited libido. Sex, not love, is therefore the prime motive. And since the fundamental tendency of the nervous system is to restore a state of unstimulated equilibrium, the total passivity of death is its ultimate objective; rage and

destructiveness are merely disguises and transformations of the death instinct.

8. *Objects* (that is to say, other people) are important only insofar as they provide stimuli that set the psychic apparatus in motion and supply the necessary conditions for the reduction of internal tensions that brings it to rest again. Relationships as such are not real, however; a psychology can be complete without considering more than the individual apparatus and events within it, plus the general class of external stimuli. Reality contains "only masses in motion and nothing else" (Freud, 1895, p. 308).

9. The genetic emphasis is not very different for Freud as mechanist and as humanist, except in a rather remote theoretical extension: the humanistic approach assumes that there is historical causality, whereas the mechanistic one basically assumes an ahistorical, instantaneous causality. Nevertheless, the parallelogram of forces at t_1 causes motion and a new alignment of forces at t_2, for the mechanist; hence, he recognizes the validity of tracing the historical sequence of events leading to the present parallelogram of forces as a way of assessing the latter when they cannot be directly measured.

10. Since man's behavior is strictly determined by his past history and by the contemporary arrangement of forces, free will is an illusion. To allow the idea of *autonomy* or freedom of choice would imply spontaneity instead of passivity in the nervous system, and would undermine the scientifically necessary assumption that behavior is determined strictly by the biological drives and by external stimuli.

I think it should be apparent that psychoanalytic theory as we know it is a tissue of compromise between these two opposing images. The influence of the mechanistic image is clearest in metapsychology (e.g., Freud, 1900; 1915a,b,c), in which the general structure of the major propositions, as well as a good deal of the terminology, can be seen to derive directly from the explicitly mechanistic and reductionistic model of the Project. The most striking change was Freud's abandoning an anatomical-neurological framework for the abstract ambiguity of the "psychic apparatus," in which the structures and energies are psychic, not physical. Unwittingly, Freud took a plunge into Cartesian metaphysical dualism, but continued to stave off what he felt as the antiscientific threat of the humanistic image by continuing to claim ultimate explanatory power for metapsychology, as opposed to the theoretically less ambitious formulation of clinical observations in language that was closer to that of everyday life. And in the metapsychology, by the device of translating subjective longings into the terminology of forces and energies, Freud did not have to take the behavioristic tack of rejecting the inner world; by replacing the subjective, willing self by the ego defined as a psychic structure, he was able to allow enough autonomy to achieve a fair fit with clinical observation.

The mechanistic image of man is most familiar to all of us, of course, in the various transformations of behaviorism or behavior theory. Even in its modern guises, S-R theory is antihumanistic, seeking always to view man as a machine and to find ways of disparaging and neglecting his subjective world of meanings, yearnings, and fantasies, and his role as active agent rather than as passive reactor.[3] The mechanistic image of behaviorism differs most sharply from that of Freud on the issue of the unconscious: oddly enough, despite their antagonism to the preceding introspectionist psychologies of consciousness, the behaviorists are so offended by the notion of unconscious processes that they go to great lengths to try to show that everything important is conscious. This is less surprising when one reflects that after 1900, Freud insisted on a strange *psychic reality* for unconscious processes, thus embracing a kind of metaphysical mentalism that is anathema to the behaviorist. Ironically, he need not have done so had he been writing today: he could have seen that meanings, the stuff of experience, can be encoded in electrical impulses and can interact as meanings in this encoded form, in a nervous system or in a computer, without the need to postulate a psychic unconscious in either system.[4]

THE TWO IMAGES EVALUATED

But let us go back to Freud's two images, and try to evaluate them. Since I have tried to formulate them in explicit propositions, we can and should inquire first to what extent these may be said to be true or false. And since neither is an explicit model so much as it is a silent force, tending to steer thought and action, we must also consider the broader implications and ramifications of each.

To consider first the truth-content of the mechanistic image, it is a mixture of a general scientific outlook and a particular doctrine that was already becoming outmoded in physics before the end of the nineteenth century. Like other structures of half-truths, it is difficult to oppose successfully without seeming to be against the valid parts, which are subtly intertwined with the invalid ones.[5] The machine is a powerful image, but a poor model for a universe made up largely of radiant energy, electromagnetic fields, and atoms that lose their classical attributes of solid substantiality the more closely they are studied. Relativity and quantum theory made the mechanistic model of the universe a dead letter generations ago in the physical sciences. In biology, the machine was a fruitful model for a long time in that it encouraged detailed studies of structures and processes by available scientific methods, yielding much useful knowledge. But the reductionistic strain in mechanism has long been seen to be fallacious; one does not need to retain a trace of vitalism to maintain that it is valid and necessary for each science to consider its problems on its own level of description and explanation. One can no more explain the resolution of a psychological conflict in terms of the neurological processes mediating it alone than one can explain

---

[3] This point has been well developed by Chein (1962).

[4] For a further discussion of the mind-body problem and its bearing on psychoanalytic theory, see Rubinstein (1965) and Holt (1972).

[5] For a useful general critique of mechanism and the illusory pursuit of complete objectivity in science, see Polanyi (1958), Grene (1969), and Yankelovich and Barrett (1970).

the solution of an algebraic problem in terms of the electrical pulses mediating it in a computer: neither psychoanalysis nor algebra can be reduced to physics. At the same time, a complete explanation of conflict resolution must take account of both psychological and neurobiological processes, among others.

Further, Freud's mechanistic image of man incorporated a number of factual assertions assumed by nineteenth-century neurology to be true, but now known to be false (Holt, 1965a). The nervous system, far from being a passive reflex apparatus, is an incessantly active communication network, in which energy plays virtually no role except as a transmitter of encoded information. The tension-reduction theory of motivation is under widespread attack, if not yet quite defunct, and the psychic energies postulated to replace Freud's original working quantity, the neural excitation, are increasingly being recognized as unmeasurable and theoretically redundant.

What then about free will vs. determinism? Briefly (see also Holt, 1967a), the two concepts are *not* antithetical: both are necessary and the two can coexist. To maintain that the subjective experience of being able to make a deliberate choice among alternatives is a delusion on the grounds that freedom means a capricious act unrelated to anything else is to miss the point entirely. Truly free behavior is not acting on an unpredictable whim, but acting in *self-consistent* ways, in harmony with one's ego-values. The person who is able to exert will power against temptation and to act with a sense of autonomy is just as much a part of the lawful natural world as one who feels utterly compelled by influences beyond his control, whether these are unconscious needs or external compulsions. Freedom of the will (or, more generally, ego autonomy) is not a philosophical absolute, it is a quantitative psychological variable, which can be diminished or enhanced in ways that are lawful and predictable. Smith (1971a, 1971b) and Chein (in press) have reached the same conclusion by well-argued lines of reasoning.

Let us begin our scrutiny of the indirect effects of these two images within psychoanalysis by asking what their implications are for its therapeutic work. I believe that to the extent that the mechanistic residue of physicalistic physiology continues to color psychoanalytic theory, it has an antitherapeutic effect (Holt, 1968). The metapsychological language constantly points us away from real human beings, their concrete sufferings and aspirations, and invites us to see instead a bloodless battle of ego, superego, and id, anticathexis being pitted against cathexis, energies being fused, neutralized, and what not, while structures interact with objects, and real people disappear behind an impressive cloud of words. Personal dilemmas and life crises become defects in an apparatus, conceived of as ultimately bodily—a set of silent assumptions that urge us away from treating psychological problems psychologically and in the direction of drugs and other somatic therapies. Recall, in this context, Freud's prediction that the era of psychotherapy would be a short one, since he expected that chemical remedies would soon make it unnecessary. The emphasis on energy and its discharge can lead to a false expectation that aggression has to be vented, and to an overevaluation of what can be accomplished by "catharsis" (Holt, 1967b,

1970a). The mechanistic image encourages treating the patient in the way so many patients want to be treated: as a passive machine, to be manipulated back into chugging properly, rather than as a partner in a joint enterprise of trying to increase his ability to function for himself in a free, mature, responsible way.[6] Since, in psychoanalytic theory, the phenomenological richness and subtlety of affective experience is reduced to quantities of pleasure and unpleasure, the analyst is not encouraged in his therapeutic role to pay a great deal of attention to fine shadings of emotional meaning—a gap into which existentially oriented psychotherapists have moved.

This conflict between images of man is a great deal more than a squabble within the realms of pure science and psychotherapy, for it ramifies to the gravest dangers mankind has ever faced. The single most obvious and important implication of the image of man one is guided by is that humanism biases one in a humanitarian way, while mechanism creates a dehumanizing bias. (Note that I have considered validity separately, being wary of condemning a theory because it makes me feel anxious, or of thinking that it must be true if it seems socially constructive.)

In the following paragraphs, I recognize that I am going considerably beyond what can be proved scientifically; indeed, this is hardly more than a plausible interpretation. It may well be that I have confounded the issue of how science is used or misused with the intrinsic implications of reductionistic mechanism in science. It is also manifestly difficult to say how far mechanism is involved as a cause and as an effect in the following relationships. Because of their great social importance, however, I believe that these hypotheses are worthy of our attention and of further study.

The mechanistic world view, as Lewis Mumford (1970) brilliantly argues in his latest book, especially when it is used to conceptualize man as a machine, gnaws at any faith in his capacity to influence his own fate, at any trust in his capacity to become a mature and responsible citizen of a democracy, and thus at any hope of his achieving an egalitarian and just society. Instead, as Mumford shows, the rise of mechanism in science was accompanied by the emergence of absolute monarchy, partly because authoritarian rulers (who supported the work of the mechanists) intuitively saw that the mechanistic man was the perfect model of the docile subject, and mechanists like Descartes saw in absolute monarchy the ideal actualization of their model of the state as a smoothly functioning machine.

If, as Lord Acton said, power corrupts, it does so by making the man in the upper part of a power hierarchy contemptuous of whatever and whomever he has power over, and encourages his belief that the less powerful are not

---

[6] The analyst's temptation to slip into the role of an inscrutable and unquestioned authority, who assumes power of veto over the patient's entire personal life and often infantilizes him, may well stem in part from the mechanistic image. Schafer (1970b, p. 438f.) shows by a clinical example how a characteristically complex transference reaction can be biased and oversimplified if one conceptualizes it in terms of functions and energies: these concepts "do not even do the work they are supposed to do. They give the illusion of deep and exact 'scientific' understanding when in fact they are blurs."

fully human. They may therefore appropriately and justly be exploited or even destroyed. A mechanistic image of man subtly supports the theory that the disadvantaged are not really human. This is the basis for the theory of genocide —a master race has the power and thus the right to exterminate a "lesser breed." It is the theory of slavery, surviving in only slightly modified form as racism, ethnocentric prejudice, and discrimination. It is the theory of patriarchy or male supremacy, embodied in religion, in science, and in many other aspects of our culture, as women like Kate Millett (1970) are beginning to show us. And it is the theory of political authoritarianism, whether it is expressed in feudalism, monarchy, the communist dictatorship of the proletariat (more precisely, of the *apparatchiks* speaking in the name of the masses), or the fascist dictatorship of the lower middle class in league with an economically powerful and privileged elite. This same assumption that the underdog or the enemy is not fully human underlies war as an instrument of policy, and deterrence as an attempt to keep the peace (for deterrence always assumes that the "enemy," being indifferent to moral or ethical or humanitarian considerations, cannot be trusted to obey laws, and will therefore respond *only* to the threat of force).

Many writers have pointed out how mechanism is the ideal theory of a mass society, for the necessary assumption of mass production for mass consumption, manipulated by mass media, is that members of the mass are like the standardized, interchangeable parts of a machine. Huge, hierarchically organized industries or bureaucracies (like those of the church, the state, or the army) cannot function efficiently on the assumption that everyone concerned is a unique individual of equal ultimate worth, regardless of his hierarchical position; in the form we know them—Mumford says that this was the social invention of the Pharaohs and alone made possible the construction of such stupendous and symbolic works as the pyramids—hierarchical organizations require tight discipline, uniform functioning, and no interference from man's emotional, passionate side. Thus, the ideal citizen of an authoritarian state or institution is the robot.

The other major sociopolitical implication of mechanistic views of man is to rob him of freedom and responsibility. If freedom of choice is only an illusion, then no matter how much one affirms the necessity of preserving that fiction so as to give people the feeling that it makes sense for them to exert effort and to act responsibly, the argument cannot be more than halfhearted. Fatalism, the feeling of powerlessness, and a conviction of the futility of struggling against powerful and inscrutable forces are the logical results of the mechanistic worldview, still so widespread in science. At the present critically dangerous moment, when we are faced by difficult choices that will mean the difference between famine, desperate poverty, environmental destruction, and nuclear annihilation on the one hand, and the possibility, on the other hand, of a world of peace and plenty, it is of the greatest importance that people everywhere be helped to overcome the alienating and paralyzing feeling of pessimistic impotence. As we have seen, this doctrine—that man's freedom of choice is an illusion and his efforts make no difference—happens to be widely believed by scientists and yet based on fallacious reasoning; hence it behooves psychoanalytic theorists to combat it as vigorously as possible. For though we have (in Freud's humanistic image) the elements of a theoretical base from which to fight it, psychoanalysis is itself pervaded by the mechanistic world-view, which is basically antithetical to many of the values Freud stood for. It would be megalomanic to believe that making a theoretical change within psychoanalysis will reverse a long historical process and undo the widespread alienation of today; but it would be irresponsible—especially since the stakes are so high—not to do what we can to stop giving intellectual respectability to a socially pernicious doctrine, and to replace it by one that is both more valid and more constructive.

The implications of the humanistic image are, by and large, personally and socially constructive. It has a built-in therapeutic orientation: it assumes that people can change themselves, can reflect on their behavior and take responsibility for it, and that everyone is worth helping, capable of being understood and even loved. It is a life-affirming, hopeful outlook. Socially, it conduces to a democratic and egalitarian society rather than to a repressive and authoritarian one. It is true that Freud's own version of the humanistic tradition did contain some anti-egalitarian elements, notably a patriarchal conception of women as inherently inferior and an aristocratic disdain for the ignorant, uncultured, prejudiced masses. Nevertheless, in its most internally consistent form, this image encourages those who hold it to empathize with all other men, and to recognize through such acts of identification that we are all one species; it also provides the basis for confidence that we can learn to cooperate enough to survive. Destructive, blindly selfish, and shortsightedly pleasure-seeking behavior does not have to be either denied or pessimistically accepted as inevitable; rather, it is seen as characteristic of a relatively low level of development and thus as possible to transcend through changed methods of bringing up children. In short, a humane therapy, polity, and morality can more easily be derived from it than from the mechanistic image of man.

All very pretty, it will be objected, but what has all this sweetness and light got to do with science? This image of man is shot through with value premises, and it stresses the very aspects of people that are compatible with treatment by the humanities—literature, philosophy, religion—rather than by science. If it is to become consistently humanistic, would psychoanalysis not have to give up its ambition to be a science?

Let us look carefully at the first of these objections. Yes, there are explicit statements of value in the humanistic image; but in large part they are the opposites of the values inherent in the mechanistic image. Indeed, this is one reason to speak of these systems of ideas as images rather than theories, for the convention is automatically to formulate scientific propositions in such a way as to conceal their implicit commitment to values. Even the fourth of the above propositions in the mechanistic image—the one that abjures values—is itself a value-statement: evaluative and other affective, subjective states are downgraded. Not being considered fit objects for scientific consideration, they are subtly derogated as "objectivity" is enthroned. The reductionism of the mechanistic image similarly tends to degrade cultural achievements, spiritual aspirations, individual uniqueness, altruistic and tender affection, and most subtleties of interpersonal relationships, meanings, emotions, and other subjective states. The humanistic image declares all of these to be worthy of respectful attention and study, but in its largely belletristic embodiment (in literature, rather than in scientific writing) explicit endorsement of these values and even exhortation are common.

Here we enter upon one of the great continuing controversies in the behavioral sciences, about which I can do no more than comment briefly. My personal conviction is that all of us continually do make value judgments, and that it is not difficult to show how they operate in the behavior of scientists who are most thoroughly committed to objectivity. Therefore, a truly value-free science is precisely the same kind of obsessional distortion as the related ideal of rational thought, completely free of affect. The solution is to be as conscious and explicit as possible about one's values, to adopt truth as the first among them, and to try to guard as carefully as possible against the subtle influences of other values on the process of inquiry.

Humanistic inquiry, yes; but humanistic science? Is that not a contradiction in terms? Many writers on both sides have argued that it is; and this brings up another of the major unresolved issues in the methodology of the behavioral sciences: the possibility of making a science out of subjective human feelings and meanings. A group of German philosophers beginning with Dilthey, during the last quarter of the nineteenth century, argued that the natural sciences could be no guide in the world of the human mind and the meanings it generates; rather, a wholly separate set of disciplines, the *Geisteswissenschaften*, were necessary. As Windelband and Rickert put it, the sciences must follow a nomothetic methodology, seeking general laws, while the methodology of the humanities is idiographic and *verstehende:* it seeks to grasp the nature of individual persons, events, or books by a direct empathic or intuitive understanding. The fallacies of this position have been repeatedly exposed (see, for example, Kaplan, 1964; Holt, 1962; and Yankelovich and Barrett, 1970), yet the same arguments are continually advanced as if they were newly discovered (e.g., by Home, 1966). It was reasonable enough for Dilthey and his followers to reject science as applicable to the subject matter of the humanities, for the natural science of their day was precisely the discipline in which Freud was trained and which gave rise to the mechanistic image of man in his work. Today, there is less justification for such a narrow view of what science is, although contemporary spokesmen of the mechanistic outlook do tend to perpetuate the misunderstanding by claiming that they are the only true representatives of science. Surely, if behaviorism were the only possible scientific psychology, then we should have to agree with Home, Schafer (1970a,b), and Klauber (1968) that psychoanalysis cannot be a science but must be one of the humanities, like history.

Science, however, is not procrustean. Home (1966) to the contrary notwithstanding, it is not defined by its subject matter but by its method; therefore, it is in no way enjoined from dealing with meanings, qualities, or unique individuals. To be sure, methods do differ somewhat from one science to another, depending on the nature of the subject matter; but, since the death of vitalism, there have been no biologists of any scientific stature who claim that studying living instead of non-living objects requires a method or a logic fundamentally different from that of the inorganic sciences. Since the brief flare-up of physicalism in the middle decades of this century, few scientists or philosophers of science have espoused reductionism. It is now generally conceded that the phenomena of biology are emergent with respect to physics and chemistry, those of psychology emergent with respect to biology, and those of sociology and anthropology emergent with respect to psychology; moreover, that it is legitimate for each level of analysis to treat the phenomena peculiar to it by means of its own concepts. As to the claim that it requires a different logic to deal with motives as compared with physical causes, it remains just that—an empty claim, not backed up by any detailed demonstration of what is lacking in the logic of the scientific method, or what the new and different logic might be. Elsewhere (Holt, 1961), I have examined the methods used in such humanistic disciplines as literary criticism and history, and attempted to demonstrate that— to the extent that they are disciplined—these methods are substantially identical with those of science.

Klauber (1968) has raised another supposed obstacle keeping psychoanalysis from becoming a science: the psychoanalyst finds "multiple explanations for unitary events," a "logical method which contrasts strongly with the usual method of science . . . finding unitary explanations for multiple events." A similar objection is that science works with single variables in controlled experiments seeking simple laws, whereas the complex phenomena the analyst deals with are so interdependent that they do not allow the controlled manipulation of one variable at a time. The difficulty with these objections is partly that they inappropriately compare the concrete situation of the analyst interpreting a dream with the idealized one of the physicist formulating a law. The analogue of the working psychoanalyst is the civil engineer building a bridge, not the physicist. The engineer too is dealing with a concrete case, with its own peculiarities, which calls for a knowledge of many laws of physics and of other sciences; he does not carry out single-variable experiments any more than the analyst does, but he must know and use the essentials of scientific method, if his bridges are not to fall. In short, there is no difference between the *logic* of focusing on multiple explanations for single events (characteristic of applied work) and that of seeking the abstract unity in many observations (characteristic of pure research).

Schafer (1970b) speaks of the "natural-science approach" in psychoanalysis as "an option, useful and costly at the same time." Unfortunately, he does not specify what he thinks the uses and costs are, nor—even more important—does he make a similar cost-benefit analysis of the alternatives. We must beware the allure of the "freedom" that is apparently bestowed by renouncing the intention to make psychoanalysis a science; it becomes all too easily a license to make the sky the limit to speculation, and to substitute vague, emotionally allusive language for precision and verifiability—in short, to perpetuate the worst features of contemporary psychoanalytic writing. I feel confident that this is not Schafer's intent and that it would not be his practice. Nevertheless, the danger of turning to a putatively separate logic and methodology of the humanities is that it is very difficult to find any such, and psychoanalysis has great need of as much guidance toward intellectual responsibility and as much protection against self-deception as it can get.

A remarkable feature of the arguments against the possibility of treating meanings scientifically is their naive or willful ignoring of the great quantity of scientific work of just such a kind that is actively going on. Modern structural linguistics has enormously advanced the direct study of the mediation of meaning through language by applying scientific method to it. In the related science of psycholinguistics, the work of Osgood and associates (1957) is noteworthy for its bold and successful attempt to quantify the evaluative and connotative aspects of language. In the Project, Freud (1895) maintained that science could deal only with quantities, not with qualities; yet Fechner's psychophysics was already well-established as the quantitative study of perceptual qualities. Today, psychophysical methods have been extended even to the quantification and control of such meanings as the quality of "cuteness" in drawings of girls' faces (Hochberg and McAlister, 1953). During the past four decades quantitative content analysis has become a mainstay of political science, sociology, and social psychology, and through the work of Murray (1938) and his followers (e.g., McClelland et al., 1953; Atkinson, 1964; Holt, 1966) has become a major technique for measuring human motives. Ironically, it was only by abandoning the pseudo physicalism of the attempt to define the primary process in terms of unbound energy, and by focusing on Freud's phenomenological discussions of primary-process thinking, that I was able to develop a technique of measuring this central psychoanalytic construct with satisfactory reliability and to verify Kris's hypothesis about regression in the service of the ego and artistic creativity (Holt, 1970b). The work of Dahl (reported in this volume) is an excellent demonstration that quantitative methods drawing on both psycholinguistics and content analysis can be fruitfully applied to the basic data of the psychoanalytic hour (see also Spence, 1968). The burden of proof has been shifted to those who maintain that quantification (and the precise definition of concepts that it requires) is the kiss of death for psychoanalysis or other humanistic approaches to the study of man.

Traditionally, the humanities have been sharply segregated from the sciences, and there are many in both of Snow's "two cultures" who still believe that there can be no integration here. A heterogeneous but rapidly growing group of workers has begun to gather around the banner of *humanistic psychology*, but many of them distrust the ideals of rigor, control, quantification, and empirical verification. It is indeed difficult to retain the rich and human view of people conveyed by the humanistic tradition while still pursuing the intent of building a science; yet it is both necessary and possible, and it is actually under way.

What should be the place of metapsychology in a reconstructed psychoanalysis, purged of its mechanism? My late friend and colleague, George Klein (in press), urged that the existing metapsychology must be replaced in a major attempt to systematize and introduce scientific rigor into the clinical theory, supplemented by a new set of higher-order abstractions and principles. A psychoanalytic theory, he argued cogently, must employ *meanings*, as metapsychology does not. Much as I agree with this emphasis and with his main line of thought, I find it incomplete. It must, in my opinion, be part of a larger model of the human organism and person, in which purely psychological, meaningful propositions have a major place as one level of analysis among several.[7] True, psychoanalytic methods deal only with this level, and the observations of the clinical analyst are confined almost entirely to verbal and nonverbal (but still meaningful) communications. Nevertheless, the subject matter of psychoanalysis, the set of presenting problems it has tried to explain, has always been psychosomatic. The emotions, sexuality, hysteria, not to mention the disorders sometimes called organ neuroses—these are all prime concerns of psychoanalysis, as they must be of any theory of human beings that has any aspiration to comprehensiveness, and they all comprise both subjective and bodily occurrences. Fortunately, today it is possible to build a theory that will be comprehensive enough to give the body its due without having to undermine the psychological. In brief, it can be organismic, not reductionistic, and it can provide for sociocultural levels of analysis, too. In other papers (Holt, 1967a,b) I have sketched out some specifications for such a theory, following the lead of Benjamin Rubinstein (1965, 1967).

One of the great advantages of our era, as compared with Freud's, is that we do not have to frame a science of man in mechanistic terms. We can keep the richness, the humaneness, the concern with vital and meaningful issues that characterized the humanistic side of Freud's work, without having to give up the scientific ideals of rigor, testability, clarity, internal organization of concepts, and systematic linkage to other sciences. True, the psychology of personality has not yet produced a full-blown theory that incorporates the best of psychoanalysis, but I think we are seeing the beginnings. We still have to resist easy dichotomies and to strive for an integrated theory, which neglects neither the physiological, anatomical, and biochemical, nor the social, cultural, and philosophical aspects of man. But in a world where the dominant psychologies are so narrowly mechanistic, where the reductionistic and dehumanizing strain in science is causing many people to reject the entire scientific enterprise, and where the contribution of psychology will probably be so vital to the solution of desperately critical problems, a truly adequate psychological theory—both humanistic and scientific in the best sense—is a worthy enough goal to warrant herculean efforts.

[7] An alternative formulation, which is perhaps more realistically modest, is that of Yankelovich and Barrett (1970, p. 291, 294): One major "purpose of a revised metapsychology is to link clinical psychoanalysis to the closely related sciences, psychology, ethology, sociology, anthropology, biology, and behavioral genetics. This linking is important to psychoanalysis, because psychopathology cannot be studied in isolation; it is important to the other sciences because psychoanalysis throws light on crucial aspects of their own subject areas. . . . We are not suggesting that the metapsychology become either a general philosophy of human nature or the sum of all the other human sciences, but simply that it tie psychoanalysis to its sister disciplines at those strategic points needed to preserve the integrity of the clinical theory—which means to preserve the integrity of the human person."

REFERENCES

Amacher, P. (1965). Freud's Neurological Education and Its Influence on Psychoanalytic Theory. *Psychological Issues,* Monograph No. 16. New York: International Universities Press.

Andersson, O. (1962). *Studies in the Prehistory of Psychoanalysis. The Etiology of Psychoneuroses and Some Related Themes in Sigmund Freud's Scientific Writings and Letters 1886–1896.* Stockholm: Svenska Bokförlaget.

Atkinson, J. W. (1964). *An Introduction to Motivation.* Princeton, N.J.: Van Nostrand.

Bernfeld, S. (1944). Freud's Earliest Theories and the School of Helmholtz. *Psychoanalytic Quarterly,* 13:341–362.

Chein, I. (1962). The Image of Man. *Journal of Social Issues,* 18(4):1–35.

———— (1972). *The Image of Man and the Science of Behavior.* New York: Basic Books.

Ellenberger, H. F. (1970). *The Discovery of the Unconscious: The History and Evolution of Dynamic Psychiatry.* New York: Basic Books.

Freud, S. (1895). Project for a Scientific Psychology. *Standard Edition,* 1:295–387. London: Hogarth Press, 1966.

———— (1900). The Interpretation of Dreams. *Standard Edition,* 4 & 5. London: Hogarth Press, 1953.

———— (1913). Totem and Taboo. *Standard Edition,* 13:1–161. London: Hogarth Press, 1955.

———— (1914). On Narcissism: An Introduction. *Standard Edition,* 14:73–102. London: Hogarth Press, 1957.

———— (1915a). Instincts and Their Vicissitudes. *Standard Edition,* 14:117–140. London· Hogarth Press, 1957.

———— (1915b). Repression. *Standard Edition,* 14:146–158. London: Hogarth Press, 1957.

———— (1915c). The Unconscious. *Standard Edition,* 14:166–204. London: Hogarth Press, 1957.

———— (1920). Beyond the Pleasure Principle. *Standard Edition,* 18:7–64. London: Hogarth Press, 1961.

———— (1921). Group Psychology and the Analysis of the Ego. *Standard Edition,* 18:69–143. London: Hogarth Press, 1955.

———— (1925). An Autobiographical Study. *Standard Edition,* 20:7–74. London: Hogarth Press, 1959.

———— (1927). The Future of an Illusion. *Standard Edition,* 21:5–56. London: Hogarth Press, 1961.

———— (1930). Civilization and Its Discontents. *Standard Edition,* 21:64–145. London: Hogarth Press, 1961.

———— (1939). Moses and Monotheism. *Standard Edition,* 23:7–137. London: Hogarth Press, 1964.

———— (1940). An Outline of Psycho-Analysis. *Standard Edition,* 23:144–207. London: Hogarth Press, 1964.

———— (1960). *Letters of Sigmund Freud,* ed. E. L. Freud. New York: Basic Books.

Grene, M., ed. (1969). Toward a Unity of Knowledge. *Psychological Issues,* Monograph No. 22. New York: International Universities Press.

Hochberg, J., and McAlister, E. (1953). A Quantitative Approach to Figural "Goodness." *Journal of Experimental Psychology,* 46:361–364.

Holt, R. R. (1961). Clinical Judgment as a Disciplined Inquiry. *Journal of Nervous and Mental Disease,* 133:369–382.

———— (1962). Individuality and Generalization in the Psychology of Personality. Revised version in: *Personality: Selected Readings,* ed. R. S. Lazarus and E. M. Opton, Jr. Penguin Modern Psychology UPS 9. Baltimore, Md.: Penguin Books, 1967.

—————— (1963). Two Influences on Freud's Scientific Thought: A Fragment of Intellectual Biography. In: *The Study of Lives*, ed. R. W. White. New York: Atherton Press, pp. 364–387.

—————— (1965a). A Review of Some of Freud's Biological Assumptions and Their Influence on His Theories. In: *Psychoanalysis and Current Biological Thought*, ed. N. S. Greenfield and W. C. Lewis. Madison: University of Wisconsin Press, pp. 93–124.

—————— (1965b). Freud's Cognitive Style. *American Imago*, 22:163–179.

—————— (1966). Measuring Libidinal and Aggressive Motives and Their Controls by Means of the Rorschach Test. In: *Nebraska Symposium on Motivation, 1966*, ed. D. Levine. Lincoln: University of Nebraska Press, pp. 1–47.

—————— (1967a). On Freedom, Autonomy, and the Redirection of Psychoanalytic Theory: A Rejoinder. *International Journal of Psychiatry*, 3:524–536.

—————— (1967b). Beyond Vitalism and Mechanism: Freud's Concept of Psychic Energy. In: *Science and Psychoanalysis*, 11:1–41, ed. J. H. Masserman. New York: Grune and Stratton.

—————— (1968). Freud, Sigmund. *International Encyclopedia of the Social Sciences*, 6:1–12. New York: Macmillan and The Free Press.

—————— (1970a). On the Interpersonal and Intrapersonal Consequences of Expressing or Not Expressing Anger. *Journal of Consulting and Clinical Psychology*, 35:8–12.

—————— (1970b). Artistic Creativity and Rorschach Measures of Adaptive Regression. In: *Developments in the Rorschach Technique*, Vol. 3, ed. B. Klopfer, M. M. Meyer, and F. B. Brawer. New York: Harcourt Brace Jovanovich, pp. 263–320.

—————— (1972). On the Nature and Generality of Mental Imagery. In: *The Function and Nature of Imagery*, ed. P. Sheehan. New York: Academic Press.

Home, H. J. (1966). The Concept of Mind. *International Journal of Psycho-Analysis*, 47: 42–49.

Jackson, S. W. (1969). The History of Freud's Concepts of Regression. *Journal of the American Psychoanalytic Association*, 17:743–784.

Kaplan, A. (1964). *The Conduct of Inquiry*. San Francisco: Chandler.

Klauber, J. (1968). On the Dual Use of Historical and Scientific Method in Psycho-Analysis. *International Journal of Psycho-Analysis*, 49:80–88.

Klein, G. S. (in press). *Psychoanalytic Theory: An Examination of Essentials*. New York: International Universities Press.

McClelland, D. C., Atkinson, J. W., Clark, R. A., and Lowell, E. L. (1953). *The Achievement Motive*. New York: Appleton-Century-Crofts.

Millett, K. (1970). *Sexual Politics*. Garden City, N.Y.: Doubleday.

Mumford, L. (1970). *The Myth of the Machine*, Vol. 2: *The Pentagon of Power*. New York: Harcourt Brace Jovanovich.

Murray, H. A., et al. (1938). *Explorations in Personality*. New York: Oxford University Press.

Osgood, C. E., Suci, G. J., and Tannenbaum, P. H. (1957). *The Measurement of Meaning*. Urbana, Ill.: University of Illinois Press.

Polanyi, M. (1958). *Personal Knowledge; Towards a Post-critical Philosophy*, rev. ed. New York: Harper Torchbooks, 1964.

Rapaport, D. (1959). The Structure of Psychoanalytic Theory: A Systematizing Attempt. In: *Psychology: A Study of a Science*, Vol. 3, ed. S. Koch. New York: McGraw-Hill. Also in: *Psychological Issues*, Monograph No. 6. New York: International Universities Press, 1960.

Rubinstein, B. B. (1965). Psychoanalytic Theory and the Mind-Body Problem. In: *Psychoanalysis and Current Biological Thought*, ed. N. S. Greenfield and W. C. Lewis. Madison: University of Wisconsin Press, pp. 35–56.

—————— (1967). Explanation and Mere Description: A Metascientific Examination of Certain Aspects of the Psychoanalytic Theory of Motivation. In: *Motives and Thought*, ed. R. R. Holt. *Psychological Issues*, Monograph No. 18/19. New York: International Universities Press, pp. 20–77.

Schafer, R. (1970a). Requirements for a Critique of the Theory of Catharsis. *Journal of Consulting and Clinical Psychology*, 35:13–17.

────── (1970b). An Overview of Heinz Hartmann's Contributions to Psycho-Analysis. *International Journal of Psycho-Analysis*, 51:425–446.

Smith, M. B. (1971a). A Psychologist's Perspective on Public Opinion Theory. *Public Opinion Quarterly*, 35(1):36–43.

────── (1971b). "Normality"—for an Abnormal Age. In: *Essays in Honor of Roy Grinker, Sr.*, ed. D. Offer and D. X. Freedman. New York: Basic Books.

Spehlmann, R. (1953). *Sigmund Freuds neurologische Schriften: Eine Untersuchung zur Vorgeschichte der Psychoanalyse*. Berlin: Springer. English summary by H. Klein-schmidt in *Annual Survey of Psychoanalysis, 1953*, 4:693–706, 1957.)

Spence, D. P. (1968). The Processing of Meaning in Psychotherapy: Some Links with Psycholinguistics and Information Theory. *Behavioral Science*, 13:349–361.

Yankelovich, D., and Barrett, W. (1970). *Ego and Instinct: The Psychoanalytic View of Human Nature—Revised*. New York: Random House.

THE NATURE OF PSYCHOLOGICAL CHANGE IN INDIVIDUALS AND ITS RELATION TO CULTURAL CHANGE

Lawrence S. Kubie, M.D., D.Sc.

INTRODUCTION

It is possible to formulate with fair clarity clinical criteria of significant psychological change; but the technical problems of how to develop precise qualitative or quantitative tests for this have never been faced and consequently have never been solved. My hope in this paper is only to confront myself and my readers with some of the questions that must first be considered in any approach to these difficult issues.

Throughout life, human mental processes continue in sleep as they do in the waking state. This is one among the reasons why we must conclude that one is never wholly asleep nor wholly awake; that these states are bands along a continuous spectrum. Furthermore, everywhere along this spectrum there is an incessant input, of which only a small fraction is consciously perceived, much of it entering the central stream without conscious images or sensory awareness, i.e., as a preconscious process. There it is stored, registered, ordered, compared, coded, etc., until, out of widening ripples of central disturbances, there comes an equally continuous but variable and also largely preconscious output, emotionally colored in changing and sometimes alternating hues.

What is usually spoken of as "consciousness" is actually this continuous process of gathering fragmentary and weighted samples of this central activity and representing them by means of sensory afterimages and their projections, along with the verbal, paralinguistic, and somatic symbols and related effects. In an incessant inner activity of this kind, what constitutes significant change, change that is more than ripples and waves in the recurrent ebb and flow of activity? What changes? And what constitutes enduring change? These are basic questions. Furthermore, since most of our mental activities take place on neither a conscious nor an unconscious level, but preconsciously, the difficult technical challenge for the future is to develop methods by which preconscious processing and its changes can be studied with precision.

For many years I have been perplexed about what constitutes significant change, either in man's underlying nature or in the continuously changing currents and eddies in the stream of his inner experience. Our percepts and plans, our play, our working adjustments, our voices, enunciation, body tensions, feelings, handwritings, facial expressions are never constant. Consequently, clinical observation by itself brought me to the seemingly circular hypothesis that the only psychological change that is enduringly meaningful for individual health, for life in general, or for human culture as a whole is a change in the capacity for further change. It is on this hypothesis that I shall base all that follows; it will lead to a search for objective criteria of change in this sense, and for an answer to the question: on what does the capacity for continuing change depend? My approach to these questions derives from the clinical study of human lives, using the techniques and the data of psychoanalytic psychiatry. These methods and theories are not flawless; nor are the data always certain. And surely psychiatrists and psychoanalysts do not already know the answers: our function is chiefly to ask the question. In fact, I regard psychoanalysis largely as a penetrating instrument for the *uncovering of crucial questions.*

As Robert Waelder pointed out long ago, all human behavior and all human psychological processes are multi-determined, i.e. they are determined by many concurrent variables, some specifically organic, others psychological, others a combination of the two. Among these, the psychological variables are made up of varying mixtures of concurrent conscious, preconscious and unconscious processes.

The essence of all neurotic processes is the fact that their symptomatic manifestations are rigid, repetitive, stereotyped, insatiable, unlearning and indeed unteachable. Any behavior and any aspect of the personality that is dominated by neurotic mechanisms will manifest these characteristics. This is equally true for any self-diagnosing neurotic state, such as a phobia or a hand-washing compulsion, and for such subtle masquerades of health as compulsive benevolence or compulsive work drives.

Even in a society in which man could freely experiment with changes in the forms of his social order, he would face internal problems to which no human culture has as yet found solutions. If it is true that everything can change except human nature, what is it in human nature that limits the capacity of the individual to change, and may even block it permanently and absolutely? Furthermore, to the extent to which individual human nature operates under such restrictions as these, will this to an equivalent degree limit change in human culture as a whole?

This hypothesis about the nature of psychological change in the individual is linked to another—namely, that among the human beings who make up every human culture about which we have any searching information, there is a universal neurotic potential that both shapes and restricts psychological development, but which, for the most part, is so well masked that it can be detected only by special methods (Kubie, 1951b, 1958b, 1963). This universal masked neurotic potential evolves through a highly variable neurotic process, which is also masked more often than it is overt, but which, when it becomes overt, exhibits manifest neurotic symptoms. Most people have this latter neurotic state in mind when they speak of "a neurosis." Paradoxically, a *creative* potential that is equally universal also exists, but its development and expression are distorted and hampered by the co-existing neurotic process. Indeed, the fate of the creative potential depends largely upon the ways in which concurrent neurotic mechanisms distort and imprison it (Kubie, 1958a).

Let me describe a few banal examples of how, when neurotic mechanisms dominate man, whether openly or in hidden ways, he is rendered incapable of learning from experiences of success or failure, of pain or pleasure, of satiation or frustration, of rewards or punishments, of exhortation or criticism. Consider a cultivated, educated, bright and intelligent woman whose childhood had been shadowed by an alcoholic father. On one level in spite of that experience, but on another level because of it, she had to marry three alcoholics in succession, being convinced and determined each time that this would not, indeed could not, happen again. After her fourth marriage (this time to a *non*-drinker), she became an alcoholic herself. Is this the paradigm of our problem? Namely, man's neurotogenic tendency to defy experience instead of learning from it, and without any awareness that he is doing so?

Of course, about such a case as this, one would ask many questions: what wholly *unconscious* rivalries, needs for vengeance, hostile identifications, needs to prove herself by triumphing over both father and mother, etc., may have made an automaton of this woman, as she repeated her tragic experiment? How in general can such stereotyped necessities come to dominate human behavior even in the face of predictable pain? How do similar imprisoning stereotypes occur in different ways in every culture of which we know anything? For, whenever this happens, it produces a chain of consequences in the life of the individual, with secondary distortions of his patterns of living, feeling, and thinking, and with many psychosocial consequences for his relationships to others and to the outside world. In this way a cybernetic chain-reaction is built, in which the neurotogenic rigidities of the individual become entrenched, and which in the end tend to reinforce his own primary neurotogenic stereotypes and those of the culture as well. This produces a further restriction in the range and capacity for human change, whether upward or downward in any value system. This sounds as though mankind is doomed; yet it also carries at least one optimistic implication—namely, that if and when we learn how to resolve the early and universal neurotic episodes of childhood *as they occur,* so that buried residues do not accumulate to produce the masked and overt neuroses of adult life, it will become possible for mankind to attain a new dimension of freedom.

But what lies behind all this? We have both experimental and clinical evidence that in all human beings there is a continuous, concurrent interplay among conscious, preconscious, and unconscious processes, out of which evolves our every moment of thought, feeling, purpose, and behavior. There is further evidence that whenever the unconscious ingredients among these processes play the dominant role, they predetermine the automatic and stereotyped repetition of the resulting behavior, a repetitive pattern that continues without regard to consequences (Kubie, 1953). This is a basic fact of human psychology; and it is no less important merely because, in addition to psychological determinants, certain organic processes can contribute to these obligatory and stereotyped repetitions, as has been shown by the work of Brickner (1940), Penfield (1952; Kubie, 1951a), Olds (1955, 1958, 1959, 1961) and many others.

WHAT CHANGE IS NOT

It will be difficult to decide what psychological change is, until we can agree on what it is not. This makes necessary certain basic differentiations, which should be obvious but have been strangely neglected—such as, for example, the difference between changes in underlying processes and the mere masking or unmasking of these processes. Throughout life there is an incessant shifting between latent and overt manifestations of the same unchanged inner conflicts and processes, as these operate on concurrent conscious, preconscious and/or unconscious levels. In every person at different times and under different circumstances, the impact of internal conflicts, or of external events and of specific triggering experiences, together with the subtle effects of insight determine the direction, the speed, and the constancy of these shifts. In fact, the fluctuations between masked latent processes and their manifest representations go on incessantly when we are awake, quite as much as they do when we are asleep and dreaming. Among these determining processes, those that are unconscious will be both represented and masked by condensed fragments of symbolic behavior, thought, and feeling, which are interwoven with others that represent concurrent conscious processes without distortion. The shifting dominance between the two groups will alter dramatically the stream of thought, feeling, and behavior; yet this does not imply a real or lasting change.

Less obvious but equally important for the study of change is an understanding of the identity of opposites in the language of unconscious mental processes, such as Yes and No (Spitz, 1957), Yesterday and Tomorrow, Near and Far, etc. On a conscious level, I may change my mind about a plan from yes to no, from doing something to not doing it, from staying where I am to traveling a thousand miles, from doing it now to doing it next year. On an unconscious level, these may be interchangeable equivalents, implying no basic change in me. Yet certainly all of the external aspects of my life will vary dramatically according to the decision that is finally put into effect; and this in turn will produce practical and emotional alterations in my life. For a time I may even *feel* different; yet I, the individual, and my neurotic potentials will not have changed. In psychiatry, this has much to do with the difference between sickness as a process and a sick life, a distinction which has received almost no consideration, even among analysts. These simple facts are of basic import in our consideration of the nature of change.

The obverse is also true. Wide swings of overt thoughts and feelings may occur *without* changes in underlying, latent processes and problems. This clinical fact is obvious and well known, but not its implications for the concept and the criteria of change. We see this constantly in daydreams and in night-dreams—for example, in the seesaw between bland dreams and nightmares, which may follow each other in swift succession in any individual, with widely varied affects even when the same conflicts are being expressed behind different disguises. Here the apparent "change" is limited to the mask. We see this also in the wide sweeps of a cyclothymic cycle.

Furthermore, changes in manifest behavior can be simulated consciously, preconsciously, and unconsciously. There are even facsimile psychoses (Kubie, 1964, 1966). Such changes can be unconsciously determined, preconsciously selected and rejected, or sometimes consciously and purposefully withheld and masked (although this is less frequent) or overexpressed with deliberate over-emphasis. Many statistical studies are based on such changes as these, giving fallacious support to the illusion that significant change has occurred.

There are still other pitfalls that make it difficult to recognize what apparent changes are occurring in the incessant stream of preconscious ("imageless") processing that underlies all human behavior, whether the apparent changes occur "spontaneously" or under the influence of therapeutic efforts. Shifts may occur in a patient who seems dramatically "improved" (or alternatively "worsened") at the very moment when the family or the general physician first urges him to consult the psychiatrist, or on the day he enters a psychiatric hospital. Moreover, such sudden symptomatic shifts from latent to overt, or from manifest to latent, or from affirmation to denial may endure for days or weeks. This does not mean that enduring changes have occurred in that complex mixture of buried conflicts among purposes and identifications, etc. that makes up the personality out of which illness has arisen.

Let me describe a concrete example. A woman had a severe but masked claustrophobia, of which she had been wholly unaware throughout a successful career. Her work had kept her constantly on the move. During many years of outstandingly successful professional activity, she complained earnestly that her peripatetic job kept her away from home and friends. She had no suspicion that the very thing she complained about was precisely what made it possible for her to maintain a convincing simulation of health, free from any overt symptomatic manifestations of her hidden phobic neurosis. In fact, she would have denied with amused impatience any suggestion that she had neurotic difficulties of any kind. Yet these caught up with her for the first time in her adult life when she married happily and then two years later found herself tied to her home by the care of her first son, for whose arrival she had been waiting impatiently. At this critical juncture the latent claustrophobia became overt and precipitated her into a period of acute, stormy, and symptomatic illness.

The underlying neurotogenic conflicts that had given rise to her latent neuroses had been there during all the years when their only manifestation had been her "counterphobic," overdriven but successful roving career. Without knowing it, she had actually been enslaved to this career as a defense against a neurosis whose existence she did not even recognize, until marriage and motherhood triggered a violent symptomatic eruption of overt phobic distress out of her latent claustrophobia. This led her swiftly into acute alcoholism and then to secondary and tertiary guilt, shame, rage, and suicidal depression. Of course, at this point her whole *life* was changed, and she herself looked and acted changed in every way. Yet in a truer sense her inner self remained unaltered.

Her *life* had become "sicker," but the underlying processes of sickness were not different. There had only been this shift from latent to overt, which brought the process of illness into the open and made it symptomatic. At the same time, however, this change made her heretofore masked neurosis accessible to treatment. Only when long analytic treatment had altered the neurotogenic mechanisms that had hitherto determined the whole shape and quality of her years of "successful" and socially productive living, did she herself begin to change, in the sense that she achieved the psychological freedom to try different ways.

This life-story challenges the prevailing confusion between, on the one hand, those enduring changes that may result from fundamental alterations in underlying pathogenic processes and, on the other, those temporary changes in surface manifestations that can result from altering the circumstances of a man's life—particularly when these external circumstances are changed in such a way that he will pay either a greater or a lesser price for an underlying and often recognized neurosis. To move a man with a height phobia from New York City to a flat plain may diminish or even eliminate all his symptomatic suffering, thereby altering his life dramatically for a time while leaving his underlying neurosis untouched.

Another example of partial or surface change without basic underlying change was seen in an illness that produced episodic obsessional furors of homosexual ruminations and activities. Even with incomplete treatment, this patient became able to marry and to have children, and thus to surround himself with a family's love, to which he in turn could respond with devotion. Nevertheless, from time to time under special circumstances, or in response to specific trigger stimuli, the distressing furors of homosexual preoccupations would recur. These were brief and he could control, limit, and understand them; but each time they were triggered off he paid for them with a period of anxiety and tormenting depression. The underlying process of the illness itself, it is true, had changed sufficiently to enable him to marry; his hitherto crippling symptoms were diminished, and this in turn made possible such extraordinary changes that his life looked totally different. Yet, because the inner changes were incomplete and inconstant, he was unable to experience a total eradication of the underlying neurotogenic conflicts. Subsequently, with further treatment, the outbursts of obsessional, homosexual turmoil disappeared, and were replaced by episodic flurries of driven, hypomanic activity, alternating with bouts of paralyzing depression. These new symptoms brought about a new group of tertiary subjective and objective changes in his life. Thus the underlying process of illness continued, profoundly altered but still not eradicated.

These examples highlight again the difference between a sickness, a sick man, and a sick life, and between changes in the essential underlying processes of sickness and symptomatic changes.

To relieve a patient, even temporarily, of painful and life-disrupting symptoms, is obviously important; but it is equally evident that at some point efforts to alter behavior significantly and enduringly, whether by chemotherapy or psychotherapy, education, improved milieu, or other cultural forces, must do more than interdict the symptomatic manifestations. They must alter not only the originating processes, which had their roots in earlier years, and the behavior that these had produced, but also the sustaining processes and the complex secondary feedback from them. Otherwise, symptomatic change and improvement may merely hide a continuing process of disease. By itself, it should never be regarded as certain evidence of fundamental change.

Still another example is from the story of a young woman who had led a life of abject submissiveness, interspersed with episodes of self-mutilation and kleptomania, along with periods of gorging, followed by self-induced vomiting, and still other phases of deliberate starvation. Under treatment, certain elements in the underlying constellations changed, and with them their symptomatic expressions—for example, the tendency to self-mutilation and the cycles of fasting alternating with compulsive eating disappeared. She was able to hold a job and to enjoy at least some relationships with men. Yet this latter aspect of her life was still neurotically restricted, as shown by the fact that she could express it only in debased and debasing relationships, through which she secretly ventilated her pent-up and in many ways justified hostility toward all of those who had been closest to her in childhood and adolescence.

Obviously, partial changes had taken place in the underlying processes that had produced her symptomatic behavior; and these changes in turn had made secondary changes possible in the symptoms themselves, changes that fed back different tertiary consequences for her life and for her human relationships. Yet all this was still partial: her *life* became less sick, and the process of illness was significantly ameliorated, without being fully resolved. She herself was not yet basically changed, and her capacity for further change was still limited.

Quite evidently, every moment of psychological activity is a moment of apparent change. But for the most part these are changes in the surface disguises worn by unchanged, underlying or latent and masked thoughts, feelings, conflicts and purposes. One form of symbolic representation is substituted for another, often with changes in affective coloring, all of which may look very different, even when it covers up an unchanged base. Furthermore, we are continuously in transit between one such mixture and another, between one point in a temporary, unstable equilibrium and another, yet without ever returning precisely to the preceding point of departure.

What all these examples have in common is the simple fact that in the mosaic of the *concurrent conscious, preconscious, and unconscious processes* that govern every moment of all human life, lasting and significant change requires a release of psychological processes from domination by the dictatorship of unconscious mechanisms. Only this can produce the freedom to go on experimenting, trying now a turn to the right and now to the left, free from unconsciously determined compulsions or fears that force the subject to move like a robot in either direction. The freedom to modify and alter one's course, the

freedom to experiment with changes of patterns and to learn from the consequences of these changes, the freedom to respond appropriately to changes in
inner and outer cues—these are the internal freedoms that are made possible
only by a change in the distribution of influence among the conscious, preconscious and unconscious determinants of all psychological events.

The charge often leveled at psychiatrists is that they merely teach people
to "adjust," to alter their "masks," to change their behavior so as to make it more
acceptable to the outside world, and perhaps to make it possible for the patient
to learn how to gain more of the material rewards the society has to offer. Such
therapists, if they exist, are not attempting to cure, but only to persuade people
to adjust to what may fairly be called an irrational society. But the kind of cure
I am talking about, when I define change as the capacity to change further, is not
as circular as it sounds, because it means freeing the patient from imprisonment.
I would not claim that this is always possible for individuals or for large numbers
of people today.

WHAT THEN IS CHANGE?

It is a source of many human tragedies that, starting with the first acquisition
of language in early childhood and continuing throughout life, the freedom to
change with which we are endowed at birth gradually lessens under the cumulative influence of neurotogenic and other restricting events. Among these the
acquisition of the tools of symbolic communication is of prime importance. The
story of how the processes of education and the mere acquisition of language
can frequently initiate the imprisonment of psychological freedom is one of the
many important problems that educators have never faced adequately, but must
ultimately face and solve. Most of the earliest manifestations of this take the
form of masked compulsive and phobic mechanisms. In their production, somatic
variables also play a role, the precise degree and nature of which is unclear. Only
rarely are these early manifestations of neurotic deviations easily recognized
through self-evident symptoms. Usually only the fully evolved neurotic state is self-
diagnosing. A man with a hand-washing compulsion needs no psychiatrist to
convince him that he has a neurosis for which he needs help. He comes com-
plaining of his neurosis and asking for help. Another man may be destroying his
career and his life and his human relationships through a compulsive work drive,
compulsive benevolence, or an insatiable and compulsive gregarious need, none
of which he may recognize or acknowledge even to himself as symptoms of
illness, even though they may be driven by an unstable interplay among phobias
that are touched off by his being alone or even by any future prospect of his
being alone, a situation against which he defends himself by one or another of
these counterphobic drives.

Such a man may struggle to his last breath to deny his neurosis, and to
defend himself and his way of living as "normal." Yet ultimately this insatiability
ends in depression, sometimes in efforts to drown this in alcohol, often decom-
pensating later in life into an agitated depression. In still another man, a counterphobic hand-washing compulsion may cause severe skin troubles, yet its general

secondary consequences are not as destructive to the patient, to those around him, or to society in general, as are the consequences of many more insidious but socially accepted symptoms. Frank neurosis may paralyze an individual, yet may pass unnoticed because it has little impact on society. (Similarly, a mother or father with a neurotic fear of heights may produce less distortion in a child than would that same mother or father with subtly concealed neurotic personality traits.) Moreover, the frankly symptomatic neurosis is actually less frequent than are those masked and subtle neurotic distortions of human development that are universal in all cultures of which we have more than superficial knowledge.

INDICATORS THAT THE CAPABILITY FOR CONTINUING CHANGE HAS ALTERED

Clearly, I must accept the challenge of attempting to characterize as precisely as possible what constitutes criteria of change in behavioral patterns. To do this, I have first to present my concept of how we think and feel, and of what I consider to be the one essential criterion of normal thought and feeling. With this goal in mind, I shall repeat here that, to be termed "normal," any pattern of behavior must have the capability of changing in response to changing cues, whether these cues reach the individual from changes in the outside world or in the biological tides within his own body, or in the accumulated residues of past experiences, or from changes in the projections from past experiences into the future, in the form of anticipations of the future. No matter what the pattern of action may be, no matter how creative and constructive is the impact of any particular act, if its freedom to change in response to changing cues has been impaired or limited, then that very same act has become a neurotic symptom. But if this essential capacity to change in response to changing signals is to be preserved, then the constellation of both the psychological and the physiological processes that determine all behavior must also be free to change.

My own definition of psychopathology has been that *whenever the complex cluster of concurrent somatic and psychological processes that determine behavior* predetermines its automatic and obligatory repetition (even in the face of success or failure, rewards or punishments, satiation and fulfillment, frustration or deprivation, anxiety or reassurance, anger or fear, happiness or depression), that pattern of action must be regarded as pathological. Furthermore, the secondary feedback from any pattern of behavior, the repetition of which has become obligatory, is a secondary intensification of the process of illness with new conflicts and new symptoms, which in turn develop a new and third order of distorting consequences. This principle applies to all forms of activities, even the simplest and most elementary biological instinctual activities such as breathing, eating or drinking. It is equally applicable to sexual activity and to all complex social, economic, political, artistic, cultural, or religious behavior, etc. It is, finally, true of all the activities that we call creative, whether in art or science.

From this it follows that the only psychological change that carries lasting significance must arise out of a change in the distribution of control among conscious, preconscious, and unconscious processes in the direction of conscious and preconscious dominance, thus freeing the capacity for further change. In other words, the significant change in human life is a change that brings with it an increase in the freedom to learn from experience, with a consequent capacity for growth and development. This then is the ultimate criterion of psychological change. Unless human beings achieve this, they remain imprisoned.

Almost every patient who comes for treatment wants to be free of pain, but not really to change. Indeed, it is easy to want to be free of pain, but it is not easy to want to be a different kind of human being, or even to conceive of what such a difference in one's self might mean. Unhappily, the same is true of the social structure of society, of government, or of any of our cultural institutions. As with individuals, governments and social structures want to be "tax-exempt": they want to be free of pain; they want not to have to pay for their defects with pain; but they do not want to change. This is why the individual's struggle through therapy to break out of his personal imprisonment within the neurotic process is an essential first step in any effort to increase the freedom to change in our social structures and in our culture.

A few subtle indicators of the freedom to change and of variations in that freedom are available to us. Of these one has to do with the speed of certain processes of search and retrieval. This will undoubtedly be a valuable indicator, but its application will require the development of new methods of measuring. Another has to do with the degree of freedom of what we call "free associations." This can be gauged more readily by determining the speed of the process, the word frequency, the duration and periodicity of rhythm of silent interludes, the presence or absence of stereotyped and repetitive patterns both of content and of form. With appropriate recording devices one can also study the stereotype of voice-volume, intonation, pitch and their rhythms, as well as the patterns of the accompanying paralinguistic language. None of this is easy; but all of it is possible. Therefore we are justified in saying that it is almost certainly predictable that these devices will be used in future basic studies of the impact of drugs and of psychonoxious and/or psychotherapeutic experiences on the freedom of the individual for continuing and evolving change. Comparable indicators of the freedom to change on the part of cultures and societies are more elusive.

IMPLICATIONS FOR CULTURAL CHANGE

As with individual human beings, cultures have a relatively rigid core even when they seem to be fluid processes. They reinforce the rigidity of the individual by written laws, authoritarian edicts, and those unwritten laws we call traditions, customs, mores. There are often incompatibilities among these ingredients of culture, because almost invariably the unwritten elements in a culture are expressions of irreconcilable but neurotically entrenched biases. They are not easy to alter, because they represent not only our ethical standards but also those unconscious conflicts and their derivatives that together make up the neurotic components of all human nature. This makes it difficult and sometimes impossible to change a culture in any significant way, unless the individuals who compose the culture become free to change. And that is precisely the problem that I have been considering in the preceding pages: that is, what meaningful change constitutes for the individual and how this can be achieved. Clearly cultural change is limited by the restrictions that are imposed on change in individual human nature by concealed neurotic processes.

At the same time, there is a continuous cybernetic interplay between the culture and the individual—that is, between the intrapsychic processes, which make either for fluidity or for rigidity within the individual, and the external processes, which make either for fluidity or for rigidity in a culture. This interplay is sometimes clearly evident, sometimes subtly concealed; either way, it is at the heart of the resolution of one of the basic obstacles to human progress. It would be naive to expect political and ideological liberty to provide internal liberty to the individual citizen unless he had already won freedom from the internal tyranny of his own neurotic mechanisms. Political liberty allows him to experiment with changes in the external forms of the society in which he lives; but only his attainment of internal liberty will make it possible for the individual to make the most of his external freedom. A free society does not automatically bring psychological freedom to the individual; it makes it possible for him to strive for it. Nor does the free individual automatically create a free society; his own freedom makes it possible for him to struggle towards it.

The great neurophysiologist, Paul MacLean (1962, 1963, 1964), pointed out that the human animal has not merely one brain but a hierarchy of at least three: a reptilian brain at the core; a lower mammalian brain a step above this; and the higher mammalian brain struggling, often unsuccessfully, to rule the others. He compared us to a 1960 car with a 1940 carburetor and a 1920 generator. It is not remarkable that this jerry-built apparatus contributes to our vulnerability to those obligatory repetitions that are at the core of all that is neurotic in human nature, and to which a variety of experiential, social, biochemical, and structural variables make their contributions. Clearly, all who are concerned with cultural progress must search for ways to eliminate or at least to limit those somatic and psychological factors that restrict the freedom of the human being himself to change.

This search should focus first on infancy and childhood, because that is where the restriction of the capacity to change is first observed. Such a search requires a close comparison of the effects of different child-rearing traditions. It would be helpful to study this in the past as well as the present; but since we cannot go back to compare with the present the manifestations of these phenomena in earlier centuries, we must instead subject all existing cultures to microscopic study—those that we call "primitive" as well as those that we euphemistically call "advanced"—seeking for correlations between cultural variables and the freedom of the infant to grow, the freedom of the adult to change, and the freedom of the culture to make experiments.

As I contemplate the role in human culture of such institutions as education, art, literature, religion, the humanities, and indeed all of the life sciences, I ask this same question: What is their effect, if any, on the individual's freedom to change and to keep on changing, and consequently on the capacity of an entire culture to evolve? Admittedly, this question itself gives me an uneasy feeling, since even savants and creative artists and scientists are not noted for their flexibility. This leads directly to still another question: What effects do our educational processes in general have on our ability to transmit to succeeding generations any fragment of wisdom that we may acquire in our own allotted time? And this in turn brings me to my ultimate concern, which is whether and to what extent the early resolution of the universal neurotic episodes of childhood would free the enormous untapped creative potential that is latent in every man. Here of course is the meeting place of the two streams, i.e., the freedom of the individual and the freedom of society for continuing change. If the second depends upon the first, then the prognosis for cultural change is indeed very gloomy. For we know the impossibility of making available to every citizen the kind of self-inquiry that offers at least the possibility for enduring change.

But if we try to think in long-range terms—in terms of generations—then the place to start is in earliest childhood. We already know that at this stage the manifest restriction of the child's psychological freedom takes many forms—for example, tic-like repetitive patterns of sound and movement; automatic crying; disturbances of breathing, ingestion, and excretion; sleep disturbances; such automatisms as bedwetting and sleepwalking; nightmares or equally unreasonable daytime terrors; arbitrary repugnances to certain foods or places or people. In later childhood, these may reappear in new symbolic disguises, such as persistent or transient phobias and compulsions.

If those involved in the rearing of children—parents, teachers, doctors, nurses—can be trained to recognize these signals of disturbance and to explore at their inception the originating causes of these early imprisonments of the child's freedom to learn and change, so as to regain this freedom for the child as promptly as possible, some hope may exist for the future possibilities of cultural change.

The work of researchers in normal child development, in pathology, in medicine, endocrinology, and genetics, might all converge to teach us what are the truly optimal conditions for normal growth; how to correct genetic defects; how to alleviate or cure organic conditions that interfere with psychological functioning. If the push of society were in the direction of finding ways to rear healthy children, who are capable of change, these children might be able to grow into and work out the creative society of which humanists dream.

This sounds like the naive reverie of someone who has lost faith in solutions. And perhaps it is. But society is made up of institutions, and the institutions are composed of men. One can change institutions, but unless man is able to change, he will continue to endow his institutions with the rigidities, the compulsive beliefs, the irrational determinations that stem from his unconscious processes when these hold dominant control.

Take just one example: compare two children, each with the same intellectual and creative endowment. Rear one in an atmosphere in which his personal freedom is nurtured; rear the other in an atmosphere in which he is made to feel powerless, dispossessed of volition, so that he simultaneously hates and envies the magically powerful adults around him. What would they reach for as they grew up? What if the first reached for achievement for the sake of the feeling of competence, and the second reached for achievement for the sake of power, the right to dominate? What kinds of societies would each prefer? and create?

We have seen the outer forms of societies change radically, yet retain the aggressions, the inequalities, the inhumanities that haunt mankind. If we are to hope for a society capable of productive change, we must find a way to produce people capable of change. Where can we start, except with the children?

REFERENCES

Brickner, R. M. (1940). A Human Cortical Area Producing Repetitive Phenomena when Stimulated. *Journal of Neurophysiology,* 3:125–130.

Kubie, L. S. (1951a). Discussion of Dr. Penfield's Address on Memory Mechanisms. *Transactions of the American Neurological Association* (76th Annual Meeting, Atlantic City, June 1951). Richmond, Va.: William Bird Press, pp. 31–39. Reprinted in *Archives of Neurology and Psychiatry,* 67:191–194.

———— (1951b). The Neurotic Potential, the Neurotic Process, and the Neurotic State. *United States Armed Forces Medical Journal,* 2(1):1–12. Reprinted in *Digest of Neurology and Psychiatry,* Series 20 (Jan. 1952), p. 15.

———— (1953). Some Implications for Psychoanalysis of Modern Concepts of the Organization of the Brain. *Psychoanalytic Quarterly,* 22:21–68.

———— (1958a). *Neurotic Distortion of the Creative Process.* Lawrence: University of Kansas Press (esp. Chap. 3, pp. 104–127).

———— (1958b). The Neurotic Process as the Focus of Physiological and Psychoanalytic Research. *British Journal of Mental Science,* 104:518–536.

———— (1963). Neurosis and Normality. In: *The Encyclopedia of Mental Health,* 4:1346–1353, ed. A. Deutsch. New York: Franklin Watts.

———— (1964). Traditionalism in Psychiatry. *Journal of Nervous and Mental Disease,* 139:6–19.

———— (1966). Book review of *I Never Promised You a Rose Garden,* by Hannah Green. *Journal of Nervous and Mental Disease,* 142:190–194.

MacLean, P. D. (1962). New Findings Relevant to the Evolution of Psychosexual Functions of the Brain. *Journal of Nervous and Mental Disease.* 135:289–301.

———— (1963). Phylogenesis. In: *Expressions of the Emotions in Man,* ed. P. Knapp. New York: International Universities Press, pp. 16–35.

———— (1964). Man and His Animal Brains. *Modern Medicine,* Feb. 3:99–106.

Olds, J. (1955). *Physiological Mechanisms of Reward.* Lincoln: University of Nebraska Press.

———— (1958). Self-Stimulation of the Brain. *Science,* 127:315–324.

———— (1959). Higher Functions of the Nervous System. *Annual Review of Physiology,* 21:381–402.

———— (1961). Differential Effects on Drives and Drugs on Self-Stimulation at Different Brain Sites. In *Electrolysis Stimulation of the Brain,* ed. D. E. Sheer. Austin: University of Texas Press, pp. 350–360.

Penfield, W. (1952). Memory Mechanisms. *Archives of Neurology and Psychiatry,* 67:178–198.

Spitz, R. (1957). *No and Yes: On the Beginnings of Human Communication.* New York: International Universities Press.

QUESTIONS ABOUT MAN'S ATTEMPT TO UNDERSTAND HIMSELF

Frederic G. Worden, M.D.

INTRODUCTION

When I read the title *Psychoanalysis and Contemporary Science,* it was the "and" that caught my attention because of the relationship it implies between the effort by man to understand himself through psychoanalysis, and his efforts through science to understand those other elements of his world that are perceived as not-self. Over some years of clinical experience in psychoanalysis and psychiatry and of laboratory research in neurophysiology, questions about the nature of this relationship had occurred to me in a number of different forms and contexts. The problems are old ones, epitomized by such antitheses as subjective–objective, private–public, and mind–brain. It is not clear, at least to me, how much progress, if any, we have made on the body–soul problem in the 2000 years since the Greeks formulated it. It seems appropriate, nevertheless, for the first issue of this new annual, to reexamine the relationships between science in general and those psychological disciplines that attempt to deal with man as an experiencing, self-aware subject.

My aim is to clarify some questions rather than to provide answers. This expresses a conviction that psychoanalysis (and psychiatry) should spend more energy distressing itself with questions and less energy comforting itself with apparent answers. Indeed, it seems to me that, in the history of science, progress has been retarded less by the difficulty of the questions faced than by man's incredible need to think that he knows, and therefore to accept almost any answer, however simplistic, superstitious, or irrelevant, in preference to living with a feeling of ignorance. Much of being a scientist involves the fight to overcome this irrational fear of ignorance, and to search for, welcome, and define gaps in knowledge.

Albert Einstein, according to one of his friends, once attributed his intellectual success to the fact that, when he was a little boy, his mother always inquired, when he came home from school, "Did you ask any good questions today?" Presumably she was less interested in whether he had gotten any good answers. In the hope of encouraging that kind of questioning attitude, I shall ask some questions and state some opinions about matters for which I believe few answers are yet available, taking "answers" to mean statements whose validity can be settled in terms of evidence. Opinions, on the other hand, are assertions for which the evidence is sufficiently equivocal so that the question of who is making them becomes helpful in evaluating them. This is by way of suggesting that it will be easy to refute my opinions by citing authorities who disagree; but, unless I have made some unwitting breakthrough, it will not be easy to reject them on the basis of decisive evidence. This is not merely a peculiarity of my remarks; it reflects something of the current status of attempts to establish a scientific understanding of the human mind, its biological substrates, and the social matrix within which its normal and pathological manifestations develop. The prevalence of opinions, and of authorities who express them, tends to be self-perpetuating, because schools are established in which informing the student about the details of various opinions and controversies inculcates a sense of expertise that placates his need to know, and prevents the development of that vigorous questioning without which the Emperor's nakedness continues to be accepted as a fine example of fabric and tailoring. The questions that follow are intended to encourage an attitude of wondering, "Did I ask any good questions today?"

What is a good question? In the first place, a good question has to be a valid one. That is, it must not only have the grammatical form and appearance of a question, but it must, at the semantic level, actually state the terms defining the form and fitness of an answer. We humans are so vulnerable to struggling with invalid questions as if they were real that one might expect a field like psychiatry to place much emphasis on teaching its students to discriminate between valid and invalid questions. Nothing could be further from the truth. Some twenty years of observing psychiatric education has persuaded me that invalid questions are more often answered than recognized, and thereby encouraged rather than discouraged.

Year after year, questions are asked on the order of "Is intensive psychotherapy an effective treatment for schizophrenia?" and answers are provided in erudite terms concerning the nature and course of schizophrenia, the design of experiments with matched controls, the problem of quantifying behavior and obtaining follow-up data, and other considerations, all of which obscure the fact that no question has been asked, or, more explicitly, that whatever has been asked has not been specified in the question. Regrettably, it is not enough for a teacher to point out that the terms need definition, or even to provide such definitions. Rather, the task is to help the student discover that a term like "intensive psychotherapy" is meant to refer to a reality that defies operational definition, because it is such an awesome task to know which aspects of that reality are significant and which are trivial. If one looks across different schools of psychotherapy, and across therapists within a school, it seems clear that what therapists think they do with patients comprises only partial aspects of what actually goes on in the therapeutic relationship, and that it is easy to be convinced about which aspects of therapy are important even though others are equally convinced about conflicting propositions, and it is not easy to know for sure.

The other terms in the question, "effective treatment" and "schizophrenia," obscure equally difficult problems, leading directly to such mysteries as the nature of mental health, the equilibrium between individual and group values, and the purpose of human existence. There is today a widespread conviction among youth that "shrinks" are agents of a sick society set upon making people "adjust"; in an earlier era, psychoanalysis was widely suspected of favoring the freedom of animal instincts, even at the cost of overthrowing the restraints of society.

A second factor in judging the goodness of a question concerns the amount of difference it makes to answer it one way rather than another way—provided of course that "difference" is taken to refer to matters beyond the personal feelings of the questioner. More difference is likely to hinge on the question of whether to cut here or there during a major surgical operation than is likely to hinge on whether or not to give an electroconvulsive treatment. Even less difference is likely to depend on the question of whether aggression arises only by deflection from the death instinct, or whether it is an instinct in its own right. Unfortunately, for psychiatric questions it is often inordinately difficult, or even impossible, to know how much difference, if any, one answer will make, as compared with another answer. This problem could stand more attention in psychiatry than it is generally accorded.

For example, much emphasis in psychiatric training is placed on the question of what to say to patients, how to say it, and when to say it. Implicit in discussions of this topic is the assumption that what we say is going to make a difference, yet for any given instance it is usually difficult to know whether the difference will be slight or great. Obviously, the importance of what we *say* is partially a function of what we *are* to the patient. Sometimes just being with a patient is so important that what we say probably holds about as much import as the verbal content of a mother's vocalization when she attends to a preverbal infant. At other times, we are so unnoticeable to the patient that almost anything we might say will remain subliminal for him. Unpredictably enough, there *are* moments when the details of what we say may have momentous consequences for the course of therapy. In general, it seems to me that the common error is to overestimate the importance of what we say. This error is a pleasant one to make so long as patients tend to improve, but it becomes very unpleasant when patients deteriorate or kill themselves. Taking undeserved credit for recoveries would be a more popular folly for psychotherapists if it were easier to enjoy without having to accept undeserved blame for bad outcomes and suicides. This is not to say that a few words can *never* precipitate a move toward recovery or toward death, but only that it is not easy to know when words are going to be that important.

Some years ago, "direct analysis" of schizophrenic patients was introduced by Rosen (1947). An incidental sidelight was the surprise among many psycho-analysts and psychiatrists at the blunt and free-wheeling way Dr. Rosen talked to his patients, which conflicted with an opinion widely held then that one must choose words carefully in speaking to schizophrenic patients because they are inordinately sensitive to, and influenced by, words. As is usual for psychiatric anecdotes, little can be concluded except that the import of words is not neces-sarily self-evident, even to experts. Man likes to talk and to overrate the im-portance of words, but there are probably many moments in the course of human affairs when debating about this or that word is nitpicking, because there aren't any words, or even deeds, that could make much difference.

If psychotherapists tend to overestimate the power of words, patients often tend to underestimate them, as expressed in the query "How can just talking help?" A considerable part of becoming human rests on "just talking," as is evident in the fate of children with congenital deafness, the vulnerability of personality functioning to stimulus isolation experiments, and the contribution of interpersonal communication to human experience. There is little doubt that talking is the most human, and perhaps the most important, activity of men, but the problem lies in knowing, for a given instance, whether words are going to be meaningful or meaningless.

A third aspect of a good question is its simplicity. No matter how complex a system one confronts, the best question to ask about it is probably the simplest question that one can devise at that particular moment in time. For my purpose, a simple question is one that can be answered easily. A person who is a psychi-atric patient is a complex system, but this doesn't mean one has to start by asking complex questions. Simple questions about things like weight loss, sleep pattern, appetite, interests, and patterns of current interpersonal relatedness should be answered before one gets into questions on the order of whether the oral sadistic trends are primarily expressions of instinctual fixation or regression. Unfortunately, opinions about the latter are often unaccompanied by informa-tion about the former. That is to say, the differentiation of observations from inferences is less clear in psychological disciplines than it is in other sciences, and there is some tendency, especially in clinical situations, to make inferences that are distantly removed from observations, or are made prior to, and instead of, explicit observations. This leads to the rapid accumulation of opinion con-cerning very complex questions, without first establishing solid answers to simple questions that can serve as stepping-stones toward the next level of complexity. This is not merely carelessness on the part of psychological investigators; it arises from factors peculiar to the process of coming to understand another human being. Some of these are discussed in the following pages.

What does it mean to understand another person? In the psychoanalytic situation, as in other intensive psychotherapies, the patient's subjective sense of being understood is important: if his hope for this feeling falls below a certain level, he is likely to leave the relationship. Curiously enough, no matter what the theoretical frame of reference of the therapist, in successful psychoanalysis or psychotherapy, the patients tend to feel increasingly understood. The talent people have for feeling understood on almost any conceptual basis is not a trivial issue, as illustrated by experiments reported by Garfinkel (1967). He had undergraduate subjects, who thought they were participating in a search for new methods of counseling, ask ten questions about personal problems that could be answered with a "yes" or a "no." The sequence of answers, evenly divided between yes's and no's, was predecided with a table of random numbers, and delivered by the "counselor" who was concealed behind a screen. The results demonstrated that the subjects were able to make sense out of the answers, and generally felt that the advice had been helpful. When answers were startlingly incongruous, or contradictory of the preceding context, the subjects were able to minimize the incongruity by "discovering" what the counselor "really had in mind." This capacity for finding patterns of sense and understanding even in a randomized sequence of answers suggests that the validity of an understanding cannot be tested with observations from the psychotherapeutic situation.

What can be examined is the influence exerted by a given set of beliefs on personal adaptation. History reveals that man can live successfully with a great diversity of convictions regarding his own nature. It follows that utility for daily living is not a very powerful test for scientific theories about man. This statement is especially convincing because man seems willing and able to believe whatever is necessary for achieving a sense of mutual acceptance, respect, and love with significant other persons, and intensive psychotherapy inherently establishes the significance of the psychotherapist as another person, almost whatever he believes. It seems to me that the validation of scientific concepts about men will depend upon the integration of data from the clinical psychotherapeutic situation with data from all the sciences that bear on the biological processes mediating personality functioning.

Why isn't psychiatry more scientific? There are a number of answers that are popular but unsatisfactory. One is that psychiatry is a young science, which hasn't yet had time to develop. It seems to me that this is no explanation, but merely rephrases the question to: *Why is psychiatry such a young science?* Surely it is not due to lack of interest. Since the evolutionary emergence of symbolic processes, I would guess that more human brain energy has been spent on trying to understand human behavior than on any other topic. By comparison, trivial amounts of time have been devoted to chemistry, yet with spectacular scientific results. Some say, "Ah, but the phenomena are so complex and subtle, so awkward to express verbally, that it has been most difficult to develop adequate instruments." The implication here is that the problem is essentially methodological. The converse of this has also been offered as an answer—namely, that psychiatry is scientific in *method*, even though its results are so complex and subtle that it is difficult to communicate or validate them. This notion is often fortified by appeals to astronomy or Darwinian evolution, as examples of the fact that a non-experimental method can be scientific.

The relationship of psychiatry to science involves a substantial problem in underlying logic, which overshadows problems of immaturity and method. The essence of this issue is that much of dynamic psychiatry's capacity to understand troubled persons depends upon Freud's discovery that a symptom can have a meaning, and as Home (1966) has contended, in making this discovery Freud moved from the logic of science to the logic of the humanities, because a meaning is not a product of causes, but is the creation of a living subject. He writes:

The subject of meaning is known to us through an act of identification and not through an act of sense perception or scientific observation. Nor is it accessible to introspection because through introspection it is infinitely recessive. We can never observe the "I" that observes. Because meaning is an aspect of the living subject known to us through identification, it cannot be investigated by the methods and logic of science, for these are only applicable to the dead object, or to the object perceived as dead.

About a year later, in the same journal, Guntrip (1967) suggested that the contrast between living and dead drawn by Home could better be viewed as a contrast between object and subject.

The objects we are interested in are capable of being, and in fact are, subjects of experience. The objects of natural science are either not capable of being subjects, or when they are it does not matter to science, which ignores that aspect of their reality. When live objects are studied as subjects, we have psychodynamic science. On the other hand, when live subjects are studied as objects only, as is done in biology, neurology, behaviouristic psychology and sociology, then we have the classic model of "natural" science. . . .

Of the difference between scientific and humanistic logic, Home (1966) wrote:

My aim has been to make the point that science is not just an improved version of humanistic thinking; it is a different kind of thinking, with a limited field of reference, with different basic axioms and a different logical form. To apply scientific modes of thought inappropriately produces meaningless theories, in precisely the same way as the inappropriate application of humanistic modes of thought does. Abuse of either mode also has its own peculiar symptomatology. Misapplied humanism, whose intrinsic logic demands an explanation of events in terms of motivated persons, invents them and so for a time the sky was full of angels each with a compulsion or orders to push a star . . . Misapplied science, on the other hand, whose intrinsic logic demands an explanation in terms of impersonal events, invents metaphysical facts, as for example Karl Marx and his successors did in the process of creating a Science of History. Feudalism, Capitalism, Socialism, Communism, . . . Fascism, Colonialism, Imperialism, and Marxism-Leninism are some of these facts, for in Marxist theory such nouns are used as if they stood for actual objective events whose structure and development are known. And as humanism invented people to push the stars around, so Marxist science had to invent impersonal forces generated by the class war to push the people around.

The logical distinction between causes and meanings has direct pragmatic implications for clinical attempts to understand patients. Whitehorn (1947) commented on the fact that to attempt to understand the meaning of behavior is often helpful, even though causal explanations be lacking. On the other hand, the scientific search for causes often conflicts with approaches that could be helpful with the individual patient. To state this dilemma in a stark form, one can look for the meaning of an hallucination in the context of a personal relationship with another human being, but to search for the cause of an hallucination one must deal with things perceived as impersonal and dead, such as chemicals, neuronal circuits, and electrons.

For brain researchers, this dilemma has come to be called "the mind–brain barrier," and in sensory neurophysiology, it concerns the problem of how perception arises from neurophysiological processes in sensory systems. A fair bit is known about how acoustic energy is transduced into neural activities, and how these activities are transformed and transmitted upward in the brain systems concerned with hearing; but we have no idea how and where in the brain these electrochemical processes emerge in the form of an experience that fuses the inputs of both ears into a single sound image, endowed with qualities such as meaning, and a location somewhere out in space. Popular solutions include attributing perception to the soul, to a single pontifical neuron, to all the neurons of the brain as a collectivity, to a little personage somewhere in the brain, or else denying that the experience of a fused sound image is real, let alone a problem. Such an experience occurs in the so-called "private world" in contrast to the "public world" of sense perception—which is a way of saying that no one can prove it occurs for anybody else but himself.

In sum, then, it seems that psychiatry is no more scientific than it is because it wants to understand living persons, and to do this the humanistic mode of cognition, based on projective identification, is useful, whereas the scientific mode, based on sense perception of things seen as impersonal objects, is not.

What is a psychiatrist? According to my definition, a psychiatrist is surprisingly rare even within that group who have graduated from psychiatric residency training and are spending their time treating psychiatric patients. This rarity reflects a situation quite different from that which obtains, for example, for graduates of violin training, of whom one might say that Jascha Heifetzes are rare. Most of the people who claim to be fiddlers are at least playing the same instrument, even if not so well as Heifetz. It seems to me that for those who claim to be psychiatrists, not only are they not all playing the same instrument, but some are playing instruments that others disapprove of or disbelieve, or even, in some cases, instruments whose very existence is unknown to others in the group. Since all of them think of themselves as psychiatrists, and since all of them are more or less successful with patients, it would appear that it might be confusing to try to discover what a psychiatrist is in terms of these criteria.

If one shifts from the context of clinical practice to the context of research, the issue becomes clearer. In fact, my thinking on this topic stems from struggling with the question "What is a psychiatric researcher?" In the early 1950's, the NIMH established a Career Investigator Program of fellowships, to encourage and support psychiatrists and related behavioral scientists who wished to prepare for research careers. An early disappointment for this program was that not many psychiatrists leaped at the opportunity, which did, however, attract an assortment of clinical and physiological psychologists, biochemists, neurophysiologists, and others. Perhaps even more interesting was the gradual realization that, when psychiatrists were drawn into the program, they often tended to acquire an appearance of being no longer psychiatrists, but amateur experimental or clinical psychologists, biochemists, neurophysiologists, or the like. In those instances where a program did seem clearly psychiatric, questions were likely to arise as to how clearly it was research.

This situation led me to wonder whether there was an area of expertise that would define the psychiatric researcher, as distinct from the neurologist, pharmacologist, or other professional working on psychiatric problems. After struggling through various stages of thinking about it, I finally decided, as any reasonably intelligent high school student might have in the first place, that the psychiatric researcher had the skills necessary for investigating the human mind. By extrapolation, the unique expertise of a clinical psychiatrist would consist in being able to come to know the mind of another human being in depth. As I have argued, this is inherently a humanistic rather than a scientific process, in that observations are made for the purpose of establishing an identification on the basis of which the meaning of the behavior of another person can be understood.

One possible reason why psychiatrists are rare is that this task demands great, if not peculiar, talents which are not easy to recognize, and which are not, therefore, practical prerequisites for entering residency training programs. The conspicuous absence of such talents may not become evident until after rather arduous and prolonged efforts to exercise them—a problem not unlike that of predicting the talent for getting along in a marriage. A second hypothesis about why psychiatrists are rare is that to develop and exercise this talent requires a one to one doctor-patient relationship that is both intensive as to amount of contact, and prolonged over a number of years. Such experience, even with only a handful of patients, is a sine qua non for becoming a psychiatrist. From it, a first-hand view of one's own mind, and informed inferences about the mind of another person and the transactional process between two persons, can be obtained in a form that is simply not available in any other context.

After such a first-hand experience, one can then move on to group therapy, community psychiatry, clinical psychopharmacology, or behavior therapy; but no matter what one does, one retains a professional expertise on the human mind. Without such an experience, one may be successful at all kinds of activities that have therapeutic import, and yet be in the position of not truly knowing the person one is attempting to influence or treat. As I see it, the essence of this necessary experience consists of joining another person in a mutual effort to clear away all the obstacles within the patient and the doctor that prevent a shared trust from developing, on the basis of which the patient can dare to become, and thereby to discover, the kind of person he would have been all along —except for the fact that it had never seemed "safe."

In the beginning, this element of becoming, and discovering, a person applies also to the would-be psychiatrist. I believe that no matter how experienced he becomes, in intensive psychotherapy this element is never completely lost. That is to say, a good psychiatrist always emerges a little more of a person at the end of doing intensive psychotherapy than he was at the beginning of it. That this kind of experience takes years rather than months is most unfortunate, but not surprising in view of the time course of such human affairs as personality maturation, the development of intimacy in interpersonal relationships, and the natural history of psychiatric illnesses. To provide for such prolonged experience all too often conflicts with block time scheduling of other training activities in residency programs.

A third reason, I believe, why psychiatrists are rare is that there has been a trend towards depersonalizing psychiatric training and psychiatry, especially in the last decade: the need for the psychiatrist to be able to come to know, in a deeply intimate way, his patient as a person has been, and is being, belittled. In part, this reflects disillusionment with psychoanalysis, and intensive dynamic psychotherapy, as treatments. Putting it crudely, the notion is that no matter how well you come to know a patient, it won't help him much. A second factor derives from the advent of potent psychopharmacological agents and the concepts of community psychiatry. These provide effective means for keeping the patient in the social harness by manipulating his internal chemistry and his external circumstances, familial and social. A third factor, I believe, is the reflection within psychiatry of those dehumanizing trends that have become so prominently operative in the broader aspects of our society, as the individual human being grows increasingly alienated from, and submerged by, the values and products of the industrial and scientific revolutions. The result of this depersonalizing trend in psychiatric education has tended to be the production of a generation of psychiatrists who can do so much to a patient in three weeks or three months that getting to know the patient seems hardly worthwhile, especially if it is going to take anything like three years of prolonged effort. All of this has been accelerated and encouraged by the modern shift from concern as to what can be done for the few and the rich, to concern as to what can be done for the many and the poor. It is probably self-contradictory to attempt to be personal on a mass basis.

To say that the unique skill of the psychiatrist is to know other persons intimately through inferences derived from projective identification is not to deny the hope that he will also be competent in the biological and behavioral sciences. Rather it is to suggest that if he uses somewhat less personal methods, such as group therapy, drug therapy, community-based procedures and so forth, he will not forget that there is more to being human than is evident in those relatively public facades that people dare not shed except in the privacy of trusting intimacy with another human.

Is psychiatric hospitalization therapeutic or pathogenic? For this patently non-valid question, the last decade has provided a vehement answer, based on demonstrations that patients can be kept in the community, that they may deteriorate during hospitalization, and that, even if they are hospitalized, they can be gotten out quickly if the social organization and resources of the hospital are geared to the "rapid turnover" or "instant discharge" philosophy. Surely any past tendency to underestimate the dangers in psychiatric hospitalization has been overcorrected in the present anti-hospitalization fad. Kubie (1968) has written elsewhere on some of the fallacies of this position, and at the very least, it seems evident that hospitalization as an experience may vary in its effects across numerous dimensions.

It is, however, interesting to reflect on the change in values represented by this shift to community, and against hospital, treatment. Some years ago, I remember hearing Dr. Harry Stack Sullivan present the argument, based on his conceptual model of psychotherapy, that intensive psychotherapy with a schizophrenic patient might be considered successful even though the patient would have to spend the rest of his life in the hospital, being too honest, sensitive, and sane to survive in our hypocritical, harsh, and insane world. The notion that one could be too sane for the outside world is now completely reversed in the assertion that no matter how crazy you are, you don't need to be in the hospital. Gruenberg (1967), in discussing the "social breakdown syndrome," contrasts the schizophrenic who has been socially disabled by hospitalization with a non-disabled patient; he writes, "This non-disabled schizophrenic may be a street cleaner while attending to auditory hallucinations, spend his evenings in the neighborhood bar over a glass of beer, half-listening to his neighbors' conversation: he responds appropriately to the environment's insistent demands, supports his aged mother with whom he lives, and meets adequately all that his society requires in the way of self-care and conformity to community norms." It is not my intent to suggest that Gruenberg's perspective is inherently bad, but only that it is very different from Sullivan's. Moreover, I do not believe that the difference has resulted primarily from new knowledge about social factors in psychiatric illness. In fact, Sullivan was clearly aware of social factors and discriminated quite carefully between the ability to carry on in society and those goals he felt were important for psychotherapy.

I believe that the present fad expresses not so much new discoveries as a movement away from individual to group values, along the continuum suggested in Koestler's title *The Yogi and the Commissar* (1945). This movement saves society money, spares families the distress of having a hospitalized relative, and obviates the challenge for any psychiatrist to attempt the arduous task of establishing a relationship of personal intimacy within which the patient might grow a bit more human. Whether or not this is progress is part of the major question facing man today—namely, "How important, or possible, is it to be humanly personal in a mass society?"

Is a chemical cure for schizophrenia conceivable in principle? Just barely. There are formidable problems in research on the genetic factors in schizophrenia (Rosenthal and Kety, 1968), but there is no objection, in principle, to stipulating that these problems have been solved, and that the enzymatic or biochemical mediation of a specific genetic etiological factor has been identified. Given this discovery, it is easy to imagine a chemical preventive to be administered to the prospective schizophrenic from birth, or perhaps even prenatally. It might act by energizing integrative capacities, or by increasing that intransitive zest for living that Federn (Weiss, 1950) called "medial ego libido," or by lowering vulnerability to anxiety; through such actions, it might shift the balance of the potential for interpersonal activities in the direction necessary for experiences promoting personality development and maturation.

To imagine a chemical that would cure schizophrenia requires a much more difficult conceptual leap, because in addition to correcting the inborn chemical-metabolic error it would have to transmit information of the kind ordinarily acquired from those interpersonal experiences that are essential for personality maturation but are missing in schizophrenic persons insofar as they have failed to have these experiences. In other words, the pill would have to supply the patient with all those inner cognitive and emotional controls and models that constitute the internalized trappings of being a person, including such items as a conscience with a workable set of rewards and punishments, self-percepts of at least modest accuracy, social roles, and flexible patterns of loving, along with a host of other, equally intangible attributes. To provide all this is conceptually, and certainly chemically, a bigger order than straightening out twisted molecules. Even if one stipulates that the chemical transfer of information has been achieved, the problem of choosing which information to transfer to a particular patient, and who should make such decisions, might be solved by authoritarian means in the absence of a scientific basis for defining the nature and purpose of man.

Are psychiatric residents taught too much? If one travels about the country visiting departments of psychiatry, one repeatedly comes across faculty members who have horrified themselves by calculating how much of the residents' time is scheduled for didactic lectures, seminars, and supervision, and how little is left over for actually seeing patients. This tendency to overschedule teaching time at the cost of patient-care time is, I believe, more pronounced for psychiatry than for other medical speciality training. This becomes especially peculiar if one considers what would happen if all teaching were cancelled, leaving the psychiatric resident full time for his patients and his books.

At worst, it would appear that the patients would receive competent general medical care reflecting the internship [1] from which the resident had

---

[1] If the psychiatric resident has not had an internship this argument is destroyed, along with other matters of more consequence for patients.

been graduated, and that, since the resident is a human being, he would provide this medical care in the context of a doctor-patient relationship approached with at least minimal warmth and understanding. It seems appealing to me that to cancel all teaching for the medical or surgical resident might have more alarming consequences. If this is true, then it becomes necessary to explain why over-teaching should be a particular problem in just those areas of medicine where there is reason to suspect that teaching is less vital for patient welfare.

It is plausible to argue that psychiatry is more complex and subtle, and involves the personality of the resident more than is true for other specialities. Even so, the fact that the psychiatric resident is often burdened with more tu-torial scrutiny and supervision in saying "good morning" to his patient than the surgical resident is provided in opening a belly, suggests the possibility that an irrational factor may be operating. Teaching too much may enable teachers and students alike to substitute a sense of there being too much to learn for an awareness of how little is truly known. For the psychotherapist, it is of course helpful to think he knows, but for the researcher it is more important to know that he needs to think.

Where, or what, in the world is mind, or is it? How productive this question has been is open to question, for despite appearances to the contrary, I am not at all certain that the explosion of information in the neurosciences has brought us any closer to whatever the question is, let alone to its answer. In a paper called "Why the Mind Is in the Head" McCulloch (1965) argued that it had to be there because that is where the neural circuitry exists that is sufficiently complex to constitute a mind, or subserve it, or mediate it, or whatever. Unfortunately, the "whatever" unglues the whole argument. Sherrington (1951) couldn't see how a mental force could influence matters neurophysiological at all; but Eccles (1953) decided that, at the level of the synaptic knob, one got down to such tiny and lightweight things that even mental forces, however insubstantial they might be, might influence them.

Around the turn of the century, William James (1890) asked "Are our bodies ours, or are they us?" What with Skinner, Eysenck, Wolpe, and the concepts of behavior therapy, one might rephrase this and ask "Is our behavior ours or is it us?"

A twenty-six-year-old male had had bizarre and ominous psychiatric symp-toms since the age of six, had never lived apart from his parents nor been gainfully employed, and had had little experience of interpersonal relationships except with his parents, especially his mother. In a psychiatric ward he paced restlessly, failed to tuck in his shirttails, and demanded "Do I have a mental illness?" so incessantly of everyone within earshot that he quickly established himself as the greatest annoyance on the ward. The nursing staff, being much impressed with behavior therapy, organized efforts to shape his behavior through systematic social approval and disapproval. Busy as he was with agitated fears that he might lose control or kill someone, or be permanently crazy, the patient was able to show a marked tendency to tuck in his shirttails in response to a nursing chorus of "If you don't tuck in your shirttails, we won't associate with you." Satisfaction with the success of this aversive conditioning was somewhat limited, however, because he persisted in asking "Do I have a mental illness?" despite the fact that every nurse promptly responded "Stop that crazy talk, or I won't have anything to do with you."

Since this reinforcement suggests both that he is crazy and that he can stop if he wants, its lack of effectiveness may reflect a sort of double-bind quality. Because visits by the mother were being used in a mutual conspiracy to maintain symbiosis with the patient, they were stopped, precipitating decompensation in the mother, which taxed the social worker who was attempting to hold her together, and panic in the patient that he, or the mother, or both, might die or not exist.

Some months later, after he had to some extent substituted the hospital and his resident for his mother, the notion began to occur to him that, after all, at twenty-six years, it might be time to think of living away from his parents. This generated an obsessive-ruminative trend, which took the form of a litany of anxious questions such as "But who would get me up in the morning?" and "Who would make my sandwiches for me?" Since behavior therapy requires establishing good habits as well as extinguishing bad ones, a program of instruction and approval was instituted on the care and use of alarm clocks, and how to make sandwiches. Now it is not my purpose to belittle behavior therapy, nor to pretend that this represents a very sophisticated edition of it. Indeed, I am not even suggesting that these efforts were ineffective, let alone detrimental. At the very least, a context was provided within which a male who has little talent or experience with girls was able to relate to young nurses who, without much experience with psychiatric patients, were able to approach him in a confident manner, reflecting their sense of knowing what to do to be helpful.

My only intent is to suggest that the mind may not be in the head, but it is even less likely to be in the behavior. This is my way of saying that, for this rather intelligent patient, the question about sandwich-making involved more than just insecurity as to whether he could take two pieces of bread and put them together with something edible in between. As McKellar (1962) has suggested, the justification for psychological experimentation with animals does not imply that human subjects ought to be treated as "noncommunicating rats or pigeons, in the interests of a misguided sense of 'objectivity'." That is, one does not need to throw out animal experiments on the grounds that animals aren't people, but neither does one need to throw out people in order to make use of information obtained from animals.

Psychiatric residents, I have found, do not have much time or enthusiasm for wondering about where the mind is, perhaps because they are so busy attempting to cure it. For such residents, and for others who seem uninterested in questions about the nature and location of the mind, an article by Irving Good (1962) called "The Mind-Body Problem, or Could an Android Feel Pain?" provides an introduction so readable and amusing that one acquires useful and provocative information without really trying. He tackles problems of metaphysicality, consciousness, thinking by machines, and aspects of the philosophy of science.

Concerning philosophical efforts to eliminate the mind-body problem, he writes:

I am left with an uneasy feeling. Subjective experiences in other people are permitted to influence our experiments, via our ethics, but not to influence our explanations. For reasons known to God and Freud we must be kind to animals as well as people. But why stop at animals; should there be a Society for the Prevention of Cruelty to Androids? If science can give us no help with this question, we must turn to metaphysics for the answer. Thus the mind-body problem is still with us: it is only a so-called pseudo problem, it is a quasi-pseudo problem.

After discussing the possibility of constructing an android, Good continues:

It might be suggested that we are now ready to find out whether an android could feel subjective pain. We ask it. In virtue of the definition of an android, the answer given would be "yes." We might then hope to detect that this was a lie by means of the lie detector. Unfortunately, the answer might be truthful but mean something like "there are situations that I try to avoid, and when I fail I show all the overt indications that you do when you say you are in pain; and furthermore certain internal events occur that I am unable to verbalize and that I describe as unpleasant." If we then ask, "But do you feel pain?" the android might reply, "Whereof one cannot speak, thereof one must be silent."

To quote Wittgenstein (1922) so aptly is scarcely surprising for a machine stipulated to be as marvelously constructed as this android, but for it to feel pain would require a metamorphosis from object to subject so alien to our experience that it cannot yet be imagined, even in principle.

If the brain is the only object capable of being a subject, does this mean that it is in some unknown respect not a machine? Or is subjectivity a peculiarity limited to the human brain only because other machines have not yet been constructed with the level of complexity at which subjectivity is an emergent property? If the latter is true, then one might postulate that the brain is completely determinate (as machines are), and that its unpredictability is due to inability to analyze its complexity rather than to indeterminacy per se. Mackay (1969) suggests that, even if the brain and body are assumed to be mechanical as clockwork, there are logical grounds for asserting that human beings are inherently indeterminate *in the sense that there exists no determinate complete specification of their future with an unconditioned claim to their assent.*

To see this, we first observe that any complete description of a human agent must describe, at least by implication, what he believes. It follows that if the agent were himself to believe the description, it could not be valid both before and after his believing it. If valid before then it describes the agent as not believing it, and so would become invalid if he were to believe it. If, however, it were preadjusted so that when believed by the agent it would become a correct description, then ipso facto it could not be a correct description beforehand. In neither case has the purported description any logical claim on the agent; for in

*the first case he is manifestly in error if he believes it, since it will then be false;
while in the second he is manifestly not in error if he disbelieves it, since it is and
will remain false unless he believes it (p. 151).*

The strength of this argument would be easier to gauge if more experience were
at hand concerning clockworks possessed of beliefs.

That there has been little pressure to answer these kinds of questions may
reflect the fact that lack of answers has not prevented scientists from making discoveries, whether in the neurological disciplines investigating the brain or in the
psychological disciplines investigating the mind. With the accelerating progress
in neurological and psychological sciences, the gap between them narrows and
opportunities for methodological or conceptual bridging are subjected more and
more to serious scientific scrutiny. Elsewhere (Worden, 1966, p. 56), I have suggested that such "bridging" does not result in bridges so much as in the discovery
of a new conceptual mainland where two islands had formerly been thought to
exist. In other words, the search for neural mechanisms subserving psychological
phenomena, or for psychological manifestations of neural processes, does not lead
to simple additive connections between the neurological and the psychological;
rather it exposes problems and inadequacies within each disciplinary system that
are not so apparent within its own boundaries, but become painfully apparent
when attempts are made to cross these boundaries. These exposures have already
increased the pressure on scientists to ask how mind and brain are related; as
progress continues and new information accumulates, one of the important developments, I believe, will be restatements of these age-old questions in forms
providing a better chance for answers.

SUMMARY AND CONCLUSION

The relationship of psychoanalysis to science is as puzzling as the relationship
between man's direct experience of himself as a subject, and his sensory-per-
ceptual knowledge of the world of objects. For this first volume of *Psychoanalysis
and Contemporary Science,* I have advocated the need for a vigorously questioning attitude, and have stated a number of questions and opinions to encourage,
provoke, and illustrate such an attitude. My remarks have ranged broadly across
such topics as psychoanalysis, clinical psychiatry, psychiatric training, and research
in neuroscience; in each context I have attempted to highlight the need for
skepticism and for sensitivity to the difference between information supported
by evidence and opinion established by authorities.

There is a difference in the logic underlying man's attempt to understand
an object like the living brain, and his attempts to understand a subject like the
personality living with that brain. For the former, explanatory causes are sought,
whereas for the latter, explanatory meanings are sought. A further difference is
implicit and should be made explicit at this point. The scientific method is man's
most powerful tool for gaining knowledge of, and control over, the world of
objects; but it is inherently ineffective as a tool for transacting interpersonal rela-

tionships, because its explanatory "causes" are invisible to subjective experience (e.g., connectivity patterns within the brain), and it is blind to those meanings that illuminate personal life.

If the questions I have been urging psychoanalysis to ask are intended to move it into closer relationship with other sciences, would not the main thrust of my argument be to incapacitate psychoanalysis as a system for dealing with persons? On the other hand, if psychoanalysis continues to prune and sharpen only its own methodological and theoretical structure, is there anything it can hope to accomplish other than shortening a five-year analysis to perhaps four years, or developing means whereby the current percentage of analytic failures can be somewhat reduced? Is there, in principle, anything better that psychoanalysis can hope for? I do not believe there is, insofar as psychoanalysis is conceived as a treatment or research method based upon the experience of a two-person relationship within the psychoanalytic situation.

Psychoanalysis, however, has provided the most detailed data, and the most all-embracing account, of the phenomena of the human mind, and equivalent information cannot be obtained by other methods. Carrying psychoanalytic information vigorously into the context of all the neurosciences would bring sophisticated data on the mind into juxtaposition with rapidly developing new information about the brain. The potential in such a move is not to improve psychoanalysis, but to facilitate another step forward in man's long attempt to understand himself. Obviously, the new system of understanding would not replace the need for explanations and treatment in terms of interpersonal relationships, including psychotherapeutic ones; but the discovery of powerful new approaches to the biological factors underlying man's psychological frailties may substantially alter the current gloom-producing disparity between human problems and the resources available for treating them.

Lest the message in all this not be clear, I would like to close by drawing a moral from it: Sometimes it is easier to ask good questions if you are too ignorant to know any better; but usually it is not so easy to hear them if you are educated enough to know a system into which they do not fit.

REFERENCES

Eccles, J. C. (1953). *The Neurophysiological Basis of Mind.* London: Oxford University Press.

Garfinkel, H. (1967). *Studies in Ethnomethodology.* Englewood Cliffs, N.J.: Prentice-Hall.

Good, I. J. (1962). The Mind-Body Problem, or Could an Android Feel Pain? In: *Theories of the Mind,* ed. J. Scher. New York: Free Press.

Gruenberg, E. M. (1967). Can the Reorganization of Psychiatric Services Prevent Some Cases of Social Breakdown? In: *Psychiatry in Transition,* ed. A. B. Stokes. Toronto: University of Toronto Press.

Guntrip, H. (1967). The Concept of Psychodynamic Science. *International Journal of Psycho-Analysis,* 48:32–43.

Home, H. J. M. (1966). The Concept of Mind. *International Journal of Psycho-Analysis,* 47:42–49.

James, W. (1890). *The Principles of Psychology.* New York: Henry Holt.

Koestler, A. (1945). *The Yogi and the Commissar*. New York: Macmillan.

Kubie, L. S. (1968). Pitfalls of Community Psychiatry. *Archives of General Psychiatry*, 18: 257–266.

MacKay, D. M. (1969). *Information, Mechanism and Meaning*. Cambridge, Mass.: M.I.T. Press.

McCulloch, W. S. (1965). Why the Mind Is in the Head. In: *Embodiments of Mind*. Cambridge, Mass.: M.I.T. Press.

McKellar, P. (1962). The Method of Introspection. In: *Theories of the Mind*, ed. J. Scher. New York: Free Press.

Rosen, J. N. (1947). The Treatment of Schizophrenic Psychosis by Direct Analytic Therapy. *Psychiatric Quarterly*, 21:3–37.

Rosenthal, D., and Kety, S. (1968). *The Transmission of Schizophrenia*. New York: Pergamon Press.

Sherrington, C. S. (1951). *Man on His Nature*. London: Cambridge University Press.

Weiss, E. (1950). *Principles of Psychodynamics*. New York: Grune and Stratton.

Whitehorn, J. C. (1947). The Concepts of "Meaning" and "Cause" in Psychodynamics. *American Journal of Psychiatry*, 104:289–292.

Wittgenstein, L. J. (1922). *Tractatus Logico-Philosophicus*. London: Routledge and Kegan Paul.

Worden, F. G. (1966). Attention and Auditory Electrophysiology. In: *Progress in Physiological Psychology*, Vol. 1, ed. E. Stellar and J. Sprague. New York: Academic Press.

2

PSYCHOLINGUISTIC

ON HEARING, ORAL LANGUAGE, AND PSYCHIC STRUCTURE

David A. Freedman, M.D.

Abraham's (1924) delineation of six stages of libidinal development and six complementary stages of the development of object love (Table 1) was the harbinger of many subsequent refinements in the description of the epigenetic process. Continuing investigation of the interaction between those innate givens of the individual that are rooted in inheritance and which emerge in the course of development, on the one hand, and on the other the vicissitudes of experience as derived from the environment, has yielded an increasingly complex picture of the developmental process. Even at the time, Abraham noted that the stages he positioned on the same horizontal lines of his table need not occur simultaneously. That is, despite their apparent relatedness, the development of the zonal libidinal stages and the stages of object love may follow largely independent courses.

Table 1   *(from Abraham (1924))*

Stages of Libidinal Organization	Stages of Object-Love	
VI. Final genital stage	Object-love	(Post-ambivalent)
V. Earlier genital stage (phallic)	Object-love with exclusion of genitals	
IV. Later Anal-sadistic stage	Partial love	(Ambivalent)
III. Earlier Anal-sadistic stage	Partial love with incorporation	
II. Later oral stage (cannibalistic)	Narcissism (total incorporation of object)	
I. Earlier oral stage	Auto-erotism (without object)	(Pre-ambivalent)

Data accumulated during the intervening years have more than justified both the conclusion that each line of development follows its own time course and Abraham's suspicion that his analysis was incomplete. With regard to the oral period alone—i.e., the first 18 to 24 months—at least the following refinements have been introduced since 1924. On the basis of the emergence of the smiling response at three months and of stranger anxiety at eight months, Spitz (1959) divided the oral phase of ego development into three stages. Piaget (1954) had already established that, during these same first 18 to 24 months, cognitive development passes through six readily distinguishable phases. A variety of motor skills, too, have been shown to emerge through a series of identifiable steps (McGraw, 1945). For each of these developmental lines, the principle appears to hold that, however long any given phase may last, the *sequence* of the emergence of new capacities is invariant. No child manifests stranger anxiety before the emergence of the smiling response, and no child recovers a fully hidden object before he is able to recover one which is partially hidden. Whatever the environmental vicissitudes, for any given line of development the emergence of new innate genetically derived potentialities occurs in a regular and predictable sequence.

Escalona (1965) has presented these complex relations in graphic form. According to her, most behavioral and psychological developmental research has

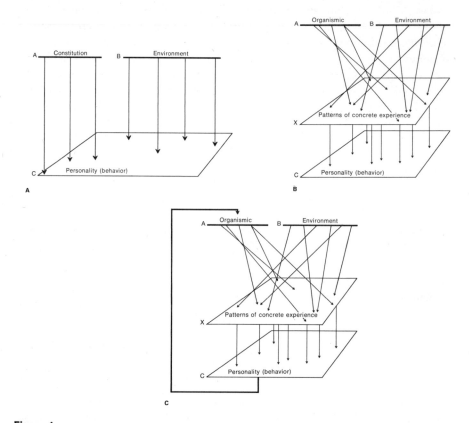

Figure 1.

implied that behavior and personality are the direct result of an interaction between the organism and the environment (Figure 1A). She points out, however, that this model fails to take into account the fact that the organism is never in a static state. Maturation of the nervous system, as well as the influence of past experience and of ongoing visceral processes, are constantly altering the tissue substructure of the mind. To this congeries of influence she has assigned the name "organismic state" (Figure 1B). The organismic state at any given instant interacts with environmental influences to yield an intervening variable, which she calls a "pattern of concrete experience." It is, she proposes, to the pattern of concrete experience that the developing individual makes new adaptations. These in turn result in what may be designated as personality or behavior or, in more general terms, the next new organismic state. One could add to the model a feedback loop, to indicate that each new organismic state includes the personality and behavior of the moment (Figure 1C).

Elkind (1970) has recently considered the special problems that are posed for the investigator of such developmental processes. He points out that the nature of the subject matter relegates the use of conventional experimentation to a secondary role. Because it is rarely possible, in the course of longitudinal human studies, to set up a controlled situation into which a single variable can be introduced, the student of human development must be prepared to identify regularities as they occur in uncontrolled situations. Such regularities, when they are clearly defined, may be regarded as reflecting consistent characteristics of the population being studied.

The identification of regularities, however, does not serve to differentiate between the roles of organismic (in the sense of both newly emerging gene-determined potentialities and already established patterns of reaction) and of environmental influences, which together determine the character of those regularities. It is for this purpose that longitudinal observation of the development of individuals suffering from congenital and/or perinatal somatic deficiencies and sensory deprivations has proven to be a useful technique. Often referred to as "experiments of nature," such populations in fact represent the converse of the typical experimental situation. In effect, a single constant—e.g., a distorted or deficient body part, or deprivation of age-appropriate experience with a particular sensory modality—is introduced into an otherwise uncontrolled situation. Regularities that distinguish those individuals who are suffering from such a specific deprivation from the general population of developing individuals can be considered to reflect the absence of some aspects of the role that the missing part or function would have played in the average expectable process of development of psychic structure. On the other hand, when the deprived individual shows behavior we are accustomed to associate with the missing function, it becomes necessary to reappraise our conception of the relation of that function to the developmental process.

Using such a research model, Lenneberg (1965) showed, with respect to the infant's cooing and babbling, how different its motivation and perceptual experience may be from that which the observing adult imputes to him. Parents regularly interpret such sounds as responses to either self-induced or social auditory stimuli. At least during the first hundred days of postpartal life, however, they would appear to be incidental to a proprioceptive reflex and to have little or nothing to do with the hearing function. Not only do they occur with approximately the same frequency in both deaf and hearing infants; they are also unaffected by the presence or absence of ambient noises. They occur with equal frequency in the children of deaf-mute parents and in the normally developing offspring of normal parents. Lenneberg's finding makes it necessary to reconsider the role of early sound-making behavior in later development. That the noises the infant makes prior to three months serve to intensify its bond to its mother seems a reasonable speculation. This, however, must be the result of the mother's affective and behavioral response to what she imputes to the baby; it is not related to the actual significance of the baby's vocalization. In terms of Escalona's model, an equivalent pattern of concrete experience can be established in the absence of any vocalization by mother or child. The assumption, furthermore, that even the normal baby's cooing is a manifestation of the operation of a vocal-auditory system would appear to be erroneous.

Other studies, which derive from the observation of congenitally blind children, have demonstrated that the infant's ability to respond to sound stimuli by modifying its behavior emerges through two distinct phases. A congenitally blind infant as young as 10 weeks old is able to discriminate his mother's voice from other similar feminine voices (Freedman et al., 1969), and sometime between his third and fifth month he will also smile in response to an auditory stimulus. Unlike the generalized smiling response described by Spitz and Wolf (1946), however, this smile is highly selective, in that it occurs only in response to the sound of the mother's or some other already familiar voice (Fraiberg and Freedman, 1964).

Despite the evidences of the ability to discriminate among complex sound stimuli at so tender an age, however, the congenitally blind infant will make no effort to reach out for sound-making objects until he is approximately 10 months old—i.e., some five months after sighted children appear to reach for sound stimuli. Because it did not seem possible to account for this discrepancy on the basis of the lack of vision, Freedman et al. investigated the emergence of the use of hearing as a guide to search behavior in normally developing youngsters. In a group of 33 such infants, the use of sound for such "cognitive" purposes did not emerge until the children were between eight and 12 months old. Up to that age the normally developing infant, like the blind baby, did not treat a sound stimulus as the indicator of the existence of an object from which the sound emanated. Rather, like a piece of sonar equipment he oriented to the sound source—for example, a bell. If in the course of doing so he made visual contact with it, he would continue to follow it with his eyes. After the fifth month, he would also reach for the object. However, when it was made to disappear behind a screen, his pursuit behavior stopped, even though the sound continued. The initial orienting response aside, his behavior appeared to be a response to the visual stimulus.

The emergence in the 10-week-old infant of the ability to respond to sound with change in affective behavior; the establishment of vocal–auditory connections in the 14-week-old, and the emergence in the eight- to 10-month old of the ability to conceive of a sound stimulus as the indicator of the existence of an object "out there" that is generating the sound—these may be regarded as points along the developmental line that ultimately eventuates in the predominance of speech as a means of communication. Unlike the emergence of the ability to understand speech and the emergence some three months later of the ability to speak (McCarthy, 1954), for an average expectable child in an average expectable environment, the emergences just referred to follow one another so smoothly that it becomes possible to demonstrate them only under the artificial conditions imposed by sensory deprivation. That they do exist, however, is a consideration that may be relevant to the effort to understand both the process of the evolution of the vocal auditory system and its ultimate role as an ego apparatus.

THE VOCAL AUDITORY SYSTEM
AS AN EGO APPARATUS

The developmental processes that lead to the ability to utilize the vocal-auditory system as an ego apparatus—i.e., a medium for the formulation and expression of thought, as well as for the receipt and transmission of messages—imply the confluence of the developments of those physiological apparatuses that are the substrata for coordinating hearing and speaking with those apparatuses that are relevant to the capacity to differentiate self and object, and to establish and cathect internalized object representations. It is therefore of relevance that the developing individual's ability to assimilate and utilize various sensory modalities for these latter purposes appears to undergo a regular and predictable shift in emphasis.

Although it is not possible to vouch for the precise contours of the curves in Figure 2, the occurrence of a sequence such as they describe is supported by data from a variety of sources.

From this standpoint, the combination of sensory inputs designated as coenesthesia (Spitz, 1945) seems to be the critical modality at least for the first half of the first year of life in human infants, as well as for extended periods in the early postpartal life of many other mammalian species. Spitz included under this designation relatively diffuse, at best poorly localized sensations having to do with equilibrium, muscle tension, posture, temperature, vibration, pitch, resonance, and poorly differentiated visual input. Failure to receive sufficient coenesthetic stimulation during the infant's critical period results in gross and probably irreversible disturbances of later affective and cognitive development.

Denneberg (1969), who studied early development in the rat, has found in that species, for example, that prior to weaning the effective property of applied stimuli is "unpatterned" and their effects on the mature animal are reflected in "emotionality, physiology and biochemistry." After weaning, on the other hand, the animal responds preferentially to "patterned" stimuli. Their later effects are

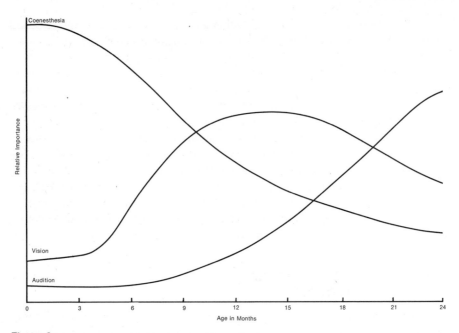

Figure 2.

reflected in tests of perception, problem-solving, cognition, and neural activity. W. Mason (1968) has succeeded in preventing the development of the Harlow syndrome by substituting, for the immobile surrogate Harlow used, a surrogate that swings freely and unpredictably in space. He was able to do this because the macaque, in addition to having fully functioning sensory transducers, is fully mobile from birth. That is, unlike the human neonate, who is restricted to the use of the mouth as an effector organ, the infant monkey has available and under his volitional control both his arms and his legs. The fact that when he is reared on an immobile surrogate he nonetheless develops the Harlow syndrome underscores the critical importance, for later development, of the provision by the environment of coenesthetic stimulation.

In the human data from the observation of thalidomide babies (Décarie, 1965), congenitally blind infants (Fraiberg and Freedman, 1964), and infants without demonstrated tissue pathology who had suffered massive neonatal maternal deprivation (Goldfarb, 1943; Davis, 1940, 1946; Provence and Lipton, 1962; Freedman and Brown, 1968), all point to the critical importance of early coenesthetic experience and the likelihood that the effects of prolonged coenesthetic deprivation are irreversible. Marked deficiencies in the development of speech, as one element of the neonatal environmental deprivation syndrome, have been noted by all the cited authors.

The evidence in this regard is in striking contrast to the findings in those few reported instances in which a youngster has received adequate early mothering and subsequently suffered significant sensory deprivation. These children appear to acquire speech very rapidly once they are exposed to an appropriate environment. The cases of Kaspar Hauser (v. Feuerbach, 1833) and Helen Keller (Dahl, 1965) may be cited in this regard. Perhaps more eloquent than either is the case reported by M. K. Mason (1942). This child was the product of an illegitimate pregnancy. Her mother, who had suffered a head injury in childhood, was mute and totally uneducated; she communicated with her family only through gestures. From the time the pregnancy was discovered, the mother and subsequently the child were kept locked in a room with drawn shades. We can infer that the child received considerable nonverbal, but no verbal, stimulation from her mother during the six and a half years these conditions continued. When she was brought to Mason's attention she had no language. In contrast to the experience of workers with youngsters who have suffered early preverbal maternal deprivation, Mason was able very quickly to engage her interest and attention and to establish a mutual affective tie. Within a year and a half she had acquired a vocabulary of between 1500 and 2000 words, and could identify coins and do simple arithmetic computations. In further striking contrast to the children reared without adequate coenesthetic stimulation, at eight and a half years she was described as an imaginative, affectionate, loving child with an excellent sense of humor.

Beginning at approximately five to six months of age, vision appears gradually to take over as the principal sensory modality through which the "average expectable" infant goes about differentiating self from non-self and defining and cathecting objects. Two lines of evidence, one direct and the other indirect, support this statement. It is well established (Gesell and Amatruda, 1941) that the coordination of hand and eye—i.e., the ability to use the hand purposefully as an organ of prehension under the guidance and control of vision—begins at this age. This is the age, too, at which blindisms—waving the hands in front of the eyes and rubbing the eyes—begin to emerge in infants with cataracts and those with retrolental fibrous dysplasia who have some light vision. By contrast, one infant with complete anophthalmia whom I have studied, and who was developing well despite the lack of any visual stimulus, never engaged in blindisms. Presumably the endogenously determined aspects of central nervous system development were proceeding in him just as they do in the sighted child and the child with cataracts. In the absence of any environmental stimulation, however, he showed neither the expected prehensile response of the normal baby nor the hand waving of the baby who can perceive only light and dark. The indirect evidence also derives from the experience of the period of the retrolental fibrous dysplasia epidemic. It was typically the case that their parents did not become concerned about the afflicted infants until they attained this age. That is, the behavior of the blind infant of less than five to six months who showed no external manifestations (e.g., cataracts or absent orbits) of his blindness did not impress even experienced parents as particularly unusual or atypical. Not infrequently the infants were described as "very good" babies, who demanded and received little attention.

The very high incidence (25 per cent or more) of an autistic-like syndrome (Keeler, 1958; Norris et al., 1958; Fraiberg and Freedman, 1964) among the con-

genitally blind appears to be associated with this lack of handling and consequent inadequate coenesthetic experience. Their problem, of course, is com-
pounded by the relative sensory vacuum in which the congenitally blind child
must exist for that period of months during which vision is normally the critical
sensory modality. The fact that as many as 75 percent of similarly afflicted children do not become autistic, and many go on to develop very well, can be
accounted for in terms of Escalona's model. It would appear that the organismic
factor "congenital blindness" increases the likelihood that patterns of concrete
experience conducive to autism will develop. The finding of an unusually high
incidence of the use of proper names by the blind (Maxfield, 1936), together
with the independent observations by Fraiberg (personal communication) and
the present author (unpublished) that blind children, even when they are developing well, show delay in the development of the use of the first person
pronoun—these findings seem to support the hypothesis that the processes of
differentiation of self and object and the establishment of ego boundaries are
hampered by the fact of blindness, even under optimal environmental conditions.

In contrast to these findings is the repeated observation in the same population of a high degree of skill in the reproduction of connected sequences of
sounds, words, and sentences. Fraiberg and Freedman's subject, Peter, who was
unable to utilize speech for purposes of communication, could nonetheless
repeat words and sentences clearly and with appropriate enunciation. He could
also sing songs with excellent control of both intonation and pitch. That his ability
to do so was not associated with any understanding of the words he used is
indicated by the following previously unpublished episode.

Peter, the child of a monolingual English-speaking family, had been hospitalized for several months in an institution in a large northeastern city. The effects
of this experience were, generally speaking, catastrophic. Upon his return home,
his parents complained that among his other disturbing new characteristics was
a tendency to talk endlessly in gibberish. When she had the opportunity to hear
him, Mrs. Fraiberg found, however, that he was repeating, in perfectly clear
Yiddish, *"der meshugene shloft noch nit . . ."* (the crazy one isn't sleeping
yet)—something he undoubtedly overheard in the hospital. In effect, Peter's well-
functioning vocal auditory apparatus, as well as his ability to retain and reproduce complex sound patterns, had not been incorporated as an ego apparatus.

Similar echolalic phenomena have, of course, been reported among the
mentally defective (Barr, 1898; Jones, 1926), as well as in autistic children in
whom no disturbance of either the primary sensory transducers or the vocal
apparatus could be demonstrated. Like the abilities of the parrot and the mynah
bird, they underscore the necessity to distinguish between those organismic
substrata that are relevant to the capacity to hear, to register, and to reproduce
complex sounds, on the one hand, and, on the other, those that are relevant to
the development of such preconditions for the ability to communicate as the
differentiation of self and object and the cathecting of objects.

The evidence for the occurrence of speech without thought is complemented by equally persuasive data that point to the conclusion that thought

occurs in the absence of speech or of any possibility of the occurrence of speech.[1] Creative thinking on the part of lower primates has been described by many psychologists. Schiller's (1957) observations, which fit so neatly with the epigenetic hypothesis, deserve special mention. He presented his chimpanzees with the problem of retrieving food that was out of their reach. Sticks that could, by being joined together, make rakes were scattered about the cage. The problem was solved by those animals who had attained the age of five to six years and had had earlier (i.e., childhood) experience playing with similar sticks. Neither the younger animals who had had extensive experience playing with sticks nor the older animals who had not had the opportunity to engage in such play during childhood were successful. Solution of the problem required both a level of maturation that is ordinarily attained at this age in this species *and* the residual effects of prior play experience with the relevant objects.

Because of the repeated failure by other workers to teach chimpanzees oral language, Gardner and Gardner (1969) elected to teach their subject the American sign language for the deaf. When she was between 30 and 36 months old—i.e., some 22 months after they began their work with her—she had learned 30 signs, which she was able to use in sentences of two or three words. She was also able to generalize the use of signs. For example, she spontaneously used the sign for "open" in the sentence "Open the box" although she had learned it in the sentence "Open the door." Consistent with the general thesis that the establishment of object-relations is critical for the ability to communicate is Gardner and Gardner's emphasis on the sociability of the animal. They feel that the chimpanzee's propensity for forming strong attachments to humans was an indispensable element in their subject's ability to learn language.

Recent studies of human beings who had undergone section of the corpus callosum (Gazzaniga and Sperry, 1967) have also shown that the ability to learn,

---

[1] The necessity to distinguish between those processes that have to do with thought and feeling, on the one hand, and those that have to do with the use of the vocal auditory system as a medium for communication was explicit in Freud's formulations of both the topographic and the structural models of the mind. In his earliest attempts to develop a neurological model (1895), he pointed out that the neuronal system that subserves perception could not also subserve memory. One year later (1896), he wrote to Fliess, "Our psychical apparatus comes into being as the result of a process of stratification: the material present in the form of memory traces being subjected from time to time to a rearrangement in accordance with fresh circumstances—to a retranscription." He postulated that at least three such transcriptions must occur between a perception and its later recall into consciousness. Only with the third—which corresponds to the preconscious—were the memories "attached to word presentations and corresponding to our official egos." He reiterated the same formulation in Chapter 7 of *The Interpretation of Dreams* (1900), "The Unconscious" (1915), and in Chapter 4 of *Beyond the Pleasure Principle* (1920). Again, in "A Note upon the 'Mystic Writing-Pad' " (1924), he used that device as a mechanical analogue to the process of the registration and transfer of perceptions into memories that he had postulated in his earlier formulations.

Both his recognition that the process of repression by its very nature must be unconscious and at the same time an ego function, and the connection that Freud observed between the compulsion to repeat and an unconscious sense of guilt—i.e., the two phenomena that led to the formulation of the structural model (1920, 1923)—also clearly assume discriminating ego functions which are unconnected to word representations.

to abstract, and to generalize is preserved even in the absence of any possibility of attaching linguistic symbols to the thought processes in question. These authors state, "When stimulus material was presented to the minor hemisphere under conditions in which its comprehension could be indicated by purely non-verbal responses, it became evident that the mute minor hemisphere was quite capable of perceptual understanding and of forming ideas and concepts well beyond the image of the stimulus. Not uncommonly, these test performances seemed to involve some abstraction, generalization and mental association."

Studies of the congenitally deaf also underscore the importance of distinguishing the vocal auditory apparatus as a device that can be used for the purpose of formulating and expressing thought and feeling from the phenomena of thinking and feeling per se. Thirty years ago Eberhardt (1940) concluded, "Experiments have shown that the world of the deaf is already organized beyond the perceptual level and that this organization closely follows that of speaking people. They show clearly that language is not essentially for organized conceptual thought at least during its first stages . . . Much of the first language development of the young deaf child consists in learning words for ideas that he already has and uses in his everyday life, not as one might believe a priori in the development of language symbols in a child whose world up to then has been a more or less unorganized one." In more recent studies, in which adequate care has been taken to control for the influence of speech, the congenitally deaf have also shown no intellectual deficit as compared to the hearing (Vernon, 1967). Furth (1966), for example, has shown that the deaf readily learn to manipulate the symbols of symbolic logic. VanderWoude (1970) found that congenitally deaf and hearing children show no characteristic differences of approach to problem solving.

Rainer's finding (Rainer and Altshuler, 1966), in the New York State Hospital system, that the admission rate for schizophrenia among the congenitally deaf is identical with that for the normally hearing population, indicates that lack of speech and hearing is by no means incompatible with the process of differentiation of psychic structure.

Freedman, Canady, and Robinson (in press) studied five girls with severe congenital hearing loss secondary to prenatal rubella infection. The subjects, who were followed from age two and a half to age 5 years were selected because of the similarities of their cultural, economic, and medical backgrounds. In areas that did not involve the use of language, their performance on developmental tests was on a par with that of their normally hearing age mates. Despite both the marked delay in their beginning to use any oral language and the gross deficiency of their speech, they showed none of the already described characteristics of the environmentally deprived children or the congenitally blind. All had formed strong self-identities, as well as the capacity to enter into mutual interactions and attachments to others. Lack of language aside, when compared with normally hearing children they differed only in that they tended to translate their wishes into action more readily than do normally hearing youngsters, and were more likely to attempt to solve problems without appealing for help. Because of these qualities, they tended to be regarded as brighter and more alert than their normally hearing age mates. This impression, however, was not borne out by developmental testing.

Despite the fact that their lack of hearing made them unable to be aware of conventional oral expressions of prohibition, permission, praise, or blame, their processes of internalization and identification did not appear to be adversely affected. All the subjects were distinctly feminine in their interests and behavior, and they had all developed well-defined internal regulators of behavior. The authors conclude that, its special usefulness as a medium of communication notwithstanding, spoken language—i.e., what is referred to in this essay as the vocal auditory system—is not a prerequisite for nor even a significant factor in the early phases of ego development. Again, to refer to Escalona's model, despite the absence of speech and hearing, appropriate environmental adjustments made it possible for these children to have patterns of concrete experience equivalent to those of normal preoedipal children.

It is probably the case that the relative independence and somewhat frenetic activity manifested by these children are the earliest manifestations of organismic factors that will eventuate in later typical characteristics of the deaf. Certainly, their inability to appreciate the nuances of meaning conveyed by spoken language cannot help setting the deaf apart from the hearing, as the use of the vocal auditory system becomes increasingly important in human activities. In contrast, however, to the situations of the environmentally deprived individual and of a very high percentage of the congenitally blind, by the time the use of speech and hearing become critical, the deaf individual characteristically will have experienced a considerable degree of psychic structuralization and differentiation of self and environment. His response to the isolation and frustration he must inevitably experience will be determined at least in part by the introjects he has already formed and, in his efforts both to account for and to compensate for his plight, he will be guided by established object-relations and expectations. One would, therefore, anticipate that his adaptive efforts will approximate those of the normally endowed individual who is confronted with the necessity of making an adjudication between the demands of id, of superego, and of external reality. The already cited studies indicate that this is indeed the case.

REFERENCES

Abraham, K. (1924). A Short Study of the Development of the Libido, Viewed in the Light of Mental Disorders. In: *Selected Papers on Psychoanalysis,* trans. D. Bryan and A. Strachey. London: Hogarth Press, 1949, p. 496.

Barr, M. W. (1898). Some Notes on Echolalia, with Report of an Extraordinary Case. *Journal of Nervous and Mental Disease,* 25:20–30.

Dahl, H. (1965). Observations on a "Natural Experiment": Helen Keller. *Journal of the American Psychoanalytic Association,* 13:533–550.

Davis, K. (1940). Extreme Isolation of a Child. *American Journal of Sociology,* 45:554–565.

——— (1946). Final Note on a Case of Extreme Isolation. *American Journal of Sociology,* 52:432–437.

Décarie, T. (1969). A Study of the Mental and Emotional Development of the Thalidomide

Child. In: *Determinants of Infant Behavior,* 4:167–187, ed. B. M. Foss. London: Methuen.

Denneberg, V. H. (1969). Different Effects of Pre- and Post-Weaning Stimulation in Rats. In: *Stimulation in Early Infancy,* ed. A. Ambrose. London and New York: Academic Press, pp. 64–67.

Eberhardt, M. (1940). Studies in the Psychology of the Deaf. *Genetic Psychology Monographs,* 52:4–55.

Elkind, D. (1970). Developmental and Experimental Approaches to Child Study. In: *Cognitive Studies,* 1:44–56, ed. J. Hellmuth. New York: Brunner/Mazel.

Escalona, S. (1965). Some Determinants of Individual Differences. *Transactions of the New York Academy of Sciences,* Ser. 2, 27:802–816.

v. Feuerbach, A. (1833). *Kaspar Hauser.* London: Simpkin and Marshall.

Fraiberg, S., and Freedman, D. A. (1964). Studies in the Ego Development of a Congenitally Blind Child. *Psychoanalytic Study of the Child,* 19:113–169.

Freedman, D. A., and Brown, S. L. (1968). On the Role of Coenesthetic Stimulation in the Development of Psychic Structure. *Psychoanalytic Quarterly,* 37:418–438.

———— Canady, C., and Robinson, J. R. (in press). Speech and Psychic Structure—A Reconstruction of Their Relation. *Journal of the American Psychoanalytic Association.*

———— Fox-Kolenda, B. J., Margileth, D. A., and Miller, D. H. (1969). The Development of the Use of Sound as a Guide to Affective and Cognitive Behavior—A Two-Phase Process. *Child Development,* 40:1099–1103.

Freud, S. (1895). Project for a Scientific Psychology. *Standard Edition,* 1:295–387. London: Hogarth Press, 1966.

———— (1896). Letters to Fliess: No. 52. *Standard Edition,* 1:233–239. London: Hogarth Press, 1966.

———— (1900). The Interpretation of Dreams. *Standard Edition,* 5:533–549. London: Hogarth Press, 1958.

———— (1915). The Unconscious. *Standard Edition,* 5:166–204. London: Hogarth Press, 1957.

———— (1920). Beyond the Pleasure Principle. *Standard Edition,* 18:7–64. London: Hogarth Press, 1955.

———— (1923). The Ego and the Id. *Standard Edition,* 19:13–66. London: Hogarth Press, 1961.

———— (1924). A Note upon the 'Mystic Writing-Pad.' *Standard Edition,* 19:227–232. London: Hogarth Press, 1961.

Furth, H. G. (1966). *Thinking without Language.* New York: Free Press.

Gardner, R. A., and Gardner, B. T. (1969). Teaching Sign Language to a Chimpanzee. *Science,* 165:664–672.

Gazzaniga, M. S., and Sperry, R. W. (1967). Language after Section of the Cerebral Commisures. *Brain,* 90:131–148.

Gesell, A., and Amatruda, C. (1941). *Developmental Diagnosis,* 2nd ed. New York: Paul B. Hoeber.

Goldfarb, W. (1943). The Effects of Early Institutional Care on Adolescent Personality. *Journal of Experimental Education,* 12:106–129.

Jones, H. E. (1926). Phenomenal Memorizing as a "Special Ability." *Journal of Applied Psychology,* 10:367–377.

Keeler, W. (1958). Autistic Patterns and Defective Communication in Blind Children with Retrolental Fibroplasia. In: *Psychopathology of Communication,* ed. P. Hoch and J. Zubin. New York: Grune and Stratton.

Lenneberg, E. (1965). The Vocalizations of Infants Born to Deaf and Hearing Parents. *Human Development,* 8:23–37.

Mason, M. K. (1942). Learning to Speak after Six and One Half Years of Silence. *Journal of Speech Disorders,* 7:295–304.

Mason, W. A. (1968). Early Social Deprivation in the Nonhuman Primates: Implications for Human Behavior. In: *Environmental Influences,* ed. D. Glass. New York: Rockefeller University Press and Russell Sage Foundation, pp. 70–100.

Maxfield, K. E. (1936). The Spoken Language of the Blind Pre-School Child: A Study of Methods. *Archives of Psychology,* No. 261.

McCarthy, D. (1954). Language Development in Children. In: *Manual of Child Psychology,* 2nd ed., ed. L. Carmichael. New York: John Wiley, pp. 520–526.

McGraw, M. (1945). The Neuromuscular Maturation of the Human Infant. New York: Columbia University Press.

Norris, M., Spaulding, P. J., and Brodie, F. (1958). *Blindness in Children.* Chicago: University of Chicago Press.

Piaget, J. (1954). *The Construction of Reality in the Child.* New York: Basic Books.

Provence, S., and Lipton, R. (1962). *Infants in Institutions.* New York: International Universities Press.

Rainer, J. D., and Altshuler, K. Z. (1966). *Psychiatry and the Deaf.* U.S. Dept. of Health, Education and Welfare Publication.

Schiller, P. H. (1957). Innate Motor Action as a Basis for Learning. In: *Instinctive Behavior,* ed. C. H. Schiller. New York: International Universities Press, pp. 264–287.

Spitz, R. (1945). Diacritic and Coenesthetic Organizations: The Psychiatric Significance of a Functional Division of the Nervous System into a Sensory and Emotive Part. *Psychoanalytic Review,* 32:146–161.

———— (1959). *A Genetic Field Theory of Ego Formation.* New York: International Universities Press.

———— and Wolf, K. (1946). The Smiling Response. *Genetic Psychology Monographs,* 34: 57–125.

VanderWoude, K. W. (1970). Problem Solving and Language. *A.M.A. Archives of General Psychiatry,* 23:337–342.

Vernon, M. (1967). Relationship of Language to the Thinking Process. *A.M.A. Archives of General Psychiatry,* 16:325–342.

ON METAPHOR AND RELATED PHENOMENA

Benjamin B. Rubinstein, M.D.

Metaphors play an important role not only in the communications between patients and psychoanalysts but, as Hartmann, Kris, and Loewenstein (1946) among others have noted, in the formulation of psychoanalytic theory as well. In the present paper I shall consider neither of these questions. My focus will be primarily on certain aspects of metaphor itself, normal as well as deranged, and on a number of related phenomena.

It may seem to some that I dwell too much on the intricacies of normal metaphor, on its theory, varieties, functions, and possible evolution. In my view, however, this is a largely neglected area of inquiry, significant not only to the literary critic and the linguist but also to the psychoanalytic theoretician who wants to establish a baseline of normality with which to compare both the abnormal ways of thinking and the fleeting imagery of the dream that constitute his primary field of interest.

A TENTATIVE THEORY OF THE NATURE OF METAPHOR

It is not possible to formulate even a tentative theory of the nature of metaphor without considering certain aspects of modern linguistics, particularly as elaborated by Chomsky and his followers. Most of these authors have only incidentally referred to metaphor; but what they have had to say (as well as what they imply) is nonetheless important. One may not always agree with them, but their views cannot be disregarded. The following formulations should be viewed as a first approximation to a theory. I hope they will be carried forward by those who are more expert in the field than I am.

Other views, of course, cannot be disregarded either. Some of them I will briefly consider in the second section of this paper.

Let me start with Chomsky. He (1964) regards metaphors of at least a certain type as representing grammatically deviant or *semi-grammatical* sentences (p.

387). Thus he groups the metaphor "Misery loves company" with such other semi-grammatical sentences as "John frightens sincerity" (p. 386). Although Chomsky assigns the same *degree of grammaticalness* to the two sentences, he makes it quite clear (in two papers co-authored with Miller) that sentences of the first type are interpretable in the light of their "analogies and similarities" to grammatically well-formed sentences, whereas those of the latter are not (Chomsky and Miller, 1963, p. 291). According to Miller and Chomsky (1963), a person can impose an interpretation on the interpretable sentences "much as he can impose an interpretation on an abstract drawing" (p. 446).

Chomsky and Miller do not specify the kind of "analogies and similarities" to well-formed sentences that they have in mind, nor do they make a clear formal distinction between interpretable and uninterpretable semi-grammatical sentences. Ziff (1964), who acutely examines certain aspects of semi-grammatical sentences, hardly considers these questions. Katz (1964), on the other hand, addresses himself specifically to them. He refers to interpretable semi-grammatical sentences as *semi-sentences,* and insists on the formulation of rules specifying how these sentences are (a) comprehended, and (b) distinguished from such *in part* flawlessly structured nonsense strings as "John frightens sincerity." Like Chomsky and Ziff, Katz includes in the class of semi-sentences not only metaphors but also such simple semi-grammatical sentences as "Man bit dog," "House the is red," etc. Briefly stated, in his view each semi-sentence becomes associated with a set of grammatical sentences, the *comprehension set* of the semi-sentence (p. 411). Katz believes that we understand a semi-sentence by virtue of the transfer to it (according to certain rules) of the *meaning(s)* of the sentence(s) of its comprehension set. Nonsense strings, in contrast, whether partly structured or not, are not associated with a comprehension set.

The comprehension set of the semi-sentence "Man bit dog" includes such grammatically well-formed sentences as "The man bit a dog" and "A man bit the dog." Katz does not specifically consider the sentences that constitute the comprehension set of a metaphor. These are not always easy to identify, even when we understand the metaphor intuitively, so to speak. Take again the metaphor "Misery loves company." According to English grammar, the verb 'loves' requires an animate subject. To arrive at a grammatical sentence we must therefore replace the word 'misery' by a noun phrase—i.e., a word or expression that refers to such a subject. Let us try the noun phrase 'a miserable person.' This substitution yields: "A miserable person loves company." This is clearly a grammatical sentence. But it is patently false. If anything, a miserable person shuns company. Since "Misery loves company" is nevertheless felt to be true—at least in a general sort of way—the suggested substitute cannot belong to the comprehension set of the metaphor. It seems that either the word 'loves,' or the word 'company,' or both, must also be replaced. I shall not examine these replacements, which are quite complex. Suffice it to say that one sentence of the comprehension set of the metaphor runs as follows: "A miserable person prefers the company, real or imaginary, of other miserable persons to that of persons who are not miserable." In this sentence the expression 'imaginary company of other miserable persons' is used in a wide enough sense to include reference to *hearing about* the misery of others.

In what follows, I shall consider only metaphors of a simpler type—i.e., sentences in which the metaphor hinges on the meaning of only one or two words. As an example I shall take the metaphor "Mr. X is a fox." It seems justified, in this case, to ask whether the metaphor really represents a semi-grammatical sentence. If we disregard the possibility of certain odd uses, such as that somebody has a table he calls "Mr. X," "Mr. X is a table" is obviously a semi-grammatical sentence. But then it is not a metaphor. In the present connection the word 'table' can be regarded as *unambiguous*. At any rate, unless Mr. X plays at being a table this word cannot be interpreted so as to make sense of the sentence "Mr. X is a table." This gives us a clue. May it not be that the word 'fox' is simply an *ambiguous* word, meaning 'sly person' on the one hand and 'particular sort of furry animal' on the other? The word *does* in fact have these two meanings. In the context "Mr. X is a fox," we would automatically select the meaning 'sly person' for 'fox.' Selection of 'particular sort of furry animal' clearly leads to a contradiction.

Let me pursue this matter a little further. Katz and Fodor (1964) and Katz and Postal (1964) have elucidated the complex semantic factors that determine the proper selection of words for sentences. Among them are what they call *semantic markers, distinguishers,* and *specific selection restrictions.* The semantic markers and the selection restrictions are of particular interest. The former represent the classes and subclasses under which the referent of a word may be subsumed. For example, Mr. X is clearly a member of the class of human beings. Therefore the word 'fox' as it occurs in "Mr. X is a fox" must refer to a subclass of the class of human beings—i.e., in view of the fact that, according to our assumption, the word 'fox' can be used in the meaning 'sly person,' more specifically to the class of sly persons. Because in the context "Mr. X is a . . ." the semantic marker *human being* becomes attached to whatever Mr. X is supposed to be, in this case to the word 'fox,' the meaning 'particular sort of furry animal' cannot be selected. The meanings of ambiguous words are obviously selected in the same manner as are words. Thus it seems that, if we look at the word 'fox' in the indicated way, and if we take the so-called *semantic component* (Chomsky [1957, 1968]; Katz and Fodor [1964]) of English grammar into account, we can explain how a sentence like "Mr. X is a fox" is understood and also, in part, how it may be generated.

Comparison with other ambiguous words, however, shows that this analysis is only partly correct. Take the word 'ball,' which Katz and Fodor and Katz and Postal use as an example. Like 'fox,' this word has two commonly accepted meanings. On the one hand, it refers to a globular object of a certain size, consistency, and weight (meaning$_1$), and on the other to a social occasion characterized by a particular type of dancing (meaning$_2$). We should note that when we use the word 'ball' in meaning$_1$ (as in "He hit the ball"), it does not occur to us to think of it in meaning$_2$, and when we use it in meaning$_2$ (as in "She enjoyed dressing up for the ball"), it does not occur to us to think of it in meaning$_1$. Not so, however, with the word 'fox' as it occurs in "Mr. X is a fox." Even though in this sentence 'fox' is clearly understood in the meaning 'sly person,' the meaning 'particular sort of furry animal' is not completely suppressed but hovers in the background of our comprehension of the sentence "Mr. X is a fox." It follows that, although the word 'fox' is ambiguous, it is not ambiguous in exactly the sense in which 'ball' is.

'Fox,' of course, means primarily 'particular sort of furry animal.' How did it acquire the meaning 'sly person'? To begin with, foxes are proverbially sly creatures. Now it seems that a word can sometimes acquire the meaning of an attribute of the class it stands for. Bickerton (1969) calls a word used in this meaning a "marked sign" (p. 39). In our example, the word 'fox' is marked in respect to the attribute of *being sly*. The important point is that, according to Bickerton, a marked sign can cross the boundary between certain classes that in its unmarked condition—its ordinary, direct meaning—it cannot cross (p. 46). In the rather simple case with which we are concerned, the condition for the crossing of such a boundary is obviously that all members of the class the unmarked sign refers to, and at least some members of the class into which the sign is supposed to cross, possess the attribute that the sign in its marked condition represents. It follows, then, that it is because the word 'fox' is marked in respect to *being sly* that it can cross the boundary between the class of animals and the class of human beings. And it is clearly as a result of crossing this boundary that the word acquires the meaning 'sly person.'

The marked and unmarked conditions of a sign evidently correspond to the two meanings of a metaphorically used word. To speak about crossing boundaries, however, is itself metaphorical. It seems that the essential meaning of Bickerton's theory can be rendered in a much simpler way. When we say that, as a sign marked in respect to *being sly,* the word 'fox' crosses the boundary between the class of foxes and the class of human beings, what we mean is that the word now comes to refer to a class that *subsumes* the class of foxes, *as well as* a particular subclass of human beings—namely, the class of sly persons. We may speak about a class of sly creatures. The remarkable thing is not this classification, but the name given to the class last mentioned, which is the name of one of its subclasses, the class of foxes. The word 'fox' is thus in this sense ambiguous. For the sake of clarity I shall treat it as if it were not one word with two meanings but two separate words. In its reference to the class of sly creatures or to any member(s) of this class I will capitalize the word. We now have a class of FOXES, which includes Mr. X, and a class of foxes, which does not include him. A fox, on the other hand, is both a fox and a FOX. The modified Venn diagram (Figure 1) shows these class relationships.

We can also render these relationships more simply in the following schema:

FOXES   (Mr. X; foxes).

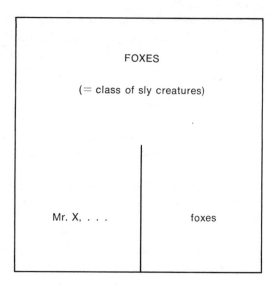

Figure 1.

This schema is to be understood as indicating that, while Mr. X is a FOX and a fox is a FOX, Mr. X is not a fox. In contrast to the *phrase markers* used by Chomsky and by Katz and his co-workers, it represents logical, not grammatical, relationships. In a way it does summarize sentences, but it does not show how these sentences are generated. Since I am more interested in the logic than in the grammar of metaphor, I shall hereafter be making extensive use of schemata of this type.

It follows from these considerations that the metaphor "Mr. X is a FOX" is a grammatically well-formed sentence while, unless we have in mind a fox named "Mr. X," the sentence "Mr. X is a fox" (after the distinction between foxes and FOXES has been made) is a partly structured nonsense string, comparable to the sentence "Mr. X is a table." This point is clearly consistent with Cohen and Margalit's claim (1970) that metaphors are not grammatically deviant. I may mention that, even though according to the view just presented "Mr. X is a FOX" is not a semi-sentence, it may still be associated with a comprehension set. This set clearly includes such sentences as "Mr. X is a sly person."

It seems reasonable to assume that the classifications just mentioned are fundamentally prelinguistic, in the sense that they are not based on, but provide a basis for, linguistic expressions (see Lenneberg [1967], pp. 332f). If so, they are presumably reflected (perhaps in the form of semantic markers) in what Chomsky (1957) calls the deep structure of sentences, in this case of the sentence "Mr. X is a FOX." The peculiar naming of the class to which the metaphor assigns Mr. X, on the other hand, is unlikely to be prelinguistic in this sense. It is probably part of the deep sentence structure itself—or, rather, of the linguistic processes embodied in that structure.

To indicate what Chomsky means by the deep structure of a sentence, let us take the sentence "A wise man is honest," which he uses as an example

(1968, p. 25). In a simplified form, the deep structure of this sentence is rendered as follows:

[a man [man is wise] is honest].

This organization is clearly a reflection of the statement that the class of honest men includes the class of wise men.

By analogy, the deep structure of "Mr. X is a FOX" may be rendered as

[a man (Mr. X) [man (Mr. X) is sly] is a FOX].

This organization reflects the statement that the class of FOXES includes the class of sly men, of which class Mr. X is a member. For the classification itself, it is irrelevant whether the superordinate class is called the class of FOXES or something else, for example, the class of REPTILES or, for that matter, the class of NETZGELOS. If foxes are classified together with Mr. X, in the first of the alternative cases they would evidently be REPTILES and in the second NETZGELOS.

We can now see why we tend to think of a fox when we say that Mr. X is a FOX. We tend to think of other vertebrates (such as fish, dogs, and horses) when we say that humans are vertebrates, and of other primates (such as chimpanzees and gorillas) when we say that they are primates. When I referred to foxes as REPTILES, wasn't there a tendency to think of actual reptiles of some sort? Generally speaking, it seems that if a class is superordinate to other classes, the use of the name of this class evokes in us a readiness to think of the members of at least some of its subclasses. Now, not only is the class of FOXES superordinate to the class of foxes but, phonetically and as ordinarily written, it also carries the name of this class. Therefore, as I have indicated, it is by no means remarkable that we should think of a fox when we say that Mr. X is a FOX. Contrary to Brown's contention (1958, p. 140), however, the sameness of the name does not appear to be the decisive factor. The class of balls in the sense of globular objects is not in the indicated manner related to the class of balls in the sense of occasions for social dancing. Accordingly, in spite of the sameness of the name, when we use the word 'ball' in the first sense we do not tend to think of it in the second. To become effective, sameness of name apparently requires a super-subordinate relationship of the classes.

In this connection, I may mention that Dylan Thomas's phrase 'a grief ago,' which Chomsky (1964) characterizes as semi-grammatical, is not in my view a metaphor—or at least not of the same type as "Mr. X is a FOX." The word 'grief' occurs in its ordinary lexical meaning (as synonymous with sorrow); but it is put to a highly original use. The phrase presupposes an endless succession of griefs so that the interval between griefs can be used as a measure of time. A further presupposition is that griefs are the most (or only) memorable and hence significant events of the past, and that it therefore makes sense to measure time in terms of their occurrence, even though, according to conventional time measures, they may occur at quite irregular intervals. Levin (1967), while emphasizing the semi-grammaticalness of Thomas's phrase, interprets it in a somewhat similar manner.

I shall comment briefly on Brown's (1958, p. 144) interpretation of a sentence by e.e. cummings (1953, p. 12) as a metaphor. There is a sudden shift of frame of reference in the middle of this sentence so that the death of the writer's mother is referred to as 'the beginning' instead of as 'the end,' which the context leads us to expect. In this sentence the word 'beginning' seems to be used in its lexical meaning and would therefore not represent a metaphor. It is possible, however, to claim that what is the end in reality is the beginning in what we may think of as a particular REALITY. Accordingly, the word 'beginning' is not used in its ordinary sense of a real beginning but rather in the sense of a REAL beginning or of a BEGINNING—i.e., in a sense that is at least reminiscent of metaphor.

OTHER THEORIES OF THE NATURE OF METAPHOR

A comparison of the present theory with other theories of the nature of metaphor will serve to amplify some of the points made above.

Although Goldstein (1948) did not specifically address himself to the subject under consideration, he made an important contribution to it. He found that patients with amnesic aphasia suffer marked impairment of their capacity for abstraction and classification. The significant point is that their ability to understand metaphors and related linguistic productions, such as proverbs, is similarly impaired (see particularly pp. 25, 111, and 270). This finding is clearly compatible with the theory outlined above, according to which metaphor depends entirely on certain abstract operations, primarily the formation, on the basis of some similarity between classes, of classes of a higher degree of generality and therefore of abstraction. Ogden and Richards (1923, p. 214) have also emphasized the relationship between metaphor and abstract thought.

The view that similarity is crucially significant for metaphor has a venerable ancestry. It was already recognized by Aristotle, who asserted that "a good metaphor implies an intuitive perception of the similarity in dissimilars" (quoted in Burnshaw [1970], p. 87). No subsequent writer has quarreled with this formulation. Langer (1962), for example, writes that metaphors are based on the abstraction of similar attributes from otherwise dissimilar objects and events (p. 157). Brown (1958), who focuses on the classificatory aspects of the process, calls the similar attributes the *criterial attributes* for the classification (p. 10). We should note, however, that he uses this term in reference to linguistic classifications generally, not just in reference to metaphor.

Jakobson (1956) sees the similarity relationship as part of the basic structure of language itself. He distinguishes two fundamental aspects of language: "Speech implies a selection of certain linguistic entities and their combination into linguistic units of higher degree of complexity" (p. 58). Jakobson believes that combination results in contexts made up of contiguous elements, whereas selection (or at least one form of selection) is a substitution for one another of elements from a pool of similar elements (pp. 60f). One of his central points is that combination and contiguity characterize metonymy, and substitution on the basis of similarity characterizes metaphor. According to this view, metaphor is rooted in one of the fundamental aspects of language.

Not every substitution on the basis of similarity, however, is a metaphor. For example, the substitution of 'burrow' for 'hut' in "He went into his hut" is a metaphor, but the substitution of 'cabin' for 'hut' in the same sentence is not. 'Cabin' and 'hut' are simple synonyms, and the substitution of one for the other does not yield a metaphor (p. 77). Jakobson does not say how synonyms are distinguished from metaphorical substitutes. The distinction is not difficult to make, however. We have seen that metaphorical substitutes (phonetically and as ordinarily written) are always ambiguous in a very specific sense. Synonyms, on the other hand, are not. According to the convention I have adopted, in the indicated context the phoneme sequence /burrow/ should be written 'BURROW.'

Jakobson's focus on substitution raises a question that I have not so far considered: What determines the substitution of a metaphorical for a direct expression? If a speaker has the verb phrases 'is sly' and 'is a FOX' available, what determines his selection of the latter phrase? I shall try to answer this question in a later section of this paper.

The main shortcoming of Jakobson's theory is his failure to consider the part played by classification in the formation of metaphor. Brown (1958, pp. 139ff) is the only author I know of who clearly recognizes that metaphor depends on the relationship of super- and subordination of two classes having the same name. As I have indicated, however, I cannot go along with his contention that the sameness of the name is exclusively responsible for why, in our example, we tend to think of a fox when we say that Mr. X is a FOX. This contention is all the more surprising since Brown is fully aware of the fact that *only* if a sentence is a "live" metaphor does the use of an ambiguous word in one meaning tend to evoke its other meaning.

Burnshaw (1970) and Wheelwright (1962, p. 71) both make the somewhat astonishing claim that the distinction commonly made between simile and metaphor is unimportant. According to Burnshaw (p. 87), a simile is a metaphor in which the word 'like' has been inserted at an appropriate place. This view takes no account of the shift in meaning when a word is used metaphorically. That is, while it makes sense to say "Mr. X is like a fox," the string "Mr. X is a fox" is, as we have seen, nonsensical. The word 'like,' in other words, is not inserted into a metaphor. In the sentence "Mr. X is like a FOX," on the other hand, the word 'like' introduces an ambiguity. If we say that Mr. X is like a FOX, then we imply that he is not really a FOX, just as when we say that he is like a fox we imply that he is not really a fox. In this case, the insertion of the word 'like' in effect destroys the metaphor.

Here let me say a word about the hypothetical processes involved in simile formation. These processes obviously do not include the peculiar naming that is characteristic of metaphor. On the other hand, it is not clear whether the pre-linguistic processes proceed *beyond* the establishment of a similarity to the classification together of the similar items on the basis of their established similarity. In other words, in the case of simile do the prelinguistic processes describable as a classification of Mr. X as sly and of foxes likewise as sly lead directly to the recognition that (in respect to *being sly*) Mr. X is like a fox? Or do these prelinguistic processes first lead to the establishment of the superordinate class of sly creatures, any member of which can then (in respect to *being sly*) be said to be like any other? It seems to me that we can well describe any detected similarity as equivalent to a classification. Either alternative, however, is compatible with the data available at present.

VARIETIES OF SIMPLE METAPHORS [1]

Everyday speech abounds in metaphors like "Mr. X is a FOX." Here a noun is transformed into a metaphor. Proper names are sometimes transformed in the same way; for example, "Peter is a little NAPOLEON." The principle is the same as in the case of the noun 'fox.' Some characteristics of Napoleon Bonaparte are taken as the criterial attributes for the formation of the superordinate class of NAPOLEONS. The relationships between the classes may be represented by the following schema:

NAPOLEONS   (Peter and other people who in a characteristic way resemble Napoleon; Napoleon).

The name Napoleon as it occurs after the semicolon stands for a one-member class.

Metaphors are common not only in everyday speech, but also in primitive thinking and poetry. The following example is an unusually good one. Many primitives believe that their ancestors were animals. At least some of them, however, seem to be aware that this belief is not literally true. As quoted by Lévi-Strauss (1966), an Osage gave this explanation to his interlocutor (J. O. Dorsey): "We do not believe that our ancestors were really animals, birds, etc., as told in traditions. These things are only *wa-wi-ku-ska'-ye* (symbols) for something higher" (p. 149 fn). In other words, according to this Osage, the ancestors of his people were not animals but ANIMALS. Primitives generally believe that animals are endowed with the most admirable qualities: wisdom, cunning, strength, etc. (see Leach and Fried [1949], p. 61). Thus, the members of any group, such as the ancestors of the Osage, who were thought to possess these qualities, may be said to be ANIMALS in exactly the sense in which Mr. X is said to be a FOX and Peter a little NAPOLEON.

A few examples from poetry will suffice. I shall not consider the poetic merits of the lines to be cited, only their metaphoric structure. Walt Whitman's

the silent SEA of faces

---

[1] Hereafter, words used metaphorically are consistently capitalized.

(from *When Lilacs Last in the Dooryard Bloom'd*) is rather straightforward. We have the schema:

SEA   (vast homogeneous, or seemingly homogeneous, softly rolling mass (of faces); sea).

The following line, from Roethke's "The Manifestation,"

The worm, INTREPID SCHOLAR of the soil

(Roethke [1958], p. 71), is more intriguing, but not impenetrable. At least one way of explicating the meaning of the word 'SCHOLAR' in this context is by the use of a number of additional metaphors. We may say that a scholar BURROWS into his subject matter as a worm burrows into the soil. Worm and scholar are thus both SCHOLARS in that they BURROW "singlemindedly" into something. A worm, like a scholar, may further be said to EXAMINE whatever it burrows into, at least in the sense, say, of TAKING NOTE OF obstacles and adjusting its movements accordingly.

(These remarks, as well as the explanatory remarks appended to the metaphors that follow, may be regarded as extracted from the comprehension sets of the metaphors.)

The reason for capitalizing 'intrepid' is fairly plain. A worm may be said to be intrepid in the sense of being, as far as one can tell, completely oblivious to the manifold reasons for trepidation that continually surround it. This is not to be intrepid in the ordinary sense of the word, however. The worm, as it were, is intrepid by default, not by inclination, and is therefore best regarded as being INTREPID, not intrepid.

Let me turn now to Marianne Moore's (1951) line from "The Monkey Puzzle,"

the lion's ferocious CHRYSANTHEMUM head

(p. 80), quoted in Blackmur (1952, p. 243). Here we have a startling juxtaposition of what *seem* to be radically incompatible elements. Once it is pointed out, however, the *purely configurational* similarity between a chrysanthemum and a lion's head, on which the metaphor is based, becomes quite obvious. The schema is clearly

CHRYSANTHEMUMS   (heads of lions; chrysanthemums).

So far I have considered mainly nouns that have been subjected to metaphoric transformation. e.e. cummings' (1954, p. 394) "a salesman is an it" provides an example of the metaphoric transformation of a pronoun and a verb:

a salesman is an IT that STINKS to please

Here 'an IT' clearly stands for a human who is really subhuman (and hence contemptible). The following schema indicates one possible meaning in the given context of 'STINKS':

STINKS   (bows and scrapes and is in every way ostentatiously submissive; stinks).

T. S. Eliot (1963, "The Love Song of J. Alfred Prufrock") provides a beautiful illustration of a partly metaphorically transformed verb phrase:

> Would it have been worth while,
> To have BITTEN OFF THE MATTER with a smile

Judged by the context in which it is embedded, THE MATTER may be anything, from a casual conversation or a foolish remark to the author's (or Mr. Prufrock's) philosophical ruminations; it may include the universe, or anyone's view of it, or the author's, or all of these. The class of objects and events that 'THE MATTER' stands for seems endlessly variegated; it may even be meant to include itself as a member. I shall therefore consider only 'to BITE OFF.' The schema is fairly clear:

to BITE OFF   (to stop one, or some, or all of the things 'THE MATTER' has reference to; to bite off).

The role of the smile is interesting. The person in question may consider the possibility of smilingly BITING OFF THE MATTER or of letting a smile BITE IT OFF.

Everyday speech also makes use of metaphorically transformed verbs: for example, "They KICKED the idea AROUND," and "It is KILLING me."

It seems clear from these examples that a metaphorically transformed verb represents a member of a class of activities or events that is named after one of its subordinate classes. In respect to the class relationships involved, metaphorically transformed verbs therefore do not differ from metaphorically transformed nouns.

This seems to be true also—at least on the face of it—of a number of metaphorically transformed adjectives. Examples are such phrases as 'a SAD landscape,' 'HEAVY skies,' 'a WEEPING willow.' We may further note Roethke's use, cited above, of 'INTREPID.'

Asch (1955) has called attention to a group of adjectives that are primarily applied to physical objects, but secondarily acquire psychological meanings as well. Examples are 'hot,' 'cold,' 'hard,' 'straight,' and 'crooked.' The remarkable finding is that these terms have rather similar double meanings in a number of unrelated languages—namely, English, Hebrew, Greek, Chinese, Thai, Malayalam, and Hausa (pp. 35ff). Asch also noted that, while children three to four years old understand many of these words in their physical applications, it is only several years later that they become aware of their psychological meanings (Asch and Nerlove [1960]).

Partly relying on introspective evidence, Asch claims in a later paper (1961) that the concepts corresponding to these words (which he now calls *dual terms*)

"have little in common with abstract logical operations. They are not generaliza-
tions of what is common to an array of different instances" (p. 333). He nevertheless admits that the dual terms refer to common "functional properties and
modes of interaction" exhibited by the persons as well as by the physical objects
to which they apply (p. 332). In both instances, for example, 'hard' refers to
something unyielding, something that resists change. I shall tentatively put forth
the claim that, in its psychological application, each dual term represents a metaphorical transformation of the same term when it is understood as referring to a
physical attribute. According to the convention I have adopted, it would be
nonsensical to say that a person is hard. A stone is hard. A person, on the other
hand (if he qualifies for the description), is HARD.

Quine (1960) raised an interesting question, using the word 'hard' as an
example. He observes that this word is used about chairs as well as about questions, and that its second use is a "figurative extension" of the first. He then
asks: "Are we to treat this extension as a second sense of a thenceforward
ambiguous term, or are we to treat it as an extended application of a thenceforward more general term?" (p. 131). It follows from the preceding discussion
that the term is *both* ambiguous and more general, in that a chair may be said to
be hard as well as HARD whereas a question can only be HARD, not hard.

We may note in passing that at least some of Asch's dual terms apply not
only to persons and physical objects. A HARD question is neither a physical
object nor a person. This is true also of HOT issues, the COLD WAR, SOFT
music, etc.

We may note further that in their metaphorical uses at least some of the
adjectives of the group we are considering may be said to be dead, or as
MacLeish (1960, p. 81) puts it, "half-dead" metaphors. Thus, when we say that
a person is HARD, we do not necessarily think of the hardness of a stone
(although we may).

I shall conclude this discussion on a note of uncertainty. The tentativeness
with which I put forth the claim that in their psychological applications dual
terms are metaphorically transformed reflects a certain difficulty that this claim
brings with it. If we accept it, we can obviously say "He is HARD." And we can
also say "He is a STONE." But should we say "He is hard as stone" or "He is
HARD as stone"? The latter expression is obviously correct. Both STONES and
stones are HARD, but only stones are hard.

It would be a mistake, however, to think that that is all there is to it. It
seems that "HARD" and "hard" refer to partly overlapping *conglomerations* of
attributes and that the overlapping parts of the conglomerations are the true
criterial attributes of the class of STONES. These include *being unyielding* in a
certain way. But can stones and STONES (e.g., persons) be said to be unyielding
in the same sense of the word? It does not seem so. In fact, it appears that,
whereas stones are unyielding, STONES are UNYIELDING. We should note that,
even though, for example, Mr. X and foxes may be said to be sly in different
ways, the difference between *being sly* in the one case and *being sly* in the other
is not of the same fundamental nature as between *being hard* and *being HARD*
and between *being unyielding* and *being UNYIELDING*.

We are now prepared to consider a theory of metaphor advanced by Levin. It differs in an interesting way from the view I have proposed. Following Chomsky, Levin (1963) characterizes metaphor as a particular sort of violation of grammatical rules. In a later paper (1965) he states, more specifically, that an "analogizing process" brings about a "conflation" of certain words with words or notions of a different kind, "with consequent enrichment of the expression" (p. 236). In reference to Eliot's line "My self-possession gutters," for example, he states that "the intransitive verb *gutter* is limited in its co-occurrence range to just about the words (*burning*) *candle* or *flame,* so that self-possession and flame are fused in a metaphor" (p. 236). According to Levin, in other words, the word 'gutter' makes 'self-possession' acquire a new meaning. In my view, on the other hand, it is the word 'gutter' that is changed metaphorically: I would, without hesitation, write "My self-possession GUTTERS." As used by Levin, the expressions 'analogizing process' and 'conflation' are purely descriptive and, to my mind at any rate, do not have theoretical implications of a kind that would make his view preferable to the one proposed here.

EMPTY METAPHORICAL FORMS
AND OBSCURE METAPHORS

Consider the noun phrase 'colorless green ideas' in Chomsky's well-known example of a semi-grammatical sentence, "Colorless green ideas sleep furiously" (1957, p. 15; 1964, p. 386). In their literal meanings the two attributes, 'colorless' and 'green,' are clearly contradictory. The expression therefore makes no sense. But what if we take these words metaphorically? Then we get the following schema for 'colorless':

COLORLESS (bland, undistinguished, prosaic; colorless)

And for 'green' we get:

GREEN (not ripe, immature, inexperienced; green).

We often speak about a COLORLESS style of writing, and we may say about a person that he is rather GREEN. Wheelwright (1962) quotes from a poem by Dylan Thomas in which the expression 'GREEN age,' meaning 'youth,' occurs (p. 77; capitalization mine). Bickerton (1969) cites a few other interesting uses of 'GREEN' (p. 49; capitalization mine).

If we now transform the noun phrase we are considering into the phrase 'COLORLESS GREEN ideas,' we find that the phrase ceases to be contradictory. Thus transformed, it refers to ideas that are bland and immature.

It still does not sound right, however, and the main reason why the metaphorically transformed expression is not readily accepted is fairly clear. As is the case with metaphors generally, the use of a metaphorically transformed word tends to elicit the literal meaning of that word. The contradiction inherent in 'colorless green ideas' will therefore easily be evoked by 'COLORLESS GREEN ideas.' When such a contradiction occurs, a metaphor is likely to break up and become meaningless. The force of the superordinate classification, which is supposed to reconcile the contradiction, is apparently weaker than the force with which contradictions, once spotted, are rejected.

Apart from being somewhat pedestrian, 'COLORLESS GREEN ideas' is at best a strained and therefore rather shaky metaphor. It is not particularly obscure, nor is it an empty metaphorical form. Its comprehension set is easily extracted from the schemata for 'COLORLESS' and 'GREEN.' Consider now the expressions 'honest geranium' and 'spinster insecticide,' which Katz and Postal (1964, p. 16) and Katz and Fodor (1964, p. 508), respectively, use as examples of anomalous combinations. Taken as such they are obviously nonsensical. But what about the expressions 'HONEST geranium' and 'SPINSTER insecticide'?

Offhand, it does not seem that the metaphoric transformation of the two attributes renders the expressions more meaningful. It does, however, make us stop for a moment and ask whether the expressions may not be meaningful after all. Is there something about an insecticide that makes it comparable to a spinster? Perhaps both may be said to be in a certain sense CAUSTIC and STINGING. Similarly, is there something about a geranium, perhaps in its appearance or general configuration, that suggests to us some characteristic feature of the attribute *being honest*? The last question, at least, I do not think can be answered in the affirmative. It is significant, however, that these questions are suggested by the metaphorically transformed expressions. Because they make us look for perhaps nonexistent similarities, I shall refer to such expressions as *empty metaphorical forms.*

Empty metaphorical forms should not be confused with what Beardsley (1958) calls *logically empty attributions* (pp. 139 ff). He includes under this heading redundancies of a certain type (e.g., two-legged biped), tautologies, self-contradictions, and genuine metaphors. It seems to me that the inclusion of metaphor in this motley group is based on a partial misunderstanding of its nature. I shall not discuss this question beyond mentioning that what I refer to as empty metaphorical forms Beardsley regards as "nonsense of a particular kind" (p. 143). It is of interest that, as Beardsley points out, it is not always easy to draw the line between this kind of nonsense and what he terms *obscure,* but valid, *metaphors.* Different persons may also draw the line differently. Among other such borderline metaphors, he lists the expression 'RUBBER joy,' which he constructed by analogy with e.e. cummings' 'RUBBER questions' (p. 143; capitalization mine). 'Participial biped,' on the other hand, Beardsley regards as almost unquestionably a nonsensical attribution.

The following lines from T. S. Eliot (1963, "Morning at the Window") exemplify a metaphor that is obscure at best:

> And along the trampled edges of the street
> I am aware of the DAMP souls of housemaids
> SPROUTING despondently at area gates.

I shall consider only the first of these metaphors. Grover Smith (1956) regards it as "barely plausible" (p. 30), which means, according to the terminology adopted here, that it is on the borderline between being an obscure metaphor and an empty metaphorical form.

Another obscure metaphor is St.-John Perse's (1949) phrase from "Exile"

> . . . the CANCER of SILENCE

(p. 17). Judged by the context, its comprehension set may include 'the disintegrating effect of solitude.' But this is by no means an obvious interpretation, nor is it the only possible one in the context. Wheelwright (1962) refers to metaphors of this type as "plurisignative" (pp. 57ff, 90). To some, however, the quoted expression may simply represent an empty metaphorical form.

The following metaphors from cummings' (1954), "anyone lived in a pretty how town"

> he sang his DIDN'T he danced his DID

(p. 370), which Levin (1967) comments on from the point of view of their degree of grammaticalness (which clearly is quite low), seem closer to being empty metaphorical forms than either of the poetic metaphors just quoted. This quality, apart from the bafflement it creates, may well enhance the purely musical value of the line.

Levin (1965) makes an interesting observation about the expression "a pretty how town," which occurs in the first line of the same poem. His point is essentially that either the expression is nonsensical or the adverb 'how' must be interpreted as being *in effect* an adjective (p. 235). Following the convention adopted here, we may write "a pretty HOW town." It seems to me that Levin's contention is at least compatible with my view of this expression as an empty metaphorical form (or a form that is closely related).

ON THE DEATH AND SO-CALLED REVIVAL OF METAPHORS

Let us take a hypothetical case. We have the word 'leg' in its reference to the legs of men and animals. Let us assume that at one point the word had no other meaning. Now let us assume that we suddenly discover a similarity between legs and the vertical supports of chairs and tables. Accordingly, we begin to refer to the latter as LEGS. We have the schema:

LEGS (vertical supports of chairs and tables; human and animal legs).

Gradually the metaphor wears out. When we speak or think of the LEGS of a table or a chair, the legs of humans and animals no longer come to mind. But this means that now the vertical supports of chairs and tables have become legs; they are not LEGS any more. The superordinate class of LEGS has simply disappeared. Instead, the word 'leg' has become an ambiguous word in exactly the same sense as the word 'ball' which I referred to earlier. When the metaphor has reached this stage, it is commonly said to be dead.

We have again arrived at the conclusion that, without a logical relationship of super- and subordination, the sameness of name of two classes cannot establish a psychological tie between them.

Sometimes a dead metaphor *appears* to be revived. I. A. Richards (1960) described the lines by Robert Frost

> Mother can make a common table rear
> And kick with two legs like an army mule

"as a nice example of reviving a dead metaphor" (p. 434). But is this really so? Let us call the legs of the mule $legs_1$ and the legs of the table $legs_2$. (I shall consider only the kicking with the legs, not the rearing of the table.) $Legs_2$ cannot kick; only $legs_1$ kick. The following point is decisive: Even before the death of the metaphor, the LEGS that are now $legs_2$ were not supposed to kick. According to our assumption, they were originally called LEGS simply because, like legs, they are slender vertical supports of something. Therefore when we say that the $legs_2$ of the table kick we are not reviving a metaphor but confusing these legs with $legs_1$. There is a superficial similarity with a metaphor, however. In saying that the table, like a mule, uses its vertical supports (i.e., its $legs_2$) for kicking, Frost makes us think of the mule as it in fact uses its vertical supports (i.e., its $legs_1$) for kicking. This is not a metaphor, however, and hence no metaphor has been revived; it is a tall story based on overstretching an analogy.

ON THE FUNCTIONS OF METAPHOR

Metaphors have a number of functions, some of which are functions only in the sense that the metaphors in question have certain determinate effects. I shall discuss only a few of the more important functions of metaphors.

A. The most ancient and perhaps most powerful function of metaphor is to extend the reach of language. Innumerable concepts, and the words representing them, were derived from metaphor, from seeing similarities in widely different objects, events, etc. As the metaphor died, the corresponding word acquired a new meaning, seemingly unrelated to the original one. The transition from leg_1 to LEG to leg_2, described above, illustrates the process. Brown (1958) gives as an example the transformation through metaphor of the anatomical 'foot' to 'foot of a mountain' (p. 140). Langer (1962) offers, among other examples, the transformation of 'cap,' as a particular kind of headgear, into 'cap,' meaning a cover for the hub of a wheel (p. 158). According to Empson (1930), "metaphor, more or less far-fetched, more or less complicated, more or less taken for granted . . . , is the normal mode of development of a language" (p. 2). Langer expresses a very similar view. Hulme (1965) likewise contends, perhaps with some exaggeration, that "Prose is . . . the museum where the dead metaphors of the poets are preserved" (p. 130).

As we have seen, a metaphor represents a class that is superordinate to at least two classes. In this respect, metaphor formation does not differ from the formation of superordinate classes (or concepts) generally. Take the class of vertebrates. We might arbitrarily give this class the name of one of its subclasses— i.e., we might turn the classification into a metaphor. Consider the sentence: "With the possible exception of human beings, of all MICE in the world the lion is the most ferocious and the nightingale the most bewitching singer." There can be little doubt that the word 'MICE' in this sentence has the meaning 'vertebrates,' or 'members of the ANIMAL KINGDOM,' or 'living THINGS,' etc. A metaphorical concept of this type would of course be rather unwieldy, but it does show that apart from the specific naming there is no difference in the processes of metaphor formation and the formation of other superordinate concepts.

Another point that emerges from this example is that, contrary to the authors just cited, metaphor formation is not always a step in the formation of new concepts. In many instances a superordinate class is named after some conspicuous attribute shared by all members of the class. Usually, the criterial attribute of the class is drawn upon. Examples are 'vertebrate,' 'mammal,' and 'locomotive.' The word 'vertebra,' which is derived from the Latin *vertere,* meaning 'to turn,' is a nice example.

Although the choice of criterial attributes may differ, in this respect there is no difference between our own modes of thinking and primitive ones. According to Lévi-Strauss (1966), the Nuer, an African tribe, group red ants and cobras together because of their similar color (p. 63). Concepts may also be formed on the basis of contiguity—by primitives as well as by ourselves (p. 63).

B. A second function of metaphor is indicated in the following quotations. According to Hulme (1965), to preserve the "individuality of the emotion" the artist must "invent new metaphors and new epithets" to express his experiences. Everyday language is defective and often "will not carry the exact thing [he] wants to say" (pp. 134f).

Considering specifically modifier-subject combinations (like 'RUBBER hopes'), Beardsley (1958) notes that often "the subject singles out for attention a hitherto unnoticed connotation of the modifier" (p. 144). Metaphor may thus lead to the discovery of hidden meanings of words. His main point, however, is that "In this way a metaphor is able to mean something that no literal combination of words in existence can mean" and that it thus "augments the resources of our language" (p. 144). In their own way, Cohen and Margalit (1970) also emphasize this point.

If we disregard his metaphysics, we recognize in Wheelwright (1962) a related view of the limitations of ordinary (including scientific) language and the necessity of metaphor. Speaking primarily about poetry, he states first that metaphor reveals previously unseen similarities between the known and the usually more important unknown (pp. 73f). He then says that metaphor (or *epiphor,* as he calls it) thus "hints significance" (p. 91), in part creating and in part disclosing—incompletely, to be sure, yet more completely than the language of science—"What Is," the inner meanings of things (pp. 51, 130f, 173).

The authors cited seem to agree on at least one point—namely, that a metaphor may be able to express something that is not otherwise expressible. This may be because what we want to express is so vague, so evanescent, so merely felt, so complex, or so devoid of practical significance, that language has not developed a corresponding vocabulary. But it may also be because what we want to refer to is, although quite tangible, so newly discovered that words for it have not yet been invented.

Poetry is not the only mode of expression in which metaphors of the first type are resorted to. The BIG BANG theory of modern cosmology is an example from a different field, and so are a number of psychoanalytic concepts, for instance, EGO and INTROJECTION.

Werner (1948) reports an example of metaphor formation of the latter type—i.e., the use of metaphor to refer to a newly discovered object. The Boloki, an African tribe, when faced with an umbrella for the first time, called it a "bat." Obviously, what they had in mind was that the umbrella was a BAT. Although recognizing the metaphorical character of the naming, based as it was on obvious similarities between umbrellas and bats, Werner insists on the primitive character of the process. To him it represents merely "a preliminary step toward generalization" (p. 243). He believes that in the minds of the Boloki "umbrella and bat (by virtue of concrete abstraction) become, in a particular sense, concretely united" (p. 244). It is difficult to see what Werner means by "concrete abstraction." It seems, rather, that in this case metaphor formation follows exactly the same logic as it does in so-called civilized societies. Werner apparently had not been able to free himself from the notion that primitive people are incapable of abstract thought, a notion that Lévi-Strauss (1966) disproves with a wealth of examples.

C. The BAT metaphor is a clear illustration of the function of metaphor to compensate for certain deficiencies of ordinary language. But what about metaphors like "Mr. X is a FOX"? They are certainly not resorted to in order to make up for a language defect. There is no need for us to say that Mr. X is a FOX. We can express the same idea more simply by saying that he is a sly person. So, since we have available the verb phrase 'is sly' as well as the verb phrase 'is a FOX,' why choose the latter rather than the former?

Assume that we call an automobile a beetle. According to Morris (1946), "Since an automobile is not literally a beetle, to call it a beetle *forces the interpreter to attend with special care* to the automobile in order to determine in what sense the automobile is like (and unlike) a beetle" (p. 137; italics mine). In discussing empty metaphorical forms, I noted that the mere appearance of a string of words as a metaphor compels us to look for the (sometimes nonexistent) characteristics that would indeed make it a metaphor. T. S. Eliot's 'DAMP souls of housemaids,' as I indicated, may owe its force largely to this effect. Thus, when we say "Mr. X is a FOX" we force the listener to look for the attribute Mr. X has in common with foxes, which—or so it seems—makes this attribute stand out with greater poignancy than when we say simply that Mr. X is a sly person. In this sense a metaphor, in Black's word (1962, pp. 39ff), functions as a "filter," augmenting what Mr. X has in common with foxes, while suppressing what he does not have in common with them.

If we disregard the function of metaphor in the development of language, we can say that metaphors have two main functions: (1) to compensate for the insufficiencies of existing language, and (2) to emphasize characteristics that for one reason or another we feel deserve the special attention of our audience. These functions, clearly, can also be described in motivational terms. In the next section I shall consider how, in some cases, unconscious motives may influence the choice of metaphors.

A NOTE ON THE DETERMINATION OF THE CHOICE OF METAPHORS BY UNCONSCIOUS FACTORS

Considering the frequent use of metaphors in psychoanalytic theory and practice, it is rather surprising that psychoanalysts have written so little on this topic. Sharpe (1940) believes that metaphors generally arise in connection with early bodily experience and in their own way reveal that experience, which is often of a traumatic nature. This is an odd statement. Most commonly used metaphors show little or no trace of such a connection. Neither does it seem, as Aleksandrowicz (1962) claims, mainly following Sharpe, that "the metaphor is archaic in form and often in content" (p. 97). Everything I have said so far contradicts this claim. Indeed, Aleksandrowicz himself cites examples of metaphor that do not fit his own formula. It is nonetheless likely, as Beres (1965) points out, that in some cases the choice of metaphor may be determined by unconscious factors (pp. 15f).

In conformity with her theory of the origins of metaphor, Sharpe distinguishes oral, anal, urethral, and what she calls "miscellaneous" metaphors. She gives a great number of examples of each kind but analyzes, in the psychoanalytic sense, only a few, and none in the sense of logical or linguistic analysis. The psychoanalytic analyses are quite cursory. Like a poet, she relies mostly on the immediate effect on the reader of the metaphors she presents.

This way of going about things does not inspire confidence. Nonetheless, I will assume that the clinical confirmation of the effect of unconscious factors on the choice of metaphor is substantial enough to warrant at least some belief in its reality. This assumption is of course not an arbitrary one but is based on the informal confirmation provided by clinical experience. Ill-defined though it may be, it must still be taken seriously. Within the framework of the present paper, the next question is how an effect of this kind may conceivably be brought about.

Among the many "oral" metaphors listed by Sharpe is the following:

"I have wandered off the point and can't find it again."

The patient has obviously not managed to say what he originally intended to say and has now forgotten what it was. I shall consider only the first part of this statement. It almost goes without saying that it will hardly occur to us to inquire about the possible unconscious determination of the choice of a metaphor of this type unless we are satisfied that the speaker uses it excessively or in a specific context. The following considerations should be viewed with the first of these alternatives in mind. The second alternative I shall briefly consider later.

'To WANDER OFF the POINT in talking' is a common metaphor and not hard to understand. It is not, however, easy to explain. It is the word 'POINT' that makes for the difficulty. Let us consider two of the largely interrelated meanings of the word 'point' in modern usage. Take the point of a pencil or of an arrow. The point of a pencil is (a) its tapering-off end and (b) its functionally most significant part. The point of an arrow fits the same description. Now take the POINT of a story. As the word is commonly used, the POINT of a story is its most significant part, its essential meaning. In terms of another metaphor, the POINT of a story may also be said to be what the story NARROWS DOWN TO, a concept that is clearly related to tapering off. We can construct the following schema:

A POINT   (the comparatively most significant part of something that has no point in a literal sense, i.e., no tapering-off end, but that can be said to be what this something NARROWS DOWN TO; the comparatively most significant part of something that literally has a point, i.e., a tapering-off end, which is also its most significant part).

In the given context 'to WANDER OFF' clearly means 'to talk about a lot of mostly irrelevant things.' Accordingly, when the patient said that he had WANDERED OFF the POINT, what he had in mind was that he had talked about a lot of things but not about the most significant part of his story—that is, not about what he had intended to talk about.

If we assume that the choice of 'to WANDER OFF the POINT' as a mode of expression is unconsciously determined, then the determiner of the choice may itself be expressible in these very terms. For the sake of argument, I shall take this view, referring to it as the basic hypothesis underlying Sharpe's thesis. A rough sketch of the essential lower-level clinical hypotheses will do in this connection. They flow naturally from Sharpe's classification of the metaphor as "oral." We shall assume that, as an infant, the patient often lost the nipple and felt distressed (in the way infants may be presumed to feel distressed). As a consequence, he developed a *fear* of losing the nipple and, more specifically, of moving in such a way as to lose it. We shall assume further that a disposition not only for the fear but also for the distress persisted and now determines, among other things, the choice of metaphors such as the one we are considering.

The following considerations indicate that something may indeed be said in favor of what I have just referred to as the basic hypothesis underlying Sharpe's thesis. To begin with, a nipple is also a POINT. It is (a) the tapered-off, slightly elevated center of a breast, and (b) at least for an infant, the breast's functionally most significant part. Although, according to this analysis, a nipple is almost literally a point, we do not generally refer to a nipple as the point of a breast. Therefore it must be regarded as a POINT. It follows that, if the patient does indeed have an unconscious fear of moving in such a way as to lose the nipple, and *if he were to express this fear in words,* he might say metaphorically that he is afraid of WANDERING OFF the POINT. In the indicated connection, 'to move' is in effect 'to WANDER OFF.' If this is correct, we can provisionally claim that the metaphor and other equivalent expressions (or, rather, the underlying classifications and perhaps also the deep structures of the corresponding sentences) are in a state of at least some degree of readiness to become active. In the same way, distress about having lost the nipple may be expressed in terms of HAVING WANDERED OFF it.

The claim made by the basic hypothesis is therefore at any rate thinkable. But I have not as yet indicated how the state of affairs just outlined may conceivably determine the choice of the metaphor in question to express an entirely different state of affairs. Let us go back to the original situation. The patient experiences dismay at having talked about a lot of things but not about the most significant part of what he had intended to talk about. *If he were to express this dismay in words,* he might say metaphorically that he is dismayed at HAVING WANDERED OFF the POINT. If this is correct, we can provisionally claim that the metaphor and other equivalent expressions (or, rather, the underlying classifications and presumably also the deep structures of the corresponding sentences) are in a state of at least some degree of readiness to become active.

The principal remaining assumptions are: (1) that even in its nonverbal aspect the felt dismay has enough in common with the distress for it to trigger this distress; (2) that of all the equivalent expressions of the distress, and of all the equivalent expressions of the dismay, only 'HAVING WANDERED OFF the POINT' (and perhaps a few others) are capable of expressing *both* the distress and the dismay; (3) that the *convergence* of the two *potential* uses of this metaphor determines the patient's choice of it to describe his experience. The convergence, in other words, turns a state of readiness to become active into a state of activity.

This is all highly speculative and requires clarification on several points. It should not be taken too seriously, perhaps, except as a *demonstration* of the thinkability, from the point of view of possible processes, of specific unconscious determination of the choice of metaphor.

In the following example, it is the *context* which suggests that the choice of metaphor is determined by unconscious factors. A young woman, whose father had administered enemas to her until she was eleven or twelve, could not achieve an orgasm with her husband. Only when she masturbated did she reach a climax. Her most frequent masturbation fantasy was that she was being given an enema by a young doctor in a hospital. Although the relationship between her desire for an enema and her failure to achieve orgasm in intercourse had often come up during the psychoanalysis, she always managed to "forget" it again. I am not concerned here with the transference implication of her "forgetting." The point I want to make is that in an hour when I once again indicated that she apparently prefers an enema to sexual intercourse she seemed surprised, as if she had never heard this before, and exclaimed: "Oh, that's awful—I have to WASH THAT OUT, that desire!" And again, just before she left that day, she asked: "Will I feel free to talk about it next time—or do I again have to DREDGE IT UP FROM THE BOTTOM?"

The remarkable thing is that the patient, who was intelligent and alert, was completely unaware of the metaphorical character of these utterances. It should also be noted that, as a rule, her speech was straight—i.e., nonmetaphorical. Since her desire for enemas was discussed in the hour, and since she was unusually emotional about it, we may surmise that, at least unconsciously, *the desire itself* was alerted. If this surmise is correct, we can see how it may have determined the choice of the metaphors—perhaps in the manner indicated above. The point is clearly consistent with Arlow's (1969) statement (provided this statement is taken to apply only to cases of particular types) that "Metaphor constitutes an outcropping into conscious expression of a fragment of an unconscious fantasy" (p. 7).

A related but less specific question concerns the relationship between certain personality characteristics and the preference for certain types of metaphor. One facet of this question has been investigated by R. H. Knapp and J. T. Garbutt (cited by Brown [1965]). High and low scorers on the achievement motive were presented with a set of metaphorical descriptions of time, for example, "A DASHING WATERFALL," "A STRING OF BEADS," and asked to judge the appropriateness of each. It turned out that high scorers preferred metaphors expressing speed, directionality, or purposiveness, whereas low scorers preferred quiescent ones (p. 443). This finding lends some support to the hypothesis that choice of metaphor is determined by unconscious factors.

One might claim that, in addition to the functions of metaphor considered in the preceding section, metaphor has yet another function, which is to serve as a vehicle for the expression of unconscious wishes and fears. Aleksandrowicz (1962) in fact makes this claim and, if I understand her correctly, so does Sharpe. Maybe in some cases the claim is valid. A particularly telling example is Aleksandrowicz's interpretation of the statement of a very disturbed young girl that "the WEEDS may also be pretty" as an expression of "her feelings of worthlessness and her need to be accepted" (p. 94; capitalization mine). Aleksandrowicz does not, however, present evidence for the assumption that the feelings and the need were unconscious. Besides, the context in which the statement occurred is not described in enough detail for an independent observer to be able to evaluate it properly. I am therefore not persuaded by the general claim that one function of metaphor is to provide an outlet for unconscious motives. I am even less persuaded by the claim that the patient is unconsciously trying to communicate something to the therapist. In most cases, only the weaker claim—that the choice of metaphor is sometimes unconsciously determined—seems justified.

The view just presented is compatible with Voth's (1970) careful analysis (in the psychoanalytic sense) of a number of probably unconsciously determined metaphors produced by patients. Voth, who is mainly interested in the therapeutic use of metaphors, hardly discusses the theoretical issues involved.

ON UNCONSCIOUSLY DETERMINED METAPHORICAL READINGS OF MESSAGES AND SITUATIONS

The following incident concerns not the production of metaphors but the apparent interpretation as a metaphor of a statement that was quite obviously meant to be taken literally. It involves a writer in his mid-thirties who gave ample evidence of the presence of intense unconscious castration anxiety. He had mentioned several times that he had been circumcised at the age of five and that his mother on that occasion had said, "That's what happens when you play with yourself." From then on he had hated his mother, he said.

One day the patient came to his hour fuming with rage. He had submitted an article to an important magazine and had just received a letter from the editor requesting him to cut the article. Considering his castration fear, we can most simply explain his inordinate rage on the assumption that he read the letter as requesting him, not to cut_1 (i.e., to shorten) the article, but to cut_2 (i.e., to cut off) the ARTICLE (i.e., his penis and/or testicles). In other words, without being aware of what he was doing, the patient seems to have transformed the editor's request in accordance with his fear and then to have reacted violently to this reading of the request.

Transformations of this type are not necessarily based on metaphor (see, for example, Arlow [1969], p. 2). Accordingly, without further confirmation, the hypothesis that the patient read the message metaphorically is at best no more than plausible. A metaphorical reading of a message of a different type is an idiosyncratic interpretation of an indisputable metaphor. Such interpretations are obviously more likely if the metaphor is obscure or borderline. Somebody might, for instance, see a urinary connotation in Eliot's 'DAMP souls of housemaids.' We should note, however, that seeing a urinary connotation in this metaphor does not necessarily indicate the presence in the reader of an unconscious urethral wish or fear of some kind. Even a tentative statement to this effect requires *some* additional evidence.

The following is an example of a metaphorical reading involving an entire situation, not just a message. It is often said about a patient in psychoanalysis that he sees the analyst as his mother, his father, etc. Let us take the (presumed) analyst-mother equivalence. What may be meant is that the patient sees the analyst as a MOTHER, or as a MOTHER of the same type of MOTHERS as his own mother. In this sense the analyst may be a good or a bad MOTHER. The term 'mother figure' is apparently synonymous with MOTHER as used here. We should note that the metaphorical reading in cases like this is *inferred* from the patient's productions and may not even be seen by him as consonant with his experience.

It should be noted that the inference is based in part on the analogy between the analyst-patient and the parent-child situations, in part on a similarity between the patient's known (or surmised) attitudes toward his mother and his attitudes toward the analyst. As a rule the metaphor is therefore, at least originally, produced by the analyst, not the patient. The hypothesis is, however, that the patient has made the relevant prelinguistic classifications and is acting accordingly.

PHENOMENA RELATED TO METAPHOR

A number of phenomena are in one way or another related to metaphor.

A. Suppose that somebody draws the image of a fox and provides it with a caption reading "Mr. X." We would have no difficulty in deciphering the message: obviously, it is that Mr. X is a FOX. Innumerable cartoons are based on this principle. In the case we are considering, the image of a member of the class of foxes, which is a subclass of the class of FOXES, is used, together with the caption, to indicate membership in the latter class.

Similarly, justice is commonly represented in the form of a rather buxom, youngish woman holding a pair of scales in one hand. I will disregard the metaphorical significance of the fact that she is often blindfolded and holds a huge sword in her other hand. The scales are clearly meant to depict the act, not of weighing, but of WEIGHING. JUSTICE WEIGHS the evidence. I will consider only the following schema:

WEIGHING the evidence (comparing the evidence *for* with the evidence *against* a statement; weighing concrete objects).

Such concrete representation of an abstract concept is often called *symbolic*. In cases like these I shall speak of *deliberate nonarbitrary symbols*.

Assume the not uncommon depiction of the woman without a blindfold and without a sword in one hand. In these circumstances, if it were not for the caption "JUSTICE" (and if we could explain her usually solemn or stern expression in everyday terms), we would have before us the image of a rather pretty woman weighing some concrete object, say, a fish or a bunch of vegetables. But even in this case we might interpret the image correctly, simply because we are *used to* seeing justice represented in this way. Beardsley (1958) speaks here about the "conventional basis" of symbols (p. 289).

A contemporary example is a sculpture by George Segal, which is intended to represent the condition (or feeling) of being BOXED IN. One of Segal's typical plaster-of-Paris figures sits in a black box turning its back to the viewer. The space inside the box is so cramped that part of the skull and part of one arm are cut off by the walls of the box. This makes the figure seem most uncomfortably boxed in and adds to the feeling of being BOXED IN.

Many heraldic figures have their origin in metaphor. For instance, the image of a bald eagle, usually stylized, is used to symbolize the United States. Like the United States, the eagle is thought to be in the highest degree free, independent, and powerful (see also Beardsley [1958], p. 289).

The flag of a country, by contrast, is a *purely arbitrary* or *conventional symbol*—that is, it is not linked by metaphor to what it symbolizes.

B. Make-believe objects are closely related to deliberate nonarbitrary symbols. Suppose that a group of boys are brandishing sticks and umbrellas at one another. To the boys the sticks and umbrellas represent swords: they have the same general shape and are used, up to a point, in a similar fashion. In reality, however, they are not swords but SWORDS, as indicated by the schema:

SWORDS   (sticks and umbrellas; swords).

Another example: According to Evans-Pritchard (quoted by Lévi-Strauss [1966], p. 224), the Nuer used to sacrifice cucumbers instead of oxen. It is quite clear from the description of the ceremony (as well as from the plump, elongated form of both cucumbers and oxen) that to the Nuer the cucumbers were OXEN.

C. A further phenomenon related to metaphor is acting. Suppose that Mr. Y plays Hamlet and does so excellently. Can we say about him that he is an excellent Hamlet? If he ever existed, there has been only one Hamlet, Prince of Denmark (and perhaps a few forgotten Danish princes of the same name). Mr. Y is merely impersonating Hamlet. Since he may be presumed to have something in common with Hamlet while he is playing the role, we can say that Mr. Y is an excellent HAMLET. Not being Hamlet, however, he cannot be said to be an excellent Hamlet. 'Hamlet' is, strictly, a proper name. We must distinguish two classes. The people whose name is or was Hamlet belong to the class of Hamlets. Mr. Y does not belong to this class; he belongs, with other actors, to the class of HAMLETS. The class of HAMLETS is clearly superordinate to the class of Hamlets. To say that Mr. Y is a HAMLET is essentially, but (as we will see presently) not quite, comparable to saying that Mr. X is a FOX.

It may be objected that in the play Hamlet exists quite independently of whether a real Hamlet ever existed. The objection is no doubt valid. It seems that we must distinguish between real and REAL, between reality as we know it and the REALITY of the play. Within the REALITY of the play, which exists primarily while it is being played or thought about, Mr. Y *is* Hamlet. In reality, however, when we talk about him as being excellent or poor in the role, he is an excellent or a poor HAMLET, a more or less "convincing" impersonator. We should note that only if the actor is "convincing" is the REALITY of the play likely to emerge. For somebody to be Hamlet in REALITY, in other words, he must be a "convincing" HAMLET in reality. Similarly, of course, a person who, in a Passion Play, has the part of the Virgin Mary is *the* Virgin Mary within the REALITY of the play, provided in reality she is at the same time a "convincing" VIRGIN MARY.

It is obvious that we must not confuse the REALITY of a play with the reality of which its being played is a part. For example, the naïve theatergoer, who is so captured by the REALITY of the play that he does not see Mr. Y but only Hamlet, has an entirely different experience than does the critic who, firmly rooted in reality, sees only Mr. Y as a convincing HAMLET. These are extreme positions, of course; a reasonably sophisticated person may be simultaneously tuned in to the REALITY of the play and to reality. Accordingly, he will simultaneously see Hamlet and Mr. Y as a convincing HAMLET on the stage.

We should note that, while Mr. Y may be said to be a HAMLET only in reference to his playing the role, Peter, to whom I referred above, can either be said to be more permanently a little NAPOLEON or he cannot be said to be a NAPOLEON at all. Similarly, when we say that Mr. X is a FOX, we do not envision him as being a part-time FOX but a FOX more or less forever.

D. Let us look at some of the above examples from a slightly different point of view. Even though we may say metaphorically, for example, that a stick is a SWORD and a cucumber an OX, we more often say instead that the stick *represents* a sword and that the cucumber *represents* an ox. We must, therefore, examine somewhat more closely the relationship of representation as it is expressed in these examples.

It appears that an object of a class of objects having a set of attributes, abc, can in certain circumstances be said to represent (in the sense of the word just indicated) an object of another class of objects having the same set of attributes. Take two classes having the attributes abcem and abcfn, respectively. We shall call the first class k and the second l. It follows from our assumption that k and l are both subclasses of a class having only the attributes abc. In accordance with the above usage, we may refer to this class either as K or as L.

We commonly say that an object k_1 of class k represents an object of class l if k_1, or an image of k_1, is actually present while the l's are merely being thought about. In this case it would be highly unusual to say that the thought of an l (e.g., of l_1) represents, say, the image of k_1. That being the case, we may say metaphorically that k_1 is an L. Although the statement "k_1 represents an l" and the metaphor "k_1 is an L" are not synonymous, the one expression is readily transformed into the other. In the same way the metaphors "The stick is a SWORD" and "The cucumber is an OX" are readily transformed into statements involving the relationship of representation—namely, the statements indicated above that a stick represents a sword and a cucumber an ox.

Not every metaphor can ordinarily be transformed this way. For example, as commonly used, the metaphor "Mr. X is a FOX" is not transformable into the statement "Mr. X represents a fox" and, as implied by the Boloki, neither is the metaphor "The umbrella is a BAT" transformable into "the umbrella represents a bat." The meaning of the word 'represents' in the last two statements is not consistent with the ordinary use of this word. It seems that an object can be said to represent another only if it is used *in the same way as,* or is *somehow functionally related to,* or *occurs instead of,* the other object. In this sense, Mr. Y may be said to represent Hamlet, not in the REALITY of the play, but in reality. Similarly, if in a play or opera (such as Stravinsky's *Renard*) Mr. X is cast in the role of a fox, he may be said to represent a fox. An umbrella, on the other hand, may be said to represent a bat if it is used to demonstrate, for example, how a bat flaps its wings.

The cartoon described earlier involves a representation of a somewhat different sort. What the cartoonist had in mind was clearly that Mr. X is a FOX. Now, it is of course impossible to draw a FOX—that is, a picture that *without explanation* will be recognized as the likeness of a FOX. Therefore he drew a fox instead, which represents not Mr. X but, together with the caption, the metaphor "Mr. X is a FOX."

A TENTATIVE THEORY OF DREAM SYMBOLISM

The fact that a cartoonist cannot draw a FOX but must draw a fox instead brings to mind Freud's (1900) concept that "considerations of representability" are among the factors that determine the way in which an idea may get into a dream (pp. 339ff). It seems natural—and not only for this reason—to ask what relationship, if any, there is between a metaphor and dream phenomena. According to Kris (1952), "Metaphor serves as a stimulus to functional regression because the primary process is itself metaphoric and imagistic. The dream life .   . shows a marked tendency to note similarities" (p. 258). Of the so-called primary-process mechanisms believed to operate in dreams, symbolism is most unequivocally based on similarity. Hence, as Morris (1946, p. 276) and Jakobson (1956, p. 81) have indicated, Freud's dream symbols seem to be closely related to metaphor.

One cannot deny the resemblance—at least from an interpreter's point of view—between dream symbols and the representation of Mr. X, the FOX, by a fox, of WEIGHING evidence by weighing concrete objects, of swords by sticks, and of oxen by cucumbers. In all these and similar cases, however, the fact that the seen object (or action) stands for something else is clearly indicated, whether by caption, gestures, or in some other manner. In a dream there are no such indicators.

Let us assume for a moment that we are psychoanalytically naïve. We hear that somebody has dreamed about a snake. We are told that a snake in a dream is not as a rule simply a snake but represents something else. What? That we are not told. In this situation we may recall, say, the Nuer ritual and then try to identify significant attributes of snakes generally. For one thing, snakes are often poisonous. Usually they are also quick, striking like lightning. They are proverbially treacherous and cunning—at least, some of them are. One thing that all snakes have in common, however, is that they are long and slender. Let us choose these last two attributes. We thus include snakes in a class of elongated objects. Taking this as a superordinate class to the class of snakes, our next step is to ask what other objects belong to it. Sooner or later we will hit on the sub-class of penises of the class of elongated objects. As interpreters of the dream we might then say that the snake represents a penis, or we might say meta-phorically that the snake is a PENIS. If this interpretation is correct, the snake *occurs instead of* a penis and thus represents it, in essentially the sense in which a stick may represent a sword and a cucumber an ox.

There is a difference, however. The boy who brandishes a stick *knows* that the stick represents a sword, and similarly the Nuer in all probability *knows* that the cucumber represents an ox. They *know* it even without putting their knowl-edge into words and often without corresponding imagery. The dreamer, on the other hand, *does not know* that the snake represents a penis, or anything else for that matter.

The "knowing" on the part of the boy and of the Nuer is contingent on (a) the classification together of the two disparate objects, and (b) the establish-ment of a relationship of representation between them, so that the object that is present is experienced as representing the absent object. As I have just described it, these processes also underlie the interpretation of the dream snake by an interpreter. In this case, obviously, the image of one object is supposed to repre-sent the "idea" of the other.

Can this be said about the dreamer too? Do the same processes occur but without corresponding awareness? We can obviously invent an additional process that cancels out the awareness but does not interfere with the essential processes—that is, those of classification and of establishing the relationship of representation between an idea, or, rather, an unconscious idea, and an image.

Assuming that symbol formation does in fact occur in dreams, I shall briefly outline an alternative hypothesis, or set of hypotheses, according to which the unconscious state of the idea to be represented and the processes of representa-tion are explained without recourse to the quite unlikely notion that unconscious processes and processes involving awareness are essentially similar, except that the former for some reason do not involve awareness. Freud's (1915) explanation of the difference between conscious and unconscious processes was in part de-pendent on the concept of hypercathexis (see also Kris [1950]). The inadequacy of explanations that in any way depend on the concept of psychic energy has been commented on by many authors (e.g., Holt [1967]; Kubie [1952]; Peter-freund [1971]; Rosenblatt and Thickstun [1970]; Rubinstein [1967]).

Chief among the hypotheses I have in mind is the one that the idea of an object can be described as the class of all relevant classifications of that object. A penis is thus classified as an elongated object, an object of such and such a size, a body organ, etc. According to a second hypothesis, these classifications do not merely represent what may be thought of as a filing system, but together they also function as a penis classifier (and hence recognizer), a penis image organizer (or program), and a selector of the word 'penis.'

The crucial hypothesis in the present connection is that, in dreaming, because of a *specific instability* of the activated classifier under these conditions, one of the constituent classifications may function as an independent subclassifier and image organizer. Thus if the subclassifier "elongated object" of the penis classifier organizes, *independently* of the rest of the classifier, the image of another elongated object such as the image of a snake, the dreamer obviously cannot "know" that there is a connection between the image of the snake and the idea of a penis. Accordingly, even though the image of the snake may be said to *occur instead of* this idea, we cannot say that from the dreamer's point of view the former represents the latter—at any rate not in the sense in which I used the word 'represents' above.

The specific instability may be a characteristic of the dream state, or it may be a function of repression. The second alternative is compatible with Jones's (1948) view that the role played by repression in symbol formation in dreams is decisive (p. 116).

Enough has been said in the present connection. Obviously, many questions remain unanswered; most of them have not even been explicitly stated. A fuller treatment of the problem, however, must be reserved for another occasion. I shall add only that the process of interpreting dream symbols seems more closely related to metaphor than does symbol formation itself. Accordingly, Kris's statement that "the primary process is itself metaphoric" is not quite accurate.

Dream symbols are clearly nonarbitrary. In contrast to other nonarbitrary symbols, however, they are not deliberate.

THE PATHOLOGY OF METAPHOR

Certain pathological forms of thinking are more or less directly related to the process of metaphor formation. I shall discuss a few types that seem important.

A. Suppose I ask somebody: "Why is it that we sometimes say about a person that he is a FOX?" And suppose the answer is: "Because both have two ears, the person and the fox." Someone who gives an answer of this kind has obviously grasped that the person in question and foxes have been classified together on the basis of some common characteristic, and that the resulting superordinate class is named after one of its subclasses, the class of foxes. What he fails to see is that the classification is based on the humanly significant common attribute of *being sly*. Instead he picks, presumably at random, an obvious but not distinctive common attribute, the possession of ears. Whereas all humans have ears, only some of them may be said to be sly

B. Suppose we say to someone: "Mr. X is a FOX." And suppose the person retorts: "But he doesn't have a tail!" This person has obviously failed to form the superordinate class of FOXES. What he heard is not that Mr. X is a FOX but that he is a fox.

The failure to form this type of superordinate class is often referred to as literalization of metaphor. It is regarded as an expression of a tendency to concrete thinking. As Goldstein (1948) pointed out, it is characteristic of certain kinds of aphasia. It is also characteristic of some forms of schizophrenia. McKellar

(1957) cites a nice example. A schizophrenic patient "when asked to explain 'When the cat's away the mice will play,' replied that it meant: 'If nobody's in the kitchen the soup will boil over' " (p. 103). The proverb is close enough to a metaphor to serve as an illustration. The patient was clearly able to abstract the relevant attributes from the situation described in the proverb and to find another concrete situation characterized by the same attributes. Apparently, however, he was not able to form a superordinate class subsuming both situations (such as the class of some kind of supervisory activities by an authority); or, if he did form such a class, he was not able to describe it in words.

Benjamin (1944) recorded even more literal responses to the same proverb. One of his schizophrenic patients explained: "If there isn't any cat around, the mice will monkey around, and maybe get into things" (p. 73).

C. The logic underlying derangements of these sorts has been investigated by von Domarus (1944) and Arieti (1955). According to von Domarus, schizophrenic thinking follows a logic of its own, characterized by the exclusion of the law of contradiction (pp. 108ff). Von Domarus calls this thinking *paralogical*. He gives two examples which, since he relies largely on traditional formal logic, are appropriately rendered in the form of syllogisms:

> Certain Indians are swift.
> Stags are swift.

Therefore:

> Certain Indians are stags.

The second example was provided by a schizophrenic patient. (I shall abbreviate it slightly. Since von Domarus had the patient refer to Jesus and a saint interchangeably, I do not think that the example is distorted by my using the latter reference only.)

> A saint is surrounded (by a halo).   ·
> A cigar box is surrounded (by a tax band).

Therefore:

> A saint is a cigar box.

In both cases the reasoning is "paralogical" only in the sense of being logically invalid. The syllogisms are characterized by what is known as the fallacy of the undistributed middle term.

We may conclude that schizophrenic thinking is in this sense illogical. There is, however, another way of looking at the data. In both cases, the conclusions may be meant to be metaphors. If so, they would be homemade, and therefore unfamiliar, variants of the FOX metaphor. We would then have the following syllogisms:

> All swift creatures are STAGS.
> Certain Indians are swift creatures.

Therefore:

> Certain Indians are STAGS.

And:

> All in some way surrounded objects are CIGAR BOXES.
> A saint is surrounded in a certain way.

Therefore:

> A saint is a CIGAR BOX

Both these syllogisms are valid, and in both the conclusion is clearly a metaphor. On the face of it, the metaphor constituting the second conclusion is obscure and might seem to be an empty metaphorical form. In this case, however, the patient himself provided the criterial attribute of the class of CIGAR BOXES, namely, *being in some way surrounded*. The most striking thing about this mode of reasoning is not the logic involved, but the lack of distinctiveness of the criterial attribute and the lack of practical and/or theoretical significance of the resulting classifications. Another example is the fictitious case cited above of classifying a person together with foxes "because both have two ears."

If the criterial attribute of a classification is in some sense acceptable, whether aesthetically or in some other way, the classification may make sense without being practically and/or theoretically significant. It is instructive to compare the CIGAR BOX metaphor to Marianne Moore's "the lion's ferocious CHRYSANTHEMUM head." Moore's metaphor is as little practically and/or theoretically significant as is the metaphor of von Domarus's patient. But whereas the *sharpness* of the unexpected similarity between a chrysanthemum and a lion's head is the outstanding feature in the one case, the *fuzziness* of the unexpected similarity between a saint and a cigar box is the equally outstanding feature in the other. The logic—that is, the actual process of reasoning—however, is the same in the two cases.

Even if we assume that the reasoning in the schizophrenic case proceeded in the way just indicated, it is entirely possible that the superordinate class, once formed, was immediately lost. This would of course be consistent with the tendency to concreteness that is presumed to be characteristic of schizophrenic thinking. If so, we would end up anyway with the statements that certain Indians are stags and that a saint is a cigar box. An example is the statement "He has twisted my eyes; now I have twisted eyes" which (in a slightly different form) Freud referred to as an instance of "organ-speech" (1915, p. 198). It seems quite plausible that the patient, a young girl, in referring to the alleged hypocrisy of her lover, must have said (or thought) something like "He has TWISTED my eyes" *before* she could have said "He has twisted my eyes."

Arieti (1955) expands von Domarus' views. He believes that schizophrenic thinking is "paleological," a regression to more primitive forms of thinking in response to emotional needs (pp. 188ff; p. 201). He regards these forms of thinking as literally more primitive—that is, as resembling the thinking of children and primitive peoples. He also notes the similarity between schizophrenic thinking and dream symbolism (pp. 199f). Arieti believes that, like the law of contradiction, the laws of identity and of the excluded middle are characteristically absent in paleological thinking (pp. 205ff), that similarity is likely to turn into identity (p. 194), and that, in contrast to the normal person, the paleological thinker considers only the denotations of his terms, not their connotations (p. 210).

I need hardly mention that Arieti's belief in the "paleologic" of primitives is roundly refuted by Lévi-Strauss's work. Otherwise my criticism of von Domarus applies in the same measure to Arieti. Most of the points he makes can be explained in terms of metaphorical classification with possible subsequent loss of the superordinate class. He cites the case of a patient who thought she was the Virgin Mary *because she too is a virgin* (p. 195; but see also p. 203). Now, what the patient may have had in mind is that she is a VIRGIN MARY, not in the sense in which Mr. Y is said to be a convincing HAMLET, nor in the sense in which our man Peter is said to be a little NAPOLEON, but in the sense in which a person may be said to be a *reincarnation* (perhaps one of a series) of another, long since dead. We may, however, also understand the patient's idea by analogy with the Virgin Mary of the Passion Play. In this case we would say that, although in reality she is not, in the REALITY of her psychotic world the patient is IN FACT *the* Virgin Mary. We may note that, in contrast to the REALITY of the play, which is a public REALITY, the REALITY of the patient's psychotic world is, obviously, strictly private. An outsider may *infer* its existence. But only for brief moments can he, as it were, imaginatively immerse himself in it.

As far as I can see, Henle (1962) makes a similar point when she writes, in reference to Arieti's thesis, that the patient's conclusion that she is the Virgin Mary is not deduced from the premises as stated by Arieti but "belongs rather in the category of revealed truth or intuition" (p. 375). This statement, as I shall show presently, does not imply that Henle embraces some sort of mysticism. But let me first state her general position. She believes, partly on the basis of controlled observations, that although, as a rule, thinking does not assume a syllogistic form, even when errors occur "it can often be shown that it does not violate the rules of the syllogism" (p. 377). According to her, it is not the reasoning process itself but "the materials with which thinking works" that may be affected, for example, by misunderstanding of the task, by motivationally induced errors in the premises, etc. (pp. 373–375). This is an interesting conception. If we add the choice in some cases of irrelevant and/or fuzzy criteria for classification, and the inability in specific instances to retain superordinate classifications for long, or even to form them at all, it is in essence compatible with the view put forth above.

In his response to Henle, Arieti (1963) writes that, to her, "logic is exclusively a normative discipline" and that her reference to "revealed truth or intuition" fails to explain anything (p. 62). I disagree with both points. Henle's claim is precisely that logic is *not* exclusively a normative discipline but may reveal something about the psychology of thought. As to the second point, it seems fairly clear that the patient's "revealed truth" is the truth of her REALITY which, since it does not touch reality, cannot contradict it either. At least from a formal point of view, this assumption explains the patient's *apparent* contradiction, without recourse to (presumably nonexistent) paralogical or paleological thinking.

D. I want to present briefly a case I have had occasion to observe. The patient, a highly disturbed schizophrenic man in his late twenties, saw his apartment as a breast. Sometimes the houses on the streets he walked along also appeared as breasts. It turned out that the apartment was a BREAST because he felt secure in it. The houses, on the other hand, were BREASTS because they LOOKED DOWN ON him like breasts that THREATEN TO DEVOUR one. These are quite obscure metaphors. They do not, however, seem to be empty metaphorical forms. The interesting point is that the criterial attributes involved in the apartment-BREAST and the houses-BREASTS classifications are provided, not by the objects in question, but by the patient's highly subjective reactions to them. It would seem that, whereas his reactions to the apartment and the houses were to the objects themselves, his similar reactions to breasts were most probably to imaginary breasts of some kind.

The patient suffered from intense anxiety. It is important to note in this connection that in a previous therapy he had been told that he feared and hated his mother's breast. He had thus been given a *form* through which his anxiety could readily be expressed. Accordingly, when he felt oppressed, and hence THREATENED, by the houses surrounding him, they became BREASTS. He had learned in his therapy that this was the way to classify and name THREATENING things. We have not shown, however, that the houses did not become BREASTS because an unconscious factor prompted both the classification and the naming. In spite of the previous therapy, this may indeed have been what happened, but the available evidence is inconclusive.

I should mention that, at least when I saw him, this classification and naming did not ameliorate the patient's anxiety, if it ever had. It seems clear, on the other hand, why in the apartment-BREAST classification a BREAST could also serve as a source of security. That, obviously, is one of the *normal* roles of any BREAST.

E. The following is an example of a less serious disturbance. It involves a clearly *motivationally determined* use of a metaphor, followed by dissolution of the superordinate class. A young man tried to justify his homosexual inclinations by pointing out that, ever since he was a little boy, he had been told that to play with girls *only* is to be a sissy. He now apparently transformed this sentence into the sentence: "To PLAY with girls *only* is to be a sissy." The latter sentence he then interpreted as meaning that to have sexual relations with girls *only* is to be a sissy. Hence homosexuality is not merely admissible but desirable for a man—that is, for a nonsissy. Clearly, his reasoning was based on the schema:

To PLAY with   (to have sexual relations with; to play with).

It seems that the patient's need to justify his homosexuality prompted the activation and subsequent (transient) death of a particular metaphor, which indeed had the effect, at least to the patient's satifaction of justifying his homosexually.

F. In a number of cases pathological classifications similar to some of those mentioned above may occur, but without leading to metaphor. One patient, for example, a so-called borderline case, classified the following incidents together on the basis that they all involved telephones: (a) having received bad news over the telephone once several years ago; (b) getting annoyed when his boss calls him on the telephone at home; (c) having to compile a telephone directory at the office on clients and prospective clients, which he hated to do; and (d) having gotten terribly upset when a previous therapist continually answered the telephone during his hours. He realized that the mere involvement of a telephone in these incidents did not make for a very meaningful classification, but nevertheless insisted that "there is something about telephones," a mysterious attribute that makes the classification meaningful but which he is at a loss to identify.

A NOTE ON METAPHOR AND DEFENSE

So far I have not mentioned defense. The reason is that there is very little I can say about it in the present connection. We may note, however, that, according to Aleksandrowicz (1962), metaphors generally serve a defensive purpose. This, he thinks, is because they are *indirect* expressions of whatever they express. In some instances this is true—and not only because metaphors are indirect expressions. The play on 'play' and 'PLAY,' cited above, may be classified as a rationalization. And the patient with the enema conflict presumably revealed both her desire for an enema and the partial repression of this desire in her exclamation, the metaphorical character of which she did not recognize, that she had to WASH OUT the desire. As a *general statement,* however, Aleksandrowicz's thesis seems to me unsubstantiated. Not all indirect expressions are indirect in the same sense.

CONCLUDING REMARKS

The preceding pages are highly speculative. They may not present any solutions. But at least they suggest problems that, if not new, are looked at in a new way. One of the main premises underlying the above exposition is that processes of classification constitute an important part of mental functioning and thus ultimately of the functioning of the CNS. This is not an original idea. But it has generally been overlooked in relation to most of the questions discussed in this paper.

What is meant by a classification is not very clear. It may consist not in an actual grouping of elements but merely in an emphasis of some sort on certain common features of these elements. In discussing simile, I made a suggestion to this effect. But there may also be other possibilities. The important point in the present connection is that the word 'classification' itself stands for a class of possible processes describable as related in some perhaps quite tenuous way to the grouping of elements.

One point that has emerged from this discussion is that, while the posited prelinguistic classifications underlying metaphor are closely related to those underlying certain cartoons, deliberate nonarbitrary symbols, and some forms of the relationship of representation, they are less closely related to the "pre-imagistic" class formations (or programs) that, according to a theory briefly outlined here, operate in the production of dream symbols. Another point is that metaphors, and particularly deranged metaphors, may play a larger part in pathological forms of thinking than they are ordinarily credited with.

A third point is that, because of its close relationship to concept formation and to the often sudden discovery of unexpected similarities, nonpathological metaphor throws light on an important aspect of what Freud (1895, 1900) called secondary-process thinking. Considering particularly the sharpness, the illuminating effect, and the economy of many poetic metaphors, it does not seem very felicitous to regard them as promoted by what Kris referred to as ego-regulated regression (1950, pp. 551f; 1952, p. 312), or "regression in the service of the ego" (1952, p. 177). On this point, I am in full agreement with Schachtel (1959, pp. 244ff).

It is likely that the production of poetic and pathological metaphors is contingent on what we may think of as a high degree of flexibility of class boundaries, in the sense that new superordinate classes are readily formed. The view that this flexibility is regressive, however, appears to derive at least in part from seeing it as a function of increased mobility of psychic energy, which, according to Freud (e.g., 1900, pp. 599ff; 1915, p. 188), is a defining characteristic of the primary process (see also Kris, 1950; Arlow and Brenner, 1964, p. 91). There seems to be little doubt that this is mistaken theory. Besides, as far as we can tell, it is not the flexibility as such that is abnormal, or that borders on the abnormal, but the choice of fuzzy and/or exclusively nonpublic criteria for the formation of the superordinate classes, and in some cases, if they are formed at all, the comparative ease with which these classes are lost

SUMMARY

1. Metaphors, or at any rate the metaphors I have examined here, do not represent semi-grammatical sentences. Properly interpreted, the sentences expressing them are seen to be grammatically well-formed.

2. A metaphorically used word refers to a class that is superordinate to the class to which this word refers in its literal meaning, *as well as* to at least one other class or to a subclass of one other class. If the sentence "Mr. X is a fox" is interpreted metaphorically, the word 'fox' refers to a class that is superordinate to the class of foxes (in the literal meaning of the word 'fox'), as well as to the subclass of human beings to which Mr. X belongs. From the meaning of the metaphor as it is commonly used, we derive the criterial attribute of the superordinate class, which is *being sly*. In this paper I have adopted the convention of capitalizing metaphorically used words. The indicated sentence should accordingly be written "Mr. X is a FOX."

3. Interpreted in this way, a metaphorically used word represents a higher-level concept than the word used in its literal meaning. The difference between ordinary concept formation and the formation of metaphor lies exclusively in the *naming* of the superordinate class. Only in the latter case is the superordinate class given the name of one of its subclasses. This peculiarity of naming is clearly responsible for the seeming ambiguity of metaphorically used words.

4. The theory of metaphor presented here draws on a number of sources but differs from each in one or more respects.

5. Metaphors are used in ordinary as well as in poetic and scientific language. Examples were given of metaphorical uses of proper names, nouns, verbs, and adjectives. Some problems presented by the latter were briefly considered.

6. Whereas some apparent nonsense strings can be given a metaphorical interpretation, others can not. Empty metaphorical forms are *presentations as metaphors* of nonsense strings that cannot be interpreted metaphorically. The line between empty metaphorical forms and valid but obscure metaphors is not easy to draw. Different persons may draw it differently.

7. Ordinary language is studded with dead metaphors. Apart from thus enriching language, metaphor serves mainly (a) to express the otherwise inexpressible, and (b) to lend specific emphasis to particular ideas. It is of interest that most authors apparently recognize only one or the other of these functions and therefore see *it* as the exclusive function of metaphor.

8. An attempt was made to outline a *possible* mechanism for the probably unconscious choice of particular metaphors in certain cases. Since one can conceive of such a mechanism, the unconscious choice of metaphor, apart from other considerations, becomes at least thinkable also *from a strictly process-oriented point of view*.

9. A number of phenomena were seen as related to metaphor, mainly cartoons of a certain type, the artistic representation of some abstract concepts, and particular forms of make-believe, including acting.

10. The *formation* of dream symbols can also be seen as related to metaphor. However, this relationship is apparently less close than the relationship to metaphor of the *interpretation* of dream symbols. A tentative model of some of the processes involved in dream symbol formation was briefly outlined.

11. It was argued that, in their basic logical structure, certain forms of pathological thinking can likewise be seen as related to metaphor. A few examples were presented. The question of how representative these examples are was not considered. On the other hand, they seemed plausible enough to warrant further investigation of the issue.

12. Since poetic metaphor, like metaphor generally, is closely related to the formation of comparatively high-level concepts, and thus exhibits the characteristics of the so-called secondary process, there seems to be no justification for regarding its emergence as contingent on what Kris called "regression in the service of the ego."

13. Even though symbol formation in dreams and certain forms of pathological thinking were considered, no attempt was made to relate these events to the so-called primary process. It would have taken us too far afield from the main concern of this paper to have included a discussion of displacement (in its broad sense) and condensation. I will, however, add at this point that the concept of a specific instability of complex classifiers, which is an essential part of the suggested model of symbol-formation in dreams, may also be relevant to the understanding of other primary-process events.

14. Our spotting of metaphor or a probable metaphor in a patient's productions may provide additional confirmation of what, on different grounds, we take to be one of his basic conflicts, or it may give us a first hint of the possible presence of such a conflict. Some of the clinical material cited above is relevant to this question. A further discussion of it, however, must be reserved for another occasion.

REFERENCES

Aleksandrowicz, D. R. (1962). The Meaning of Metaphor. *Bulletin of the Menninger Clinic,* 26:92–101.

Arieti, S. (1955). *Interpretation of Schizophrenia.* New York: Robert Brunner.

———— (1963). Studies in Thought Processes in Contemporary Psychiatry. *American Journal of Psychiatry,* 120:58–64.

Arlow, J. A. (1969). Unconscious Fantasy and Disturbances of Conscious Experience. *Psychoanalytic Quarterly,* 38:1–27.

———— and Brenner, C. (1964). *Psychoanalytic Concepts and the Structural Theory.* New York: International Universities Press.

Asch, S. E. (1955). On the Use of Metaphor in the Description of Persons. In: *On Expressive Language,* ed. H. Werner. Worcester, Mass.: Clark University Press.

———— (1961). The Metaphor: A Psychological Inquiry. In: *Documents of Gestalt Psychology,* ed. M. Henle. Berkeley and Los Angeles: University of California Press.

———— and Nerlove, H. (1960). The Development of Double Function Terms in Children. In: *Perspectives in Psychological Theory: Essays in Honor of Heinz Werner,* ed B. Kaplan and S. Wapner. New York: International Universities Press.

Beardsley, M. C. (1958). *Aesthetics: Problems in the Philosophy of Criticism*. New York: Harcourt, Brace.

Benjamin, J. D. (1944). A Method for Distinguishing and Evaluating Formal Thinking Disorders in Schizophrenia. In: *Language and Thought in Schizophrenia*, ed. J. S. Kasanin. Berkeley: University of California Press.

Beres, D. (1965). Symbol and Object. *Bulletin of the Menninger Clinic*, 29:3–23.

Bickerton, D. (1969). Prolegomena to a Linguistic Theory of Metaphor. *Foundations of Language*, 5:34–52.

Black, M. (1962). *Models and Metaphors*. Ithaca, New York: Cornell University Press.

Blackmur, R. P. (1952). *Form and Value in Modern Poetry*. New York: Doubleday.

Brown, R. (1958). *Words and Things*. Glencoe: Free Press.

———— (1965). *Social Psychology*. New York: Free Press.

Burnshaw, S. (1970). *The Seamless Web*. New York: George Braziller.

Chomsky, N. (1957). *Syntactic Structures*. 'S-Gravenhaage: Mouton.

———— (1964). Degrees of Grammaticalness. In: *The Structure of Language*, ed. J. A. Fodor and J. J. Katz. Englewood Cliffs, N.J.: Prentice-Hall.

———— (1968). *Language and Mind*. New York: Harcourt, Brace and World.

———— and Miller, G. A. (1963). Introduction to the Formal Analysis of Natural Languages. In: *Handbook of Mathematical Psychology*, Vol. 2, ed. R. D. Luce, R. R. Bush, and E. Galanter. New York: John Wiley.

Cohen, L. J., and Margalit, A. (1970). The Role of Inductive Reasoning in the Interpretation of Metaphor. *Synthese*, 21:469–487.

cummings, e.e. (1953). *Six Nonlectures*. Cambridge, Mass.: Harvard University Press.

———— (1954). *Poems 1923–1954*. New York: Harcourt, Brace.

von Domarus, E. (1944). The Specific Laws of Logic in Schizophrenia. In: *Language and Thought in Schizophrenia*, ed. J. S. Kasanin. Berkeley: University of California Press.

Eliot, T. S. (1963). *Collected Poems, 1909–1962*. New York: Harcourt, Brace.

Empson, W. (1930). *Seven Types of Ambiguity*. New York: New Directions.

Freud, S. (1895). Project for a Scientific Psychology. *Standard Edition*, 1:295–387. London: Hogarth Press, 1966.

———— (1900). The Interpretation of Dreams. *Standard Edition*, 4 & 5. London: Hogarth Press, 1958.

———— (1915). The Unconscious. *Standard Edition*, 14:166–204. London: Hogarth Press, 1957.

Goldstein, K. (1948). *Language and Language Disturbances*. New York: Grune and Stratton.

Hartmann, H., Kris, E., and Loewenstein, R. M. (1946). Comments on the Formation of Psychic Structure. *Psychoanalytic Study of the Child*, 2:11–38. New York: International Universities Press.

Henle, M. (1962). On the Relation between Logic and Thinking. *Psychological Review*, 69:366–378.

Holt, R. R. (1967). Beyond Vitalism and Mechanism. In: *Science and Psychoanalysis*, 11:1–41, ed. J. H. Masserman. New York: Grune and Stratton.

Hulme, T. E. (1965). Bergson's Theory of Art. In: *The Problems of Aesthetics*, ed. E. Vivas and M. Krieger. New York: Holt, Rinehart and Winston. (Originally published 1936.)

Jakobson, R., and Halle, M. (1956). *Fundamentals of Language*. 'S-Gravenhaage: Mouton.

Jones, E. (1948). The Theory of Symbolism. In: *Papers on Psycho-Analysis*, 5th ed. (Originally published 1916.)

Katz, J. J. (1964). Semi-Sentences. In: *The Structure of Language*, ed. J. A. Fodor and J. J. Katz. Englewood Cliffs, N.J.: Prentice-Hall.

———— and Fodor, J. A. (1964). The Structure of a Semantic Theory. In: *The Structure of Language*, ed. J. A. Fodor and J. J. Katz. Englewood Cliffs, N.J.: Prentice-Hall. (Originally published 1963.)

————— and Postal, P. M. (1964). *An Integrated Theory of Linguistic Descriptions.* Research Monograph No. 26. Cambridge, Mass.: M.I.T. Press.

Kris, E. (1950). On Preconscious Mental Processes *Psychoanalytic Quarterly,* 19:540–560.

————— (1952). *Psychoanalytic Explorations in Art.* New York: International Universities Press.

Kubie, L. S. (1952). Problems and Techniques of Psychoanalytic Validation and Progress. In: *Psychoanalysis as Science,* ed. E. Pumpian-Mindlin. Stanford: Stanford University Press.

Langer, S. K. (1962). *Philosophical Sketches.* Baltimore: Johns Hopkins Press.

Leach, M., and Fried, J., eds. (1949). *Standard Dictionary of Folklore, Mythology and Legend.* New York: Funk and Wagnalls.

Lenneberg, E. H. (1967). *Biological Foundations of Language.* New York: John Wiley.

Levin, S. R. (1963). On Automatic Production of Poetic Sequences. *Texas Studies in Literature and Language,* 51:138–146.

————— (1965). Internal and External Deviations in Poetry. *Word,* 21:225–237.

————— (1967). Poetry and Grammaticalness. In: *Essays on the Language of Literature,* ed. S. Chatman and S. R. Levin. Boston: Houghton Mifflin.

Lévi-Strauss, C. (1966). *The Savage Mind.* Chicago: University of Chicago Press.

MacLeish, A. (1960). *Poetry and Experience.* Cambridge, Mass.: Riverside Press.

McKellar, P. (1957). *Imagination and Thinking.* New York: Basic Books.

Miller, G. A., and Chomsky, N. (1963). Finitary Models of Language Users. In: *Handbook of Mathematical Psychology,* Vol. 2, ed. R. D. Luce, R. R. Bush, and E. Galanter. New York: John Wiley.

Moore M. (1951). *Collected Poems.* New York: Macmillan.

Morris, C. (1946). *Signs, Language and Behavior.* Englewood Cliffs, N.J.: Prentice-Hall (New York: George Braziller, 1955).

Ogden, C. K., and Richards, I. A. (1923). *The Meaning of Meaning.* New York: Harcourt, Brace, Harvest Book Edition.

Perse, S.-J. (1949). *Exile and Other Poems.* New York: Pantheon Books.

Peterfreund, E. (1971). Information, Systems, and Psychoanalysis. *Psychological Issues,* Monograph No. 25/26. New York: International Universities Press.

Quine, W. V. O. (1960). *Word and Object.* New York: John Wiley.

Richards, I. A. (1960). Discussion. In: *Style in Language,* ed. Thomas A. Sebeok. New York: John Wiley.

Roethke, T. (1958). *The Far Field.* Garden City, New York: Doubleday.

Rosenblatt, A. D., and Thickstun, J. T. (1970). A Study of the Concept of Psychic Energy. *International Journal of Psycho-Analysis,* 51:265–278.

Rubinstein, B. B. (1967). Explanation and Mere Description: A Metascientific Examination of Certain Aspects of the Psychoanalytic Theory of Motivation. In: Motives and Thought: Psychoanalytic Essays in Honor of David Rapaport, ed. R. R. Holt. *Psychological Issues,* Monograph No. 18/19. New York: International Universities Press.

Schachtel, E. G. (1959). *Metamorphosis.* New York: Basic Books.

Sharpe, E. F. (1940). Psycho-physical Problems Revealed in Language: An Examination of Metaphor. *International Journal of Psycho-Analysis,* 21:201–213.

Smith, G. (1956). *T. S. Eliot's Poetry and Plays.* Chicago: University of Chicago Press.

Voth, H. M. (1970). The Analysis of Metaphor. *Journal of the American Psychoanalytic Association,* 18:599–621.

Werner, H. (1948). *Comparative Psychology of Mental Development.* New York: International Universities Press.

Wheelwright, P. (1962). *Metaphor and Reality.* Bloomington: Indiana University Press.

Ziff, P. (1964). On Understanding "Understanding Utterances." In: *The Structure of Language,* ed. J. A. Fodor and J. J. Katz. Englewood Cliffs, N.J.: Prentice-Hall.

THE ROLE OF VERBAL CLUES IN CLINICAL LISTENING [1]

Donald P. Spence, Ph.D., and Marta Lugo, *Licenciada en Quimica*

Clinical skills have traditionally been taught in a master-apprentice relationship with all of its usual assumptions. So long as we provide the student with access to a qualified practitioner, the argument goes, we can assume that sooner or later the necessary skills will be acquired. The student will learn *by example* how to become a good clinician, armed with his supervisor's wisdom and a handful of aphorisms culled from the literature.

Many good clinicians have developed from such a system and its partial success has blinded us to its obvious faults. Take clinical listening as a case in point. It seems indisputable that specific kinds of listening are needed to decode the latent content of a patient's statements, yet in how many cases is the student given specific training in this technique? Moreover, how many clinicians understand the way in which they themselves listen, to the extent that they can explain it to someone else? As in many kinds of complex skills, we rely on the master-apprentice mode of teaching because we have nothing else to offer; too little is known about specifics to set up a formal course of training.

Two dimensions of clinical listening can be isolated at the outset—*mode* and *content*. By *mode* we refer to the size of the unit being considered—does the clinician pay attention to every word or only to certain underlying themes? By *content* we refer to the specific sets of meanings—words or themes—that are considered important. The two dimensions can vary independently; thus, we can listen to a specific theme (e.g., birth fantasies) as it is expressed in the total sweep of the material, or as it appears in discrete words. In the latter case, we would be alerted to specific words, such as delivery, term, issue, etc., even when the

[1] Supported by NIMH Grant No. 13,615 and Research Scientist Award No. 14,120. Thanks are due to Helen Golden, Kris Lincoln and Adele Shumsky for assistance in testing subjects, and to Lester Luborsky and Suzette Annin for their help in criticizing the manuscript. Additional thanks are due to Lester Luborsky for providing the clinical materials.

context belied a pregnancy meaning; in the former case, we would be alerted to such words *only* when the context was supportive. When we draw attention to slips of the tongue, we are listening in a *word-by-word* mode; when we summarize material for an interpretation, we are listening for particular *themes* with no restriction as to mode. As one example of the second case: we might combine a dream with a slip of the tongue so long as a single theme was common to both.

TYPE OF WORD AFFECTS THE SIZE OF THE UNIT CHOSEN

At least two types of words can be distinguished. One set stands by itself— help, fire, no, etc.; a second set depends on context. Listening in a word-by-word mode is obviously much easier with words in the first set than with those in the second, and one can see how the nature of the material might force the listener to adopt one or the other mode of listening. Although the mode of listening is determined by the listener, it is in continuous interaction with the nature of the material, or more specifically, with the nature of the verbal clues. If the meanings are highly dependent on context, it would be easier to listen to themes, even though it might make more sense from a clinical standpoint to listen to words. One can see how specific training is necessary to overcome the tendency to let mode of listening be shaped by the material.

Once mode and content are determined, the listener must decide how to combine the units so as to reach a clinical conclusion. Traditionally, two models are proposed: a *linear* model, in which the units are simply added together (with or without differential weighting), and a *configural* model, in which the pattern is taken into account. Here again the novice clinician is usually left to his own devices; indeed, we are only just beginning to learn what kind of model is used by experienced clinicians so that we can begin to pass it on to our own students.

So much for an introduction to the major issues. It is the purpose of this paper to study the function of different verbal clues in a variety of different listening tasks, in order to draw conclusions about the concepts of mode and content in clinical listening, and the kinds of models used in forming clinical judgments. But before discussing particular experiments, we shall begin with some clinical applications.

Consider an ulcer patient during a psychotherapy hour. He is talking about his relationship to his girl friend and suddenly breaks off with "There goes my stomach again"—he has felt a sharp pain. At another time, he is talking about having been in a fight and has another stomach pain. Is there a common theme running through such instances? Luborsky and Auerbach (1969) thought so, and asked three judges to distinguish between 24 pairs of symptom instances and matched controls. The judges' guesses turned out to be no better than chance. When they were told, however, that the symptom had to do with helplessness and a need for narcissistic supplies, two of the three judges performed at better than chance level. Helplessness and a need for supplies apparently had been encoded by the patient as a stomach pain; the passages could be decoded by listening for these themes and translating them into the concept of stomach symptom.

How did the judges make their decisions? Goldberg and his associates (1968) have made a strong case for the possibility that clinical judgments are primarily generated from a linear model which can be expressed by the traditional formula Y (judgment) $= B_1 X_1 + \cdots B_k X_k$, where $X_1 \cdots X_k$ are the clues used for the decision and $B_1 \cdots B_k$ are the weights supplied to each clue. In the second part of the Luborsky study two clues were given (helplessness and concern for supplies) and the weighting was determined by the instructions that these were important contributors to the symptom of stomach pain.

One limitation of Goldberg's formulation lies in the nature of the clues to which it is applicable. This model may be most appropriate to situations in which explicit clues are provided. In a study by Hoffman, Slovic, and Rorer (1968), seven signs of ulcer malignancy (e.g., ulcer contour regular, ulcer crater small, etc.) were provided by a gastroenterologist. Hypothetical profiles were generated by taking all possible combinations of the seven signs. Since each sign could be either present or absent, 2^7 or 128 profiles were produced. Plausibility of the profiles was checked by a specialist, who eliminated 32 because of a logical inconsistency in the patterns. The remaining 96 profiles were given to nine radiologists to judge on a 7-point scale, ranging from definitely benign to definitely malignant.

Each judge tended to combine the clues in a more or less regular manner (reliabilities for judgments across two trials ranged from .60 to .92 in a group of nine judges). Analysis of the data also showed that the clues were being combined in a linear rather than a configural manner. Other studies supporting the linear model have tended to be of this type.

A naturalistic situation, however, seems to require a more complex model. In Luborsky and Auerbach's material, the clues are more inferential and must be deduced from the context, in contrast to the explicit clues given by Hoffman et al. and in similar studies. This difference can be conceptualized by the linguistic terms "signal" and "symbol." A signal is "an indicator of existence—past, present, or future—of the same event or condition. Wet streets are a signal that it has rained. Patter on the roof is a signal that it is raining. The fall of the barometer or a ring around the moon is a signal that it is going to rain . . ." (Langer, 1951, pp. 57–58). A symbol, on the other hand, does not carry the same explicit meaning. "A term which is used symbolically and not signally does not evoke action appropriate to the presence of this object . . . symbols are not proxy for their objects, but are vehicles for the conception of objects" (Langer, 1951, pp. 60–61).

Both signals and symbols belong to the larger class of signs. As defined by Morris (1946, p. 354), a sign is "something that directs behavior"; a symbol is a sign "produced by its interpreter . . . that acts as a substitute for some other sign for which it is synonymous"; a signal is "a sign that is not a symbol, that is, not produced by its interpreter . . ." Morris uses pretty much the same rationale as Langer in distinguishing signal from symbol.

In the Hoffman et al. study, the judges were given a series of signals in the sense that each clue was unequivocal, never varied, and always carried the same meaning; in the Luborsky and Auerbach study, the judge was presented with a series of symbols (language) that could be decoded in a variety of ways. One segment of the patient's production might at one time mean narcissistic supplies, while at another time the same words could mean depression. However, in clinical inference, both signals and symbols are usually used. The patient's choice of words, degree of emphasis, or implied meaning can be understood as symbols. Signals are used when a depressed look is taken to mean a depressed state, when the holding out of hands is taken to mean that the patient is asking for help, or when a single word is used over and over.

Langer suggests many distinctions between symbol and signal, but for our purposes the key difference lies in the fact that the relationship between a signal and what is signalized tends to be invariant—crying usually means sadness, a red light usually means stop, "no" usually means negation, etc. Symbols, on the other hand, have a fluctuating relationship to their referents—a relationship that depends heavily on context. Taken in isolation, a symbol does not convey a clear meaning in the same way as a red light does. The meaning of the word "table," for example, depends on whether or not it is preceded by the word "multiplication." Most words (with the exception of *onomatopoeic* words) have an arbitrary relation to their referents. We usually cannot define a symbol unless we know how it is being used.

As a result of this difference, we must listen to signals and symbols in quite different ways. Because a signal can be interpreted in isolation, it can be decoded with only a relatively brief burst of attention. Symbols, on the other hand, because they depend heavily on context, cannot be interpreted unless we listen with close attention. The more complicated the grammar and the more involved the syntax, the more attention must be paid, and the units necessary for understanding become larger and larger.

The more primitive signal can thus be picked up quite easily with fragmentary or "free-floating" attention, and this is the mode of listening traditionally prescribed for clinical listening. Rosen (1969) has suggested that primary-process thought is largely conveyed by signals, pointing out that they would facilitate the high speed of discharge assumed to be characteristic of this mode of thinking. It can be argued, therefore, that free-floating attention is appropriate in clinical listening because it is particularly sensitive to the primary-process content that is conveyed by means of signals. Rosen (1969) further argues that secondary-process thought is usually conveyed by symbols. Secondary-process material would therefore require close listening to decode its highly symbolic meaning, since the more abstract symbols presumably require more sustained attention; and complex material is in fact usually listened to attentively.[2]

We can argue that because the two types of clues have different listening requirements, a person's mode of listening will determine which clues are picked up. By manipulating the amount of attention at the person's disposal, it should be possible to influence the selection of clues. Suppose a subject is asked to predict when an ulcer patient in psychotherapy will report a stomach disturbance, but is allowed to give only a small part of his attention to the task. We would expect him to use more signals than symbols for his assessment, on the assumption that signals require less attention. If he is permitted to use somewhat larger units of attention, however, he should use more symbols to aid his decision. In Experiment 2, below, we investigated this possibility.

We can also influence which clues are registered, by priming certain ones. Here again the distinction between symbol and signal is important. Signals are relatively unchanging, presumably easier to learn and to listen for, and we would therefore expect signal-priming to be more successful than symbol-priming. We would also expect both symbol- and signal-priming to result in increased sensitivity to the relevant categories. We tested this assumption in Experiment 3 described below.

CLINICAL MATERIALS

The clinical materials used were taken from the transcript of a patient treated in psychotherapy by Luborsky (see Luborsky and Auerbach, 1969, p. 79). Eighteen months before treatment started, the patient was diagnosed as having a "superficial ulcer"; he spent two weeks in the hospital and was convalescent for the next fifteen months. His stomach continued to bother him during treatment; accordingly, he was asked to report stomach pains whenever they occurred.

For Experiments 1 and 2 we chose 17 segments of about 150 words each, nine that had been immediately followed by a report of stomach pain (symptom segments) and eight that had not (control segments). Samples of each type are given below.

Symptom

I'm going to weed out these small committees as quickly as I can weed them out by the end of this semester—weed out most of the bulk of them and get my interest centered on some of these smaller committees in large organizations— I may keep on working on them—I'm looking forward to getting up on the

---

[2] Symbol in the linguistic, not the psychoanalytic, sense. The two meanings are exactly opposite. Secondary-process thinking depends on linguistic *symbols;* primary-process thinking uses linguistic *signals,* which are frequently *psychoanalytic* symbols. The separate usages are, by now, so well established that a general terminology seems out of the question; see Morris (1946, p. 276) for a more general statement on the meanings.

higher rungs of the ladder with some of these things I've been learning in a fairly good sized way—another thing I can see more plainly, too—I have got to take better care of myself—it's all well and good to build up these other people, organizations, and so on—I do it at the expense of my own health, vigor, and so what I shall build won't amount to anything—so I figure on paying a little more attention to myself. [My old stomach kicks around again].

Control

I'm afraid—I knew there was a weak outfit—take a lot of shoulder work and I had planned on putting it in—I went in my International Friendship Committee meeting and supposed to give them my answer—I thought about it while the meeting was going on—I made up my mind that I would take the position—but that I still hadn't figured out how to get these things taken care of—explained the situation to them and told them just how it stood—the cabinet just almost has to be all together—it is important to be there—anyone missing just leaves a gap there—so I accepted just the same—they were sorry the work had those things—weren't trying to take me away from the other organizations but that was just the way it was—of course, that's just the way it is, so . . . I went home and I felt pretty irked about the whole situation.

The 17 segments were randomly ordered and given to a naive speaker to record on a tape. Because the speaker did not know which segments were symptom and which were control, he was not likely to convey any difference between them in his mode of delivery. The information conveyed by the passages probably came from their *lexical* aspects (from the patient) rather than from their *paralinguistic* aspects (from the speaker).

The ulcer patient is popularly understood to be overambitious, overachieving, and covertly dependent. Alexander, French, and Pollock (1968) have described the dynamics of the ulcer patient as follows: "Certain dynamic factors seem to be the frustration of dependent desires originally oral in character. The most common defense against both oral-dependent and oral-inquisitive impulses is overcompensation. The latently dependent or inquisitive person overtly appears as an independent, hard-working individual who likes responsibility and taking care of others. He responds to challenges with increased activity and ambition, works hard and assumes greater and greater responsibility" (pp. 15–16). On the assumption that our subjects would rely on part of this syndrome to detect when a stomach pain was about to erupt, we scored each of the 17 segments on the categories of Mastery, Achievement, and Wish (to pick up ambition themes), Family (to pick up dependency themes), I (to pick up independence), Negation (to pick up the incipient stubbornness so often implied in a passive-aggressive syndrome), and Anxiety (to pick up the helplessness detected by Luborsky). Mastery and Achievement represent the obverse of helplessness. Concern for supplies, Luborsky's other category, could not be defined by the categories we had available. Other categories that might have been appropriate were rejected because they did not appear often enough in the 17 segments to give us a meaningful distribution of scores. All categories but "I" were detected by the McWilliams Need Affiliation–Need Achievement Dictionary and a PL/1 computer program that tallied the number of times each category appeared in each of the segments (Spence, 1969).

The category Family can be used to illustrate the procedure. For this patient, the category includes such words as Child, Dad, Mother, Parent, etc. (see Table 1). Suppose five of these words appeared in a segment; it would be scored 5 on the Family category. If one Family word appeared five times, a score

Table 1 CATEGORIES USED IN CONTENT ANALYSIS OF 17 SEGMENTS

	Symbols				Signals		
	Mastery	Anxiety	Achieve-ment	Wish	Family	Negation	I
	Accomplish	Afraid	Build	Afraid	Child	No	I
	Build	Agitated	Direct	Anxious	Dad	Not	
	Busy	Anxious	Discuss	Hope	Fellow		
	Direct	Disappoint	Explain	Wonder	Girl		
	Discuss	Pain	Fight	Wondering	Mother		
	Explain	Sad	Find		Parent		
	Fight	Sorry	Fix				
	Fix	Worry	Formulate				
	Formulate	Worried	Learning				
	Made		Made				
	Make		Make				
	Makes		Manage				
	Learn		Progress				
	Problem		Prove				
	Prove		Put				
	Putting		Putting				
	Resolve		Resolve				
	Think		Speak				
	Thinking		Thought				
	Try		Try				
	Work		Writing				
			Working				
Aver. Syl/ Word	1.6	2.2	1.6	2.2	1.2	1.0	1.0
No. Diff. Words	21	9	22	5	6	2	1
Over-all Summary	Symbols: 1.7 syllables/word				Signals: 1.1 syllables/word		
	14 words per category				3 words per category		

of 5 would also be given. That is, no distinction was made between the use of five separate words and the repetition of one word five times. Other categories were scored in the same way.

The words in the Negation and Family categories were used in a concrete, literal way that does not require any interpretation. These two categories and the "I" category are here designated as signal categories. Wish, Mastery, Achievement, and Anxiety, on the other hand, which convey their respective meanings through context as well as individual words, are categorized as symbol categories. Both signal and symbol categories are listed in Table 6-1. All the words listed appeared in one or more of the 17 clinical segments.

EXPERIMENT 1—NO DISTRACTION CONDITION

The purpose of the first experiment was to get baseline data on the 17 segments. Twenty-five subjects (college undergraduates) were tested individually. Each subject was asked to listen to a tape of the 17 passages presented in a fixed random order. The subject was told that all passages had been taken from the records of a single patient in psychotherapeutic treatment, and that about half of them had been immediately followed by a report of stomach pain. The subject would hear each statement played once; he would then decide whether or not stomach pain had occurred by saying "symptom" or "no symptom" and give a confidence rating from 1 (very unsure) to 5 (very sure).

RESULTS

The mean number of correct predictions in the sample of 25 subjects was 8.64—almost exactly the chance level of 8.50 (or 17/2). Correct responses did, however, differ significantly from incorrect responses in confidence (mean 3.63 for correct, 3.23 for incorrect, .05 level, two-tailed sign test). The subjects' higher confidence when they were correct indicates that, even though they were not consciously discriminating between symptom and no symptom, they were aware at some level of a systematic difference.

The number of symptom calls (the number of times the subject replied "symptom") varied from 5 to 13. Because some symptom calls were incorrect, the "hit" score, as already indicated, did not exceed the chance level. Nevertheless, it is possible that the segments were not labeled completely unsystematically but, rather, that the subjects were responding to the wrong sets of clues. To investigate this question further, we used a multiple regression analysis to determine which of the categories mentioned earlier (Mastery, Wish, etc.) were the best indicators that the response "symptom" would be given, whether or not the response was correct.

The results are presented in Table 2. Column 2 lists, in order of importance, the five categories that best indicated symptoms calls: Mastery first ($R = .48$), "I" next (adding .19 in R^2), and so on. For purposes of comparison, the five best predictor categories of the criterion—the five that actually discriminate

Table 2   FIVE BEST PREDICTORS OF CITERION AND SYMPTOM CALLS FOR 17
SEGMENTS (Multiple R's listed opposite each predictor)

Criterion		Symptom Calls per Condition					
		No Distraction		Slow/Fast		Fast/Slow	
**Anxiety	.31	**Mastery	.48	**Anxiety	.55	**Achievement	.44
*I	.41	*I	.67	**Mastery	.58	*Family	.56
**Wish	.49	**Achievement	.72	**Wish	.63	*Negation	.61
**Mastery	.54	*Negation	.74	*I	.64	*I	.66
*Family	.63	**Wish	.75	**Achievement	.67	**Wish	.72
Aver. Syl/Word		1.61		1.71		1.58	
Aver. No. Diff. Words		10.2		11.6		7.2	

* Signal
** Symbol
For significance at the .05 level, multiple R must be .48 or higher for 1 predictor and .77 or
higher for 5 predictors.

between symptom and no symptom—are shown in column 1; these are the categories that would give the highest "hit" score. The more of these categories used, the greater would be the number of hits. A comparison of columns 1 and 2 shows why the No Distraction group was performing at only a chance level. First, they did not use Anxiety—the best predictor—in any way. Second, they depended heavily on Mastery, the fourth-rated predictor. Third, they used Achievement and Negation, the two categories that do not even appear among the best five predictors. Nevertheless, they did seem to be responding in a systematic way. The almost significant multiple R for the five predictor categories (column 2) strongly suggests that the subjects were, in fact, relying on the frequency of these categories in arriving at a decision. Only if there were no correlation between symptom calls and one or more of these categories would we conclude that the subjects were behaving more or less at random.

A closer look at the categories used by the subjects in Experiment 1 suggests that they accepted the stereotyped picture of the ulcer patient described above. According to this stereotype, he is a frustrated over-achiever, who is trying to deny strong dependency needs by active independent mastery. As Table 2 shows, the subjects placed their strongest reliance on the categories of Mastery (which includes such words as "accomplish," "direct," "formulate," "resolve," "think," etc.), "I" (a possible token of independence), and Achievement (which includes many of the same words as Mastery). This cluster of categories can reasonably be interpreted as belonging to the popular ulcer syndrome described in Alexander et al. (1968). The difficulty in applying these categories to the patient in question is that they do not correspond to his dynamic make-up. The subjects seem to have been trying to rediscover in the material the cultural stereotype of the ulcer patient, rather than listening to clues that are, in this patient, idiosyncratic (see Chapman and Chapman, 1967, for a similar phenomenon in beginning clinicians' interpretations of figure drawings).

EXPERIMENT 2—DISTRACTION CONDITIONS

We have been assuming that specific categories triggered the symptom calls, but so far we have no hard evidence that that was the case. To gather such evidence was the goal of the second and third experiments. Their aim was systematically to influence each subject's choice of categories by manipulating the mode and content of his style of listening.

We manipulated mode by requiring subjects to write a series of random numbers as they listened to clinical material. Two different intervals between numbers were used, one somewhat longer than the other. The longer the interval between numbers, the more uninterrupted attention the subject could devote to the clinical material and the greater the likelihood of his using symbols as the main clues. The shorter the interval, the greater the likelihood of his using signals. In the long-interval (slow) condition, subjects generated random numbers at the rate of one every 2.33 seconds; in the short-interval (fast) condition, the rate was one every 1.75 seconds. Interval size was changed midway through the segments to test the effects of speed change on subjects' performance. Fourteen subjects (Slow/Fast group) were given the long-interval condition during the first eight segments and the short-interval condition during the last nine segments. Twelve subjects (Fast/Slow group) were given the reverse order. In both groups, the subjects were told to generate a random series of numbers, using the digits 0 to 9, while they listened to the tape. They were asked to distribute their attention about equally between tape and numbers. A random series was defined as a string of numbers that might be pulled out of a hat by picking out one number at random, replacing it and picking out another, and so on. After each segment, subject responded "symptom" or "no symptom," and rated his confidence on the 5-point scale described earlier. The subject wrote numbers on a moving strip of paper driven by a motor. A shield covered the moving paper so that the subject could not see what number he had just written. For each segment of the tape subjects generated an average of 35 numbers during the long-interval condition and an average of 49 during the short-interval condition.

RESULTS

Sensitivity. Total "hits" averaged 10.5 for the Slow/Fast group and 7.2 for the Fast/Slow group (difference significant at the .01 level, two-tailed Mann-Whitney test). The two groups and the No Distraction group of Experiment 1 are compared in Table 3; the No Distraction group falls midway between the two distraction groups. Taking 8.5 as the chance number of "hits" and dividing each group at this point, all but two of the Slow/Fast group fall above chance, all but one of the Fast/Slow group fall below chance, and the No Distraction subjects are almost equally divided above and below chance. Chi square for this distribution is 15.47 ($p < .001$, 2 degrees of freedom).

The pacing of the number-generating task seems to have had a profound influence on sensitivity. The condition of long-interval pacing followed by short-interval pacing in the Slow/Fast group seems to have alerted subjects to the critical clues needed to discriminate symptom from control segments. The reverse combination of fast followed by slow pacing seems to have made subjects relatively insensitive to the critical clues. The five main categories used by each group are shown in columns 3 and 4 of Table 2. If we compare the categories actually used by each group with the ideal categories (column 1), we can see why sensitivity should be higher for the Slow/Fast group and lower for the Fast/Slow group, relative to the No Distraction group. The Slow/Fast group used one signal and four symbol categories—a set of five that included four of the best five predictors of the criterion (column 1). As a result, they scored more "hits." The Fast/Slow group, on the other hand, used three of the best five categories, but the one that contributed most (Achievement) to their symptom calls was not among the best five. Use of it as the primary category must, therefore, have led to a good deal of error. Thus the Slow/Fast group was forced by the pacing speed to focus on categories that turned out to be good predictors and as a result, their "hit" score was increased. The Fast/Slow group, on the other hand, was forced to rely on categories that were not efficient predictors and their "hit" score went down. The No Distraction subjects, who were not restricted by pacing speed, seem rather to have been influenced by their stereotyped impression of the typical ulcer patient; this impression did not agree particularly well with the clinical material and as a result their "hit" scores were only average.

How exactly did pacing speed affect choice of category? Some suggestive evidence is presented at the bottom of Table 2, where average number of syllables found in the words of the best five categories is listed for each condition. The average number of syllables per word is lowest in the Fast/Slow condition, highest in the Slow/Fast condition, and in between in the No Distraction condition. Similarly, the average number of different words in each category is lowest in the Fast/Slow condition, highest in the Slow/Fast condition, and in between in the No Distraction condition. The probability of achieving this distribution of the two scores by chance (they are independent measures) is given by $p = 1/3^6$, or $p < .01$. These figures suggest that the Fast/Slow condition, by restricting the time available to scan incoming material, forced subject to attend to shorter words (fewer syllables) and to a smaller number of different words. Conversely, the Slow/Fast condition, by allowing him more time to scan and process the material, enabled him to deal with larger words and a larger number of different words. The amount of attention determined by pacing speed at the start of each condition (slow or fast) appears to have remained in effect for its duration, as shown by the fact that the predictors used (Table 2, columns 3 and 4) were derived from all 17 segments.

On the other hand, there also appear to have been certain changes within conditions, triggered by the change in pacing speed. Table 4 lists the best predictors of symptom calls within each group in each condition. The category listed in each case is the one that has the highest correlation with symptom calls within each designated subgroup; that is, Anxiety correlates highest with symptom calls in the slow condition for the Slow/Fast group, and so on. Note that for both groups in the slow condition the best predictor is a symbol category (Anxiety and Wish); in both categories words average 2.2 syllables, and the number of different words is nine and five respectively. In both fast conditions, on the other hand, the best predictors are signal categories (Family and Negation) which are much shorter (1.2 and one syllable per word, respectively) and cover six and two different words respectively. The longer interval between numbers in the slow condition may have made it possible for the subject to assimilate larger words and/or a broader range of words. When the speed changes and the "window" becomes smaller, the subject changes strategy; he seems to depend more on words that are smaller and less varying and therefore easier to respond to in a distracted state.

The odds for this distribution of predictors happening by chance were determined by the conventional method of combining probabilities. Since four of the seven categories are symbols, the chance of getting a symbol as the best predictor is 4/7. The chances of getting a signal as best predictor is 3/7. The chances of getting this particular combination of predictors is $4/7 \times 3/7 \times 4/7 \times 3/7$, or $p < .06$.

The extent to which the choice of a category is dependent on pacing speed is shown more clearly in Table 5. Here the four best predictors listed in Table 4 are scored separately for each group in each condition. Without exception, a good predictor for one condition is a chance predictor for the other, even though the subjects are the same. Thus for the Fast/Slow group, Anxiety is a good predictor in the Slow condition but a poor predictor in the Fast condition. Conversely, Family, the good predictor in the Fast condition, is a chance predictor in the Slow condition. The initial pacing speed (fast or slow) seems to have oriented subjects to the appropriate category; thus subjects in the Slow condition used Anxiety, a category with relatively long words, and subjects in the Fast condition used Negation, a category with relatively short words. A change in pacing speed sensitized the subjects to a second, more appropriate category. Nevertheless, the initial speed seems to have determined the main order of preference. Thus in both groups (Table 2) the first category used (Anxiety or Negation) is a stronger predictor (higher in the list of categories) than the second. The change in pacing speed seems to have modified rather than revolutionized subjects' listening strategy.

Randomness. The number series generated by each subject was scored for randomness by using Attneave's formula for fisrt-order H (see Attneave, 1959, p. 20). For each subject, a separate score was determined for each clinical segment, and the 17 scores averaged. The higher the value of H, the more closely a subject approaches a perfectly random distribution of numbers and, presumably, the more attention he is investing in the number task.

Mean H was 3.15 for the Slow/Fast group and 3.10 for the Fast/Slow group; the difference is significant at the .05 level by a two-tailed sign test. The Slow/Fast group was apparently paying more attention to the random numbers and was able to generate a slightly more random series; presumably, then, they were paying less attention to the clinical material. But, as we have already noted, the

Slow/Fast group was more sensitive to the clinical material (see Table 3) than the Fast/Slow group, and we assume that that was because the Slow/Fast group used categories with larger words and a wider range of words. The slow pacing speed, then, apparently enabled them to listen to larger chunks of material: even though the total amount of attention was restricted, it was focused on the best predictors. This is one explanation for the apparent paradox that subjects who paid less attention to the clinical material were better able to distinguish symptom from control segments.[3]

Table 3 SUMMARY OF SENSITIVITY IN THREE CONDITIONS

Groups	Subjects Scoring Above Chance	Subjects Scoring Below Chance	Total Subjects
No Distraction	12	13	25
Slow/Fast	12	2	14
Fast/Slow	1	11	12
	25	26	51

$X^2 = 15.47$
$p < .001$, 2 d.f.

If we combine all the findings from Experiment 2, we can say that the restriction on listening time appeared to focus attention on short words and on a smaller range of words. If a restriction was imposed at the beginning of the procedure, it apparently remained in force throughout; if it was imposed after the subject had become familiar with the material, his early choice of categories still seems to have prevailed. As a result, subjects in the Fast/Slow group were restricted to undifferentiated categories of short words throughout the 17 segments, while subjects in the Slow/Fast group were sensitized to broader categories of longer words.

Table 4 BEST PREDICTORS OF SYMPTOM CALLS

Group	Condition	
	Slow	Fast
Slow/Fast	Anxiety (Symbol) 9 diff. words 2.2 syll/word	Family (Signal) 6 diff. words 1.2 syll/word
Fast/Slow	Wish (Symbol) 5 diff. words 2.2 syll/word	Negation (Signal) 2 diff. words 1 syll/word

$p = .06$ (4/7 × 3/7 × 4/7 × 3/7)

[3] This paradox—that less attention increases sensitivity—supports Freud's recommendation (1912) to listen with evenly divided attention.

Partly for accidental reasons, the categories that differentiated symptom from control segments in this patient were largely made up of many different long words. Any procedure that would prevent subjects from attending to a wide range of long words would interfere with sensitivity, because awareness of these clues was necessary for correct identification of the segments. Therefore the Slow/Fast subjects were helped by the distraction procedure and the Fast/Slow subjects were hindered by it. Even though the Slow/Fast group was paying relatively more attentiono to the random numbers (mean H was 3.15), as compared with the Fast/Slow group (mean H was 3.10), they still were better able to discriminate symptom from control segment, because they were attending to the most differentiating themes. Conversely, although the Fast/Slow group was paying relatively less attention to the random numbers (and therefore more to the clinical material), they still did poorly, because they were focusing on the wrong sets of words. Therefore we can conclude that the amount of attention is not as critical as how it is being distributed.

Table 5 CORRELATIONS WITH SYMPTOM CALLS

	Slow/Fast Group	
Category	Slow	Fast
Anxiety (Symbol)	.78	.06
Family (Signal)	.02	.49
	Fast/Slow Group	
Negation (Signal)	.70	.18
Wish (Symbol)	.08	.66

$r_{.05} = .48$
$r_{.01} = .60$

EXPERIMENT 3—PRIMING CONDITION

Another way to influence choice of predictor is by priming specific contents. We have seen that the size of the distraction "window" can be influenced indirectly by pacing speed; we next attempted directly to control the window by giving subjects specific clues. For this experiment, we added some new clinical material from the same patient of Luborsky's and ended up with a set of 30 segments, each 100 words long. Fifteen of these occurred immediately before the patient reported a stomach pain and the other 15 were taken from control sessions when no pain was reported. One symptom segment and one control segment are given below.

Symptom

This fellow Young—never known him before—he called me some radical name and he was about 21 then—an amateur boxer I found out later—had a friend of his along, another amateur boxer—this fellow Young about as big as I am now—this fellow along about 6'2"—I don't know how I got into it, but anyhow he kept picking on me—he wanted to start a fight—I don't remember a thing—things happened so darned fast—they both set into me—I was a pretty sorry sight—never really felt any pain after that—my face was all bruised and swollen up.

Control

Then I'm thinking of the follow-up work, the continuation of a good job—I hope we're going to get down there to really develop in the Y some extra good leaders and make it strong. I'm thinking about how I want to cut out a lot of these committees I'm working on—I can't cut them out very soon. I have to stay with them at least until the summer semester—kind of wondering in my mind whether I'll go to school or whether I'll take some kind of trip to Europe or something of that sort.

Analysis of the 30 segments with the Need-Affiliation/Need-Achievement dictionary revealed two categories that were moderately correlated with the criterion (symptom/no symptom) and negligibly correlated with each other ($r = -.096$). The two categories were Negation (somewhat expanded from the category used in the previous study; it now includes such words as "don't," "can't," "won't," etc.) and Activity (words like "choose," "direct," "prepare," "finish," etc.). Negation correlated $-.278$ and Activity $-.322$ with the criterion; that is, fewer words of either category occurred in the Symptom than in the Control passages. The first of the new categories is a signal because it covers a relatively circumscribed set of words, even though it has been expanded from Experiment 2. The second category is a symbol because its category boundaries are much less distinct and because it covers a much larger set of words (23). From 0 to 6

Table 6 SEVEN BEST PREDICTORS OF CRITERION AND SYMPTOM CALLS FOR 30 SEGMENTS

Criterion		Symptom Calls per Condition					
		Control		Negation Priming		Activity Priming	
Down	.44	Down	.45	Negation	.76	Mastery	.42
Up	.56	I	.57	Down	.78	Supplies	.50
Activity	.62	Activity	.63	Supplies	.81	Up	.56
Negation	.68	Up	.66	Wish	.83	Negation	.60
Fantasy	.70	Helpless	.68	Affiliation Set.	.85	Affiliation	.64
Darn	.71	Need	.70	Activity	.86	Down	.66
Affiliation	.72	Negation	.71	Up	.87	I	.67

For significance at the .05 level, multiple R for 1 predictor must be at least .36, and for 7 predictors at least .66.

Negation words and from 0 to 7 Activity words appeared in each of the 30 segments.

The best seven predictors of the criterion (symptom or no symptom) are shown in Table 6. They were determined by entering categories counted from the dictionary into a multiple regression equation, with the clinical picture (symptom or no symptom) as the criterion. To these categories were added another containing swear words, and the two single words "up" and "down," all of which seemed clinically important. Table 6 reveals that "down" and "up" are the two best predictors, followed by Activity, Negation, Fantasy, Darn, and Affiliation. Thus the two categories chosen for the priming study were the two best *category* predictors; their multiple correlation with the criterion is −.45. If a subject were primed for Negation, we would expect this category to move up in the list of predictors and, we hoped, end up as the strongest predictor; Activity, because it is uncorrelated, should not be affected. Conversely, if he were primed for Activity, then Activity should move up and Negation should not be affected.

Thirty-six new subjects were tested in four groups of nine each. The two experimental groups (nine in each) were told that they would hear segments of the productions of a patient with a stomach symptom, and that content was frequently expressed as a symptom instead of in words. One group was told that the symptom expressed negation; the second that it expressed activity. The Activity category was defined by a list of 23 words ("choose," "direct," "put," "try," etc.), which were read to the subject; the Negation category was defined by a list of 10 words ("no," "not," "can't," "didn't," etc.). Because both categories were negatively correlated with the criterion, we needed to explain to the subject that symptoms were best predicted by the *absence* of the key words. To make this idea more convincing, we said that a particular clinical theme could be expressed either by a symptom or by words. Therefore, the best guide to the presence of a symptom was the *absence* of critical words; their *presence,* on the other hand, would indicate that the segment was symptom-free. Thus a subject primed for negative words would be expected to rate a segment symptom-free when he heard negation words, and to call it a symptom segment if negation was *not* heard. The 30 segments were played in a prearranged random order; after each segment, the subject indicated his decision—symptom or no symptom— and rated his confidence in a 5-point scale.

Each of the experimental groups was then given the same protocol and told that a second symptom—dizziness—was also related to the presence of a certain set of words. Subjects primed for negation in the first session were primed for activity in the second; subjects primed for activity in the first session were primed for negation in the second.

Eighteen control subjects were given the same 30 segments with no priming instructions: nine were told that the patient's principal complaint was dizziness, and nine were told that it was stomach pain. They were all asked to judge whether or not the symptom was present at the end of each segment, and to indicate their confidence on a 5-point scale.

RESULTS

Priming Effectiveness. Table 7 presents the relation between category frequency and subjects' responses for each of the four experimental conditions. The frequency of the categories of Activity and Negation in each segment was correlated with the total number of subjects in each group who called that segment

Table 7 CORRELATIONS BETWEEN ACTIVITY OR NEGATION WORDS AND CONTROL CALLS UNDER ACTIVITY OR NEGATION PRIMING

GROUP I		GROUP II	
Activity Priming (1)		Negation Priming (1)	
Activity Words	*Negation Words*	*Activity Words*	*Negation Words*
.24	.05	.08	.75
Negation Priming (2)		Activity Priming (2)	
Activity Words	*Negation Words*	*Activity Words*	*Negation Words*
−.01	.66	.34	.07

$r_{.05} = .36$
$r_{.01} = .46$

symptom-free (since symptom and clue were negatively correlated). In each of the four conditions, the correlation with the primed category is higher than with the nonprimed category; thus, under Activity priming, Group I, the correlation of symptom-free calls with the frequency of Activity words (.24), is higher than with the frequency of Negation words (.05). The chances of this relationship occurring 4 times is $1/2^4$ or $p = .06$. Two of these correlations are highly significant; they both occur with Negation priming. Activity priming, on the other hand, though larger than the comparison figure, is not significant in itself.

Hits. Subjects in the Control conditions averaged 17.0 hits out of a possible 30. We divided the group into those who had 0–15 hits and those who had 16–30 hits. But chance, we would expect an even division between the two groups; in fact, 14 subjects got 16 or more hits, 4 subjects got 15 or fewer hits, and the 14/1 split is significant at $p = .03$, two-tailed sign test.

In Negation priming, subjects averaged 17.2 hits out of a possible 30. Sixteen out of 18 subjects got 16 or more hits, and the 16/2 split is significant at $p = .002$, two-tailed sign test. Thus Negation priming improved performance, although the increase over Control is probably not significant.

In Activity priming, subjects averaged 15.7 hits. Eleven subjects got 16 or more hits, and the 11/7 split is not significant. Activity priming seems to have impaired performance.

Confidence. Mean confidence for hits was not significantly greater than for misses in any of the three conditions.

Multiple regression. We now asked which content categories best accounted for symptom calls in each of the three main conditions. Control (No-symptom) calls were totaled for subjects in the Negation priming, Activity priming, and Control conditions, and used as the criterion measures in three multiple regression analyses. Sixteen predictors were entered: two words ("up" and "down") and 14 categories from the Need–Affiliation dictionary. Table 6, column 2, shows the seven best predictors in the Control condition; they include four of the seven best predictors in the Control condition; they include four of the seven best predictors of the criterion (column 1), and three of the top four. This choice of predictors helps to account for the significant hit rate in the control condition. Subjects in this condition were told that the patients' principal complaint was *either* dizziness or stomach pain; perhaps for this reason, the set of predictors does not agree in any general way with the predictors used by the No Distraction group in Experiment 1.

Table 6, column 3, shows the seven best predictors in the Negation priming condition. Negation has moved up from No. 7 to No. 1, and presumably the shift was a consequence of the priming instruction. Also added are Supplies, Wish, and Affiliation Setting; the first correlates positively with Negation (.20) and the third correlates negatively ($-.23$). But they are poor predictors, not listed in column 1; thus the hit rate for subjects in this condition is lower than it might have been, because the good predictors (Negation, Activity, and "down" and "up") are weakened by three poor ones.

Table 6, column 4, shows the seven best predictors in the Activity priming condition. The Activity category fails to appear; in first place is Mastery, which contains many of the Activity words. Thus the priming is only partially successful; for some reason it alerted subjects more to Mastery than to Activity. We have seen (column 1) that Mastery is a poor predictor of the criterion, and when subjects use it as their foremost category, their hit scores suffer, as noted above.

Negation and Activity Keys. Another view of Negation priming can be obtained by scoring each protocol by the Negation key. A segment was keyed Symptom if it contained 0–1 Negation words, and Control if it contained two or more Negation words. Scoring in this way resulted in a roughly even distribution of Symptoms and Control segments. If the subject's response coincided with this key, it was scored a hit. Hits averaged 20.4 in the Negation priming condition, 14.7 in the Control condition, and 15.8 in the Activity priming condition. Negation and Activity conditions were compared with a 2×2 analysis of variance with repeated groups; the effect of order (Negation or Activity priming first) was not significant, while the effect of priming (Negation or Activity) was highly significant, with Negation priming accounting for significantly more hits than Activity priming ($F = 31.37$, 1/16 d.f., $p < .001$).

A similar analysis, scoring the segments for Activity words, showed an average of 14.9 hits in the Activity condition, 15.6 in the Control condition, and 15.5 in the Negation condition. These means are not significantly different from one another, but there was a significant order effect: subjects who were given the Negation priming first scored more hits on the Activity key *regardless of priming* than did subjects who were given the Activity priming first ($F = 8.29$, 1/16 d.f., $p < .05$).

In sum, Negation priming seems to have been more successful than Activity priming on all measures. Not only was the latter less precise, it also interfered with overall sensitivity. Possible reasons for these differences will be discussed below.

DISCUSSION

Goldberg and his colleagues (Goldberg, 1968) have made a strong case for the linear model of clinical judgment, in which clues, appropriately weighted, are combined to form a final judgment. The present study asks how specific clues are selected and provides suggestive evidence that the size of the judgment "window" determines the type of clue that is used. Sensitivity was increased in the Slow/Fast condition, probably because the subjects were given a "window" large enough to assimilate the more powerful predictors. Sensitivity was decreased in the Fast/Slow condition, probably because the size of the "window" was limited and subjects were forced to use short, undifferentiated, and, as it turned out, less efficient predictors. Window size was not controlled in the No Distraction condition; in this case, subjects seem to have been influenced by the stereotyped conception of the ulcer patient.

Clue selection was also influenced by preliminary priming, more by Negation words than by Activity words. Here subjects' attention was focused on a certain range of content, and the Negation clues were probably easier to identify because they represent a part of speech that does not depend on context and thus can be more readily identified. The word "can't," for example, has an unambiguous meaning whatever its place in the sentence, but the word "finish" (an Activity word) can be either a noun or a verb, and the meaning of Activity, since it is carried only by the latter use, must depend on the context. The decoding problem is therefore somewhat more complex in the case of the Activity words and requires the subject to listen to larger chunks of text, in order to determine the meaning being expressed. The point is that we can influence the size of the subject's listening window by cueing him to certain types of words. Negation words require a smaller window than Activity words.

Three other points should be mentioned. Negation words may have an advantage because they are easier to learn (10 as compared to 23 in the Activity category), because they are shorter (Negation words average 1.50 syllables, whereas Activity words average 1.75 syllables), and because, as a group, they are easier to infer—show more common meaning—than Activity words.

Although sensitivity was influenced by two different procedures, both seem to rely on the same mechanism—adjustment of the listening "window." In the distraction experiments, we controlled the window by regulating the pacing speed and letting the subject pick up whatever segments of the text the window would allow. In the priming studies, we controlled the window by controlling content. Because Negation words can be detected in isolation, Negation priming imposed a much smaller window on the subject than Activity priming.

If attention is free-floating and mainly signals are being heard, how are they combined? Our data do not shed much light on the linear-configural controversy (see Hoffman et al., 1968), because it was only in Experiment 3 that subjects were given explicit clues, and no more than one at a time; therefore, we had no opportunity to study possible combinations. Nevertheless, we might speculate that whether the clues are combined in a linear fashion (using a linear regression model) or configurally (using an analysis of variance model) may, like clue selection itself, depend on the subject's mode of listening. If he listens with free-floating attention, we would expect him to deemphasize rational forms of thought and not keep very strict track of the numbers of each signal being processed, the weight assigned, etc.; a configural model seems more appropriate. If he is listening with close attention and an emphasis on secondary-process thinking, a more logical and linear model would presumably be used.

These predictions can be tested. If we alerted a subject to two sets of signals, he would not need to pay maximal attention to the material because the clues would be relatively easy to identify. Hence he could listen with largely free-floating attention and might be expected to combine the clues in a less rational, more configural manner. If we alerted him to less explicit clues, he would need to pay more attention and the resulting more rational attention should thus produce a more logical, "straight-line" processing of the data.

THE THERAPEUTIC SITUATION

What do the findings indicate about the naturalistic situation of therapist listening to patient? First, we have seen (Experiment 2) that the amount of attention being paid to the material is less important than the way it is being distributed. Second, the selection of clues may be determined by our conception of the patient (Experiment 1), by the amount of attention we have available (Experiment 2), or by initial priming instructions (Experiment 3). Third (Experiment 2), the way we learn to listen at the beginning of the material strongly influences how we listen later, and it would not be surprising if this rule also applied to the other experiments and to other listening situations.

Each of these experimental findings has a counterpart in the clinical situation. We have all had the experience of listening very closely and finding that no amount of extra effort clarifies the material. We have here an example of the first finding—namely, that an increase in the amount of attention does not necessarily increase sensitivity. When such a clinical situation arises, we are presumably attending to the wrong set of clues. What determines our selection of clues? Many of the same factors that appeared in the three experiments. We often form an initial impression of the patient that alerts us to specific themes and prevents us from noting others. Our expectation of what form the material will take may also prevent us from detecting the critical themes. At other times, particularly during supervision, we may be told to listen for particular clues, and again our sensitivity may be affected—positively if the clues are appropriate, and negatively if they are not. Finally, we may choose clues in accordance with our mode of listening. If we follow Rosen (1969), close attention, because it sensitizes us to symbols, should alert us to secondary-process content—the logical, rational thread of the material. Our own data would support this supposition because we have seen that subjects in the Slow/Fast condition who had a more leisurely distraction task were sensitized to the symbol categories. If we listen with free-floating attention, on the other hand, we should be sensitized to smaller units of material. These units tend to be signals, and, according to Rosen, primary-process content is carried primarily by signals. Thus free-floating attention is best suited to picking up preconscious and unconscious meanings. Freud made a similar argument in his early papers on technique (Freud, 1912, p. 111); the present findings support his suggestion.

But Freud may have gone too far in advising the beginning analyst to maintain the same "evenly-suspended attention" in the face of all that he hears. We have seen how the judge's mode of listening will determine the kind of category he selects from the material; listening with evenly divided attention may be detrimental as well as useful. On the basis of the present evidence and Rosen's theoretical argument, we would assume that free-floating attention tends to alert the therapist to a succession of signals that carry the patient's primary-process message. But this kind of unconscious message would be of little use to the therapist early in treatment because the patient could not yet assimilate an interpretation of it; thus the therapist would have to change his listening style and listen closely, in order to pick up secondary-process meanings. He might also wish to vary his mode of listening within the same hour, using a free-floating mode when dream associations are being reported and a closely attentive mode when the patient is recounting a piece of his day's experience. If the therapist's style of listening were flexibly shifted from one mode to the other, he would be able to pick up both primary- and secondary-process material and to gain the greatest information from an hour. But if he rigidly assumed one mode or the other, he would hear only part of the message.

Thus, flexible listening is to be recommended. But, as we saw in Experiment 2, the mode of listening used at the start of the material seems to have been maintained throughout, despite interferences to the contrary, and we might conclude that changes in mode of listening were more often the exception than the rule. Part of the difficulty in changing the mode of listening lies in the fact that, to many people, free-floating attention seems counter-intuitive: when they are confused, they tend to listen more closely rather than to relax and listen only to occasional words. The times when they should shift from close to relaxed listening are usually times when an increased amount of primary-process material has emerged (such as dream material), and it is at just such items that the therapist's confusion is increased. Thus the recommended procedure goes directly against the grain; it is like asking a driver to steer into a skid. How about the reverse? Listening with free-floating attention probably requires less attention in the first place; to ask the therapist at some point during the hour to listen *more* closely is to ask him to increase his total amount of attention, and he may be reluctant to make this change. Here again he might tend to remain in his initial listening mode rather than to shift to another.

Perhaps the most important conclusion to be drawn from the experimental findings is that change in *mode* of listening has a greater influence on sensitivity than change in *content*. When we compare the Slow/Fast and the Fast/Slow group in Experiment 2, we find that the number of subjects responding above the chance level in the first condition was 12 times the number in the second condition. Moving to Experiment 3, we find that Negation priming increased the number of subjects responding above chance only from 78 per cent in the control condition to 88 per cent in the experimental condition. Even after allowing for the fact that the Negation category was not a very powerful predictor, the change in hit rate seems minimal at best, and certainly insignificant, as compared with the changes brought about in Experiment 2. These differences suggest that the instruction to listen for a particular theme (during supervision, for example) may be much less efficient than the instruction to adopt a new mode of listening or, more broadly, to become aware of the two main modes of listening and to be prepared to change from one to the other. A particular mode alerts the therapist to a choice of categories (signal or symbol), and he can select from among them those that are most useful at the time. A particular theme, on the other hand, alerts him to a relatively specific set of meanings, and there is probably a limit to the number of items that a therapist can keep in mind. But there is an even more serious difficulty. The instruction to listen to a specific set of meanings does not simultaneously impose a certain mode of listening on the therapist, and yet certain clues can be detected only if certain listening modes are assumed. If the listener's habitual mode does not coincide with the mode most appropriate to the clue in question, the priming instruction will probably have no effect. This line of argument suggests that the different conditions of Experiment 3 could have been more effective if the mode of listening had also been controlled.

To sum up, it seems that listening mode is basic to the judgment process and must be controlled before specific content is selected. If mode of listening is determined, then content may be selected as well, but if content is selected without first controlling for mode, any change in content may have little or no effect on the listening process. Further experiments will be necessary to devise ways of monitoring mode of listening that interfere less with the judgment process (less, for example, than random number generation), so that changes in mode may be studied in a naturalistic situation. Such studies could determine how thematic focus is influenced by listening mode, when changes in mode are triggered by changes in content, and how therapists with different amounts of experience vary in style of listening. Ultimately, it might be possible to devise ways of training therapists to become aware of, and to use at will, the two basic modes of listening, so that they might thereby become more sensitive clinicians.

REFERENCES

Alexander, F., French, T., and Pollock, G., eds. (1968). *Psychosomatic Specificity*. Chicago: University of Chicago Press.

Attneave, F. (1959). *Applications of Information Theory to Psychology*. New York: Holt, Rinehart and Winston.

Baddeley, A. D. (1966). The Capacity for Generating Information by Randomization. *Quarterly Journal of Experimental Psychology,* 18:119–129.

Chapman, L. J., and Chapman, J. P. (1967). Genesis of Popular but Erroneous Psychodiagnostic Observations. *Journal of Abnormal Psychology,* 72:193–204.

Freud, S. (1912). Recommendation to Physicians Practicing Psychoanalysis. *Standard Edition,* 12:111–120. London: Hogarth Press, 1958.

Goldberg, L. (1968). Simple Models or Simple Processes? Some Research on Clinical Judgments. *American Psychologist,* 23:483–496.

Hoffman, P. J., Slovic, P., and Rorer, L. G. (1968). An Analysis of Variance Model for the Assessment of Configural Cue Utilization in Clinical Judgment. *Psychological Bulletin,* 69:338–349.

Langer, S. K. (1951). *Philosophy in a New Key.* New York: New American Library.

Luborsky, L., and Auerbach, A. (1969). The Symptom-Context Method: Quantitative Studies of Symptom Formation in Psychotherapy. *Journal of the American Psychoanalytic Association,* 17:68–99

Morris, C. (1946). *Signs, Language and Behavior.* New York: Prentice-Hall.

Rosen, V. (1969). Sign Phenomena and Their Relationship to Unconscious Meaning. *International Journal of Psycho-Analysis,* 50:197–207.

Schimek, J. G., and Wachtel, P. L. (1969). Exploration of Effects of Distraction, Competing Tasks and Cognitive Style of Attention Deployment. *Perceptual and Motor Skills,* 28:567–574.

Spence, D. P. (1969). PL/1 Programs for Content Analysis. *Behavioral Science,* 14:433.

————Wolitzky, D., and Pezenik, J. (1969). Random Generation of Digits as a Measure of Attention: Relation to Text Redundancy and Recall. *Journal of Verbal Learning and Verbal Behavior,* 8:9–15.

A LANGUAGE CONSTRUCTION APPROACH FOR THE EXAMINATION OF SELF/OBJECT REPRESENTATION IN VARYING CLINICAL STATES [1]

Irving Steingart, Ph.D., and Norbert Freedman, Ph.D.

A review of selected elements from both the experimental and clinical literature supports the importance of language construction analysis for psychoanalytical research. We present data for three such measures, together with clinical, theoretical literature supporting the interpretation that such measures are indicative of the following: (1) the degree of differentiation between self-representations and object-representations; (2) the relative balance between narcissistic libidinal attachment and libidinal attachments to objects; (3) the division of selective attention between interactional and solitary features of the representational world. We consider that, relatively, our present data support this last interpretation only weakly. We also suggest that those states of consciousness that we designate as persecutory paranoid, psychotic depression, moderate non-psychotic mania, and schizophrenia possess distinctive configurations of such constructs. Finally, we suggest future psychoanalytic research areas and specific problems for which such language construction measures would appear to be pertinent.

We shall describe a procedure for the analysis of language behavior; we shall also present results that support the use of such a procedure, and suggest further areas of research that can be pursued with this approach. However, first, we shall present material from linguistics and psycholinguistics, experimental psychopathology, and the literature on developmental psychology that points in general to the importance of language behavior for psychoanalytic research.

Two investigatory attitudes (biases) have guided us throughout: first, that we should choose as the source of our data the language of a patient undergoing psychotherapy; second, that a *selection* of such data, according to changes in the independently defined clinical state of a patient, would act as a prism and

[1] This study is supported in part by Grant #MH-1483-01 from the National Institute of Mental Health, United States Public Health Service.

We want to acknowledge work done by Miss Joanne Daly, Miss Sheryl Jacobsen, Mr. James O'Hanlon and Mr. Robert Unger, who acted as Research Assistants during various phases of this research.

We want also to acknowledge the technical assistance of Mr. Charles Sleeth, Department of English, Brooklyn College.

result in a diffraction of linguistic phenomena into some theoretically meaningful array.

Certain kinds of grammatical diversity, so obtained, suggest some important, quantifiable dimensions for constructs pertaining to representations of self and objects in varying clinical states. In turn, this framework for the evaluation of representations may contribute to at least a partial assessment of states of consciousness.

*   *   *   *   *

The utterance by a patient of something that a therapist recognizes and understands as language presupposes that the patient has available two kinds of learning: first, how to construct individual words and then put words together (this is called the grammatical aspect of language); second, how to use a word as a sign to "point" to things, and to signify a concept. These latter two aspects refer to what is usually called the semantic (or meaning) aspects of language.

Two further considerations require immediate amplification. We often speak of a "correct" use of grammar and semantics. A distinction must be made between linguistics, thought of as a discipline existing in its own right—like logic—and the psychology of language. A theory of the psychological phenomena of language must deal not only with shared attributes of language behavior, but also with intra- and inter-individual differences in the acquisition and use of language. This aspect of language, both its general and specific relationship to the language user, has been called pragmatics (Morris, 1938); it constitutes, we believe, an important field of study for psychoanalytic research. We also speak about a *recognition* as well as an understanding of language, and we use this term to refer to an important distinction between grammar and semantics.

Suppose, for example, a patient makes the following statement to his therapist: "Furry jewelers create distressed stains." A therapist, indeed anyone who has learned the English language, will respond with a definite sense of recognition that English is being spoken. There can also occur even some vague sense that this patient is "trying to say something," even though the meaning of the sentence remains unclear. This sense of recognition derives in part from the fact that the grammar of this sentence is intelligible, even though the semantics is not. The way in which our hypothetical patient has constructed a string of adjectives, nouns, etc., is "correct" English—which contributes to the communicative impact of the sentence. Such an influence of grammar upon meaning can be demonstrated experimentally (Brown, 1957). Grammatical and semantic attributes must undoubtedly interact in complex ways to produce some actual pragmatic relevance for a language user or listener. Miller (1964) and his associates have recently begun to examine with experimental procedures such complex interactive effects as they influence perception and learning. The sentence described above was constructed by these experimenters and compared with other sentences that were systematically varied in terms of syntactical and semantical coherence.

Such a sentence, or at least something like it, with perhaps a somewhat narrower semantic range,[2] might be produced by a psychotic patient. Such language—appropriate grammar but inappropriate semantics—seems very often to be what clinicians mean by a "thought disorder," and we shall discuss the implications of that idea later in this paper.

Language is a species-specific characteristic distinctive to man (Lenneberg, 1967). Consequently, it comes as no surprise that theorists as divergent as Freud (e.g., 1911a, 1915a, 1923), Piaget (e.g., 1923, 1928, 1945) and Skinner (1957) have emphasized the relevance of language learning for the kind of cognitive advance that is also distinctive to man. Generally speaking, objective investigation of psychopathology via language has dealt more with language content—i.e., semantics (e.g., Auld and Murray, 1955)—than with grammaticality. Lasswell (1935) pioneered in the analysis of language content derived from recordings of patients in psychoanalytic sessions. He coded such content in terms of whether or not it contained any reference to the therapist; in addition, he coded certain paralinguistic features of speech such as pauses, rate, etc. Subsequent research added to these initial types of analyses—linguistic content and paralinguistic—a third type of analysis, having to do with the grammatical characteristics of language. Examples of research approach can be cited that place their emphasis on one or another of these major data sources (e.g., Mahl, 1956; Mowrer, Light, et al., 1953; Gottschalk et al., 1961b; Grummon, 1953). Inasmuch as our work stresses grammar-related properties of language expressed by a patient, we shall limit our review to studies that are relevant to this approach.

Lorenz and Cobb (1952, 1953, 1954) obtained evidence for distinctly different patterns of grammatical expression among various diagnostic entities: for example, neurotic patients showed a significant increase over normal subjects in their use of substantives, adjectives, prepositions, conjunctions, and articles. Balken and Masserman (1940) have demonstrated interesting grammatical differences in the T.A.T. stories of obsessive-compulsive, anxiety state, and conversion-hysteric patients. Obsessive patients showed the greatest use of "qualifying" adverbs and adjectives; conversion hysterics made little use of such qualification, and also had low verb/adjective proportion; on the other hand, persons with anxiety hysteria demonstrated the reverse, a high verb/adjective ratio. None of these findings have been cross-validated, however.

Zimmerman and Langdon (1953) found distinct changes in the use of the grammatical person as patients progressed in therapy; presumably, these grammatical changes are indicative of a more "healthy" clinical state. For example, instances of the use of the first person singular pronoun ("I") showed a downward trend with progress in therapy; the incidence of third person singular pronouns ("he," "she"), second person singular ("you"), and the first person plural ("we")

---

[2] See, for example, Laffal (1965) for a procedure that evaluates such semantic range through a coding of 114 content categories. Content categories are based upon a kind of "family" semantics, which includes but is not limited to synonymity. For example, the words "book," "newspaper," "read," "write," "pencil," "alphabet," "language," "ink," and "print" are all included in the same category "written language."

showed a corresponding increase with such movement. Systematic changes also occurred with respect to grammatical tense as patients progressed in treatment: the use of the past tense decreased, and the use of the present and future tenses increased. Grummon (1953) performed a study similar to that of Zimmerman and Langdon and obtained identical results with respect to grammatical-tense changes as patients progressed in treatment. In addition, Grummon found that the use of the form of the grammatical negative ("no," "can't," etc.) decreased with the movement toward greater health.

Weintraub and Aronson (1963) have already pointed out that an association between some manifest clinical state and a specific kind of grammatical expression cannot be regarded as two independent descriptions of a person. Wittingly or unwittingly, grammar forms peculiar to one type of patient, rather than another, enter into the diagnosis. But the use of grammar, like any behavior, can also be taken as evidence for theoretical constructs with more general import, relevant to the comprehension of *any* personality. Common sense argues that *what* a person says is much more influenced by transient situational characteristics than how he says it. Therefore, as between language content and grammar, grammar would appear a priori to possess certain advantages for the exploration of such personality constructs. Weintraub and Aronson's (1964, 1965) findings suggest that the presence of different kinds of grammatical forms in an individual's language can be used as evidence for important attributes of intrapsychic conflict and defense.

Another linguistic distinction must now be introduced before we can describe further the work of Weintraub and Aronson. Grammar itself has to do with ". . . two convenient but not precisely delimitable subdivisions: morphology, the description of the more intimate combinations of . . . what are familiarly called words; and syntax, the description of larger combinations involving as basic units the combinations described under the morphology of the language" (Gleason, 1961, pp. 57–58). Thus, morphological analysis of a sentence's grammar deals with individual word construction as the unit of study—for example, the pluralization of noun forms. By contrast, syntactic analysis of language focuses upon combinations of words as the unit of study. These word combinations have traditionally been analyzed by linguists as a series of progressively larger word constructions, termed "immediate constituents" (I.C.'s), which begin with the grammatical sentence (Gleason, 1961). For example, consider the following simple declarative active sentence: "I see the problem." The largest construction unit is, of course, the sentence itself. This is followed by its immediate constituents which consist of a noun phrase (NP "I") plus a verb phrase (VP "see the problem"). The VP is composed of its immediate constituents, a verb ("see") and another NP ("the problem"). Finally, the NP ("the problem") is immediately composed of two units, an article ("the") and a noun ("problem").

This kind of syntactic analysis of this sentence's word construction will be sensed immediately as correct by any reader, or even banal. But that is exactly the point. The fact that a reader will recognize this syntactic ordering as the "correct" way to look upon this sentence's construction already suggests important *organizational* influences at work in the production of a sentence. (For example, a reader would not accept or consider such a word construction unit as "see the" as a correct syntactic unit of analysis for the sentence "I see the problem").

The grammatical findings we have cited thus far are reported as changes in the morphological characteristics of language associated with different clinical states. Weintraub and Aronson apparently combine morphological and syntactic grammatical data in their assessment procedure. For example, these authors operationally define the defensive process of undoing as being evidenced by language that demonstrates a "retractor"—". . . any *word, phrase or clause,* which partially or totally detracts from the statement which has immediately preceded it" (italics ours, 1963, p. 175). Consider then the following two examples: "John is an honest person, sometimes" (constructed by us); "John is an honest person. Of course, he has been involved in some shady deals" (illustration offered by Weintraub and Aronson). Both these language examples show a similar retractive function. One word construction unit is being used to detract or nullify in some way the meaning of another syntactic unit. A construct of some sort of undoing, defensive process is indeed a useful hypothesis, at least partially, to account for the production of such language expressions. But, in terms of linguistic construction, one case deals on an overt level only with an adverb ("sometimes") that performs the retracting function; in the other, this same retracting function is carried by a complete sentence. The procedure for the evaluation of language construction that we employ, and which we shall shortly describe, maintains a consistent distinction between such overt syntactic and morphological analyses.

Some of Grummon's work (1953) has already been cited. We now can add some important syntactic findings obtained by Grummon involving clause production. The length of clauses appears to discriminate between an initially neurotic and a psychotic status of subjects. Also, length of clauses was associated with changes in adjustment status, as the result of improvement due to treatment. Longer clauses were associated with better initial and later adjustment. Psychotic patient subjects, in particular, used few subordinate to independent clause relationships at the beginning of treatment, whereas their use of these relationships had increased markedly by the end of treatment. Grummon attributes these kinds of variable production of clauses, in some general sense, to initial differences and changes in the ego-integrative capacity of his patient-subjects. This work by Grummon, which emphasizes overt syntactic rather than morphological analysis, finds a historical precedent in work done by Newman and Mather (1938); they examined language samples of forty patient-subjects who exhibited different types of extreme affective psychotic disorders. The language analysis performed by these experimenters emphasized content and paralinguistic features of speech, but it also included attention to syntactic structures. They noted that individuals who suffered from depressive and manic disturbance showed different patterns of language construction in a severely acute psychotic state, as well as during periods of gradual remission. Gradual remission from psychotic depressive states involves an increasing ability to produce grammatically coherent sentences; these remain, however, syntactically "meager" and "limited."

However, remission from psychotic, manic excitement is marked by an increasing ability to produce grammatically coherent sentences, possessing syntactic structures that are "rich" and "diversified." Interestingly, in the severe psychotic manic state, one observes an effort to use these same, more elaborate syntactic structures, but without success; what occurs is incomplete sentence structure.

Some subsequent research done by M. A. White (1949) elaborates on the very damaging effect that extreme ego disturbance can have upon the ability to produce syntactic structuring in spontaneous language. White used schizophrenic patients and asked these subjects to write sentences constructed out of a presented, standardized list of words. She found that schizophrenic patient-subjects showed significantly more incomplete sentence formation, as compared with a normal group.[3]

We have already mentioned that the discipline of linguistics, in its study of what in the immediate constituent analysis of a sentence causes it to be recognized as grammatical, suggests organizational influences that are psychologically important. Grammaticalness is not simply a matter of whether or not separate words that have been connected to make a sentence follow expected transitional probabilities of association. Different sentences can be constructed that will contain similar associational probabilities among words, or even word classes, and yet the grammatical quality of each sentence can vary greatly (Lenneberg, 1962). N. F. Johnson (1965) has obtained findings that point to the organizational influence of such syntactic units upon memory. In a carefully controlled series of studies, he has demonstrated that the ease with which a word is recalled by an adult is in accordance with the manifest immediate constituent analysis of a sentence of which that word is a part. The same word placed in different syntactic environments will show different rates of recall, despite similar word-to-word associational probabilities.

Further, linguists have pointed out that the production of an English sentense can demonstrate a kind of indefinite, "self-embedding" expansion which is consistently grammatical (Miller, 1962). This is a kind of sentence formation that expands by repeating "within itself" its entire immediate constituent struc-

---

[3] Newman and Mather's results are, however, presented only in impressionistic form, through language samples from selected cases. Aside from matters of case compatibility, procedure for language sample selection, etc., these authors do not provide any objective system for *ordering* syntactic complexity in spontaneous language production. Such a system, however, is certainly implied in this pioneering investigation. Syntactic failures—i.e., the incomplete sentence formation observed by Newman and Mather, as well as by M. A. White—would provide a logical and psychological low end-point for any such ordering measurement of syntactic complexity. These ideas are incorporated into the system for the analysis of language construction that will be described shortly.

ture.[4] Because of these and other characteristics of grammaticalness, some contemporary linguists have come to think of a grammar as a device that functions *to derive* the infinite and creative (i.e., never heard) sentences, termed "surface" syntactic structures, that can be expressed by a person. The grammar does this by the use of a much smaller number of postulate-like rules, termed "transformational rules," which determine how word units can act upon the immediate constituent structure of "deep" kernel grammatical strings. "Grammaticalness" is an intuitive recognition that such rules, indeed, underlie the structural derivation of any particular sentence uttered. This entire view is formally similar, say, to the structure of Euclidean geometry; N. Chomsky (1964) in particular is associated with this linguistic concept, which he terms a "generative-transformational" grammar. While this grammar is not complete, certain major classifications of derivational history can be described that are relevant to this sort of research. The most elementary use of derivational rules can produce a simple, active declarative sentence ("I hit the ball"). Somewhat more involved derivational processes involve relatively simple *coordinations* of kernel strings ("I hit the ball and swing the bat"). Finally, there are still more extended kinds of derivational processes that serve to generate various sorts of "embeddings," so as to produce all manner of complex sentence surface syntax. ("I, who am older than you, hit the ball for you to learn"). Certain derivational rules are requisite for grammatical sentence production; others are optional.[5]

Miller (1962) and his associates have used a sentence-matching technique to demonstrate that the amount of time required for adult subjects to transform presented sentences (surface structures) from one grammatical form to another accords with what would be hypothesized from a generative-transformational grammar. Following upon such original research, other investigators have demon-

[4] It may be likened to looking at an expanding series of Chinese boxes: the outermost structure (box) contains within itself an immediate constituent structure (box) which mirrors exactly the immediate constituent analysis of this outer sentence structure; the next to outermost immediate constituent structure contains within itself an immediate constituent pattern which, again, mirrors itself exactly, etc. Miller uses as an example of such "self-embedding" expansion a verse familiar to children: "The rat ate the malt; the rat that the cat killed ate the malt; the rat that the cat that the dog worried killed ate the malt, etc., etc." (p. 754).

[5] N. Chomsky states: "The motivation for adding transformational rules to a grammar is quite clear. There are certain sentences (in fact, simple declarative active sentences with no complex noun or verb phrases—or, to be more precise, the terminal strings underlying these) that can be generated by a constituent structure grammar in quite a natural way. There are others (e.g., passives, questions, sentences with discontinuous phrases and complex phrases that embed sentence transforms) that cannot be generated in an economic and natural way by a constituent structure grammar, but that are systematically related to sentences of simpler structure. Transformations that are constructed to express this relation can thus materially simplify the grammar when used to generate more complex sentences and their structural descriptions from already generated simpler ones.

"The problem is to construct a general and abstract notion of grammatical transformation which will incorporate and facilitate the expression of just those formal relations between sentences that have a significant function in language" (1964, p. 129).

Later developments (N. Chomsky, 1965) admit into deep structures the generation of strings that underlie certain kinds of complex sentences.

strated that the ability to remember sentences that vary in their surface structure accords with what would be hypothesized from such a generative-transformational grammar device (Mehler, 1963; Savin and Perchonock, 1965). The upshot of this development in linguistic and psycholinguistic research is that sentences must be thought of as being produced by the activation of something like a *program*, rather than by any kind of word-to-word associational probabilities. Sentence production is always a total constructional pattern—i.e., it is produced by the application of learned change rules, which always operate from the standpoint of some total patterning of syntactic units. It is this essential idea—that differences in manifest sentence structure reflect variations in some kind of programmatic complexity—that points to the relevance of variability in language construction for the evaluation of ego (dis)organization.[6]

There is, finally, evidence for the organizational nature of language construction from studies with young children. Numerous investigators (e.g., Brown and Bellugi, 1964; Ervine, 1964) have observed that, when a young child begins to express two-word combinations (at about eighteen months of age), the sequential placement of such words reflects an organizing grammar at work. Only certain words are consistently placed first in such two-word "sentences," and only certain other words are consistently placed into the second or final position. The kind of two-word combinations uttered by children are not simply imitations of word sequences actually spoken by adults about them. Indeed, an adult would never utter some of these two-word combinations, since to do so would be ungrammatical—according to adult syntax. (Consequently, we can suspect that precocious imitation in a child's grammar, and probably in its semantics as well, is indicative of *unhealthy* rather than healthy ego formation. Also, we can wonder about the effect of a verbal-conditioning technique on the ego formation of an autistic child, inasmuch as such a technique usually strictly imitates all aspects of adult language.)

A steady patterned progress occurs from a child's grammar to the organizational forms of adult syntax (e.g., Brown and Bellugi, 1964). The two-word "sentences" that children first produce are composed of words that linguists term "contentives." Contentives are especially nouns and verbs, because these are words with a perceptually substantive reference, words that refer to impelling surface attributes of experience. A child's grammar then begins to incorporate words that linguists call "functors"—words whose semantic content is really *inseparable from their grammatical functions*. Auxiliary verbs, articles, prepositions, conjunctions are examples of functors. The meaning of a functor is estab-

---

[6] But whether language behavior actually includes mechanisms that would correspond to a generative-transformational grammar is still far from definitive (e.g., Bever, Fodor, et al., 1966; Slobin, 1966). Linguists and psycholinguists refer to this issue as the competence vs. performance problem. Excellent reviews of the recent literature on this subject are available (Fodor and Garrett, 1966; Wales and Marshall, 1966). Notwithstanding such controversy, we believe that these substantive points remain: first, that sentence production involves some type of programmatic (organizational) activity; and, second, that the complexity of such programs can at least in part be ordered according to syntactic construction.

lished by context, not in isolation. For example, the choice of functors describes a particular illustration of a class (". . . the car"), as against any instance of a class (". . . a car"). Brown and Bellugi state: "The meanings that are added by functors seem to be nothing less than the basic terms with which we construe reality . . . it seems to us that a mother in expanding speech may be teaching more than grammar; she may be teaching something like a world view" (1964, pp. 147–148); the same authors conclude ". . . that growth of grammatical language is more reminiscent of the biological development of an embryo than it is of the acquisition of a conditioned reflex" (1964, p. 161).

We are impressed by the following implications of the literature, which has been reviewed for methods of investigating psychopathological influence upon the grammatical aspect of language: first, methods for the analysis of grammar have been relatively slow to make the study of surface syntactic construction of equal importance with the study of morphology; second, attention must be paid to complexity of syntactic operations, as a language construction variable that can reflect interference with or depletion of symbolic processes, because of ego disorder; third, the (sentence) syntactic environment of a particular unit—the clause—may be especially critical in this regard; fourth, language variation brought about by morphological change in grammatical person ("I" vs. "we" vs. "they"), etc. may be indicative of a change in clinical state from a psychopathological condition to relatively greater mental health. These aspects of language construction have been incorporated into our linguistic assessment procedure, which will now be described.

THE ASSESSMENT OF LANGUAGE CONSTRUCTION FROM CLINICAL INTERVIEWS

In this section, we shall detail the rationale and approach to the assessment of linguistic expression from clinical interviews. In most general terms, our effort is guided by the assumption that, through the examination of certain attributes of language construction obtained in clinical (diagnostic and/or psychotherapy) interviews, we can obtain measures of both stable and variable aspects of psychological structure that pertain to self- and object-representation. The work at hand is thus part of a broader research program, which seeks to arrive at objective measures that pertain to symbolizing ability and form in the area of representation, that are expressed during interviews, and that may be observed to vary with change in clinical state. We mean by symbolizing ability and form the following: first, an ability to produce some form of representation of experience with symbols that are effective for the communication of such experience to another; second, an ability to represent in some form an increasingly complex synthesis of experience with communicative symbols.[7] A first research project (Freedman, Grand, et al., 1966) reported changes in a patient's ability to com-

[7] We use the term "representation" in Piaget's (1945) wider sense. That is, it refers to diverse symbolic expressions of intelligence that are evident in language and does not include only more primitive sensorimotor "knowledge."

municate a dream verbally, immediately upon REM completion awakening, following changes from an acute to a remitted clinical state. More recently, we have emphasized as the source of our data the behavior of a patient during the clinical interview; we have identified certain units of hand-movement behavior; and we have conceptualized such units so as to provide evidence for variations in symbolizing capability in the area of self/object representation. A more recent research project showed that a change in the ability to communicate a dream experienced during the night is associated with more effective verbal communication in group therapy, and that enhanced verbal skill in both situations is again associated with the change from a pathological to a remitted clinical state (Grand, Freedman, et al., 1969). Another research project demonstrates how depressed, paranoid, and remitted clinical states show differences as to how hand movements may or may not be recruited into the service of some verbal communication to another person (Freedman and Hoffman, 1967).

ASSESSMENT OF LANGUAGE CONSTRUCTION

Our objective is to examine those features of language construction that are evident in all content that conveys information about personal and social adaptation. "Adaptation" is deliberately given a very broad definition here. It is meant to convey any and all information that is in any way pertinent to the patient's experience of satisfaction or dissatisfaction with himself as a person. Language is included that describes themes of safety and security, control, initiative, competence, work capacities, intimacy and loneliness, a sense of harmony or disharmony, etc. We exclude statements of fact that do not appear, either in themselves or from the immediate semantic context, to have any such relevance to adaptation. For example, statements such as "I was a nurse's aide" or "I am thirty-three years old," both offered in response to a question by the therapist, were judged to have no relevance and were therefore not included for scoring. In actual practice, thus far, the language content that remains and is scored involves from 88 to 97.5 per cent of the entire language output in a given sample. Such language content may convey information about the person himself, about a significant other or significant other thing, or about a relationship between the person and a significant other or significant other thing. Information that pertains to a significant other, or significant other thing, is put into a more general category term "object." On the whole, therefore, we consider that such content conveys information about the patient's self- and object-representational world (Sandler and Rosenblatt, 1962) as it is expressed in language.

Our quantification of language construction focuses upon the syntactically defined independent or subordinate clause. However, whether these clauses occur in complex sentences—and, if so, in what type of complex sentence—or in some kind of simple sentence, defines the basic categories used in the quantification of the scoring system. We evaluate certain ways in which linguistic form and content may be integrated in each such clause unit and this produces an assessment of what we term Language Code, Status, and Focus.

ANALYSIS OF LANGUAGE CODES. Language coding refers to the complexity of syntax in which a particular clause is embedded. In the broadest terms, we distinguish between Fragmented Language (grammatically incoherent sentence structure), Narrative Language (surface simple-sentence language structure), and Complex Language (surface complex-sentence structure). In each case, we total the number of clauses, or (ungrammatical) verbal units, that participate within each class of language expression and appear in a transcript.

In order to accomplish this objective, we must first establish a procedure for the identification of sentences. Initially, we disregard all punctuation marking as it appears in the transcript. We then begin a word count, and stop *as soon as* one grammatically well-formed sentence *ends* and another well-formed sentence *can begin.* For example, according to this rule, the following thirteen-word sequence produces two separate sentences: ("I don't really know who is making the noise") ("That's the whole trouble—"). The first sentence so formed in this sequence is termed complex, which means that it contains a subordinate clause (". . . who is making the noise"), representing an inseparable grammatical elaboration of the major clause idea ("I don't really know . . ."). The second sentence in this sequence is called a simple sentence. Grammatically, a simple sentence is conventionally said to contain only a single independent clause (idea), which contains both a subject term ("that . . .") and a predicate form (". . . is" (finite verb), "the whole trouble"). We consider all clause units that participate in such simple sentence structure to be instances of a *Simple Narrative Language,* and we total the number of clause units so produced.

Two further subclassifications are made among simple sentences. First, a simple sentence that contains, either and at least, one word or phrase conveying information about *time* or *quantity* (including intensity and much evaluation of the sort that is often called quality) is considered separately. A phrase is a group of words that can act grammatically as a single, modifying term; its constituent analysis does not contain a verb and its subject. For example, ("I managed *very well*"); ("I was feeling depressed *for the last couple of days*"). We consider all clause units that participate in such more elaborate sentence structure to be instances of a *Specified Simple Narrative Language,* and we sum all such instances.

A second kind of distinction among simple sentences has to do with an important modification of the basic rule by which sentences are formed. The extension of what could otherwise stand alone as an independent sentence is permitted, so long as such an extension involves (1) only the stringing together of a series of simple sentences connected (2) by the coordinate conjunction "and"; for example: ("I was terribly afraid and it could have not been anything, and I could have been imagining things") ("and I could have been seeing things cause I didn't open the door"). The word string from "I was" through "imagining things" contains three simple sentences, strung together by the "and" coordinating conjunction. The final, thirteen-word sequence in this example, while initiated by the conjunction "and," is also an instance of a complex sentence, which must thus be separated off from the preceding simple-sentence string. We consider clause units that participate in such extended simple sentence chains to be instances of an *Extended Simple Narrative Language,* and we sum all such instances.

The rationale underlying subclassifications having to do with surface complex-sentence structure requires further elaboration. From a grammatical point of view, a complex sentence is defined as possessing a major and at least one subordinate clause. However, we make a basic distinction between a complex sentence that contains at least one instance of a certain type of adverbial subordinate clause and all other surface complex-sentence subordinate clauses. (We also believe that there exists a distinct possibility that future investigation may reveal that other kinds of psychological relevance exist for the various syntactic devices we are now describing, as well as others not mentioned by us.) The type of adverbial subordinate clause we score separately is called variously a clause of "purpose," "cause," "result," "consequence" (Curme, 1947). The presence of at least one such clause in the syntax of these complex sentences enables the speaker to describe a deductive or explanatory framework for self/object representation. Some examples: ("But because I felt that she might be upset by it . . . I neglected to say it"); ("I could have in some way . . . eliminated some of that friction . . . mmh . . . by really telling Mrs. Mc. when I noticed her do things that might be irritating to Miss W").

There is another surface type of syntactic device through which the expression of such an explanatory or deductive framework can be accomplished. This involves the *contiguous placement* of two sentences (any combination of simple and complex). The syntax of the second sentence, then, can establish an explanatory or deductive framework, with an important part played by the introductory use of some kind of causal or illative (inference-making) coordinating conjunction. The second sentence can also accomplish this conditional reference by using the introductory employment of a personal pronoun, possessive adjective, demonstrative pronoun, demonstrative adjective, or adverb. Some examples: ("I'll fight it with all my might." "See? In *that* way I won't get myself down and out . . . that down-and-out feeling I used to have.") Or: ("He doesn't want to give them up. . . ." "*So* I said I really don't know how I can solve this situation, because I still can't accept these people as normal.") In the first example, the demonstrative adjective "that" contributes importantly to the conditional frame of reference, while in the second the coordinating conjunction "so" accomplishes that purpose. We consider clause units that participate in such complex sentences, or contiguous arrangements of sentences that accomplish such an explanatory or deductive contingency framework, to be instances of a *Contiguous* or *Complex Conditional Language,* and we sum all such clauses.[8] All remaining complex

---

[8] One might raise a question about the categorization of a simple sentence such as the following (constructed by us): "He makes me happy" or "She caused me happiness." Such a sentence does not convey that special kind of *contingency* information by which we classify Conditional Language.

sentences, which do nothing more than describe experience more elaborately than does a simple sentence, are grouped together as instances of a *Complex Portrayal Language,* and we sum the total number of clause units that participate in such sentence formation. Some examples of the latter kind of complex sentence are as follows: ("All I know is that I heard it.") . . . ("Now, these are the things that bother me.").

The application of these procedures for sentence formation also produces two types of incomplete sentence, and leads to the identification of the third major subdivision of language codes—namely, *Fragmented Language.* The two types of incomplete sentence fall between grammatically well-formed sentences. First, an incomplete sentence occurs because of *absent* or *incomplete predication* of a *proper noun* or *personal pronoun* subject term. Such a subject term can be "dropped" before any grammatical coupling takes place with an appropriate predicate term. This can apply to what could become an independent or main clause, as well as to the subordinate clause of a complex sentence that already possesses an established main clause. Further, while such a subject term can begin to be predicated, and this can include its finite verb, such predication may be grammatically insufficient. Some examples of these possibilities are: ("I uh"); ("That's what I mean"); ("This is *what I'm* . . ."); ("Now these are the things that bother me"). This last example demonstrates insufficient predication for a subordinate clause. We do not, incidentally, regard any error in "agreement" (as to person, number, etc.) between a subject term and its predicate term as constituting an incomplete sentence. That sort of grammatical error does not affect the scoring of the language construction patterns that interest us.

All other instances are considered to be examples of a second type of incomplete sentence called, variously, "amorphous language," "predicate language," etc. (see, for example, Curme, 1947). Here, a word, phrase, or clause is uttered without any *readily* evident subject term (a main clause subject term, in the case of a completely formed subordinate clause). A subject term is considered to be not "readily" evident if the utterance is not *contiguous* to a grammatically relevant subject term, or not attached to another word construction unit that is itself (eventually) contiguous to the grammatically relevant subject term. The following is an example of such a scored incomplete sentence, followed by a comparison wherein the same content is not considered to be such a sentence fragment. ("No ah, I, I, I, feel terribly irritated") (*"everything"*) ("since I came back to the ward I just can't get myself together") ("and everything irritates me. Everything"). The initial utterance of the word "everything" is considered to lack an evident subject term and was therefore scored as an incomplete sentence (even though this same pronoun is actually used later as a subject term in the final sentence of the sequence). The final use of this same utterance is considered to be part of the final sentence in this sequence, and technically (grammatically) is a repetition of the subject term.[9] Both such types of incomplete sentences we

[9] That is, if one were to write this final sentence in a grammatically coherent fashion, it would read as follows: "And everything irritates me, everything." A judgment

as to how readily evident is a grammatical subject term is obviously as much semantic as it is grammatical. It is well to point out that the presence of certain pitch and pause characteristics is not a reliable guide for such a judgment. This kind of paralinguistic data is reported to be a useful index for the marking of constituent units *within* a sentence, but not for sentence identification itself (Loban, 1963).

Whenever a so-called "eliptical independent" clause (Loban, 1963) or any kind of "abridged" clause (Curme, 1947) that does not possess complete predication is judged to be connected with a readily evident grammatical-subject term, it is then tallied, along with grammatically complete clause formations, according to sentence type as defined by our scoring system. For example: ("and you go back and *heat it up* and it was just disgusting"). This sequence is considered in our scoring system to contain three clauses. The second clause in the surface structure is a so-called "elliptical independent," less-than-full clause formation, which contains complete prediction with a finite verb form ("*heat it up*") and lacks only a grammatical-subject term. These three clauses are tallied here as part of an Extended Simple Narrative Language Code. Another example: ("I could have in some way . . . have eliminated some of that friction . . . Mmhm . . . *by really telling Mrs. Mc* . . ."). The abridged, subordinate clause introduced by the word "by" not only lacks a grammatical-subject term but also shows incomplete predication, in that a finite verb expression has been changed to the gerund form ("*telling*"). This abridged, gerund, subordinate clause is tallied along with other clause formations that together make up this complex sentence, and that are scored as instances of Complex Conditional Lanuage, on the basis of their surface structure. Again: ("I asked him not, you know, *to be around them*"). This final clause also contains incomplete predication, with a finite verb expression replaced by a *to* plus infinitive form ("to be"); here it is tallied along with other clause formations as an example of Complex Portrayal Language.

The clause reductions just described represent only three among various kinds of grammatical reductions that are considered to be evident in surface structures, according to a generative-transformational grammar. This grammar describes such grammatical reduction in surface sentence structure as resulting from the application of *deletion rules* acting upon kernel strings. Indeed, deletion rules according to this grammar might act upon kernel strings even to eliminate complex sentence arrangements altogether in surface structure, so that a phrase(s) or a single modifier(s) might appear in the surface form. We then might or might not code such a sentence formation as Simple or Specified Simple Narrative Language, depending upon whether or not any modifier(s) or phrase(s) that might be present provides information about either quantity or time.

Very recent developmental research by Hunt (1970) indicates that the ability to use such deletion rules especially to produce less-than-complete prediction is a particularly important yardstick of syntactic maturity. The consequence of such growing syntactic skill is the production of sentences that are not simply longer but whose length is constructed out of an increasing number of embeddings per sentence (i.e., they are not simple coordinations of clause units).

Hunt himself indicates that a simple and satisfactory measure does exist for evaluating total deletion, transformational activity which results in less-than-full clause formations being embedded into the sentence—the total number of words that compose the sentence. Hunt used a sentence marking procedure identical with ours, the one exception being that we permit the extension of coordinated simple sentences, and found a correlation of .87 between surface sentence structure, word length and a direct evaluation of overall, less-than-full clause formation, whenever a subject term is dropped. More importantly, the correlation between surface sentence structure, word length, and deletion that produces less-than-full predication, is .85.

The average word lengths we obtain for Simple versus Specified Simple Narrative sentences are similar (means of 5.4 and 7.4 respectively). We combined all such sentences and termed them Unextended Narrative Language. The average word lengths we then obtained for total, Unextended (Simple plus Specified Simple) Narrative, Portrayal, and Conditional Language constructions are respectively as follows: 5.5, 13.7, and 16.7. A repeated-measures analysis of variance was conducted for these three language construction variables for each of our cyclic patients' five clinical states, and an consider to be instances of a *Fragmented Language,* and we sum the total of these word, phrase, or clause units.

Utterances by the patient that are a response to a question or salutation by

---

F of 17.4 ($p < .01$) was obtained. Unextended, Narrative Language is thus significantly different in average word length from both Portrayal and total Conditional Language (respectively, $t = 9.73$, $p < .001$ and $t = 4.76$, $p < .01$). This finding makes it reasonable to infer that our surface sentence classification of both Portrayal and Conditional Language involves sentences that are produced by a significantly more complex order of syntactic programming, as compared with Narrative Language, according to some generative-transformational model of grammar. Portrayal and total Conditional Language are not significantly different from each other in average word length, but a tendency can be noted for more complex syntactic programming, according to a generative-transformational grammar, to occur with Conditional information; both Hunt (1970) and Loban (1963) in their developmental normative studies of syntactic maturity also suggest that this may be the case, and some comments made by these researchers will shortly be cited. (The average word length of Conditional Language, with contiguous sentences omitted, is still higher, 18.0, but this mean difference does not reach customary statistical significance; $p < .20$.)

Lindenfeld (1970) has already reported a growth in syntactic complexity, according to a generative-transformational grammar, in a patient who progressed from severe depression to close to clinical remission. She measured growth in syntactic complexity directly, by tallying the occurrence of certain types of embeddings, defined according to a generative-transformational grammar, which produced more complex sentence structures in the patient's spoken language. Lindenfeld's procedure did not involve a typology such as we employ—particularly our distinction between Portrayal and Conditional Language—inasmuch as our categories have to do with a frame of reference about cognitive development that is different from a notion of syntactic competence, according to a generative-transformational grammar. This is especially pertinent with respect to her use of an overall classification of adverbial subordination; this she reports as showing no consistent increase with remission, whereas we separate out different kinds of adverbial clauses so as to classify such clause formation as either Portrayal or Conditional Language.

Nor does the work of LaBrant (1933) involve categorizations such as we employ, although our procedure for the percentage evaluation of Portrayal and Conditional Language does bear some general similarity to the "subordination index" developed by her. We shall shortly present certain literature, and some results, that support the maintenance of such a distinction between Portrayal and Conditional Language.

The surface structure categories we employ bear a relationship to Bernstein's dichotomous classification of "public" vs. "formal" language (e.g., 1961). But such a dichotomous classification also does not include the discrimination which is supported by our data between Portrayal and Conditional language; nor does it include that special use of simple sentences which we designate as Contiguous Conditional Language. Further, the interpretation offered by Bernstein about the use of either public or formal language is sociological, whereas our explanations derive from psychoanalytic ego psychology. At least some of the theoretical connecting links between Bernstein's work and ours are to be found in Freud's monograph on group psychology (1921), but any such discussion is beyond the purview of this paper.

It can be asked whether what we term Fragmented Language can include a lengthy, complex sentence which only lacks grammatical completion for some final, subordinate clause formation. Such an utterance technically (grammatically) would be a sentence fragment, but intuitively it would be evident that such syntax reflects an effort at complexity in thought organization which exceeds that of simple sentence structure. In point of fact, the overwhelming majority of Fragmented utterances consist of extremely brief word strings. However, an interesting difference has been found between the Fragmented utterances of a group of schizophrenics and those of a group of nonschizophrenic but acutely disturbed, depressed patients. These findings are now being prepared for publication.

the therapist are expressly excluded from any incomplete sentence score. It is commonplace to answer a question (which contains the subject term) with an utterance that contains no subject term. For example: Th.: "How are you?"; Pt.: "Fine. Just fine, yes." All such utterances are not considered scorable material. The immediate expression of a verb form consequent upon the utterance of an initial verb form is considered a *correction* in scorable material, provided that the correction verb is in fact some finite form of the same basic verb, or is judged to be synonymous in content. For example: (I *don't*—I *didn't* know who it was or what they wanted"); or (". . . that *he's* he *keeps* nagging me about things"). A repetition of a word, phrase, or clause is considered *supplementary* verbal material, and is scored in whatever added way may be appropriate to it. Attention claimers ("Oh") ("Well") etc., filled pauses ("ah") ("uh") etc., or a sentence interrupted by the therapist, are considered *extraneous* verbal material, which is ignored: ("But today, ah, I feel you know all out of sor . . . can't get myself really interested. Th.: Uh, hum. In anything"). The scoring material for the preceding example includes a main clause ("But today, ah, I feel . . . all out of sor . . ."), within which is interpolated a subordinate clause ("you know"), and then there occurs a final, elliptical "independent" clause ("can't get myself really interested . . . in anything").[10] A sentence begun by the patient, interrupted by the therapist and not completed by the patient, is not considered scorable material.

ANALYSIS OF LANGUAGE STATUS: SELF/OBJECT.   Next we proceed to examine other features of a patient's language construction. First, the grammatical subject terms of all clause units that participate in grammatically coherent sentence structure are assigned to one of two classes: those in which the *head element* of such grammatical subject-terms possesses content that involves some description of the self, and those that involve representation about a significant other object (ani-

---

[10] This complex sentence would be written: "But today, I feel, you know, all out of sorts, can't get myself really interested in anything." The main-clause verb "feel" is an example of a "linking" (or state of being) verb, which cannot in itself predicate a subject, and serves only to connect it to a predicate complement. The predicate term is judged to be complete in this instance because, although the final word ("sor . . .") is incomplete, it still conveys reliable information. The word combination "you know" is identified either as an independent, main, or subordinate clause, depending upon the syntactic context. In addition to linking verbs (also called copulas), the English language contains intransitive verbs (to sleep, to cry, etc.) which do predicate but denote only a state of simple action. Finally, there are transitive verbs which predicate an action that carries over to a grammatical object term; when the action of a transitive carries back to the grammatical-subject term, it is termed reflexive (Curme, 1947). Certain verbs (e.g., to know) can act both transitively and intransitively. These procedures for the identification of sentence formation based upon utterances bear a close relationship to Loban's "communication unit" (1963), and the "T" used both by O'Connell, Griffin, et al. (1967), and Hunt (1970). There are, however, two important exceptions to this similarity: (1) the categorization of multiple, simple sentences (Simple Extended Narrative Code); and (2) the exclusion from scoring of less than grammatical full-clause formations that are answers to questions, rather than "completing" such sentence fragments by resort to semantic context.

mate or inanimate). We designate the head element, grammatical-subject position of each clause the *Language-Status* position in linguistic construction, and determine the prevalence of self-description that occupies this grammatical position, as compared with the description of objects. An example of *Language Status— Self* construction would be: ("*I* was feeling very depressed for the last couple of days.") An example of *Language Status—Object* construction would be: ("*My husband* told me once . . ."); or ("And the *house* was cold").

ANALYSIS OF LANGUAGE FOCUS: MONADIC/DYADIC. Finally, we examine the construction of all clauses that participate in grammatically coherent sentences in terms of two further possibilities, which deal with what we call *Language Focus.* Grammatical, subject-verb-object construction, involving content that describes only some isolated self or object representation, is termed *Language Focus—Monadic.* For example: ("*I* couldn't get *myself* interested . . ."); ("*I, I, I* don't know"); or (". . . that *he is* a *man*"); or ("And the *house was cold*"). On the other hand, grammatical, subject-verb-object clause construction that conveys a description of interactional content between a self- and object-representation, is termed *Language Focus—Dyadic.* For example: (". . . *he* acts like a husband *to me*"); ("*I* didn't *accept them* as *men*").

The different clauses of a sentence can contain different scores for *Language Status* and *Language Focus:* ("*I* only wondered uh why *he takes friends* like this"). The main clause here contains a self-representation as the Status term and also is *Monadic;* the subordinate clause contains an object-representation as the Status term and is *Dyadic.* In the case of abridged or elliptical clauses any needed scoring information about grammatical subject, object, and verb terms is extrapolated from the total sentence. An example already used to illustrate *Complex Conditional Language* will serve to illustrate this also: ("*I* could have in some way . . . have eliminated some of that friction . . . Mhm . . . *by really telling Mrs. Mc* . . ."). This gerund, elliptical, abridged subordinate clause is *Dyadic* and involves, as the implied Status term, a self-representation that is found in the main clause ("*I*").[11]

INITIAL CASE OBSERVATIONS ON LANGUAGE CONSTRUCTION IN DIFFERENT CLINICAL STATES

We shall now present language construction analyses from eight different therapy sessions. These therapy sessions involve four different patients. Our data sources are of two types: first, we examine the vicissitudes of the language construction of a single patient, whose clinical state undergoes five instances of cyclical change; second, we compare the language construction of this same cyclical patient in her initial, pathological, acute, clinical state with that of three other patient-subjects, who are also observed in such an initial, acutely disturbed clinical state.

---

[11] A more detailed description of these procedures for analyzing language construction can be obtained by writing to the authors.

Our cyclical patient is a married woman, in her early thirties, an articulate and cognitively differentiated person.[12] *The data derive from therapy segments, consisting of ten minutes from each of five different therapy sessions.*[13] *Each of these five therapy sessions coincides with a distinct clinical state, according to descriptive chart notes written by the patient's therapist and an independent evaluation of these notes by us.*

The first language sample is part of the first therapy session; it is the outcome primarily of a paranoid, delusional state, with only mild depression being reported by the therapist. The patient is preoccupied with persecutory delusional ideas: first, that her husband is unfaithful and is carrying on a secret homosexual love affair with his male friends; second, that these same male friends may forcibly intrude themselves into her apartment and do her harm.

Some two months later, the patient's clinical state has changed to what is now a predominantly depressive state. She no longer makes accusations about her husband's homosexuality and no longer mentions his friends; instead, she is reported to be only mildly suspicious, as a general character trait. Now she has shifted to complaints of mistreatment, and disappointment with her husband as a provider. Depressive mood accompanies statements that the husband does not take care of the home properly or pay his bills, and that he stays out late. The patient is concerned about the deprivation that befalls her children, and refers to the coldness and emptiness of her home.

Barely two weeks later, the patient's clinical state is changed again, to remission. Now, she expresses satisfaction with her husband and her life in general; she feels in control of herself, her mood is ebullient, and there is no evidence of paranoid, delusional, or depressive psychopathology. About three weeks later, the patient's state has changed to depression once more, with only mild paranoid, delusional experience being reported. Complaints, similar to those already described for her first depressive state, are once more in the foreground.[14]

[12] This patient-subject is defined as cognitively differentiated (field-independent) according to her performance on psychometric and projective tests (Witkin, Dyk, et al., 1962).

[13] The first ten-minute language sample corresponds to the second ten minutes of the patient's session. It was initiated by a "marker" question uttered by the therapist about the patient's clinical state. The remaining four language samples constitute the initial ten minutes of each therapy session. This one inconsistent time period is due to a procedure that had been established for data collection in an earlier research project, already described, which examined the hand movements of this patient (Freedman and Hoffman, 1967).

[14] This second instance of a depressive clinical state is described and used in an earlier research project (Freedman, Grand, et al., 1966), simply as an example of an acute clinical state, which is contrasted with remitted states showing no psychopathology of any sort. At that time, no distinction was drawn between depressed and paranoid acute clinical states, although the findings even in this earlier study suggested the relevance of such a distinction.

Neither depressive episode of this cyclical patient is melancholic—that is, it did not feature self-accusatory, self-belittlement, etc., types of statements. Rather, both depressive episodes are instances of what Jacobson (1953) terms a simple, acute, psychotic type of depression.

Finally, a week after her second depressive state, the patient's clinical condition once again becomes predominantly paranoid. Delusional material, similar to that obtained in her first paranoid condition, is once again reported by the patient's therapist, and this is considered to be primary, by comparison with any depressive affect. Treatment for this cyclic patient is ego-supportive, with outpatient or inpatient status depending on the patient's clinical condition. Maintenance doses of chlorpromazine are also included in the treatment regimen.

Our second data source compares the language construction of our cyclic patient in her initial paranoid-delusional state with that of three other patient-subjects, who were also observed in their initial acute clinical states. However, these other three patient-subjects showed various mixtures of delusional-paranoid, schizophrenic, and psychotic-depressive features.

Patient #1 (male) revealed a well-systematized persecutory delusion. It began at work when the patient began to believe that his colleagues were conspiring to spread lies about him, to the effect that the patient (in turn) spread "filthy rumors" about the sexual activities of other people. This delusion spread in a classical paranoid manner to all areas of the patient's social experience, including contacts on the ward with professionals and patients. The patient was able to offer intricately woven explanations and justifications for each new development in his growing, fixed paranoid belief. His therapist considered him, at this time, to possess only a mild amount of depressive experience and to show no manifest anxiety whatsoever.

Patient #2 (female). This woman is our cyclical patient. She also possessed a persecutory, delusional belief, but one that was much more moderate in scope and complexity. This patient, as we have indicated, believed that her husband was carrying on a homosexual affair, and that the husband and his homosexual friends were conspiring to do her harm. However, the delusional experience was restricted only to these individuals. This patient was evaluated by her therapist as possessing only a mild degree of depressive experience and no manifest anxiety whatsoever.

Patients #3 and #4 (both females). These patients each possessed transient persecutory, delusional-paranoid ideas about people, such as the idea that people "pick on me" and "give me a hard time," etc., but no systematized elaboration of such ideas was present at all. Hallucinatory experiences are conspicuous in the clinical pictures of patients #3 and #4. Patient #3, for example, could see a "flash" on a piece of paper, and th epaper then was seen by her to rise into her hand. Patient #4 heard voices tell her "I'm crazy." Neither Patient #3 nor #4 was evaluated by the therapist as possessing any depressive experience or any manifest anxiety.

In sum, then, Patients #1 and #2 present a uniform paranoid-delusional picture, much more systematized than that of Patients #3 and #4. These latter two patients show conspicuous schizophrenic, in particular hallucinatory, symptoms. Each therapy session represents the initial treatment session for each of these four patients. No patient was on any drug treatment during this initial session. Immediately after this initial session, a clinical state description was entered into the chart notes by the patient's therapist, which we evaluated independently. In addition, a Clinical State Rating Scale was filled out by the therapist, which quantifies various aspects of the patient's psychopathology.[15] Three language samples constitute the first 10 minutes of each of these therapy sessions; the fourth language sample (Patient #2) consists of the second 10 minutes of the therapy session.

Reliability

Table 1 indicates interscorer reliability for the first two language samples of our cyclical patient. Reliability is expressed in terms of percentage agreement between two judges for Language Code, Status, and Focus. (It should be noted that reliable Language Code assignment presupposes reliable sentence-boundary identification, and the reliability of such sentence identification was first established to be better than 90 per cent between the same two judges.) These figures

Table 1 INTERJUDGE RELIABILITY OF LANGUAGE CODE, STATUS, AND FOCUS
(Cyclical Patient, First Two Sessions: 12/2 and 2/10)

	CODE			STATUS		FOCUS
Session No.	N	Per cent Agreement	N	Per cent Agreement	N	Per cent Agreement
1		97		97		98
	240*		231		231	
2	233**		217		217	
		98		88		94

* Includes 9 grammatically incomplete sentence fragments.
** Includes 16 grammatically incomplete sentence fragments.

[15] This Clinical State Rating Scale was devised for earlier research projects, already cited (Freedman, Grand, et al., 1966; Freedman and Hoffman, 1967; Grand, Freedman, et al., 1969). These ratings are on a 4-point scale from minimal to severe. Some examples of items so reported are as follows: For manifest anxiety, expressions of apprehension, phobias, etc.; for depression, expressions of loneliness, hopelessness, suicidal thinking, etc.; for paranoid-delusional experience, content having to do with ideas of influence, of suspiciousness, false beliefs, etc.; for schizophrenic thinking, wholly irrelevant language, perseveration, etc.

never fall below 88 per cent agreement, thus indicating the potential of such language construction analysis as an objective research tool.

Consecutive Case Observations on Cyclical Patient

It will be recalled that the cyclical patient upon whom our language construction analysis is conducted provides us with a "naturalistic" experiment in the shape of a symmetrical design: Session 1 was marked by a (persecutory) paranoid state; Session 2 by a depressive condition; Session 3 by a symptomatic remission; Session 4 by another depressive episode; and Session 5 by the resurgence of a manifestly paranoid state. (We use the terms "state," "condition," and "episode" interchangeably here.) The language construction analysis derived from these five clinical states is presented in Tables 2 and 3. Data here are given in percentages, showing the relative incidence of each type of language construction per state, per entire 10-minute segment.

First, we ask whether different language-construction measures discriminate among the five clinical states of our cyclical patient. For this purpose, we talk about combined Narrative Language as well as combined Conditional Language. It should be noted that in these two tables we have also combined reality-oriented content with language that is delusional. Prior, separate examinations conducted for each of these two kinds of content showed findings that were identical.

Conditional Language shows a definite symmetrical pattern, which distinguishes among the five clinical states. The relative incidence of Conditional Language over total grammatical clause production for each of the five clinical states is (approximately): 21 per cent, 9 per cent, 30 per cent, 2 per cent, and 28 per cent. We call all other complex sentence structure Complex Portrayal Language. Complex Portrayal Language *and* Narrative Language, which is the less complex, simple-sentence clause production, show a symmetrical pattern among the clinical states that is *opposite* to the pattern just described for Conditional Language. For Narrative Language, the percentage figures are: 25, 35, 26, 43, and 31. Language Status—Self variation, which is self-representation content in the head (subject) position of a clause, shows a symmetrical pattern that parallels that of Narrative Language for the depressive and paranoid states (but not for remission): 29 per cent, 43 per cent, 55 per cent, 48 per cent, 36 per cent. Language Focus—Monadic construction, which deals with solitary features of the representational world, shows this same symmetrical pattern, which parallels Narrative Language for the depressive and paranoid states (but not for remission): 51 per cent, 64 per cent, 62 per cent, 59 per cent, 57 per cent.

It should be noted that the percentage figures just cited for Narrative, Conditional, Status—Self, and Focus—Monadic language construction are completely nonoverlapping with respect to the depressed and paranoid states. For example: *Both* depressive episodes show a percentage of Conditional Language that is less than *both* paranoid conditions; on the other hand, both depressive episodes

Table 2   LANGUAGE CODES FOR THREE CLINICAL STATES, CYCLICAL PATIENT

Therapy Session Date	Clinical State	Complete Language Codes**						Total Number of Complete Clause Units
		Fragmented Language* Code	Simple & Extended Simple Narrative	Specified Simple Narrative	Complex Portrayal	Contiguous Conditional	Complex Conditional	
		Per cent	Per cent	Per cent	Per cent	Per cent	Per cent	
12-2-64	Paranoid I	4	23	2	54	5	16	231
2-10-65	Depressed I	7	29	6	56	1	8	217
2-24-65	Remitted	8	21	5	44	1	29	200
3-10-65	Depressed II	6	36	7	55	0	2	101
3-17-65	Paranoid II	11	29	2	41	4	24	133

* Includes verbal units which are words, phrases or clauses; per cent based upon total number of code units, both Complete and Fragmented per state.

** Per cent based upon total number of complete clause units (from grammatically adequate sentences) per state.

Table 3   **LANGUAGE STATUS AND FOCUS FOR THREE CLINICAL STATES,
CYCLICAL PATIENT**

Therapy Session Date	Clinical State	Language Status		Language Focus		Total Number of Complete Clause Units*
		Self	Object	Dyadic	Monadic	
		Per cent	Per cent	Per cent	Per cent	
12-2-64	Paranoid I	29	71	49	51	231
2-10-65	Depressed I	43	57	36	64	217
2-24-65	Remitted	55	45	38	62	200
3-10-65	Depressed II	48	52	41	59	101
3-17-65	Paranoid II	36	64	43	57	133

* Per cent based upon total number complete clause units (from grammatically adequate sentences) per state.

show an amount of Status—Self construction that is greater than *both* paranoid conditions; etc.

We next proceed to evaluate the statistical significance of the interstate differences which we have just described for the paranoid, depressed, and remitted states. The 10-minute segments of the five clinical states of our cyclic patient are each further subdivided into five two-minute intervals. This produces 10 two-minute interval language scores for the depressive state, 10 interval scores for the paranoid state, and five interval scores for the remitted state. Tests of significance can now be applied to the mean interval scores for these clinical states; these are shown in Table 4. Only mean differences that reach a p of .15 or less are shown (two-tailed).

These language construction variables generally do discriminate among the patient's depressed, paranoid, and remitted states relative to each other. The overall pattern of such differences is expectable, on the basis of the general rationale we have thus far described for language construction analysis as well as the specific research already done by Newman and Mather (1938) and White (1949). (1) The paranoid state is significantly different from the depressed state in terms of the following: comparatively high amounts of Conditional Language, relatively low amount of Narrative Language, a comparatively low amount of Language Status—Self composition, and a relatively low amount of Language Focus— Monadic construction. (2) Remission, which descriptively is not just symptom-free but an ebullient condition, is characterized by a *mixture* of the kinds of language construction that characterize the paranoid and depressive states. (a)

Table 4   MEAN INTERVAL SCORES FOR FOUR LANGUAGE CONSTRUCTION
MEASURES BY CLINICAL STATE,
CYCLICAL PATIENT

Language Construction Measures	CLINICAL STATES			t VALUES		
	Paranoid	Depressed	Remitted	Paranoid vs. Depressed[1]	Paranoid vs. Remitted[2]	Depressed vs. Remitted[2]
N*	10	10	5			
Narrative	28	39	24	1.66 $p < .15$	n.s.	1.83 $p < .10$
Conditional	23	6	24	3.53 $p < .01$	n.s.	3.82 $p < .01$
Status-Self	33	45	57	2.35 $p < .05$	2.51 $p < .05$	n.s.
Focus-Monadic	53	62	58	2.02 $p < .10$	n.s.	n.s.

[1] df = 18
[2] df = 13
* Number of two-minute intervals per clinical state.

Remission shows low Narrative and high Conditional Language similar to the paranoid state. (b) Remission shows a relatively high amount of Language Status —Self and Language Focus—Monadic construction similar to the depressed state. But remission is significantly different from the paranoid state only with respect to Language Status—Self construction. Remission is not significantly different from the paranoid state for Language Focus—Monadic composition.[16]

A question can be raised as to whether the different language construction patterns that coincide with this cyclical patient's clinical states may be caused not by the patient's clinical condition, but by something about the therapist's behavior that varies with the patient's clinical state. We did find a reciprocal

[16] This last observation about remission suggests that an intraparanoid state difference may exist with respect to Language Focus—Monadic construction. Table 3 indicates that the second paranoid episode possesses an amount of Language Focus— Monadic construction that is almost equal to that of the second depressive condition, and that the second paranoid episode contributes relatively little to the overall paranoid versus depressed state difference for Focus—Monadic construction.
The possibility was investigated that paranoid and depressed intrastate differences might exist for Narrative, Conditional, Status—Self, and Focus—Monadic language construction, even though there is no overlap among these variables with respect to these four 10-minute language samples. No paranoid or depressed intrastate differences are present for Narrative, Conditional or Status—Self construction, but a paranoid intrastate difference does occur for Focus—Monadic construction ($p < .10$).
We have an independent clinical observation that provides the basis for an explanation for this intrastate paranoid difference in Focus—Monadic construction. We shall shortly discuss possible interpretations for this paranoid intrastate difference and for another such difference in Fragmented Language ($p < .06$), as well as for the particular language construction pattern that emerges with remission.

relationship between patient's verbal productivity and the amount of therapist's verbal intervention. For example, the lowest amount of clause production for the cyclical patient occurred in the second depressive state. The therapist, in this particular language sample, talked approximately 24 per cent more than in any other 10-minute language segment. However, it seems to us unreasonable to conclude that the fact of such a reciprocal relationship implies causality even for the issue of the patient's language productivity, let alone for the question of variations in the patient's language *construction*. Moreover, we find no systematic relation between specific *kinds* of therapist's verbal interventions and the patient's clinical state. All comments by a therapist were placed into one of nineteen descriptive categories: "direct question," "explaining," "support," etc. Most "direct questions," for example, occurred in the first paranoid state, the next largest number in the second depressive state, and the least in the second paranoid condition, etc.[17] Another possibility is that the relationship we obtained between type of clinical state and type of language construction (e.g., more Conditional Language in both paranoid therapy sessions) is due to the sheer amount of patient verbal productivity. However, while a systematic relationship is present between type of language construction and type of clinical state, there is no relationship between quantity of clause production (as a measure of language productivity) and type of clinical condition. It is these considerations that lead us to the conclusion that the different types of language construction patterns we have identified bear an intrinsic relationship to type of clinical state.

Initial Case Observations on Four Patients

Next, we present findings from our second data source. Table 5 describes the language construction of four schizophrenic patients, who show a varied mixture of paranoid-delusional and schizophrenic symptoms, at the point of their initial treatment interview. The three additional patients included (patient #2 is the fourth) were originally selected as subjects for earlier research projects already cited (Freedman, Grand, et al., 1966, and Freedman and Hoffman, 1967). They are now used so that we may compare the language construction of patients who present conspicuous schizophrenic symptoms with that of paranoid systematizers. Because we are unable to control for such variables as age, socio-economic class, etc., we present here only descriptive percentages for an entire 10-minute language sample.

An earlier analysis of the data for these four patients showed no construction differences between language content that is manifestly delusional or hallucinatory and content that is realistic, so that no such distinction is presented in Table 5. Also, we have combined in Table 5 all types of Narrative and Conditional Language, in order to highlight trends.

What Table 5 suggests is the following: First, the greater the extent of clinically evident paranoid delusions, the larger the proportion of Conditional

---

[17] These are excerpts of an analysis of therapist-patient interaction conducted by Dr. Stanley Grand on the same series of therapy sessions.

Table 5 LANGUAGE BEHAVIOR FOR FOUR PATIENTS WITH MIXED PARANOID AND SCHIZOPHRENIC PSYCHOPATHOLOGY

| | | | COMPLETE LANGUAGE** | | | | | | | |
| | | | Code | | | Status | | Focus | | |
Patient No.	Symptom Picture	Per cent Fragmented* Language	Per cent Narrative Language	Per cent Complex Portrayal Language	Per cent Conditional Language	Per cent Self	Per cent Object	Per cent Dyadic	Per cent Monadic	Total Number of Complete Clause Units
1	Well-organized persecutory delusion, mild depression	2	12	52	36	38	62	31	69	270
2 Cyclical Patient Initial Session	Moderate organized persecutory delusion, mild depression	4	25	53	22	29	71	49	51	231
3	Mild delusional ideas, conspicuous hallucinations; depression minimal	18	27	52	21	55	45	28	72	190
4	Mild delusional ideas, conspicuous hallucinations; depression minimal	14	46	38	16	57	43	30	70	203

* Includes verbal units which are words, phrases or clauses; per cent based upon total number of code units, both complete and fragmented, per state.

** Per cent based upon total number complete clause units (from grammatically adequate sentences) per state.

Language relative to Narrative Language. Second, and even more striking, is the association between the amount of Fragmented Language and the extent of clinically evident schizophrenic symptoms. Third, the hallucinatory schizophrenic patients consistently place noticeably more self-description into the subject position of their clauses, thus producing a comparatively high amount of Language Status—Self. Finally, but much more weakly suggested, is the finding that schizophrenic subjects tend to produce more Language Focus—Monadic construction then do paranoid patients. A clinical observation providing a possible explanation for the much weaker standing of this Focus—Monadic construction finding will shortly be offered.

COMMENTS ON LANGUAGE CONSTRUCTION AND SELF/OBJECT REPRESENTATION IN DIFFERENT CLINICAL STATES

It was over 40 years ago that Piaget observed the spontaneous utterances of children at play in school (Piaget, 1923). These observations, some of them conducted very much in the manner of a clinical naturalist, led to two important sets of conclusions about language. First, an examination of the language sample of younger children (four to six years old) indicated an important difference between "egocentric speech" and "adaptive information" language. Egocentric speech is neither enlisted into, nor is it provocative of, actual conversation ("dialogue"). The child can be speaking aloud while alone ("monologue"); even if the child is speaking in the presence of others, his language upon examination is seen to be actually not related to the content of the utterance of others ("collective monologue"). Language conveys "adaptive information" when it is actually recruited into, or elicits, mutual topics of conversation.

Piaget's second set of comparisons is between the "adaptive information" language of the four- to six-year-old child and a fundamentally new kind of "causal" language that begins to appear with some frequency only in the utterances of seven- to eight-year-old children. The language of "adaptive information" is primarily the language of the simple sentence, or a series of such simple sentences connected by the coordinate conjunction "and." A complex sentence may be uttered by the four- to six-year-old child, but it is usually of the briefest possible sort, and with a syntactic device that can only elaborate upon what still basically remains a *narrative description* of experience. Precausal language is the use of language as a kind of *story-telling* device. This can involve the simplest sort of story-telling, which we term Simple Narrative Language. Or, the same narrative function can become increasingly complex—what we call Complex Portrayal Language. The "causal" language of the older seven- to eight-year-old child is precisely a *selective use* of syntactic skill, which goes beyond any kind of portrayal and puts information into an *explanatory or deductive conditional framework*. These are the kinds of surface sentence structures we designate as Conditional Language Code.

Quite recent, large, and well-sampled longitudinal studies of language basically support the importance of Piaget's original findings (Loban, 1963; Hunt, 1970). These studies show that language development in general exemplifies a constant advance in sentence complexity, producing longer sentences, and that this results from all manner of syntactic devices for coordination and from various sorts of embedding. Those children who in general show the most syntax maturity are also the children who *use* language to make explicit "means and ends" (Hunt, 1970); these children attempt ". . . most frequently to express tentativeness, supposition, hypothesis, and conditional statements . . ." (Loban, 1963).[18] Another interesting fact is that language growth is apparently not uniform; instead, it shows statistically significant increases at two points in development: five to seven years, and eleven to thirteen years (O'Connell, Griffin, et al., 1967). These age periods are extremely interesting for the psychoanalytic theory of character formation, and of its re-formation with the ushering in of adolescence.

Piaget proposes that this entire growth of language, which eventuates into such new, conditional information, is determined by the emergence of a new stage in cognitive organization. This new kind of cognitive organization Piaget (1960) terms a (concrete) "grouping," and describes as follows:

What must be clearly understood if we are to arrive at the true psychological nature of the grouping . . . is that these variously closely related changes are actually the expression of . . . an act of complete conversion of thought. The distinguishing characteristic of the sensory-motor schema (perception, etc.), of the preconceptual symbol and also of the intuitive configuration, is that they are always "centered" on a particular state of the object . . . the mobile equilibrium peculiar to the grouping is that . . . thought is no longer tied to particular [perceived] states of the object, but is obliged to follow successive changes with all their possible detours and reversals (emphasis ours; p. 142).

[18] Syntactic devices that function to indicate tentativeness also include a kind of conditional information that is not identified by Piaget. For example: "It might be a gopher but I am not sure" (Loban, 1963, p. 53).

Piaget recognizes that, while a word such as "because" can appear earlier in a child's vocabulary (it can be evident at age three years), such words are not uttered with any frequency until children reach seven to eight years of age. Also, such words are not really established as a distinct type of subordination. He offers (1928) the following examples: "I lost my pen because I am not writing"; "I went with a message yesterday because I went on my bike" (p. 17). Piaget concludes: "Data show that up to the age of 7–8 the word 'because' is occasionally an equivocal term which is used for all purposes, and covers a number of heterogeneous relations—causal, consecutive, and even finalistic . . . sometimes there seems to be no need for the use of 'because' at all; it will be placed at the beginning of a proposition which bears no relation except that of simultaneity to the principal proposition of the sentence" (p. 16). ". . . Originally it would seem that the child refrains from voicing any explicit relations because its experience is limited to what may be called 'relational feelings,' among which, however, he is incapable of distinguishing one kind from another" (p. 20).

Piaget also points out that "logical causality" (i.e., syntactic forms that function to convey meaning as to deduction, inference-making, etc.) occurs still later in language development than syntactic forms that convey physical and psychological causality. This distinction, while extremely important, does not concern us here.

> . . . The question is to decide by what internal or mental criterion group-
> ing is to be recognized. The answer is obvious: where there is "grouping" there
> will be the conservation of a whole and this conservation itself will not really be
> assumed by the subject by virtue of a probable induction, but affirmed by him
> as a certainty in his thought (p. 140) . . . The elements of a complex [object]
> are conceived as constituting an unvarying whole (p. 139).

A view of language learning that emphasizes its connection with the
acquisition of progressively more complexly integrated cognitive organizations
is indeed a familiar refrain in Freud's writings. Peller (1966), who recently summarized Freud's views about language, reminded us of this fact.[19] In *The
Interpretation of Dreams,* Freud (1900) talks about the influence upon thoughts
of ". . . the mnemic *system* of language symbols" (italics ours; p. 574); and, in
the same volume, he describes how language facilitates the creation of ". . .
the new *series* of quality of attributes" (italics ours; p. 617). Eleven years later,
Freud (1911a) indicated especially how thoughts pertaining to *"relations between
the object impressions"* (p. 16) become capable of being represented by the
acquisition of language. This latter point Freud (1915a) makes even more explicit
in "The Unconscious": ". . . words may impart quality even to cathexes to
which, representing as they do only the *relations between the ideas* of objects,
no quality could accrue from the perceptions themselves. Such relations, com-
prehensible only through words, form one of the most important parts of thought
processes" (p. 135). This idea is repeated in *The Ego and the Id,* and elaborated
further when Freud (1923) talks about the special character of "visual thinking":
". . . what becomes conscious in it as a rule is only the concrete subject matter
of the thought; . . . the *relations* between the various elements of subject-
matter, which is what especially characterizes thoughts, cannot be given visual
expression. Thinking in pictures is only a *very incomplete form of becoming
conscious"* (italics ours; p. 33).[20] The upshot of all of this is, as Freud (1940) concluded in the *Outline:* Language does not *prescribe* for ideas the only way
to approach conscious experience. Instead, language provides one possible
framework for conscious ideation. And, we must add: an increasingly linguistic
organization of consciousness produces (to use Piaget's term) an increasing conservation of meaning because concepts now are structured into "groupings." Or,
to state this in another way, an increasingly linguistic organization of consciousness brings such conservation of meaning because concepts now deal (to use
Freud's phrase) with "relations between the ideas" rather than with disparate

---

[19] One can extrapolate from Freud's early writings an association theory of language learning, and cognition in general (e.g., 1891). But we believe that a more comprehensive reading emphasizes its relevance to evolving and changing cognitive strategies. See P. Wolff (1967) for a critique of this issue.

[20] See especially Klein's (1959) discussion of states of consciousness. Also pertinent is Piaget's description of pre-operational ideas, which are essentially imagistic in
content (e.g., 1960). See also Bruner's (1967) ikonic symbol and Langer's (1952) description of images as symbols, as well as her discussion of the evolution of nonverbal
symbolic forms.

concrete ideas that accrue from different perceptual aspects of what is objectively the same object.

But, in our view, Freud assigns to language an entirely different kind of significance than does Piaget. Piaget uses the presence of changes in language construction simply as facts, on the basis of which he infers a changed status in the organization of thought at a given stage in the child's development. Freud assigns to language learning a *determining* influence in the bringing about of such a changed status in the organization of thought.[21] What really held Freud's interest about language, however, was its semantic aspect, and this we believe retarded his further investigation into the relationship between language and thought. Freud's greatest contribution to language theory—the symbolism that is evident in dreams and language disorder—is a matter of repressed (hidden) meaning. He said little, if anything, about the grammar of sentence formation.[22] Today the psychoanalytic literature is showing an interest in all aspects of language, including its syntax, as it bears upon ego development and function (e.g., Edelheit, 1969; Shapiro, 1970).

Piaget's highly original observation about the existence of egocentric speech in young children has produced research that supports the idea of the intimate influence of language upon thought organization. Since Piaget's original findings, investigators (e.g., McCarthy, 1930) have raised questions about the actual incidence of egocentric speech in the young child, and point out that such factors as situation, person addressed, etc., will affect its output. But of greater importance is criticism directed to the interpretation of the concept itself. Vygotsky (1934) placed such a young child-subject in a room with deaf-mute peers, or non-peers who spoke a different language, and obtained a drastic curtailment in the output of egocentric speech. These and other related experiments led Vygotsky to conclude that egocentric speech is socially responsive, but that it is an immature transitional type of language in normal development. What is

---

[21] It is not relevant here to detail such concepts as "accommodation," "assimilation," etc. which enter into Piaget's learning theory, but only to emphasize that he does not involve language acquisition in a *determining* role.

[22] However, Freud (1933) may have had issues of grammar in mind when he stated the following about the dream: "Of course, this manifest dream exhibits all sorts of characteristics which are not entirely a matter of indifference to us. It may be coherent, smoothly constructed *like a literary composition,* or it may be confused to the point of unintelligibility, almost like a delirium . . . you must not suppose that we think nothing of this endless diversity . . ." (italics ours; p. 10).

Rosen (1967) makes the point that the signification of language used to verbalize free associations can become impaired for reasons that have nothing whatever to do with repression. Certain patients can employ extreme types of "associational style" for the mediation of their ideas, and this will cause a consistent loss of meaning to occur in the communication process with the therapist. Rosen, here, properly reminds us that, when we ask a patient to associate "freely," we do not relieve him of the responsibility to *communicate.* It is precisely when associations are obviously not repressed, but flowing easily and profusely, yet information seems to be missing, that we sense that something is "wrong" with the patient's language. Rosen believes that this kind of disturbance in language arises because of certain linguistic (mis)usages at that critical point in development when differentiation between self and objects begins to emerge. A permanently impaired thought organization is the result.

occurring is that the young child does not *functionally* separate between socially responsive *inner speech* (what will become eventually unverbalized thoughts) *for himself* and *outer speech* (linguistically delivered thoughts) *for others.* Werner and Kaplan (1967), and Piaget himself (1962), apparently concur in such an interpretation.

But an equally tenable—and not at all incompatible—psychoanalytic interpretation would hold that the child's verbalization of his ideas is not simply a failure to discriminate between the ego functions of thought and language. Rather, it is a positive effort to place his thoughts into a linguistic—especially syntactic—framework, because to do so *facilitates secondary-process thinking.* Luria's (1968) observations about how children spontaneously talk "plans" to themselves when engrossed in problem-solving make this abundantly clear. Rapaport (1951b) trained himself to write automatically at night so as to record reveries, hypnagogic hallucinations, and even dreams—all states of consciousness that we regard as involving thought largely organized according to primary process. He reports that his writing shows "definite changes of syntax" as one progresses toward the dream state: conjunctions tend to "fall out," although we are not told what sort of conjunctions these are (pp. 30, 31).[23] Sullivan (1953) terms such states as these "reverie," which ". . . continues to be relatively untroubled by *grammatical rules,* the necessity for making complete sentences and so on" (p. 185; italics ours). We have already cited demonstrations (Newman and Mather, 1938; White, 1949) that adults who suffer extreme psychotic and schizophrenic ego disturbance—again, states of consciousness that involve thought largely organized according to the primary process—become increasingly unable to apply grammatically coherent sentence structures for the organization of their ideas. Werner and Kaplan (1967) report that, when a normal subject is asked to write a simple sentence describing some stimulus for himself, his language shows the most limited kind of sentence structure, as compared to a request that he communicate his description in writing.

It is not simply that a normal subject's intention to communicate thought through language produces a longer sentence. The organization of thought brought about by the application of the linguistic framework becomes more coherent and complex; this shows itself in the production of a syntactically more complex simple sentence, which employs modifying words and phrases, such as we term Specified Simple Narrative Language. A psychoanalytic ego psychology, therefore, will distinguish between the developmental inability of the pre-school child to maintain a separate function between thought and language, which shows in his egocentric speech, and the adult loss of such differentiation because of extreme psychopathology. The normal, egocentrically speaking child verbalizes *only for himself* and expects no response. His intention is to construct

---

[23] It is clear from Rapaport's (1951b) description that his intention here was not to use language to transform his primary-process thinking for some purpose of communication, but just the opposite: to have language directly reflect such experience as much as possible. Other, important intra- and inter-individual differences undoubtedly exist as to the "syntactic match" between thought and language.

a *grammatically coherent* string of words so as to *facilitate secondary-process thinking.* When an adult tries to "converse" by conveying syntactically abbreviated thoughts directly to another, something we term Fragmented Language, he does so because of a regressive ego state of dedifferentiation between thought and language. He is unable to make use of a differentiated, syntactically organized language system for conversion of primary- into secondary-process thinking.[24]

[24] How does syntactic learning relate to such a developmental change in conceptual organization? Contemporary notions of a grammar device that possesses a deep as well as a surface syntactic structure urge upon us, even more than does some traditional grammar model, the consideration that the developing child learns grammatical concepts whose meaning is purely syntactic.

Initial stages of language learning can be thought of as involving the acquisition of fundamental syntactic ideas, which inform the child about basic grammatical categories (e.g., verb phrase = verb + noun phrase) and about grammatical functions (e.g., object-of-a-verb) that are indispensable for any kind of sentence formation. These basic grammatical functions and categories make possible the formation of hierarchically patterned, deep syntactic structures, which can be generated according to an immediate constituent (phrase) program. Menyuk (1969) reports that by the age of three a child has essentially completed the acquisition of such basic categories and functions (although errors in application continue to occur), so that, from then on, out of such deep syntactic structures the simplest types of surface sentences can be produced. It may be reasonable to suppose that, even during this early stage, certain more elementary, transformational rules have also been learned, such as the formation of the interrogative (Menyuk, 1969). Then, language learning involves the acquisition of progressively more elaborate deep structures and, very importantly, generative-transformational structures that can operate on two or more underlying base strings and come to produce all manner of complex embedding in surface sentences (e.g., C. Chomsky, 1969; Kessel, 1970; and Menyuk, 1969).

The individual word thus becomes operative through increasingly complex syntactic structures. What we ordinarily refer to as the meaning (semantics) of a sentence is considered to be essentially an attribute of deep structure in accordance with a generative-transformational grammar (N. Chomsky, 1965). But this entire growing assemblage of syntactic structure (deep and transformational) can be considered to exert a systemic influence upon meaning. Perhaps one can speak about a syntactic mobile equilibrium, which comes to be a property of the basic encoding unit. However we describe it, we consider that such a configurational influence, mediated by syntax, comes to facilitate the *use* of concepts for (concrete) conservation of meaning, which a child can begin to demonstrate in middle latency. Piaget (1960) talks about the structuralization of a concept into a (concrete) grouping as something that comes about "by a kind of thawing . . . by the sudden mobility which animates and coordinates configurations that were more or less rigid (p. 139) . . . tied to particular states of the object." (p. 142) There is a linguistic counterpart to such change in the status of concept formation, from: "I see the girl"; "the girl cries"; "the girl is pretty"; "the girl talks to her mother," to: "I see the pretty girl crying while talking to her mother." The actual information added by this last, syntactically much more skillful sentence, is essentially configurational, or, as we would prefer to say, interrelational (keeping more closely to Freud's terminology). A grammatical device has come to produce different kinds of syntactic formations—an adjective modifier, an abridged clause, etc.—that make possible the interrelating of various attributes with the subject—something that would be impossible to construct with a lesser order of syntactic competence. We assume that, when language structures move decisively in such a direction, the self- and object-representations implicated in such language ("I," "girl," "mother") have moved a step closer to the kind of intellectual suppleness described by Piaget as indicative of a (concrete) grouping. Piaget's observations also suggest that what may be especially intimately associated with the final emergence of such (concrete) conceptual conservation is a *selective use* of syntactic competence, to produce relational informa-

Once meaning is conserved by "groupings" (Piaget), or "relations between ideas" (Freud), we propose that an important change must have taken place in the *representation of interpersonal relationships.* Indeed, in normal development such conceptual conservation is perhaps initiated through a change in the representation of an interpersonal relationship. However this may be, Piaget (1960) describes another new and important information-encoding property of the "grouping" as follows: "The grouping thus realizes for the first time that equilibrium between . . . assimilation to the subject's action and . . . accommodation of subjective schemata to . . . objects" (p. 142). Psychoanalytic ego

---

tion of a special sort—conditional contingencies—or what we call Conditional Language. Our results support these observations.

We speak about syntax as only facilitating the use of concepts for the conservation of meaning, because of research done in the area of the thought organization of deaf children. Furth (1964), summarizing research with deaf children who possessed no language of any sort, states that such children show only a characteristic retardation in the eventual attainment of (concrete) conceptual conservation; this certainly suggests that language has only a facilitating effect upon such thought organization. Sinclair de Zwart (1969) has already found that children who have achieved (concrete) conservation do indeed employ a higher-order level of syntactic competence, in accordance with a generative-transformational model of grammar. On the basis of her experimentation, however, she argues that such syntactic learning is not in any way a determining influence upon thought organization, but is strictly and completely the result of a change in thought organization. Nevertheless, research already cited—for example, the work done by Luria and Yudovich (1968)—attests at least to the instrumental use made of language by normal children for the organization of their thought. And to us, it is still a moot question whether any kind of child can achieve (concrete) conceptual conservation *in the area of self- and object-representation* without such syntactic learning. Also, Sinclair de Zwart (1969) reports Piaget himself as indicating that language learning may be at least a necessary (if not sufficient) influence in the further evolution of thinking from concrete to formal operational thought. In any event, different states of consciousness can be identified for normally hearing and speaking adults according to the uses they make of syntactic structures that characterize the adult's language behavior. Consequently, the same word can be inferred to possess different semantic properties with respect to conservation of meaning, according to the overall patterning of syntactic structures that characterizes a given type of awareness. This overall patterning of syntactic structures can be described by the application of a grammatical "grid" over the surface syntactic structures of the spontaneous utterances made by the subject.

Lashley (1951), some twenty years ago, emphasized the need to posit structures to account for serial behavior in general and language in particular. See also Miller, Galanter, and Pribram (1960), for an attempt to formulate a neurophysiological foundation for such behavior. The psychoanalytic theory of thinking tends to dwell exclusively upon semantic criteria when it describes the change in concept formation from primary to secondary process; as a result, in our opinion, it has not taken theoretical advantage of the syntactic aspects of language learning. For example: The id need not be described as something that possesses *only* wordless ideas (Freud, 1915a)—a suggestion immediately contradicted by clinical observation of language in dreams. Rather, words can be present in the id but informationally encoded in different fashion, at least in part because of differences in the syntactic environment of this psychic system. Again: Rapaport's (1951a) notion of the hierarchical arrangement of drive-defense configurations can find theoretical assistance in the idea of a progressive evolution of relational information, facilitated by advances in syntactic learning. *Interrelational* information about reality is information that is of necessity less tied to *immediate perception.* Such increasing autonomy from immediate (inner and outer) perception must facilitate the structuring of drives, so as to produce behavior that we take to be indicative of a growth in "impulse delay."

psychology conceptualizes such change according to a construct of *increasing differentiation between self and objects,* and it considers such differentiation to be a significant attribute of the development of secondary-process thinking (e.g., Jacobson, 1964; Mahler, 1952). Such an ordering can be formulated in such a way as to represent major periods of "a developmental line" that is very familiar to psychoanalysis (A. Freud, 1965); to this we have added our hypothesis about language: (a) A stage of fused and often confused differentiation between self and objects. Such very extreme egocentric thought is facilitated by, and expressed through, the most abbreviated type of grammar, which we term Fragmented Language. Rosen (1966) speaks about ". . . patients [who] produce incomplete sentences or sentences with such syntactic errors as to make them all but incomprehensible. In such patients the confusion in identity results in a failure to maintain a clear separation between addressor and addressee" (p. 651). However, Vygotsky (1934) points out that such syntactic abbreviation can, in unusual circumstances, still produce effective communication of thoughts. First, this can occur because the situation is so well understood by two individuals that it in effect functions as the subject term in a verbal communication. Second, it can occur in a situation of unusual emotional closeness (". . . . when the subject is the same in two minds") (p. 141).[25] (b) The gradual establishment of firmer, but still pre-oedipal, differentiation between self- and object-representation characteristic of the pre-school child. A relatively stable introject is acquired with psychic content, for better or for worse. A characteristic ambivalence toward any important love object is present, however, and this attests to the still infantile, drive-gratifying nature of the interpersonal relationship. Cognition, while still obviously egocentric, is less so than it is in the earlier stage of development just described. It is facilitated by, and expressed through, the production of those construction forms that we designate Narrative Language, as well as through the syntactically simplest sorts of Complex Portrayal Language. (c) Finally, there occurs at the "second" stage of latency (Bornstein, 1951) a significant differentiation between self- and object-representation. Non-egocentric, "mutual" object relations are now possible (A. Freud, 1965). Cognitive organization at such a stage in middle latency is facilitated by and expressed through syntactically more complex Portrayal language, and especially through the growing *use* of syntactic skill for that special type of complex sentence construction that we call Conditional language. These cognitive and linguistic variables are, of course, necessary but obviously not sufficient conditions for such development in object relations, which must also involve dynamic factors.

[25] For example, two individuals can be waiting for a bus together. One person sees the bus approach and says only "Here." This single word can communicate a complete sentence (an organized thought) for the second person, such as "The bus is here." Vygotsky also goes on to give several charming examples of "emotionally close" language, involving the conversation of two lovers, taken from the novel *Anna Karenina.* While Vygotsky places special stress on abbreviated syntax, which involves the dropping out of the grammatical subject, the examples he cites from the novel seem to involve, as well, absent or insufficient predication. We consider both types of incomplete sentences to be instances of Fragmented Language.

A generally stated hypothesis—*that language behavior variation in the selective uses of syntactic competence to provide relational information is mediated by the degree of differentiation between self- and object-representation*—is supported by customary clinical interpretation about psychotic depressive, persecutory paranoid, and schizophrenic clinical states.

Freud (1911b) in his efforts to explain schizophrenic and psychotic states, emphasized a hypothetical "detachment of the libido together with its regression onto the ego" (p. 463). But even in such an early statement as this, both the term "regression" and the term "detachment" appeared. Freud recognized, and stated explicitly, that some general concept of libidinal withdrawal could not in itself explain either the initial break with reality or its later aberrant reconstruction. Freud described two further determinants, which he called "abnormal changes in the ego" (p. 462), and which he considered to be as critical as the libidinal withdrawal itself: (1) the "dispositional point of fixation," which formed the matrix for the initial libidinal withdrawal; and (2) the "mechanism for the return of the repressed," which brought about either hallucinatory or delusional phenomena. The following comments by Freud in this matter are particularly pertinent:

What seems to me more essential is that paranoia should be maintained as an independent clinical type, however frequently the picture it presents may be complicated by the presence of schizophrenic features. For, from the standpoint of the libido theory, while it would resemble dementia praecox insofar as the repression proper in both disorders would have the same principal feature—detachment of the libido, together with its regression onto the ego—it would be distinguished from dementia praecox by having its dispositional point of fixation differently located and by having a different mechanism for the return of the repressed (i.e., for the formation of symptoms) . . . (p. 463).

In dementia praecox this attempt at recovery (which observers mistake for the disease itself) does not, as in paranoia, make use of projection, but employs an hallucinatory (hysterical) mechanism. This is one of the great distinctions between dementia praecox and paranoia (pp. 463–464). The [paranoid] man has recaptured a relation and often a very intense one, to people and things in the world, although the relation may be a hostile one now, where formerly it was sympathetic and affectionate (pp. 457–458) . . . the object of contention became the most important thing in the world, trying on the one hand to draw the whole of the libido onto itself, and on the other hand mobilizing all the resistances against itself (p. 460; emphasis ours).

The second distinction is shown by the issue of the disease in those cases where the processes become sufficiently general. The prognosis [in dementia praecox] is on the whole more unfavorable than in paranoia; the victory lies with the forces of repression and not [as with paranoia] with those of reconstruction.

Regression travels back not merely to the stage of narcissism (manifesting itself in the shape of megalomania), but to a complete abandonment of object love and to a restoration of infantile auto-eroticism (p 464).

Recent investigations have directed our attention to a stage in the development of the libido which it passes through on the way from auto-eroticism to object love. This stage has been given the name of narcissism . . . there comes a time in the development of the individual at which he unifies his sexual instincts (which have hitherto been engaged in auto-erotic activities) in order to obtain a love object, and only subsequently proceeds from this to the choice of some person other than himself as his object (p. 446).

Freud made several important additions to this comparative study of ego pathology in the papers on narcissism (1914) and melancholia (1917). In 1911 he likened the schizophrenic, hallucinatory mechanism to an hysterical process. In 1914 he described the delusional mechanism as being similar in some way to an obsessional process.[26] He detailed the idea of a narcissistic object relation, wherein a love object is chosen on the basis of some kind of identification with it. In 1917 he argued that it is especially the presence of this kind of narcissistic object relationship that can incline an individual toward melancholia.

Abraham (1924) contributed certain elaborations to Freud's original comparative psychopathology. He emphasized that Freud's concept of autoerotic libidinal organization must be thought of as "pre-ambivalent" (p. 496), by which he meant a state of consciousness in which no distinction is yet experienced between ego and object. He assigned schizophrenic "regression onto the ego" (Freud, 1911b, p. 463) to such a state, and he considered the affective psychoses to be at a stage of narcissism in which some minimal differentiation between self- and object-representation exists. However, Abraham assigned this narcissism of the affective psychosis to be that of an earlier stage than the narcissism involved in paranoid megalomania. In the former, "total incorporation" of the object (p. 496) takes place, whereas in the latter condition, what is incorporated is only an (erotically significant) "part of the object," which in itself signifies the maintenance of "partial love" for the object (p. 496).

More recently, Hartmann (1969) formulated a distinction between the concepts ego and self. Jacobson (1953), in her studies of adult schizophrenic and psychotic states, emphasizes the concept of self- and object-*representation*— i.e., an endopsychic mental construction of the actual physical object. She elaborates the idea of a varying degree of differentiation between such self- and

[26] We believe that the complete analogy offered by Freud between these two neuroses and two psychoses has never been sufficiently appreciated. The central points of comparison are that when reality is (re)constructed according to either hallucinations or phobias the result is a *perceptual* disturbance, whereas when reality is (re)constructed according to either a delusion or preoccupation the result is a *conceptual* disturbance. We would expect certain kinds of similarities to appear in language construction in accordance with this analogy.

object-representations. And finally, she emphasizes how varying degrees of differentiation between self- and object-representation can be taken to constitute different points of regression in schizophrenic and psychotic states.

. . . in manic-depressives, the regressive processes do not proceed as far and do not result in "total identification." They result in fusions of bad or good love objects with the self image and with the superego and eventually lead to severe pathological conflict—or harmony—between the self and the superego. In schizophrenics the ego and superego systems deteriorate to a much more dangerous extent. The conflict between self and superego becomes re-transformed into struggles between the self and magical threatening love-object figures . . . leading to more or less total fusions between the self and object images. (p. 260)

We are now prepared to discuss our clinical observations in relation to language coding. Clinically, we expect the depressive states of a cyclical patient to indicate comparatively minimal distinction between self and objects, as compared with the much more highly differentiated consciousness of persecutory states. Indeed, Freud (1911b) thought that the projective mechanism for the "return of the repressed" functions to augment differentiation between self and objects, so as to enable the patient to attribute to another his ego-alien impulses. Our cyclical patient, when depressed, produced less Conditional but much more Narrative Language than when she was paranoid. Specified Simple Narrative Language also involves simpler syntax, and thus requires, we believe, only a slight degree of differentiation between self and objects; in the same way, it is relatively more pronounced in her depressive states. Clinically, we see the schizophrenic state as showing still less distinction between self and objects, as compared with both depressive and paranoid states. This leads to an expectation that language coding findings in schizophrenia should show an even greater movement toward simpler forms of syntax, as compared with either depression or paranoid clinical conditions. This is, in fact, what we have obtained. What is especially noteworthy is the more pronounced presence of Fragmented language composition with our schizophrenic patients; we believe this to be indicative of fusion tendencies in self-object representation.[27]

[27] It is not really possible to compare our results directly with published reports having to do with the relationship between extreme psychopathology and syntactic failures in language production. However, our case-study findings with respect to Fragmented Language are at least congruent with the results obtained by M. A. White (1949), who compared the writing of normal and schizophrenic groups. Also, our case-study findings with respect to Narrative Language appear congruent with case study observations made by Newman and Mather (1938), about how grammatically complete but simple language construction begins to appear during periods of gradual remission from acute, psychotic depressive states. Newman and Mather report that, in their most acute phase, their psychotically depressed patients showed anorexia, excessive psychomotor retardation, etc. Extreme symptoms such as these are not evident in the depressive episodes of our cyclic patient.

   Gottschalk and his collaborators have devised an elaborate system for analyzing language that is primarily oriented to content evaluation, but includes attention to failures in sentence formation (1958, 1961a, 1961b). These investigators did not obtain a

Research conducted by M. G. Johnson (1967) facilitates interpretation of the relationships we obtained between what we call Language Status and clinical state. Johnson first constructed a number of simple sentences, and then for each such sentence he derived an active and passive voice form so that sentence meaning (semantics) was held constant. He then placed nonsense syllables into the syntactic subject and object positions for each sentence. (For example: "The XEK hit the WUZ"; "The RIW was comforted by the FOJ"). He also controlled for any possible connotation that might derive from a nonsense syllable itself, by counterbalancing the use of each nonsense syllable in a syntactic subject versus a syntactic object position for different segments of his subject pool. Johnson then investigated *meaning that accrued to the syntactic subject and object positions* by making use of a semantic differential: All subjects rated all nonsense syllables according to 7-point bipolar scales: "progressive-regressive," "fast-slow," "masculine-feminine," etc.

Johnson found that scores for 11 such scales [28] were similarly (and statistically) significantly related to syntactic position, irrespective of whether the simple sentence was in the active or passive voice form. High ratings on all such scales were associated with syntactic subject position, whereas low ratings were concomitant with object position. Johnson's results essentially support the work done earlier by Clark, who used an incomplete-sentence technique to examine similar language behavior (1965). Finally, Johnson interpretively concluded that subject terms possess a high degree of "animateness," whereas object terms possess less such meaning. We, however, have observed a consistent tendency for more self-representational content to occupy the subject position in our cyclic patient's remitted *and* depressive states. We therefore conclude that self-representational content that is placed into the head position possesses something like "psychological status," in the sense of special libidinal significance. *Further, we hypothesize that the balance obtaining between self and objects in the head-element syntactic subject-position reflects a distribution of narcissistic versus object-libidinal investment.*

This general hypothesis is supported by our customary clinical interpretation of schizophrenic, psychotic depressive, and paranoid delusional clinical

---

significant correlation between various kinds of incomplete sentence formation and the extent of cognitive disorganization, in a group of psychiatric patients. It is clear, however, that this incongruence is due to a difference in our scoring systems. One of our research assistants, utterly unaware of the purpose, applied our language-coding scoring system to two language samples from psychotic patients, provided by Gottschalk et al. in one of their publications (1958). According to our system, a good deal of grammatically incomplete sentence structure is present.

Such language-coding findings are also congruent with findings reported by Witkin (1965), about types of ego psychopathology and cognitive capability. Witkin has reported that hallucinatory schizophrenics tend to be more field-dependent (less cognitively differentiated) people, whereas delusional paranoids tend to be more field-independent.

[28] The remaining bipolar adjective scales that were found to be significantly related to syntactic position were: "hard-soft," "heavy-light," "strong-weak," "potent-impotent," "active-passive," "energetic-inert," "subject-object," "aggressive-defensive." High scores refer to the initial adjective of each adjective pair.

states. Inasmuch as clinical observation about adult schizophrenia regards it as being the most narcissistic state, we would expect that our adult schizophrenic patients should show the largest amount of narcissistic (measured by self-representational) content in their language construction, relative to either paranoid or depressive states. This is indeed what we have obtained.

The literature on the comparative psychopathology of depressive versus paranoid states pivots on the differing effects of a narcissistic object relation upon consciousness. The psychotic depressive state is interpreted as being the *direct* expression of such a narcissistic object relationship (Abraham, 1924; Freud, 1917). The depressive individual accepts an ego-syntonic identification with the depriving and rejecting love object. A persecutory, paranoid state is also considered to be affected by a narcissistic object relation, but here the effect is indirect. Indeed, the essential function of the delusional formation is precisely to defend against acceptance of a narcissistic identification with the love object (Abraham, 1924; Freud, 1911b). According to Freud (1911b), libidinal overcathexis of the love object then takes place, because the paranoid person cannot allow himself to become aware of his own narcissistic love for the persecutory [29] figure. Consequently, we should expect—and we find—in the language construction of the persecutory paranoid patients, more libidinal object cathexis in the syntactic subject position, as compared with the verbalizations of either schizophrenic or psychotic depressed patients.[30]

Our last language construction measure, Language Focus, we hypothesize to be the expression of a *selective attentional mechanism,* which is *operative in the representation of self and objects.* Rapaport (1951a) indicates how such an attentional mechanism can be described so as to possess some varying degree of autonomy from motives. But such autonomy, according to Rapaport, is always relative.[31] It seems to us reasonable to assume that the autonomy of such an attentional mechanism from motives should be minimal in cases of severe ego disturbance, such as we are now studying, so that, for such patients, attention

---

[29] Freud (1911b) hypothesized that it is a homosexual-narcissistic object relation that is regularly being defended against in the paranoid state. He was able to demonstrate this to be the case even in an instance of female paranoia that seemed initially to run counter to this thesis (1915b). Abraham (1924), building upon earlier clinical observations by both Stärke (1920) and van Ophuijsen (1920), indicates that an anal (fecal) narcissistic object relation can be implicated in paranoia. However this may be, what is essential to our argument is that some type of narcissistic object relationship is being *defended against* in paranoia, whereas in psychotic depression this is not the case.

[30] We should like now to refer back to a finding that we have already cited: that patients making progress in treatment show a reduction of the first-person-singular pronoun (Zimmerman and Langdon, 1953). This can also be considered congruent with an interpretation that this represents reduced narcissistic cathexis, as a consequence of treatment.

[31] Rapaport (1951a) states: "*Consciousness* therefore is now conceptualized as a matter of the distribution of attention-cathexis . . ." (p. 699). "The operations of cathectic dynamics in the conceptual-organization of memory do not use solely the completely neutralized attention-cathexes—*if there are such*—but also directed cathexis of ego interests and *drive derivatives* as well. Thinking is never just a purely 'cold process' " (italics, with the exception of the first, ours; p. 710).

should be readily influenced by whatever is their predominating balance of narcissistic versus object cathexis.

Libidinal cathexis of object-representations at the expense of narcissistic self-representations, such as characterizes paranoid delusional consciousness, should deflect attention toward *relational* features of the representational world (Freud, 1911b). An opposite, or at least less dyadic, deflection should occur in psychotic depressed and schizophrenic states, so that attention will be more focused upon solitary features of the representational world.[32] This is what we find, although only weakly, as compared with our Language-Coding and Status findings.

In particular, our weak Focus findings are due to differences among our three paranoid states. We have already pointed out that the second paranoid episode of our cyclic patient shows an amount of Focus—Monadic construction that is almost equal to that of her immediately preceding depressive condition. Also, and incongruously, our other paranoid patient, who shows the most systematized paranoid delusion, also shows an amount of Focus—Monadic construction that is approximately the same as that of one of our schizophrenic patients (Table 5). A close reading of the 10-minute segment for the second paranoid state of our cyclic patient convinced us that depression was at times quite predominant in this session as well.

Consequently, we instructed a staff psychologist, who was utterly unaware of the purposes of this research, to evaluate the tapes of both paranoid states and to compare the two sessions, with respect to both paranoid delusional and depressive content.[33] Both quantitative ratings and qualitative summary descriptions were obtained for each of the two paranoid states. The second paranoid state is indeed described as a more extreme admixture. The psychologist's summary statement, for example, describes the second paranoid condition as "manifestly depressed. . . . During the initial part of the session . . . her rate of speech was retarded. . . ." This depressive manifestation is described further as "short-lived": it changes to ego-syntonic paranoid thinking, which comes to dominate the session. The affect of depression in the first paranoid condition is described only as "mild." Also, the patient is described in the first paranoid state as not being so "convinced" about her paranoid delusions. These findings suggest a "carry-over" of depression into the second paranoid condition of our cyclical patient, even though the paranoid experience itself is ultimately more ego-syntonic.

Unfortunately, we have no such prior comparative data about our other paranoid patient. We do, however, have rather dramatic information about his

[32] But we need not expect such parallel findings in neurotic disturbances. We have already reported a finding that implies a higher verb count among anxiety hysterics (Balken and Masserman, 1940). It is likely that most of these verbs are transitive but are not used reflectively. This would produce a high percentage of Dyadic—Focus, even though we might expect such anxiety hysterics to have an equally high percentage of Language Status—Self construction.

[33] Mrs. Dale Roskos performed this evaluation.

clinical status subsequent to this acute, delusional state. Two months later he developed a very severe depressive condition. At that time, he was reported by his therapist to show no paranoid delusional experience whatsoever, and he had made a serious suicidal attempt.[34] What is suggested—very tentatively—is that the mechanism of selective attention (Focus Monadic/Dyadic) in a paranoid delusional state is more readily influenced by actual or potential depression than are those structures responsible for the differentiation of, and libidinal investment in, self and objects.

Now, after having concluded our discussion of the data for our three language construction measures with respect to psychopathology, we want also to offer an interpretation for the ebullient remitted state of our cyclical patient. This remission demonstrates a very high assignment of self-representational content to the syntactic subject position (libidinal status). At the same time, language coding in remission shows a profile that is generally similar to her paranoid states. In our opinion, therefore, this remission represents a short-lived, moderately (nonpsychotic) manic state.[35]

Thus far, our discussion has been based entirely upon percentage figures that summarize different kinds of language construction for various language samples. We want, finally, to offer one example of how these same language construction measures can be used to examine the *flow* of language construction. For this purpose, we use all five language samples from our cyclic patient, in order to examine a sequential relation between Fragmented and Conditional Language. Interestingly, while Conditional Language accounts for only 10 per cent of total, complete (i.e., grammatical) clause production, Fragmented Language utterances occur, for 51 per cent of the time, closely adjacent (no more than two sentences before or after) to such Conditional Language structure. We consider this to be an indication of this cyclic patient's psychopathological vulnerability for regression to primary-process thinking, precisely at moments when she is attempting to be cognitively most differentiated (self- vs. object-differentiation). This finding now makes clear how it is that the second paranoid episode—which shows more Conditional Language than her first paranoid condition—also shows significantly more Fragmented Language. But we can envision another context in which such oscillation between differentiation and dedifferentiation possesses an entirely different clinical significance—namely, "regression in the service of the ego" (Kris, 1952).

There is an obvious need to replicate our introductory investigation with larger groups of subjects. This applies not only to cyclic studies. It would be especially valuable to be able to compare clinical states without the influence of a continuous treatment experience, so that the relevance of situational (treat-

---

[34] Unfortunately, we have no data for this severely depressed condition.

[35] The patient's ebullient mood and self-confident speech during this episode, of course, suggest a moderately manic state. In addition, the language-coding findings obtained in this episode appear to be congruent with observations made by Newman and Mather (1938) about the syntactic complexity of the sentence structure of manic patients in periods of relative remission.

ment) versus endogenous personality determinants for these language construction variables could be disentangled. If it is possible, independent measures for differentiation between self and objects, and for balance of narcissistic versus object-cathexis and selective attention, must be devised, which would permit an experimental manipulation of these variables, with language construction being treated as the dependent variable. The applicability of these language-construction measures to various normal varieties of consciousness must also be examined.[36] We have cited research that treats syntactic structures as independent variables and thereby demonstrates their effects upon different aspects of cognition. We believe that the addition of a psychopathological framework—which may enable one to examine different states of consciousness—is a useful addition to such research, and provides information for both theories of language and the study of psychopathology. Also, experimental designs should be created that treat (psychoanalytic) object relations as independent variables, and examine their effects upon language construction. The general hypothesis we have advanced, of a relation between stages of language-coding and stages in object-relations, requires an investigation that is direct, psychoanalytically oriented, and developmental.

In addition, various clinical research areas can be described that are pertinent to future validation of the constructs we assume to mediate various types of language construction.

1. *Studies of character types and of psychopathology:* What are the language-construction characteristics of the classical diagnostic entities? We have already mentioned the idea that what clinicians usually describe as a thought disorder seems to be language that still retains grammatical integrity, even though its meaning is impaired. It ought to be possible to develop a measure for the degree of such grammatical integrity, independent of sentence meaning. Then this kind of variable might be related, for example, to what clinicians judge to be the extent to which a schizophrenic patient is withdrawn. For a number of years now there has been disagreement in the literature as to the developmental implications of shame versus guilt experience (e.g., Hartmann and Loewenstein, 1962; Piers and Singer, 1953). Does verbal content expressing guilt possess a developmentally more advanced sentence structure? Are there other consistent differences in language construction, correlated with shame and guilt? What is the relationship between language construction and variation in degree and type of drive content? What is the relationship between language construction and cognitive style?

2. *Studies of different patterns of child-raising:* How demanding is a mother

---

[36] Some research along these lines has already been started. Data are being collected that bear upon language-construction patterns of normal subjects, who are typed according to different cognitive styles. Also, we have some preliminary case-study data indicating an association between narcissism—independently measured by body touching—and the amount of Language Status–Self construction.

in teaching her child grammar and semantics? How does such language socialization compare with other demands for social adjustment (toilet-training, eating regulations, etc.)? It would be interesting to search for instances in child-raising where we can hypothesize that a conflict is being created between the syntactic and the content aspects of language. For example, a child might be exposed to extremely libidinal language content, cast into complex, Conditional language syntactic form. Does the grammatical form of such language produce a "message" for extreme differentiation between self and objects, which is contradicted by the language content itself? If so, can such incongruity in language be related to "double bind" formulations (Bateson, Jackson, et al., 1956) for the etiology of at least some kinds of basic ego disturbance? [37]

3. *Psychotherapy and other forms of clinical intervention:* Coltrera and Ross (1967) report a general acknowledgment among therapists that one should speak simply when treating depressed patients. Is a therapist's language construction similar or dissimilar to the structure of a patient's utterances? That is, does the therapist (or do ward personnel) grammatically "talk the patient's language"? What effects does such congruence, or lack of congruence, have upon the treatment process? What are the language-construction characteristics of free association, and of a "good hour" (Kris, 1956)?

REFERENCES

Abraham, K. (1921, 1924, 1925). Psychoanalytic Studies on Character Formation. In: *Selected Papers on Psychoanalysis.* London: Hogarth Press, 1968, pp. 370–501.

Auld, F., Jr., and Murray, E. J. (1955). Content-Analysis Studies of Psychotherapy. *Psychological Bulletin,* 52:377–395.

Balken, E. R., and Masserman, J. H. (1940). The Language of Fantasy. III: The Language of the Fantasies of Patients with Conversion Hysteria, Anxiety State, and Obsessive Compulsive Neurosis. *Journal of Psychology,* 10:75–86.

Bateson, G., Jackson, D., Haley, J., and Washland, J. (1956). Toward a Theory of Schizophrenia. *Behavioral Science,* 1:251–264.

Bernstein, B. (1961). Aspects of Language and Learning in the Genesis of the Social Process. *Journal of Child Psychology and Psychiatry,* 1:313–324.

Bever, T. G., Fodor, J. A., Garrett, M., and Mehler, J. (1966). Transformational Operations and Stimulus Complexity. Unpublished manuscript.

Bornstein, B. (1951). On Latency. *Psychoanalytic Study of the Child,* Vol. 6. New York: International Universities Press.

Brown, R. W. (1957). Linguistic Determinism and the Part of Speech. *Journal of Abnormal and Social Psychology,* 55:1–5.

————, and Bellugi, V. (1964). Three Processes in the Child's Acquisition of Syntax. In: *New Directions in the Study of Language,* ed. E. H. Lenneberg. Cambridge, Mass.: M.I.T. Press.

Bruner, J. S., Oliver R. R., and Greenfield, P. M. (1967). *Studies in Cognitive Growth.* New York: John Wiley.

[37] Experimental designs along these lines can be constructed for adult subjects, and one can investigate the effects of hypothetically conflicting communications upon memory, affect, etc.

Chomsky, C. (1969). *The Acquisition of Syntax in Children from Five to Ten.* Cambridge, Mass.: M.I.T. Press.

Chomsky, N. (1964). Current Issues in Linguistic Theory; and on the Notion "Rule of Grammar." In: *The Structure of Language. Readings in the Philosophy of Language,* ed. J. A. Fodor and J. Katz. Cambridge, Mass.: M.I.T. Press.

—— (1965). *Aspects of the Theory of Syntax.* Cambridge, Mass.: M.I.T. Press.

Clark, H. H. (1965). Some Structural Properties of Simple, Active, and Passive Sentences. *Journal of Verbal Learning and Verbal Behavior,* 4:365–370.

Coltrera, J., and Ross, N. (1967). Freud's Psychoanalytic Technique—From the Beginnings to 1923. A Handbook for the Practicing Psychoanalyst. In: *Psychoanalytic Techniques.* New York: Basic Books.

Curme, G. O. (1947). *English Grammar.* New York: Barnes and Noble.

Edelheit, H. (1969). Speech and Psychic Structure. *Journal of the American Psychoanalytic Association,* 17:381–412.

Ervine, S. M. (1964). Imitation and Structural Change in Children's Language. In: *New Directions in the Study of Language,* ed. E. H. Lenneberg. Cambridge, Mass.: M.I.T. Press.

Fodor, J., and Garrett, M. (1966). Some Reflections on Competence and Performance. In: *Psycholinguistic Papers,* ed. J. Lyons and R. J. Wales. Edinburgh: Edinburgh University Press.

Freedman, N., Grand, S., and Karacan, I. (1966). An Approach to the Study of Dreaming and Changes in Psychopathological States. *Journal of Nervous and Mental Disease,* 143:399–405.

——, and Hoffman, S. P. (1967). Kinetic Behavior in Altered Clinical States: An Approach to Objective Analysis of Motor Behavior during Clinical Interviews. *Perceptual and Motor Skills,* 24:527–539.

Freud, A. (1965). *Normality and Pathology in Childhood.* New York: International Universities Press.

Freud, S. (1891). *On Aphasia.* New York: International Universities Press, 1953.

—— (1900). The Interpretation of Dreams. *Standard Edition,* 4 & 5. London: Hogarth Press, 1953.

—— (1911a). Formulations on the Two Principles of Mental Functioning. *Standard Edition,* 12:218–226. London: Hogarth Press, 1958.

—— (1911b). Psycho-Analytic Notes on an Autobiographical Account of a Case of Paranoia (Dementia Paranoides). *Standard Edition,* 12:9–82. London: Hogarth Press, 1958.

—— (1914). On Narcissism: An Introduction. *Standard Edition,* 14:73–102. London: Hogarth Press, 1957.

—— (1915a). The Unconscious. *Standard Edition,* 14:166–204. London: Hogarth Press, 1957.

—— (1915b). A Case of Paranoia Running Counter to the Psycho-Analytic Theory of the Disease. *Standard Edition,* 14:263–272. London: Hogarth Press, 1957.

—— (1917). Mourning and Melancholia. *Standard Edition,* 14:237–258. London: Hogarth Press, 1957.

—— (1921). Group Psychology and the Analysis of the Ego. *Standard Edition,* 18:69–143. London: Hogarth Press, 1955.

—— (1923). The Ego and the Id. *Standard Edition,* 19:12–66. London: Hogarth Press, 1961.

—— (1933). New Introductory Lectures on Psycho-Analysis. Lecture 29. Revision of the Theory of Dreams. *Standard Edition,* 22:7–30. London: Hogarth Press, 1964.

—— (1940). An Outline of Psycho-Analysis. *Standard Edition,* 23:144–207. London: Hogarth Press, 1964.

Furth, H. G. (1964). Research with the Deaf: Implications for Language and Cognition. *Psychological Bulletin,* 62:145–164.

Gleason, H. A. (1961). *An Introduction to Descriptive Linguistics.* New York: Holt, Rinehart and Winston.

Gottschalk, L. A., et al. (1958). The Speech Patterns of Schizophrenic Patients: A Method of Assessing Relative Degree of Personal Disorganization and Social Alienation. *Journal of Nervous and Mental Disease,* 127:153–166.

――――, et al. (1961a). Further Studies on the Speech Patterns of Schizophrenic Patients. *Journal of Nervous and Mental Disease,* 132:101–113.

――――, et al. (1961b). Experiments with a Method of Assessing the Variations in Intensity of Certain Psychologic States Occurring during Two Psychotherapy Interviews. In: *Comparative Psycholinguistic Analysis of Two Psychotherapeutic Interviews,* ed. L. A. Gottschalk. New York: International Universities Press.

Grand, S., Freedman, N., and Jortner, S. (1969). Variations in R.E.M. Dreaming and the Effectiveness of Behavior in Group Therapy. *American Journal of Psychotherapy,* 24:667–680.

Grummon, D. L. (1953). An Investigation into the Use of Grammatical and Psychogrammatical Categories of Language for the Study of Personality and Psychotherapy, 1950. Unpublished doctoral dissertation, University of Chicago.

Hartmann, H. (1969). Comments on the Psychoanalytic Theory of the Ego. *The Psychoanalytic Study of the Child,* 24. New York: International Universities Press.

――――, and Loewenstein, R. M. (1962). Notes on the Superego. *The Psychoanalytic Study of the Child,* 17. New York: International Universities Press.

Hunt, K. W. (1970). Syntactic Maturity in School Children and Adults. *Monographs of the Society of Research in Child Development,* 35, No. 1.

Jacobson, E. (1953). Contribution to the Metapsychology of Cyclothymic Depression. In: *Affective Disorders,* ed. P. Greenacre. New York: International Universities Press.

―――― (1964). *The Self and the Object World.* New York: International Universities Press.

Johnson, M. G. (1967). Syntactic Position and Rated Meaning. *Journal of Verbal Learning and Verbal Behavior,* 6:240–246.

Johnson, N. F. (1965). Linguistic Models and Functional Units of Language Behavior. In: *Directions in Psycholinguistics,* ed. S. Rosenberg. New York: Macmillan.

Kessel, F. S. (1970). The Role of Syntax in Children's Comprehension from Ages Six to Twelve. *Monographs of the Society for Research in Child Development,* 35, No. 6.

Klein, G. S. (1959). Consciousness in Psychoanalytic Theory: Some Implications for Current Research in Perception. *Journal of the American Psychoanalytic Association,* 7:5–34.

Kris, E. (1952). *Psychoanalytic Explorations in Art.* New York: International Universities Press.

―――― (1956). Vicissitudes of Insight during the Analytic Hour. *International Journal of Psycho-Analysis,* 37:445–455.

LaBrant, L. (1933). A Study of Certain Language Developments of Children in Grades Four to Twelve Inclusive. *Genetic Psychology Monographs,* 24:387–496.

Laffal, J. (1965). *Pathological and Normal Language.* New York: Atherton.

Langer, S. K. (1952). *Philosophy in a New Key.* Cambridge, Mass.: Harvard University Press.

Lashley, K. S. (1951). The Problem of Serial Order in Behavior. In: *Cerebral Mechanisms in Behavior,* ed. L. A. Jeffres. New York: John Wiley.

Lasswell, H. D. (1935). Verbal References and Physiological Changes during the Psychoanalytic Interview: A Preliminary Communication. *Psychoanalytic Review,* 22:10–24.

Lenneberg, E. H. (1962). Understanding Language without Ability to Speak. Case Report. *Journal of Abnormal and Social Psychology,* 65:419–425.

―――― (1967). *Biological Foundations of Language.* New York: John Wiley.

Lindenfeld, J. (1970). In Search of Psychological Factors of Linguistic Variation. Paper presented at Annual Meeting of the American Anthropological Association.

Loban, W. B. (1963). The Language of Elementary School Children. *National Council of Teachers of English Research Report No. 1.*

Lorenz, M., and Cobb, S. (1952). Language Behavior in Manic Patients. *A.M.A. Archives of Neurology and Psychiatry*, 67:763–770.

———, ——— (1953). Language Behavior in Psychoneurotic Patients. *A.M.A. Archives of Neurology and Psychiatry*, 69:684–693.

———, ——— (1954). Language Patterns in Psychotic and Psychoneurotic Subjects. *A.M.A. Archives of Neurology and Psychiatry*, 72:665–673.

Luria, A. R., and Yudovich, F. (1968). *Speech and the Developmental Processes in the Child*. London: Staples Press.

Mahl, G. (1956). Disturbances and Silences in the Patient's Speech in Psychotherapy. *Journal of Abnormal and Social Psychology*, 53:1–15.

Mahler, M. S. (1952). On Child Psychosis and Schizophrenia: Autistic and Symbiotic Infantile Psychoses. *Psychoanalytic Study of the Child*, 7. New York: International Universities Press.

McCarthy, D. (1930). The Language Development of the Pre-School Child. *Institute of Child Welfare Monograph*, Sec. 4. Minneapolis: University of Minnesota Press.

Mehler, J. (1963). Some Effects of Grammatical Transformations on the Recall of English Sentences. *Journal of Verbal Learning and Verbal Behavior*, 2:346–351.

Menyuk, P. (1969). *Sentences Children Use*. Cambridge, Mass.: M.I.T. Press.

Miller, G. A. (1962). Some Psychological Studies of Grammar. *American Psychologist*, 17:748–762.

——— (1964). Language and Psychology. In: *New Directions in the Study of Language*, ed. E. H. Lenneberg. Cambridge, Mass.: M.I.T. Press.

———, Galanter, E., and Pribram, K. H. (1960). *Plans and the Structure of Behavior*. New York: Holt.

Morris, C. W. (1938). Foundations of the Theory of Signs. In: *Encyclopedia of Unified Science*, ed. O. Neurath, R. P. Carnap, and C. W. Morris. Chicago: University of Chicago Press.

Mowrer, O. H., Light, B. H., Lauria, S., and Zeleny, M. P. (1953). Tension Changes during Psychotherapy with Special Reference to Resistance. Unpublished manuscript.

Newman, S., and Mather, V. G. (1938). Analysis of Spoken Language of Patients with Affective Disorders. *American Journal of Psychiatry*, 94:913–942.

O'Connell, R. C., Griffin, W. J., and Norris, R. C. (1967). Syntax of Kindergarten and Elementary School Children: A Transformational Analysis. *National Council of Teachers English Research Report No. 8*.

Peller, L. E. (1966). Freud's Contribution to Language Theory. *Psychoanalytic Study of the Child*, 21. New York: International Universities Press.

Piaget, J. (1923). *The Language and Thought of the Child*. New York: Meridian Books, 1955.

——— (1928). *Judgment and Reasoning in the Child*. New Jersey: Littlefield, Adams and Company, 1966.

——— (1945). *Play, Dreams and Imitation in Childhood*. New York: Norton, 1951.

——— (1960). *The Psychology of Intelligence*. New Jersey: Littlefield, Adams and Company.

——— (1962). *Comments on Vygotsky's Critical Remarks concerning the Language and Thought of a Child, and Judgment and Reasoning in the Child*. Cambridge, Mass.: M.I.T. Press.

Piers, G., and Singer, M. E. (1953). *Shame and Guilt: A Psychoanalytic and a Cultural Study*. Springfield, Ill.: Charles C Thomas.

Rapaport, D., ed. (1951a). *Organization and Pathology of Thought*. New York: Columbia University Press.

——— (1951b). Consciousness: A Psychopathological and Psychodynamic View. In: *Problems of Consciousness*. ed. H. A. Abramson. New York: Josiah Macy, Jr. Foundation.

Rosen, V. H. (1966). Disturbances of Representation and Reference in Ego Deviations. In:

Psychoanalysis—A General Psychology, ed. R. M. Loewenstein, L. M. Newman, M. Schur, and A. J. Solnit. New York: International Universities Press.

———— (1967). Disorders of Communication in Psychoanalysis. *Journal of the American Psychoanalytic Association,* 15:467–490.

Sandler, J., and Rosenblatt, B. (1962). The Concept of the Representational World. *Psychoanalytic Study of the Child,* 17. New York: International Universities Press.

Savin, H. B., and Perchonock, E. (1965). Grammatical Structure and Immediate Recall of English Sentences. *Journal of Verbal Learning and Verbal Behavior,* 4:348–353.

Shapiro, T. (1970). Interpretation and Naming. *Journal of the American Psychoanalytic Association,* 18:399–421.

Sinclair de Zwart, H. (1969). Developmental Psycholinguistics. In: *Studies in Cognitive Development. Essays in Honor of Jean Piaget,* ed. D. Elkind and J. H. Flavell. Oxford: Oxford University Press.

Skinner, B. F. (1957). *Verbal Behavior.* New York: Appleton-Century-Crofts.

Slobin, D. I. (1966). Grammatical Transformations in Childhood and Adulthood. Unpublished doctoral dissertation, Harvard University.

Stärke, A. (1920). The Reversal of the Libido Sign in Delusions of Persecution. *International Journal of Psycho-Analysis,* 1:231–234.

Sullivan, H. S. (1953). *The Interpersonal Theory of Psychiatry.* New York: Norton.

Van Ophuijsen, J. H. W. (1920). On the Origin of the Feeling of Persecution. *International Journal of Psycho-Analysis,* 1:235–239.

Vygotsky, L. S. (1934). *Thought and Language.* Cambridge, Mass.: M.I.T. Press, 1962.

Wales, R. J., and Marshall, J. C. (1966). The Organization of Linguistic Performance. In: *Psycholinguistic Papers,* ed. J. Lyons and R. J. Wales. Edinburgh: Edinburgh University Press.

Weintraub, W., and Aronson, H. (1963). The Application of Verbal Behavior Analysis to the Study of Psychological Defense Mechanisms: Methodology and Preliminary Report. *Journal of Nervous and Mental Disease,* 134:169–181.

————, ———— (1964). The Application of Verbal Behavior Analysis to the Study of Psychological Defense Mechanisms: II: Speech Pattern Associated with Impulsive Behavior. *Journal of Nervous and Mental Disease,* 139:75–82.

————, ———— (1965). The Application of Verbal Behavior Analysis to the Study of Psychological Defense Mechanisms: III: Speech Pattern Associated with Delusional Behavior. *Journal of Nervous and Mental Disease,* 141:172–179.

Werner, H., and Kaplan, B. (1967). *Symbol Formation.* New York: John Wiley.

White, M. A. (1949). A Study of Schizophrenic Language. *Journal of Abnormal and Social Psychology,* 44:61–74.

Witkin, H. A. (1965). Psychological Differentiation and Forms of Pathology. *Journal of Abnormal and Social Psychology,* 70:317–336.

————, et al. (1962). *Psychological Differentiation.* New York: John Wiley.

Wolff, P. H. (1967). Cognitive Considerations for a Psychoanalytic Theory of Language Acquisition. In: Motives and Thought: Psychoanalytic Essays in Honor of David Rapaport, ed. R. R. Holt. *Psychological Issues,* Monograph No. 18/19.

Zimmerman, W., and Langdon, J. (1953). A Preliminary Attempt to Establish Criteria for Measuring Progress in Psychotherapy. Unpublished Manuscript.

3

DEVELOPMENTAL

When Rubinstein and Peterfreund conceived the idea behind *Psychoanalysis and Contemporary Science*, one of the first people they approached was George S. Klein, convinced that his participation would be vital to bringing this new publication into reality. He became part of the original editorial board (which also included Holt, Rosen, and Wolff), a working group which made the basic policy decisions, negotiated the contracts, and did the other unseen but necessary work to launch a new publication. In all of this, his previous experience as editor in chief of *Psychological Issues*, his extensive personal knowledge of scientists in many fields, his wisdom about a host of matters ranging from the theoretical to the practical, and his characteristic energy and enthusiasm were invaluable.

The editors wish to dedicate this volume to his memory, because in many ways it is an attempt to embody several principles he stood for: the broadening and deepening of the scientific base of psychoanalysis, its enrichment by exchange with other sciences, a commitment to theoretical clarification hand in hand with empirical research—in brief, fidelity both to the methodological ideals of science and to the inner reality of living human beings. Klein is perhaps best known as a superb exponent of laboratory research on psychoanalytic hypotheses, but he was also a dedicated clinician and whenever there was a conflict between purity of method and relevance to human reality, he unhesitatingly resolved it in favor of the latter ideal. This paper, a chapter from his last major work, expresses a good many of these values. In addition, it epitomizes in its subject matter an important facet of the man George Klein—an exuberantly vital person who experienced and gave much pleasure.

THE VITAL PLEASURES

George S. Klein, Ph.D.[1]

Man's activity, Freud wrote, develops in two directions, according to whether it seeks to realize the experience of pleasure or the absence of pain.[2] For an organism that is without a preformed, adapted identity and subject to prolonged dependence, the capacity to feel pleasure, anxiety, and pain are critical safeguards of his adaptation. The structuring and education of the pleasure potential are at the heart of what Freud went on to call the "reality principle."

In the rendering of the "pleasure principle" to be followed in the pages ahead, the emphasis will be upon pleasure and unpleasure *experiences*—qualities of awareness. This emphasis is different from that of the more usual versions of the pleasure principle that have evolved in psychoanalytic theory. The version known as the constancy principle holds that an organism tends to maintain itself at an optimal level of tension: increases bring states of unpleasure; returns to the optimum, states of pleasure. The other version combines the constancy principle with a quasi-physiological model of drives pressing for discharge as "stimuli on the mind" (Jacobson, 1953). Indeed, theorists in either mold are likely to warn the reader not to equate their use of the term pleasure with pleasure experience (see, for example, Rapaport, 1960, and Schur, 1966).

In the drive-discharge version pleasure is spoken of in the language of libido. How libido came to be an all-encompassing designation of pleasure is an intricate story that we can touch on here only in outline. It had its beginnings

[1] Preparation of this paper was facilitated by a Public Health Service Research Career Program Award (No. 5-KO6-MH-19, 728) from the National Institute of Health.

[2] "[Human beings] strive after happiness; they want to become happy and to remain so. This endeavour has two sides, a positive and a negative aim. It aims, on the one hand, at an absence of pain and unpleasure, and, on the other, at the experiencing of strong feelings of pleasure. In its narrower sense the word 'happiness' only relates to the last. In conformity with this dichotomy in his aims, man's activity develops in two directions, according as it seeks to realize—in the main, or even exclusively—the one or the other of these aims" (Freud, 1930, p. 76).

in Freud's revolutionary insight that the sexuality of adulthood is linked to infancy through a potential for sensual pleasure that evolves in different forms. Libido, referring to a hypothetical energy specific to this sensual development, was Freud's way of freeing considerations of sexuality from the traditional identification of sexuality with genital maturity and the procreative function, and of describing its diverse and extensive manifestations in thought, work, and morality, both normal and deviant (Freud, 1905a).

However, libido soon became more than simply a way of generalizing sensuality; it developed into a putatively explanatory *model*, which reified libido into an energic process pressing for *discharge*, and subject to transformations ("vicissitudes") under that pressure. Discharge was the key element of the process. The model accounts for diverse variations of sensuality by explaining them as deflected or inhibited discharges, or as transformations of libido via hypercathexes, fusions, defusions, sublimation and, in a later addition by Hartmann (1952), neutralization. Taken as a model, the libido-drive-discharge theory is a quasi-physiological, hypothetical mechanism of causation, rather than an account of pleasure experience. Since the essential moving agent in motivation was not pleasure as experienced but the "push" of the drive energy, there was little need to consider the experiential nature of pleasure, which was taken to be mere description with little theoretical status.

Insofar as the experience of pleasure itself is considered at all, the tendency of the drive-discharge model is to equate all pleasure with sensual pleasure. This theory has no language for conceiving other than sensual pleasures, or of varieties of pleasure in other than the terms of the sexual theory. An analogous blurring occurs in the constancy version of the pleasure principle, which lends itself to collapsing all pleasure experiences into simply manifestations of a reduction of tension or of discharge.

The status of pleasure, then, in psychoanalytic theory presents the ironic picture of an initial emphasis upon man's consciousness of pleasure and unpleasure as a decisive factor in development undergoing sophistications of theory that steadily downgraded this very emphasis.

The difficulties of the constancy principle and the drive-discharge model are well-documented and require no review here (cf. Herold, 1941–1942; Kardiner, et al., 1959; Kaufman, 1960; Holt, 1965, 1967; Klein, 1969; Apfelbaum, 1965). But among the criticisms leveled at either of these meanings of the pleasure principle, none seems to me more important than that they lose the import of a crucial principle implicit in a number of Freud's formulations—namely, that the loss of instinctual adaptiveness makes man's survival contingent on the evolution of his *consciousness*. The point is precisely that they deflect attention from pleasure as a positive, causal, selective factor of conscious *experience* in the retaining or discarding of patterns of behavior—or, in contemporary parlance, as a reinforcer. By narrowly construing the classes of pleasure experiences, they also ignore the important possibility that motives may vary according to the variety of pleasure experience involved. This is suggested by Buchenholz's pioneering studies (1956, 1957). If pleasure is a basis for activities *becoming* desirable, then the emergence of sensibility to different conditions capable of exciting the pleasure potential is a significant facet of ego development.

It becomes important, then, to reassert the role of pleasure experience as an important contributor to a person's evolving identity and to the structuring of his motives. To return psychoanalytic theory to this base requires, first of all, that we free considerations of pleasure from the confines of the model of libidinal development that tends to equate pleasure with sensual experience alone, and set aside assumptions of a hypothetical energy which waxes and wanes as states of tension; second, that we try to delineate prototypical conditions or contexts of pleasure—different pleasure modalities; third, that we take stock of the functional role of these different sources of pleasure in the structuring of relationships.

The schema offered in the pages that follow will include sensual pleasure in its adapted, as well as its conflictful and restitutive roles in ego development. But it is assumed that there are modalities of pleasure in addition to the sensual. The principle of developmental stages, usually restricted to sexuality, is applied to other classes of pleasure as well, allowing also for a dynamic interplay among them. Such an approach in terms of distinctive prototypical pleasures invites research curiosity rather than dulling it by comfortably relegating pleasure to a single line of physiological development and to one class of pleasure capacity.

My aim, in short, is to reorient psychoanalytic theory to the essential wisdom of the pleasure principle—that we act so as to maximize pleasure or gratification and to minimize unpleasures of all kinds, especially anxiety.

Let us first get our bearings by positioning pleasure at the executive center of behavior, the ego. In this view, pleasure, even sexual, does not reflect something that is essentially external to the ego, impinging on it as a "force" to be controlled or a "stimulus" to be dealt with, or as something to be disposed of or reacted to. Rather we should think of pleasure as reflecting a number of different forms of well-being experienced in the body, which are triggered by particular contexts of stimulation, with their arousal (and inhibition) being further shaped by experiences of permissibility and restraint that come to be associated through learning with the arousal of a pleasure prototype.

It will be easier to think of pleasure as an ego experience if we consider that a precedent and a guide for doing so already exist in how anxiety has come to be regarded in psychoanalysis. At one time Freud regarded anxiety as he did pleasure—within the context of the model of drive discharge. Anxiety, in this view, resulted from either insufficient or overcontrolled discharge of libido, the extreme being the *Aktualneurose*. Later, Freud considered it more fruitful to regard anxiety as an ego function, reflected in experiences of actual or threatened helplessness and estrangement (Freud, 1926). With the present way of looking at anxiety, many previously worrisome issues have turned out to be unfruitful or even pseudo-problems. Few psychoanalytic theorists consider it important any longer to ask whether or not the energy of the anxiety signal is libidinal. Nor is it sufficient to regard anxiety solely as a quantitative problem of discharge. Although Freud put aside his model of libido and discharge in shifting from a purely quantitative conception of anxiety as an overflow of pent-up libido to the structural view, he did not give up that model where pleasure experience was concerned.

What Freud did with anxiety could well be done now with pleasure. It seems a logical extension of the theory, as Eidelberg (1962), Kanzer and Eidelberg (1960), and Szasz (1957) suggest, to regard pleasure as complementary in function to anxiety. Seen in the same light, as an ego capability, pleasure can be usefully disengaged from the assumptions of the drive-discharge model, and we are thereby encouraged to consider various *qualitative* forms of pleasure experience and their motivational significance. Just as anxiety is informative experience with regard to events that forbode helplessness and estrangement, pleasure is an informative experience of accord and well-being, through which things and objects acquire values of approachability and desirability. Pleasure and anxiety thus designate states of self-experience—the one of well-being, the other of experienced threat.[3] We can then also assume that pleasure experience, like anxiety, can have an anticipatory as well as a fully actualized aspect; that is, we can speak of "signal pleasure" as well as "signal anxiety."

To point up the relationship of ego and self to states of anxiety and pleasure we picture them together in the diagram in Figure 1. Pleasure and anxiety are seen as major and contrasting states of feeling, generated by the organism in response to contact with things, events, and people; the ego in anxiety is in a state of disjunction, fragmentation, conflicted encounter, these being experienced

		PROTOTYPIC
EGO STATE ——————→	SELF-EXPERIENCE ←——————	PLEASURE EXPERIENCES
cohesiveness	well-being	tension-reduction
continuity		sensual pleasure
integrity		pleasure in function
		effectance
		pleasure-in-pleasing
		pleasure in synthesis
		PROTOTYPIC
EGO STATE ——————→	SELF-EXPERIENCE ←——————	PLEASURE EXPERIENCES
fragmentation	helplessness	fear of suddenness
discontinuity	estrangement	fear of separation
conflict		fear of loss of love, etc.

Figure 1. Pleasure and anxiety viewed as complementary ego experiences.

[3] In this formulation, the more useful complementarity of pleasure is anxiety rather than pain or "unpleasure." Pain is a special adaptive response to stimulation beyond physiologically tolerable limits (high and low). Nor is unpleasure, the experiential accompaniment of frustration, a general enough category to stand in polar contrast to pleasure. The polarity of pleasure and anxiety is exemplified by the contrast of motivations issuing from each. Motives of pleasure involve affiliative aims, which may even encompass tolerance of pain and unpleasure; motives generated by anxiety (e.g., defense) are pointed toward the alleviation of fantasied threats to self-identity.

as estranging and threatening to one's identity. Pleasure experiences reflect and promote ego conditions of cohesiveness and continuity.

Seen as an ego potential, pleasure is no longer assumed to be, as in the drive-discharge model or the constancy principle, simply a state of modulated stimulation, defined negatively and wholly quantitatively as relief from pain, the diminished pressure of a drive, or relented frustration. Pleasure and anxiety are qualitatively distinct processes, capable of being set in motion independently. Correspondingly, anxiety and pleasure are motivating in distinctively different ways: motives arising from anxiety are designed to minimize experienced threat; those of pleasure to reinstate and to sustain contact. This is not to omit the possibility of states that complexly exemplify both anxiety and pleasure (e.g., "awe" is perhaps such an example, marked by a feeling of helplessness before a dominating entity quickly followed by the pleasure of resignation and acceptance of one's position in relation to it).

The study of anxiety in psychoanalysis was much advanced by Freud's further attempt to specify *forms of anxiety* that are prototypical for different stages of development—e.g., fear of separation, fear of loss of love, fear of castration, fear of death, etc. Freud called these forms of anxiety "motives of defense" (1926). From the standpoint of concern with the means or phenomenology of anxiety, it is more fruitful to speak of anxiety in the cognitive terms of *kind* or *quality* of threat, rather than in purely quantitative terms; it is much more important to know that anxiety occurs in the form, say, of "a fear of abandonment," than "how much" anxiety there is.[4]

Freud's view of anxiety offers the more clinically pertinent model for the study of pleasure. Rather than speaking of pleasure strictly as a sensation that one can have a "little" or a "lot" of, I shall speak of *prototypic varieties of pleasure* in their developmental and motivational aspect. Just as with anxiety, so can we assume about pleasure experiences that there are a limited number of prototypic forms, which retain importance throughout development but assume particular importance at different stages of development. Such sources of pleasure are primary in the sense of being innately given potentialities that are not further analyzable; however, they undergo continual cognitive elaboration in schemas. Just as "danger situations" are distinguishable in their internal representation as different kinds of threat, so relationships acquire an internally represented form in their pleasure aspect. Partial activation of such schemas can produce pleasure signals corresponding to anxiety signals.

The specification of pleasure prototypes should look to developmental models for clues as to qualitatively distinguishable pleasure experiences, as well as for a rationale of their adaptive utility. Here Erikson's conception of development offers a framework within which to conceive such prototypes and to relate them to psychological growth (Erikson, 1963, 1968). It is one of the few concep-

---

[4] It may be noted that this meaning-conception of anxiety has still not registered strongly in laboratory studies of anxiety, which usually focus upon anxiety in its physiological manifestation, as a phenomenon of goose pimples or GSR deflection, rather than in its different cognitive-affective meanings of subjectively experienced threats.

tions that has been an attempt to articulate a logic of ego growth that is not limited to stages of psychosexual development, and which tries to encompass the entire life of a person. Especially important for a theory of pleasure is the sensitivity of this conception to the phenomenology of self-experience at different stages. At the same time, Erikson's model neither abandons nor slights considerations of crisis and conflict as formative factors in growth. It views these, rather, as manifestations of an ever-continuing effort to bring about a balance between internalized group values (group identity) and autonomous individuality (ego identity). It thus provides a dynamic context within which to consider the economy of pleasure experiences, their management, their miscarriages and pathology, as well as their adaptive involvement in the stage-specific tasks of development. Actually Erikson has extended Freud's qualitative view of anxiety by delineating the forms of anxiety experiences for all stages of the life cycle. He has not, however, carried this view to considerations of pleasure.

Accordingly, I shall describe six prototypes of pleasure experience. These are taken to be potentials for pleasure that make their appearance in infancy but thereafter undergo a cognitive-affective elaboration, consistent with the developments in physical and cognitive capacity of different periods. We consider these pleasure prototypes to be vital in helping to affirm and crystallize the gains of each developmental stage, with its residue of "trust," "initiative," "competence," and the like. They are vital also in the sense that incapacities and miscarriages of these pleasure sensibilities will turn out to be permanent liabilities, restrictive to further psychological growth. Although they are important at every life stage, the relative importance of each pleasure is assumed to vary with the tasks and crises of selfhood at different periods of life, with particular classes of pleasure experience being especially pertinent at certain stages. In this sense of "vital" pleasure, the prototypes are specifically and collectively crucial in the delineation of self-identity.

PLEASURE IN THE REDUCTION
OF UNPLEASANT TENSION

It was once commonly thought that the world of the baby was made up mainly of satisfiers and frustrators. Recent observations, however, have suggested that the baby's experience is much wider in range than this. The world, for instance, often seems to be not so much satisfying or frustrating to him, but just interesting, holding his attention and perhaps provoking something akin to wonder. With the recognition of such states as "alert inactivity" (Wolff, 1959, 1966) the role of tension-reduction has been somewhat downgraded as a factor in the development of the baby's attachments to things and people.

Frustration is, however, an inescapable fact from the very beginnings of postnatal life. Babies do experience tension at times; they look and feel tense as they strain over a bowel movement or as they howl in hunger and pain, and they seem more content as these states subside. Although an expressive capacity for the conveying of pleasure is not very evident in the very young infant, it is not far-fetched to assume that the diminution of such tension and the "return to baseline" is experienced as a pleasurable state of well-being of some kind. We also assume, of course, that such early experiences are primitive in their cognitive elaboration.

In hypothesizing that tension-reduction is a source of pleasure, we refer to an actual *experience* of tension and its relief, not to a hypothetical condition of energic pressure. It is part of the present hypothesis that the relief of bowel pressure or of hunger, and later on the intermittent relief from teething, are not simply the elimination of unpleasure; the relief is itself experienced positively as pleasant.[5]

With developing attentional and conceptual capacity and increased options of response, the experience of tension and its pleasurable reduction becomes more and more removed from its original locus in bodily needs. A variety of cognitive conditions may create uncomfortable tension—e.g., incompleteness, interruption of a tendency (if the tendency remains active), unfamiliarity, failures of recognition, and the like. But this is not to say that the relief of somatic tensions ever loses its pleasurable aspect; for example, the cycle of anal retention-evacuation, including flatulation, is an underestimated source of pleasure.

The intimate connection between tension reduction and somatic or bodily state, as well as between the latter and sensual and function pleasures, suggests that these pleasure sources make a particularly early appearance in development. They are thus vital to a sense of physical separateness, or "body ego," which is a crucial precursor of psychological separateness and the later sense of "I" or self. Bettelheim (1967) has described an autistic child who was extraordinarily impervious to harmful stimulation and who absorbed herself in a game of holding back and letting go in defecation, as if inviting the cycle of tension and relief as a test of being "alive."

It used to be thought that the pleasure of tension-reduction was the crucial reinforcer of human attachments—for example, that the reason why a child becomes attached to a particular figure is that she feeds him and removes his other bodily discomforts. Recent evidence suggests that this is an overly simple reduction: the mere relief of hunger need not necessarily make for greater attachment to the source of gratification of food needs. (See Bowlby's review of the literature, 1969.) The reason, says Bowlby, is that, for the hungry baby, the person who gives food is only a mediator, bearer of the object that will relieve the tension; once the infant learns this distinction, the mother is not herself the

---

[5] Commenting on this passage, my colleague R. R. Holt takes issue with the assumption that reduced tension is necessarily felt as pleasurable. He points out that the actual sources of the pleasure may be the means by which tension gets reduced— e.g., through eating or defecating—and not the relief of tension. The reduction of tension may be merely a state of tranquil inertness, which is felt as neither pleasant nor unpleasant. He concludes: "I'm afraid that you are simply trying to absorb the old view by granting tension-reduction a minor place as one type of pleasure, whereas I think the implication of your paper, from the very first sentence, is that pleasure is *not* phenomenologically identical with less pain, less unpleasure, or less tension" (personal communication). Since at present the issue is not easily testable, I concede that it is debatable.

hungered-for object. Relationships would seem to depend more on other forms of pleasures shortly to be discussed, which lend themselves more naturally to and even require arousal conditions of mutual exchange and give-and-take.

Nevertheless, it is difficult to avoid the conclusion that the mother's appearance, which brings distress to an end and induces pleasure, does carry a powerful message of beneficence, affirmative to trust, and therefore contributes a motive for attachment to the mother. That is why Lois Murphy (1964), for example, insists that tension-reduction *is* important in establishing the relationship of a child to its mother. It is likely, however, that this basis of attachment is stronger in infants than it is in older children. Certainly the reliability of care in infancy, registered through the experience of tension-relief, would be a factor in producing what Erikson calls a favorable balance of trust over mistrust.

Developmentally advanced, more purely cognitive forms of tension experience and its reduction involve the circumvention of an obstacle. For example, Freud regarded this to be an important basis for the enjoyment of a joke; tendentious jokes, as Freud refers to them, have in particular a twofold advantage: they satisfy a repressed tendency in some measure, but they also afford relief from the effortful work of inhibition. The convergence of these two sources of tension makes for a particularly intense pleasure (Freud, 1905b).

Freud suggested that such lifting of inhibition (experienced as the relief of tension) also explains the pleasure that children, and adults too, get from games which deliberately create obstacles which are gotten rid of in "joyful acts of recognition." On the same assumption, Freud tried to account for the pleasure in certain games of nonsense.[6] Freud even goes so far as to offer the challenging hypothesis that in some disturbances of learning, the unconscious insistence upon bringing about such pleasure in nonsense plays a part in the child's inefficiency in learning certain operations that require the *"inhibitive* control of reason."

To bring both infantile and later developments into a conception of this pleasure prototype, we may consider the critical criterion of tension-reduction pleasure to be the relief of an experience of inhibition. In this generic formulation, tension-relief is not limited to the correction of an actual somatic deficit, but covers all occasions on which the bringing to an end of unpleasant tensions is experienced as pleasing.

------

[6] "Whatever the motive may have been which led the child to begin these games, I believe that in his later development he gives himself up to them with the consciousness that they are nonsensical, and that he finds enjoyment in the attraction of what is forbidden by reason. He now uses games in order to withdraw from the pressure of critical reason. But there is far more potency in the restrictions which must establish themselves in the course of a child's education in logical thinking and in distinguishing between what is true and false in reality; and for this reason, the rebellion against the compulsion of logic and reality is deep-going and long-lasting. Even the phenomena of imaginative activity must be included in this [rebellious] category. The power of criticism has increased so greatly in the later part of childhood and in the period of learning which extends over puberty that the pleasure in 'liberated nonsense' only seldom dares to show itself directly. One does not venture to say anything absurd" (Freud, 1905b, pp. 125–126).

These considerations raise the question of whether there develop motives specifically directed to *producing* the pleasure of tension-reduction by the intentional creation of a state of tension. Undoubtedly there are motives that deliberately court tension, and even anxiety and pain, for the sake of evoking the pleasure of relief. Usually, however, closer scrutiny of such instances suggests the presence as well of sensual pleasure and of pleasure derived from experiencing oneself as the intended agent of control (what we will call "effectance pleasure"). Even the thrill of a racing car, of the amusement park loop-the-loop, probably comes not only from the game of tension-creation and its relief, but also from admixtures of sensual arousal and effectance pleasure. For example, the counterphobic thrill may well be a mixture of anxiety and the self-reassurance that it is mastered.

SENSUAL PLEASURE

Like the pleasure of tension-reduction, sensual pleasure originates in bodily induced sensations. We would therefore expect the capacity for sensual pleasure also to be vital in affirming a sense of physical and psychological identity.

Elsewhere (see Klein, 1969), I have proposed that Freud's revolutionary precepts regarding infantile sexuality and its developmental course are most clearly appreciated when they are uncoupled from the drive-discharge model, which requires us to assume a *vis-a-tergo* force pressing for discharge.

Freud's innovations derived from several lines of evidence, which compelled him to conclude that sexuality must have an earlier origin than in puberty, indeed, one that affects how sexuality will appear in puberty. It became critical to identify this specific developmental factor, which manifests itself long before puberty, is independent of procreative sexuality, yet is continuous with it. From the standpoint of conscious experience, this prototypic sexuality (its time of first appearance is an empirical issue) reveals itself as a capacity for a distinctively pleasant experience, arousable through appropriately patterned stimulation of body surfaces; it has its own thresholds, and its own qualities, compared with other forms of sensory experiences that are also associated with the same body regions and modes that elicit sensual pleasure. The nub of Freud's proposal was that this pleasure capability undergoes development: it changes in respect to the bodily conditions of its arousal and the cognitive-affective record left behind by its arousal, this record or schema coming in time to be a factor in the regulation of the pleasure.

In this view, sensual pleasure is not simply an outcome of the removal of unpleasure or of tension; it is tied to conditions of arousal specific to itself and it is different from the pleasant experiences of other forms of satisfactions, or of rewards. Sibylle Escalona (personal communication) points out that although the occasions of sensual pleasure very often involve tension relief, sensual pleasure occurs also in contexts of fairly high tension, e.g., tickling and cradle-rocking.

Surprisingly little is known as yet, however, about the conditions of sensual arousal, even less about the informational gains from sensual pleasure or about the first appearance in infancy of sensual pleasure as a motive—that is, when activity is generated for the sake of its yield of sensual pleasure. Quite likely the capacity for sensual pleasure does not make its appearance at birth. After some weeks, however, we may assume the appearance of sensually specific activity— that is, pleasure experience that is not contingent on preceding experiences of tension, but is directly aroused by appropriate bodily stimulations that are either externally or endogenously produced. Evidence on all these matters is sparse. We are not even far advanced in the first and critical task of validating the basic claim of Freud's hypothesis, of distinguishing sensual from other forms of pleasure in infancy.

Quite possibly an important characteristic of sensuality, as compared with other forms of pleasure, is the unique way in which consciousness is dominated by the pleasure experience during sensual arousal, so that the informational yield of sensual contact is secondary to the pleasure experience itself. Sensory avenues are of course critical sources of information, but in non-sensual, sensory contacts, most of the time, the sensations themselves are not important and we hardly attend to them; it is the information about the *source* of these sensations that is important. The case is different with contacts that arouse sensual pleasure; here the pleasure experience itself preempts consciousness. Nonetheless, it be- comes a matter of great interest as to whether and to what extent the wafting movements, caressing, fondling, etc., which provoke sensual pleasure, provide in the baby some information about correlated internal states in the person who provokes it—of desiring, giving, offering, and the like—that is, social infor- mation concerning experiences of pleasure and intimacy in the other. Sensual experience in infancy may therefore be an important primary source of affiliation and attachment. At the age when such a perceptual capacity has matured enough to be said to operate in occasions of sensual arousal, sensual contact can become one means of acquiring what Harlow (1958) calls "contact comfort."

At a recent concert, I was struck by an incident of contact pleasure between parent and child, taking the form of a playful ritual or game. A father was holding his little boy in his lap as the orchestra was playing. Respecting his father's insistence that he be quiet, the little boy listened in his own way. Taking his father's large hand, he pumped the fingers rhythmically this way and that with the music, moving now this finger and then that finger to his will, turning the hand and palm up and then the palm down, running the father's hand against his face and moving it over his lips. All the time, the father was attentively focused on the concert, passively assenting to the play with his hand. Then, the father, in turn, took the boy's hand, closed it into a fist and drum beat it to the rhythm of the music; the boy passively, almost hypnotically, lent himself to the rhythmic movement of his limb with a rapt expression of quiet pleasure. Throughout one had a sense of play structured by registrations of benign messages of acceptance and affirmation, communicated through bodily responses of pleasure.

A critical attribute of sensual arousal is its *plasticity*: it can be autoerotically, heterosexually, or homoerotically aroused through the activity of bodily zones and modes that are not specifically sensual in function.

This quality of plasticity makes sensuality uniquely serviceable to a variety of adaptive aims. For example, since it is arousable autoerotically, it can be a means of *controlling* the objects of sensuality in fantasy. But plasticity is also a vulnerable asset in that it renders sensual potential uniquely susceptible to conflict. Although, in the exercise of every pleasure prototype, there develops a range of discretion and indiscretion that bounds its arousal and implementation, none seems to match the firmness of regulation and the exactitude of rules of severance that govern sensual pleasure. The requirement that development be guided toward procreation and heterosexuality and away from societally destructive choices, notably incestuous ones, runs counter to the natural tendency during the early formative years to seek and expect gratification precisely from such incestuous contact (Lindzey, 1967). Being in this way an exceptional experience, sensuality is distinctively etched in memory and concept, in an evolving record of what sensual pleasure furnishes for good and ill. This affects its arousal and regulation.

PLEASURE IN FUNCTION

Very early it seems evident that gratification of bodily needs does not account for activities that an infant seeks to engage in spontaneously and which afford him pleasure: there are times when he seems to grasp, suck, babble, squeeze and pull for no reason other than the pleasure of their repetition. Possibly included here are sensory pleasures and the exercise of distance receptors. A baby's fascination with a colorful mobile seems qualitatively different from his pleasure in having an erogenous zone stimulated. Peter Wolff (1959, 1966) has discovered this activity to be typical of intervals that he calls "alert inactivity," when the body is not occupied with feeding or other homeostatic business. Awareness of emerging sensory and motor capabilities, such as ocular fixation, prehension, phonation, locomotion, etc., generates interest and pleasure in demonstrating them, so to speak, to oneself; such pleasing repetitive play proceeds to the point when mastery of the particular manipulation is obtained. The repetitions then cease— that is, when the skill becomes available for purposes that serve other aims and other sources of pleasure. Piaget (1951) believes such pleasure in exercising function to be the inherently motivating aspect of assimilative and accommodative activity, referring to it as "desirability." From such beginnings in repetitious, playful exercise of capacity there develops a sense of and pleasure in skills themselves.

One of the first to draw attention to the pleasure in exercising function was Karl Bühler (1928,[7] 1930). In the psychoanalytic literature, it was Hendrick (1942) who first described this distinctive category of pleasure; he called it a "work

---

[7] "Indeed, the facts concerning children's activity in play are not to be explained by the supposition of a general libido and this formula alone. . . . Think of the movements themselves as endowed with pleasure, and we have formulated a fundamental, a central knowledge concerning children's play. I call it *Function Pleasure*. The fact is, certain forms of movements are themselves pleasurable. . . . In the phase of development where the child learns to grasp, the grasping movements of arms, hands, and fingers are endowed with function pleasure—and so in other phases the movements of walking, or talking, etc." (Bühler, 1928, p. 197).

principle"—the principle that primary pleasure is sought by efficient use of the central nervous system for the performance of well-integrated ego functions.

Hendrick spoke of his work principle as a "drive." Hartmann (1952) was considerably more influential in gaining acceptance for essentially the same idea, when he read into ego psychology the proposal that there is an autonomous line of conflict-free development of perceptual and cognitive functions which is fostered by associated experiences of function pleasure. Such conflict-free activity and its attendant pleasure is evident in the infant who is exploring, examining, and playing with various parts of his body, fingering his toes and his hands, pulling his ears, etc.

That there should be pleasure in the exercise of function leading to sharpened awareness of one's capabilities is consonant with what embryologists have pointed out to be an important factor in growth—the idea that a new function emerges as a state of "readiness" or potential "competence" requiring prompt exercise within a critical period. That is, if a specific chemical inductor hits the developing embryo, it will produce an effect if the competence or readiness is there; if it is not, the effect will not occur. The capacity for pleasure in function would seem to aid this process of provoking or serving the emergence of function.

Conversely, were function pleasure impeded, it would stultify awareness of function, probably with deleterious effects. Not only does such pleasure in function affirm a sense of capacity and skill; it also aids in the development of a sense of physical separateness and autogenous control, which is the necessary precursor of ego autonomy. Indeed, the sensory pleasures that are incidental to or anaclitic on the satisfaction of basic needs, along with sensual pleasures, help create the basic sense that life is good and the world a pleasant place—a sense that must enter into "basic trust."

THE PLEASURE IN EXPERIENCING SELF AS EFFECTIVE AGENT OF CHANGE: EFFECTANCE PLEASURE

The pleasure of effectance (White, 1959, 1963) resides in the perception that through one's own interference one has changed and can change the course of events once set in motion. Psychological autonomy has its beginnings in this awareness, and the practicing of this awareness becomes itself pleasurable. When the baby starts to grasp articles, sits up, crawls, tries to walk, he begins a process that eventually yields the sense that the locus and origin of these achievements is in himself. When the child thus feels the change as originating with himself, he begins to have a sense of *being* himself, a psychologically, not simply physically, autonomous unit.

Such a sense of control has an early precursor in the responsiveness that even babies show to imposed versus autogenously initiated movements of the body. For example, Piaget (1951) describes the reflex resistance with which a baby reacts to restrictive obstacles to his movements; the baby is clearly sensible of the operant movements of his own body.

Effectance pleasure can be for the infant a powerful self-affirming experience in surmounting psychological stress. Weaning, for example, is assisted by the potential for effectance pleasure. As Spock points out (1963), the infant experiences stress in the change-over of feeding routine, but the stress is alleviated by the pleasure of mastering bottle and spoon. This pleasure in effectiveness may be more than compensating, for it brings something of the environment under *his* control and initiative.

The component that distinguishes effectance from function pleasure is the pleasure in observing the successful correspondence of *intention* and effect. It differs from function pleasure in that, in effectance, the focus is not simply upon the exercise of skill or function per se, but on pleasure derived from the instrumental power of skill as a tool of one's intention.

Robert White (1960) was the first to show that the developments traditionally characterized as psychosexual stages owe much to effectance pleasure. For instance, defecation can provide an elemental form of satisfaction in "doing the job" well. Ample evidence indicates that the period of "latency," which has been left somewhat anonymous in the emphasis on psychosexual development, is actually one of aimful activity. In this period, described by Erikson as involving a dominant emphasis upon a sense of industry, a need to feel useful, to make things of significance, and exploratory identifications with those who know how to do things, the potential for effectance pleasure is an important experience that abets these facets of self-identity.

The pleasure that comes with effectance is especially important, not so much in the sense of motivating adjustment to the environment, as in motivating changes of the environment. If one thinks of growth as an active process, not simply of adjusting, but of creating adaptive variations in the environment to promote a balanced "fit" with it, one can hardly exaggerate the importance of effectance pleasure as an affirming, supportive experience that abets this process. In the child this begins with the function pleasure of making "traces," as Arnheim (1954) suggests, perhaps left on the floor or on the wall by dirty hands and feet. These are pleasurable, Arnheim explains, not only because "they involve the exciting experience of bringing about something visible that was not there before" (1954, p. 136), but also because of the child's perception of the trace as a sign of himself. Moreover, such actions control the *viewer*, a further bonus in effectance pleasure. If this is what the sign means to the child, it suggests that the creation and making of signs, of categories, of artifacts, and the sense of identity are closely related: the making of these are instruments by which one identifies oneself. Even when making traces has turned toward the higher stakes of making "art," the affirming pleasure in self-generated solution remains powerfully motivating.

Threatened self-autonomy is likely to stimulate rage and aggression. For the ego in such a state, motives of effectance pleasure can acquire ruthless intensity, reflecting the insistent, not-to-be-denied assertion of such autonomy. On the other hand, chronic deprivations in the child of a kind in which effort brings feedback only of failed influence are mortifying to selfhood and to self-respect, and may result in a resigned yielding to complete passivity. Bettelheim

(1967) points out that harm can come not merely from chronic absence of opportunity for effectance experiences but also from pushing the child too soon into reliance upon psychological independence, which too may produce returns only of failure, so that in time even extraordinary events may not reach the child's attention, because he can really do nothing about them.

Bettelheim's account of what he believes to be the essential deficit in autistic children seems to come down to a failure to experience effectance. The exaggerated rituals of order often seen in such children would appear to be symptomatic indicators of this. "It seems generally true," he writes, "that the less we are able to act where the results are important to us the more we predict. And the less we can act and predict, the more inclined we are to order" (p. 21).[8]

THE PLEASURE IN PLEASING

An infant tends to become attached to figures who initiate interaction with him. A key factor in the attachment is the pleasure aroused in the mutuality of interaction—an interaction that seems to involve a sensibility in the baby of the pleasure he is bringing about in the other. The pleasure felt is in the pleasure created. The mother seems to be communicating *her* pleasure in his activity; the baby's rejoinder of pleasure may hardly be called as yet a message of his own, but it provokes a kind of positive amplification of those maneuvers of mutuality in baby and mother that brought about this shared pleasure. Whether consciously or not, the mother seems to behave as if she senses that she is communicating her feelings to the baby by the way she responds. Surely it does not take long before the infant can react to whether her emotions are mainly positive, negative, or ambivalent.

Call (1964) has drawn attention to the infant's subtle capacity to determine and adapt to the optimal stimulus configuration of bottle or breast, utilizing the kinesthetic sensations derived from the mother's holding position. It is not far-fetched to infer from this capacity that a pleasure experience of the kind just described may arise in the baby from recording, in a primitive way, that his

---

[8] He continues: "This is why artificial feeding times, arranged according to the clock, can dehumanize the infant. The reason is not just that time-clock feeding is contrary to the natural rhythms of the body, or that it signifies a mechanical ordering of time and of the mother-child relation. More important here is that it prevents the infant from feeling that *his* actions (crying, smiling) have a significant effect on this important life experience of being fed.

"What humanizes the infant is not being fed, changed, or picked up when he feels the need for it, though they add greatly to his comfort and feeling of well-being. . . . It is rather the experience that *his* crying for food brings about *his* satiation by others according to *his* timing that makes it a socializing and humanizing experience. It is that *his* smile, or facial grimacing, evokes a parallel or otherwise appropriate response in the mother.

"Conversely, the experience that his own actions (cry or smile) make no difference is what stops him from becoming a human being, for it discourages him from interacting with others and hence from forming a personality through which to deal with the environment" (p. 25).

actions and movements are consequential in bringing pleasure to the mother. This sensibility is perhaps within the infant's capacity from a quite early age. According to Bowlby (1969), a predictable outcome of the baby's smile is that "the baby's mother (or other figure smiled at) responds in a loving way that prolongs social interaction between them and increases the likelihood of her exhibiting maternal behaviour in future . . . and . . . that the function of a baby's smile is that of increasing interaction between mother and baby and maintaining them in proximity to each other" (p. 280). The pleasure he obtains in *her* reaction further enhances his efforts to foster the same behaviors that brought that reaction about in the first place—a circular process of mutually amplified maneuvers designed to sustain pleasure in the other.

There is experimental evidence to suggest the early appearance of such a prototypic potential for pleasure. Bowlby writes: "There is good evidence that when a baby's smile is responded to in a loving sociable way he smiles thereafter more strongly" (p. 287). Brackbill (1958) demonstrated this with three-month-old babies. When the baby smiled, she smiled back, stroking and cuddling him. This response in turn brought on another smile from the baby and with several such exchanges the role of smiling increased. Bowlby's comment seems an apt description of the shared experience: "In all this each partner seems to be expressing joy in the other's presence and the effect is certainly one of prolonging their social interaction" (p. 246). Conversely, when the experimenter stopped responding to the baby's smile, its smiling became more and more infrequent until eventually it died out. Rheingold, Gewirtz, and Ross (1959) reported in another study that, if similar responses of pleasure are directed to a three-month-old baby's vocalizations, this will bring about an increase in babbling. After two "rewarded" days in which they responded to the infants' vocalizations with gestures of pleasure, the infants' vocalizations had almost doubled. It is reasonable to suppose, then, that pleasure in the pleasure one provokes in another can become an early basis of actions expressly calculated to please another; that generating pleasure in another is early recognized as a gainful occasion for being approved, for being affirmed in one's being. A potential for pleasure experience in this affiliative context may be one of the facts that justifies Scott's (1968) belief that a critical period for primary socialization exists in human development.

The fact that pleasure arises from such a source tells us too that the affiliative requirement has roots just as deep as those pleasure potentials that are more directly localized and originating in the "body ego." But perhaps an equally important implication to be drawn from this early appearing, qualitatively distinct pleasure prototype is that distinctions between self-interest and interest-in-other are probably less clearcut than has been assumed in the past. We may remind ourselves here that feeling oneself a needed part of a larger, more encompassing affiliative entity is, after all, a continuing requirement of a developing self-identity. Therefore, the pleasure in pleasing can be vital in helping to affirm both one's psychological autonomy and one's need for an accepted stature in a social entity: "I am not only that which enables me to control the environment, but I am also what another is pleased with me for being." The capacity to feel pleasure in pleasing helps growth to proceed from reaction to *interaction*, into a self that can both affirm and be affirmed by others.

The active responsiveness to another's pleasure that even infants seem capable of also is one more indication that in mother-child relationships the child has less need for passive reception than was once thought to be the case. The requirement to "belong" certainly makes an early appearance, but as something *sought*.

PLEASURE IN SYNTHESIS (AESTHETIC)

By pleasure in synthesis I mean the delighted contemplation of *restored* or *discovered* order. Substitute "lingering over" or "attending to" for the word "contemplating," and it is not difficult to maintain that something of the sort is seen quite early in development. The evidence is impressive that there are in very young children, and indeed even in primates, selective preferences for certain forms and shapes, and standards of "rightness" and "fit." Even in the first year and a half of life, we see the beginnings of a sensibility for order, for operations of making order, for correction of error, for perceiving order emerging from disorder, distinguishing match from mismatch, and for such recognitions to be accompanied by pleasure. Desmond Morris' (1962) descriptions of the paintings and scribblings of the chimp Congo seem to disclose not simply the "function pleasure" of exercising visual-motion coordinations; they reveal primitive conceptual preferences and compositional control. Particularly striking was the indication that Congo seemed to appreciate when a picture was finished. Children's "art" (Kellogg, 1969) shows similar indications of archetypical representations and formal preferences. Erikson (1963, p. 108) notes that children take pains that their play constructions be "just right." He also shows that the preferred configurations of boys and girls seem to be tied in with respective differences in the ground plan of their bodies.

The pervasive sensibility to order is well expressed by Huizinga's (1950) description of children's play. Play, he writes,

. . . *creates order, is order. Into an imperfect world and into the confusion of life it brings a contemporary, a limited perfection. Play demands order absolute and supreme. The least deviation from it spoils the game, robs it of its character and makes it worthless. The profound affinity between play and order is perhaps the reason why play . . . seems to be to such a large extent in the field of aesthetics. Play has a tendency to be beautiful. It may be that this aesthetic factor is identical with the impulse to create orderly form, which initiates play in all its aspects. The words we use to denote the elements of play belong for the most part to aesthetics, terms with which we try to describe the effects of beauty: tension, poise, balance, contrast, variation, solution, resolution, etc. . . . It is invested with the noblest qualities we are capable of perceiving in things: rhythm and harmony (p. 10).*

If something akin to aesthetic sensibility is demonstrable in apes, the question arises what adaptive usefulness this has for development. Clearly, if an aesthetic potential does exist in apes, they have not taken it very far, whereas the case is different in man. The answer perhaps lies in the necessity in man, distinguishing him from the ape, of having to create a self-defined identity. From childhood on throughout life, the effort to be at one with oneself and to find an acceptance in and accept a place within a social context is a pervasive and dominant focus of motives and actions. Since self-identity is a continuing achievement, wrought out of adjudicating and resolving incompatibilities, it is fitting that a sensitivity to dissonance, cleavage, and finiteness, and a corresponding pleasure in discovering order, in restoring order, and in ordered complexity will not only have early beginnings, but be of continuing importance throughout life.

When, because of accidental developmental shifts or conflicts, one loses a sense of essential wholeness, efforts at restructuring it in a design that reestablishes it define motivational direction. As Erikson (1963) points out, among the earliest and most sobering lessons of limitation are the experience of falling, of *sudden* loss of support, of suddenness generally, which can lead to a fear of sudden change (Chapter 11). He also suggests that the baby may very early acquire some continuing sense of loss from experiencing the mother's withdrawal of the nipple. But such sensibility to limitation and finiteness, and the distaste for it, whets the appetite for order; experiences of limitation hint at and offer an inducement of a principle of order to be learned. And we do in fact learn our body's limitations without having to be taught them formally: for instance, early experiences tell us that we cannot walk on water, or fly. Being able to sense our finiteness converts fear into thoughtful respect—a condition for pleasure in order. Familiar things that have served the efforts to achieve self-related synthesis become "right," "good," "preferred"; novel things that promise to create a sense of rectifying mismatch and disorder become valued, "worth while," "beautiful," in their proven utility. Both the familiar and the novel come to be endowed with properties of pleasingness for their restitutive capacity or in closing the gaps of incompleteness. From this standpoint, even the uniformities of children's art are images of wholeness and integration.

With cognitive and physiological development, the sensibility to cleavage and dissonance becomes even more complex; correspondingly, the appreciation of meaning and of the limits of tolerable error becomes more charged with self-consciousness, urgency, and even anxiety. It reaches its crest, perhaps, as a need, in those twilight years when irreversible finitude is finally to be faced, and the effort to bring together past, present, and a shrinking future into a self-justifying meaning has become especially poignant and difficult.

From this perspective, the capability and requirement for experiencing pleasure in achievements of synthesis are present in all men; they are not the exclusive province of the professional aesthete, nor are they confined to the ritualized aesthetic play afforded by museums and the "art world." Pleasure in things that fit and that reestablish wholeness is a vital self-affirming experience, serving to accredit as "real" or "true" those conditions, objects, relationships and symbols that help sustain a sense of coherence and continuity of self. Preoccupation with issues of making things fit and with establishing and reestablishing a sense of wholeness is one of serious engagement, although it may be specifically actualized and sought in the context of fantasy, of play, and of art.

The conditions of aesthetic pleasure are more purely cognitive than those of tension reduction and sensual pleasure. At stages of cognitive immaturity, it is possible, therefore, that the occasions of pleasurable syntheses are indistinguishably linked to the reduction of tension. With maturing cognitive capacities, the aspect of pleasure that is derived from perceiving and closing a gap with the *right* fit comes to be discernible, and deserves to be designated as a pleasure prototype in its own right. If experienced tension is involved at all in aesthetic pleasure (and it need not be), it is *tolerated tension;* indeed, the aesthetically pleasurable solution may itself be experienced as tension, but as a satisfying kind of tension—a state of active tension in balance, felt as things "falling into place."

An important aspect of aesthetic pleasure is that it involves an active integration. It would belie our understanding of aesthetic pleasure experience in its adaptive utility to regard it as implying an attitude of passive receptiveness. Rather it would seem to be more in the service of what Freud (1926) called a mental mechanism of turning passive into active, which he regarded as central to the maintenance of man's individuality and wholeness. The conditions of what we call pleasure in synthesis derive from this momentum. This tie-in with a requirement for an actively sustained identity is what links aesthetic pleasure so much more closely to the act of discovery than to sensual contact and tension reduction.

This completes the inventory of the vital pleasures. In delineating these classes of pleasure, I have considered it more useful to specify *distinguishable contexts* of a pleasure experience rather than to try to delineate varieties of pleasure *"sensation"* itself. Traditional views of pleasure as a "sensation" (see, for example, Beebe-Center, 1932) have led to futile efforts to develop criteria for measuring it, at the expense of designating its cognitive context. Yet, as Kenny (1965) and Peters (1969) point out, even efforts at simply setting up criteria for the sameness of sensations encounter the inescapable need to take into account the conditions in which they occur and what people do about them. Following Kenny's lead, therefore, the present focus has been on the circumstances of pleasure arousal, the kinds of encounters people engage in for the pleasure they afford, as distinct from habitual actions or things done from some extrinsic reason, unaccompanied by pleasure.

The six classes of pleasure refer accordingly to contexts of stimulation and action that seem to be inherently pleasurable. From the standpoint of motivation, they refer to the intrinsic motivational aspect of an action. When we argue that pleasure is in the category of a motive we are in agreement with Peters (1969), who speaks of the intrinsically motivating aspect of actions—the pleasure aspect, in respect to which things are "wanted," and "needed." Certainly a large part of motivation is searching for and doing things for the sake of a pleasure aim.

Situations and encounters and relationships become important for having proved themselves as occasions for such pleasures; they are thereafter wanted for that very reason. The pleasures do not themselves require rewards in order to be aroused; they are not themselves reinforced, but become "reinforcers."

The study of such inherently pleasurable classes of activity, or different pleasure aims, is important for education. We need to know what particular gain in pleasure frames the context of learning, how it becomes a basis for the incentive to learn, and indeed, for what is learned. Knowing *what* pleasure gain is intrinsically motivating for a person, and the conditions of action and encounter that foster and inhibit it, are important for encouraging learning. If we knew more about this, we might come to know better how to offer knowledge to children. Different pleasure aims can lead to learning that is appropriate to the situation, as viewed by a teacher: an anatomy book may offer something for learning to a sexually preoccupied adolescent that is much different from what it offers to a medical student. Merely to assume, as has been done in the past, that learning itself must be made pleasurable (or is the outcome of "reinforcement") is simply a crass beginning.

What we are saying about pleasure as motive is in sympathetic accord with what we hear these days from those (White, 1963; Hunt, 1965; Koch, 1956, 1969) who point to such intrinsically motivating dispositions as the tendencies to explore, to master, etc., which are indulged in for their own sake.

We depart, however, from Hunt and others when they take the evidence of intrinsically motivated actions as the whole story of motivation, when they caustically criticize psychoanalysis for explaining one aim in terms of another extrinsic one. They ignore the possibility that inherently pleasurable activity can be extrinsically motivated as well. It is true that psychoanalysis has tended to slight the causative and self-perpetuating influence of a pleasure experience. But the "intrinsic motivation" view neglects the understanding opened to us by psychoanalysis—namely, that there are motives *for* pleasure seeking, and thus that the different pleasures can themselves acquire *functions,* and indeed be sought and *selectively* emphasized for *unconscious* aims. It is not only necessary to know that certain conditions have the meaning for a given person of affording an opportunity for a particular kind of pleasure; it is also necessary to understand the selective emphasis he is giving to that rather than to another source of pleasure. The assumption, for example, that the different classes of pleasure can be serviceable to *defense* helps to account for repetitive insistence upon one or another form of pleasure, for extreme avoidance of certain pleasure opportunities on the one hand, and for extreme hedonism (in one or another pleasure source) on the other. It also allows for the possibility of arrests and regressions in respect to pleasure-seeking. The developmental record of the vital pleasures will vary in respect to the relative claims and dominance that each class of pleasure has in a person's life, including such variations, for example, as desiring too much of a particular pleasure or of expecting too little. Clinical therapeutic exploration consists in part of examining the relative selective emphasis on the different forms of pleasure in the patient's history.

I shall close my discussion by considering some developmental implications of the notion of pleasure prototypes.

As a means of accenting these implications, I have pictured the different vital pleasures in an Eriksonian "epigenetic" chart, which tries to reflect their relativity to other schedules of development, physical and cognitive (Figure 2). It goes without saying that this scheme is extremely tentative. My intention is only to suggest some of the fresh and possibly fruitful leads that open up to us when considerations of pleasure are viewed in this way.

The various pleasure capacities are assumed to have early origins. For example, a baby may show something like autonomy from the beginning, in the particular way in which he angrily tries to wriggle his hands free when tightly held, although his capability for responding with pleasure to conditions of effectance, and of specifically *seeking* this source of pleasure, will come only much later. The pleasure prototypes are shown to have a continuing development, as well as a time of special pertinence to a phase of ego growth. The forward-pointing horizontal arrows suggest that a given pleasure prototype undergoes modifications that reflect the ego developments of a given stage. By far the most elaborated conception of a prototypic pleasure is, of course, Freud's description of the psychosexual stages. Each of the empty boxes can be thought of as qualitative varieties of each of the pleasure prototypes, and remains to be filled in.

The diagram tells us that the study of any of the pleasure prototypes should be oriented to specifying its qualitative characteristics at different stages. For example, each life stage produces and requires norms of order and balance that condition aesthetic pleasure—a projected expression of the tasks of the stage, imagined in an ideal resolution and exhibited in the forms of play, fantasy, and activity. For the child, it may be the recognition of the mother in all her "perfection"; for the growing boy, the hero-ideal. In advanced years, the occasions for aesthetic pleasure may be symbols, in which images of the past are reconciled with those of the present and with premonitions of irreversible finitude.

The heavily etched boxes that form the diagonal indicate periods in which the pleasure prototype seems especially relevant to the tasks and crises that are developmentally specific to that period. Thus, pleasure experiences associated with reduction of tension will help create an orientation of trust. In the periods of early and middle childhood, when issues of psychological autonomy, work-initiative, and industry become paramount, the pleasure in function and effectance pleasure are particularly vital reinforcements. It is reasonable that feeling one's body in action and the effectiveness of the parts of one's body that work, and taking pleasure in so doing, will promote a sense of physical autonomy. Discovering his ability to give *intentional* sound-signs is a pleasure that leads the child to exercise it for its own sake.

The diagram should not be taken to imply that there is necessarily an even and progressive development of each pleasure prototype. A more likely possibility is that all or some reach an asymptote, as, for example, with sensual pleasure at the genital stage. It should also be pointed out that the heavily etched-in

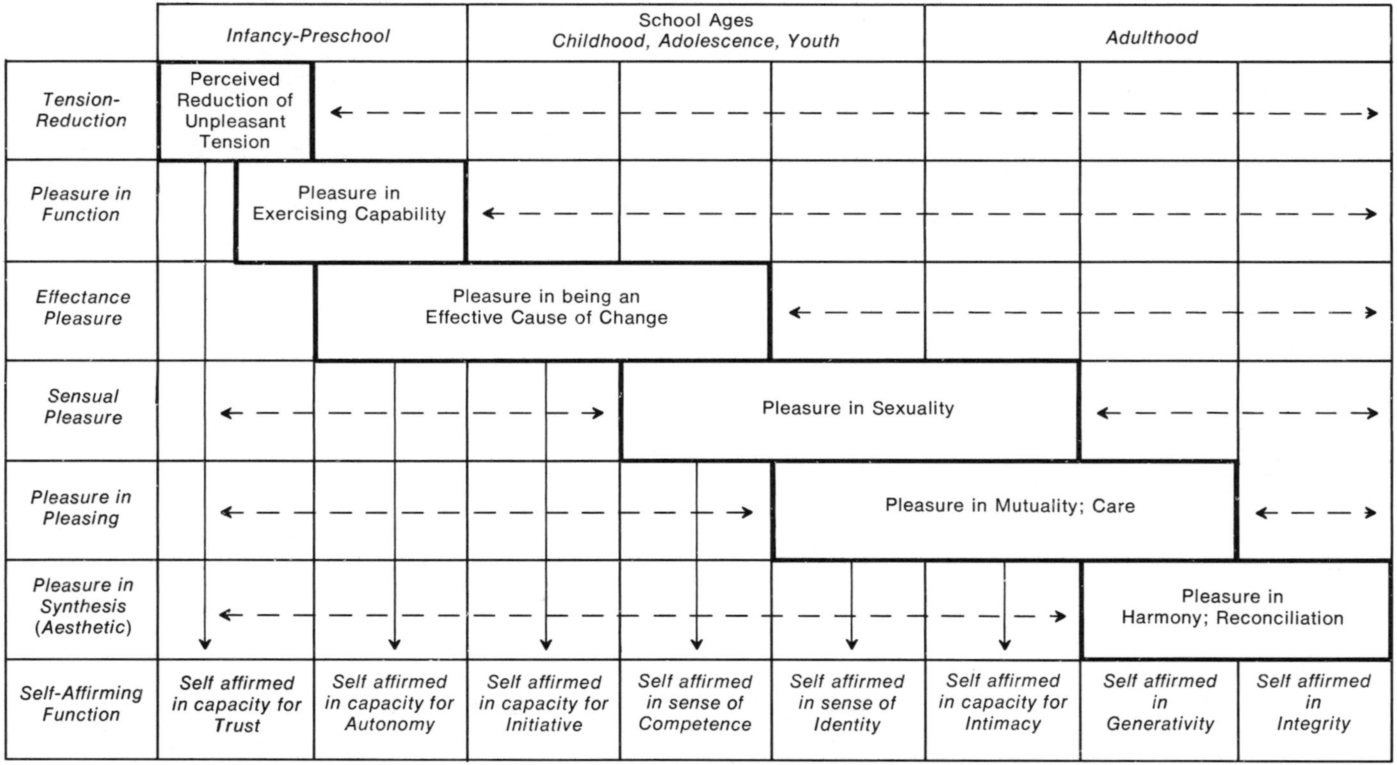

Infancy-Preschool | School Ages Childhood, Adolescence, Youth | Adulthood

Tension-Reduction — Perceived Reduction of Unpleasant Tension

Pleasure in Function — Pleasure in Exercising Capability

Effectance Pleasure — Pleasure in being an Effective Cause of Change

Sensual Pleasure — Pleasure in Sexuality

Pleasure in Pleasing — Pleasure in Mutuality; Care

Pleasure in Synthesis (Aesthetic) — Pleasure in Harmony; Reconciliation

Self-Affirming Function:
Self affirmed in capacity for Trust | Self affirmed in capacity for Autonomy | Self affirmed in capacity for Initiative | Self affirmed in sense of Competence | Self affirmed in sense of Identity | Self affirmed in capacity for Intimacy | Self affirmed in Generativity | Self affirmed in Integrity

Figure 2. The vital pleasures and critical periods of ascendance.

201

box does not imply that development of the pleasure prototype stops at that point, or that its importance for ego development was minimal before or wanes thereafter. Effectance pleasure, for example, would seem to be important at all ages. At the same time, it would appear that with increasing and changing potentialities of conflict, the potential for aesthetic pleasure undergoes continuing change throughout the life cycle.

The horizontal arrows pointing both ways suggest the possibility of regression as well as progression. Development of a prototype may be arrested at a given stage, and there may also occur regression to pleasure forms of an earlier stage. Such occurrences would characterize pathological developments in a given period.

The vertical arrows of the chart tell us that experiences of pleasure in the different prototypes are important to the emergence of what Erikson calls the *ego strengths* of different periods. Pleasure nourishes self-affirmation. Different pleasure experiences seem especially relevant to consolidating these gains of ego-strength. Correspondingly, we may infer that pleasure incapacity, or the failure to activate the different sources of pleasure at appropriate points of development, whether because of conflict, frustration, insufficient opportunity or deprivation, may contribute to chronic anhedonia and to a residue of ego vulnerability and insufficiency. Thus, following the arrows downward and in a progressive course, we find that a rich pleasure life in infancy, particularly in respect to the prompt alleviation of tension, reinforces the emerging ego strength of trust; adequate experiences of function pleasure and effectance help affirm a sense of autonomy, initiative, and industry; pleasure in genital mutuality helps actualize a sense of intimacy; and, at the later stages, pleasure-in-pleasing and aesthetic pleasures are especially relevant to consolidating achievements of "generativity" and "integrity."

In describing pleasure, we face the age-old problem of how to penetrate a private experience. Pleasure is that, of course; nevertheless, I have chosen to avoid the temptation to distinguish pleasures by variations in experienced sensation, and to specify them instead by aim and by the configuration of circumstances that elicit and reinstate them. On this basis, I have delineated six prototypic classes of pleasure. Although several of and even all these pleasures may be interactively present in particular occasions of pleasure, they are still distinguishable conceptually; the distinctions are important in the way in which height and weight are different, even though they are indivisibly associated.

I have preferred not to face the question of whether these pleasures defined on the basis of cognitive context are accompanied also by distinctive pleasure sensations, although I grant the importance of the issue. For example, sensual pleasure may indeed be unique in respect to quality of sensation, and this may have something to do with the tenacious hold of this pleasure on consciousness, as compared with the others and with the peculiarly preemptive clarity of sensual experiences.

Nevertheless, viewing pleasure from the standpoint of aim has enabled us to keep in focus the adaptive significance of pleasure as an ego resource supportive to an evolving self-identity. Especially for the human organism, confronted as it is with complexity of option and choice, pleasure is the most immediate and intimate testimony of beneficent engagement with the world. It is as vital to development to be responsive to messages of adaptive beneficence, provided by different forms of pleasure experiences, as to experience opposite ones—varieties of estrangement, evoking anxiety.

REFERENCES

Apfelbaum, B. (1965). Ego Psychology, Psychic Energy, and the Hazards of Quantitative Explanation in Psychoanalytic Theory. *International Journal of Psycho-Analysis,* 46: 168–181.

Arnheim, R. (1954). *Art and Visual Perception.* Berkeley: University of California Press.

Beebe-Center, J. G. (1932). *The Psychology of Pleasantness and Unpleasantness.* New York: Van Nostrand.

Bettelheim, M. (1967). *The Empty Fortress.* New York: Free Press.

Bowlby, J. (1969). *Attachment and Loss,* Vol. 1. New York: Basic Books.

Brackbill, Y. (1958). Extinction of the Smiling Response in Infants as a Function of Reinforcement Schedule. *Child Development,* 29:115–124.

Buchenholz, B. (1956). The Motivating Action of Pleasure. *Journal of Nervous and Mental Disease,* 124:569–577.

——— (1957). The Pleasure Process. *Journal of Nervous and Mental Disease,* 125:396–402.

Bühler, K. (1928). Displeasure and Pleasure in Relation to Activity. In: *Feelings and Emotions,* ed. C. Murchison. Worcester, Mass.: Clark University Press, pp. 195–199.

——— (1930). *The Mental Development of a Child.* London: Kegan Paul, Trench, Trubner. New York: Harcourt, Brace.

Call, J. D. (1964). Newborn Approach Behavior and Early Ego Development. *International Journal of Psycho-Analysis,* 45:286–294.

Eidelberg, L. (1962). A Contribution to the Study of the Unpleasure-Pleasure Principle. *Psychiatric Quarterly,* 36:312–316.

Erikson, E. H. (1963). *Childhood and Society,* 2nd ed. New York: Norton.

——— (1968). *Identity: Youth and Crisis.* New York: Norton.

Freud, S. (1905a). Three Essays on the Theory of Sexuality. *Standard Edition,* 7:125–245. London: Hogarth Press, 1953.

——— (1905b). Jokes and Their Relation to the Unconscious. *Standard Edition,* 8. London: Hogarth Press, 1960.

——— (1920). Beyond the Pleasure Principle. *Standard Edition,* 18:3–64. London: Hogarth Press, 1955.

——— (1926). Inhibitions, Symptoms and Anxiety. *Standard Edition,* 20:87–174. London: Hogarth Press, 1959.

——— (1930). Civilization and Its Discontents. *Standard Edition,* 21:64–145. London: Hogarth Press, 1961.

——— (1933). New Introductory Lectures on Psychoanalysis. Lecture 32. Anxiety and Instinctual Life. *Standard Edition,* 22:81–111. London: Hogarth Press, 1964.

Harlow, H. F. (1958). The Nature of Love. *American Psychologist,* 13:673–685.

Hartmann, H. (1952). The Mutual Influences in the Development of Ego and Id. In: *Essays on Ego Psychology.* New York: International Universities Press, 1964, pp. 155–181.

Hendrick, I. (1942) Instinct and the Ego during Infancy. *Psychoanalytic Quarterly,* 11:33–58.

——— (1943). Work and the Pleasure Principle. *Psychoanalytic Quarterly,* 12:311–329.

Herold, C. M. (1941–42). Critical Analysis of the Elements of Psychic Functions. *Psychoanalytic Quarterly,* 10:513–544; 11:59–82, 187–210.

Holt, R. R. (1965). A Review of Some of Freud's Biological Assumptions and Their Influence on His Theories. In: *Psychoanalysis and Current Biological Thought,* ed. N. S. Greenfield and W. C. Lewis. Madison: University of Wisconsin Press, pp. 93–124.

——— (1967). Beyond Vitalism and Mechanism: Freud's Concept of Psychic Energy. In: *Science and Psychoanalysis,* 11:1–41, ed. J. Masserman. New York: Grune and Stratton.

Huizinga, J. (1950) *Homo Ludens: A Study of the Play Element in Culture.* Boston: Beacon Press, 1955.

Hunt, J. McV. (1965). Intrinsic Motivation. In: *Nebraska Symposium on Motivation,* ed. D. Levine. Lincoln: University of Nebraska Press.

Jacobson, E. (1953). The Affects and Their Pleasure-Unpleasure Qualities in Relation to the Psychic Discharge Processes. In: *Drives, Affects, Behavior,* ed. R. M. Loewenstein. New York: International Universities Press, pp. 38–66.

Kanzer, M., and Eidelberg, L. (1960). The Structural Description of Pleasure. *International Journal of Psycho-Analysis,* 41:368–371.

Kardiner, A., Karush, A., and Ovesey, L. (1959). A Methodological Study of Freudian Theory: II. The Libido Theory. III. Narcissism, Bisexuality and the Dual Instinct Theory. *Journal of Nervous and Mental Disease,* 129:133–193, 207–221.

Kaufman, J. C. (1960). Some Theoretical Implications from Animal Behavior Studies for the Psychoanalytic Concepts of Instinct, Energy, and Drive. *International Journal of Psycho-Analysis,* 41:318–326.

Kellogg, R. (1969). *Analyzing Children's Art.* Palo Alto, Cal.: Natural Press Books.

Kenny, A. (1965). *Actions, Emotions and Will.* London: Kegan Paul.

Klein, G. S. (1969). Freud's Two Theories of Sexuality. In: *Clinical-Cognitive Psychology: Models and Integrations,* ed. L. Breger. Englewood Cliffs, N.J.: Prentice-Hall.

Koch, S. (1956). Behavior as "Intrinsically" Regulated. In: *Nebraska Symposium on Motivation,* ed. M. R. Jones. Lincoln: University of Nebraska Press.

——— (1969). Value Properties: Their Significance for Psychology, Axiology, and Science. In: Toward a Unity of Knowledge, ed. M. Grene. *Psychological Issues,* Monograph No. 22:251–279. New York: International Universities Press.

Lindzey, G. (1967). Some Remarks concerning Incest, the Incest Taboo, and Psychoanalytic Theory. *American Psychologist,* 22:1051–1059.

Morris, D. (1962). *The Biology of Art.* New York: Knopf.

Murphy, L. B. (1964). Some Aspects of the First Relationship. *International Journal of Psycho-Analysis,* 45:31–43.

Peters, R. S. (1969). Motivation, Emotion and the Conceptual Schemes of Common Sense. In: *Human Action: Conceptual and Empirical Issues,* ed. T. Mischel. New York: Academic Press, pp. 135–165.

Piaget, J. (1951). *Play, Dreams and Imitation in Childhood.* New York: Norton.

Rapaport, D. (1960). The Structure of Psychoanalytic Theory. *Psychological Issues,* Monograph No. 6. New York: International Universities Press.

Rheingold, H. C. (1966). The Development of Social Behavior in the Human Infant. *Monograph of the Society for Research in Child Development,* 31: No. 5 (Whole No. 107).

———, Gewirtz, J. C., and Ross, A. W. (1959). Social Conditioning of Vocalizations in the Infant. *Journal of Comparative Physiological Psychology,* 52:68–73.

Schur, M. (1966). *The Id and the Regulating Principles of Mental Functioning.* New York: International Universities Press.

Scott, J. P. (1968). *Early Experience and the Organization of Behavior.* Belmont, California: Brooks/Cole.

Spock, B. (1963). The Striving for Autonomy and Regressive Object Relationships. *Psychoanalytic Study of the Child,* 18:361–364. New York: International Universities Press.

Szasz, T. S. (1957). *Pain and Pleasure.* New York: Basic Books.

White, R. W. (1959). Motivation Reconsidered: The Concept of Competence. *Psychological Review,* 66:297–333.

———— (1960). Competence and the Psychosexual Stages of Development. In: *Nebraska Symposium on Motivation,* ed. M. R. Jones. Lincoln: University of Nebraska Press, pp. 99–140.

———— (1963). Ego and Reality in Psychoanalytic Theory: A Proposal regarding Independent Ego Energies. *Psychological Issues,* Monograph No. 11. New York: International Universities Press.

Wolff, P. H. (1959). Observations on Newborn Infants. *Psychosomatic Medicine,* 21:110–118.

———— (1966). The Causes, Controls, and Organization of Behavior in the Neonate. *Psychological Issues,* Monograph No. 17. New York: International Universities Press.

THE STIMULUS BARRIER
IN EARLY INFANCY:
An Exploration of Some Formulations
of John Benjamin

Katherine Tennes, M.A., Robert Emde, M.D., Anthony Kisley, M.D.,
and David Metcalf, M.D.[1]

The idea that the central nervous system is equipped with a barrier to stimulation, or a protective shield (*Reizschutz*) was originally introduced by Freud (1920, 1925). The concept has been widely used by psychoanalytic theoreticians in its implications for the development of defense mechanisms (Spitz, 1957, 1961; Hartmann, 1950), for pathological hypersensitivities (Bergman and Escalona, 1949), and as a variable in the predisposition to anxiety (Greenacre, 1958).

Within the context of a discussion of biopsychoanalytic research, Benjamin (1965) suggested that the "stimulus barrier" concept afforded an opportunity to follow biobehavioral relationships as they emerge over time in earliest infancy. In this discussion—from which we shall quote at some length—Benjamin formulated the "stimulus barrier hypothesis," composed of three propositions, each addressed to a particular developmental age.

The first of these propositions has to do with what he called the "maturational crisis" in infants at three to four weeks of age. He described the observational data and other evidence from which he derived the hypothesis as follows (1965):

As previously reported [Benjamin, 1961a, 1961b, 1963], we noted that full-term infants show a marked and relatively sudden increase in sensitivity to external and internal stimulation at the age of 3–4 weeks. The behavioral criteria are increased crying and other motor manifestations of negative affect, of unpleasure. The phenomenon is most easily accessible to naturalistic observation whenever, for one reason or another, the usual physiological needs of the infant are not well met. In all other cases, it is clearly demonstrable only when sensory stimulation in different modalities is experimentally introduced (p. 58).

[1] Dr. Emde is supported by U.S. Public Health Service Grant MH-HD 15753 and the National Institute of Mental Health Research Scientist Development Award K3-MH-36808. Dr. Metcalf is supported by National Institute of Mental Health Research Scientist Development Award K5-MH-40275.

He attempted to find evidence bearing on the assumption that the relatively sudden appearance of the behavioral change was a function of the state of neuroanatomical and physiological maturation at this particular time. Suggestive evidence was found in the longitudinal and cross-sectional investigations (carried out in association with Dr. David Metcalf) of electroencephalographic development between birth and three months. Initial examination of these records by Metcalf, independent of Benjamin's findings, had led him to the tentative statement that "There is a rather abrupt change in awake, drowsy, and sleep EEG's sometime around the age of 3 weeks, with relatively little change taking place in the period between 3–4 weeks and 7–8 weeks. What change does take place in awake and drowsy recordings in this interval is in the direction of further development of periodicity without major changes in types of frequencies" (personal communication).

Benjamin (1965) then considered the possible neuroanatomical or neurophysiological bases of these observations. He stated:

. . . when we ask ourselves just what structures and functions are maturing sufficiently at this point in time to account for these changing behavioral and EEG phenomena in the human infant, we find no easy answer; or, rather, we find a plethora of possible and plausible answers, involving cortex, brain stem and reticular system, thalamus, and thalamo-cortical and other pathways. The simple fact is that we do not yet know enough about the details of neuroanatomical and neurophysiological maturation at this particular age to answer the question we have posed (p. 59).

Benjamin related these considerations to the stimulus barrier concept, suggesting that before the behavioral manifestations of increased sensitivity and during the period of relatively unstructured EEG phenomena, the infant is protected against stimulation by the absence of the capacity to process it. From his discussion the first proposition may be stated as: *Between birth and three to four weeks the lack of functional neuroconnections in the central nervous system limits the processing of sensory input with a resultant relative lack of responsivity.* This earliest form of protection against stimulation was called by Benjamin the *passive stimulus barrier.*

A second proposition relates to the development of an "active stimulus barrier," the active efforts exerted by the older infant and young child (as well as the adult) to protect himself against excessive stimulation. "The mature organism," Benjamin (1965) stated, "has developed a variety of ways of receiving, processing and warding off stimulation. The repertoire of the young infant is much more limited with respect to all of these" (p. 62). It was his impression from many observations that "this capacity exists to a slight degree as early as 8 to 10 weeks and matures rapidly thereafter" (p. 60). He was referring primarily to inhibiting, suppressing, or regulating mechanisms in the central nervous system. It was his opinion that "another major way of dealing with excessive stimulation, through *motor action,* is not available until much later" (p. 62).

In discussing a possible neurophysiological basis for an active stimulus barrier, Benjamin (1965) stated:

. . . we must ask whether there are known physiological mechanisms pertinent to the concept of a more "active" stimulus barrier, arising later in infancy and requiring further neural maturation than our early neonatal example. The answer here is an unequivocal "yes." The whole topic of central influences on afferent transmission, . . . the focus of many neurophysiological investigations in recent years, seems directly applicable. Much is at present being learned about different mechanisms subsumable under this general heading. Rather than attempting to review details of this work, I must content myself here with a merely paradigmatic statement about one aspect of it. It has been demonstrated in a large number of species that stimulation to the sensorimotor cortex or to the reticular formation can suppress or inhibit peripherally evoked responses in dorsal column nuclei, such as the nucleus gracilis or the cuneate nucleus . . . It is obvious that these and other comparable mechanisms are applicable to the concept of an "active stimulus barrier." Once again we find that developmental work in this area has been sparse, in this case for the very good reason that it was first necessary to study and demonstrate the mechanisms themselves, a recent and still ongoing achievement, before their developmental course could usefully be made the object of systematic investigation (p. 60).

A second proposition derived from this discussion is: Beginning at eight to 10 weeks and rapidly thereafter, inhibitory or regulatory mechanisms mature, providing the infant with the ability to shut out stimuli. This later developing protection against stimulation will be called the active stimulus barrier.

A third proposition deals with the period between three to four weeks and eight to 10 weeks. Benjamin proposed that at this time the infant has developed a capacity for processing stimulation but has no protection against it. He stated (1965):

. . . there is a period of uncertain length, which we shall provisionally place between 3-4 weeks or a little earlier and 8-10 weeks or later, when the infant has neither of the two described mechanisms for warding off external (and internal?) stimulation at his disposal. The resultant enhanced vulnerability of this period, in turn, makes greater demands upon the mother or mother substitutes. Usually these are well met, with or without conscious awareness on the mother's part that the infant has become more sensitive to stimuli. Sometimes these needs for additional protection against stimulation are less well handled, probably most frequently in some institutional settings, but also in those instances where the mother, for whatever reasons, is less than usually skillful in meeting them (p. 68).

The third proposition is: There is an intervening period, between three to four and eight to 10 weeks, during which the infant is without autonomous *means of protection from the environment. Neuromaturation suddenly increases the infant's capacity to process stimuli at three to four weeks, but maturation of those mechanisms involved in inhibiting or regulating input is delayed until eight to 10 weeks.* The period between the passive stimulus barrier and the active stimulus barrier is called the *vulnerable period.*

These proposed means of protection against stimulation are, of course, relative and in no sense absolute barriers.

The present study has attempted to investigate systematically the behavioral phenomena reported by Benjamin, as well as the relationships between those behaviors and concurrent neurophysiological changes, insofar as these are accessible to indirect measures.

Implications

Benjamin's hypothesis is essentially neurophysiological, but the origin as well as the ramifications of the stimulus barrier concept involve psychoanalytic considerations. That the central nervous system is equipped with a barrier to stimulation was considered by Freud (1920, 1925) to be a primary characteristic of central nervous system functioning. It was his view that "the nervous system is an apparatus which has the function of getting rid of the stimuli which reach it, or of reducing them to the lowest possible level; or which, if it were feasible, would maintain itself in an altogether unstimulated condition" (1915, p. 120). Benjamin (1965) pointed out that:

. . . *most of the findings of modern neuroanatomy and neurophysiology speak strongly against any general validity for this particular thesis of Freud's. The fact that there is spontaneous activity not only in the brain, but also in the sense organs themselves, the discovery of positive reinforcement as well as aversive centers in the limbic system, . . . and, following Hebb's original work, the results of many behavioral studies of the effects of partial afferent isolation . .* are sufficient evidence, to which much more could be added, that the concept that the organism strives to keep stimulation at a minimum, or if possible at a zero level, is without biological foundation. Yet none of this alters the fact that sensory stimulation can be noxious as well as necessary, and obnoxious as well as pleasing, as anyone living in this age of transistor radios and captive audiences can testify. It remains a biological fact that the nervous system is equipped to reduce the impact of excessive stimulation through the mechanisms alluded to above (pp. 61–62).

That the organism both seeks stimulation and avoids it is accepted as a basic postulate in the present investigation.

Benjamin discussed at some length the theoretical relationships between the hypothesized stimulus barriers in early infancy and later developing adaptive and defensive ego functions. He suggested that the passive stimulus barrier is unlikely to be a homologous prototype or a precursor having genetic continuity with later developments; but individual variability in its duration as well as in the duration and impact of the vulnerable period might have predictive value for the predisposition to anxiety. He considered that the active stimulus barrier "may or may not in any meaningful sense be a precursor of later developing defenses against drives, but it most certainly is a 'precursor' of itself in a more advanced stage of neural maturation" (p. 62); "and beyond that may conceivably have value as an *indicator* of other defensive and adaptive aspects of ego functioning" (p. 63). These implications, though adding developmental significance to the concept, go beyond the scope of the present investigation, which is limited to the period covered by the three propositions.

Related Research

Investigations of crying in infancy (Brazelton, 1962; Stewart, et al., 1953) and of colic and "paroxysmal fussing" (Paradise, 1966; Wessel, et al., 1954) lend support to Benjamin's observation of increased fussiness at three to four weeks and its decline by the third month. The finding that prematures have a delay in onset of fussiness (Pierce, 1948) supports the suggestion that maturation is importantly involved. When individual data are given, a few infants in each group are reported to have a late onset of colic—around eight weeks—in exception to the majority in the group. In populations unselected for this variable, extreme fussiness occurs in about one-fourth of the infants, an equal proportion are reported to be content and never crying for unknown reasons, and in about half, moderate amounts of fussiness occur. The precise etiology of colic is unknown but tension in the family or disturbance in the mother-infant relationship is considered to be an important contributing factor (Stewart, 1953; Wessel, et al., 1954).

From his intensive observations of infants in the first three months, Wolff (1969) described week-by-week changes in the precipitating causes of crying and interpreted the changes he observed at three weeks as due to a shift from purely physical stimuli to events of psychological significance to the infant. White and Held (1966) report that institutionalized infants of 45 to 60 days who were given an enriched visible surround gave the impression of engaging in much more crying than the control group who lived in a bland visual environment.

In summary, there is support in the literature for Benjamin's observation of a period of increased irritability within the first three months. It is a common but not universal phenomenon, with individual variability in onset, intensity, and duration, which may be accounted for in part by the nature of the stimulation experienced by the infant.

METHOD

The present research was designed as a short-term longitudinal study to investigate the relationships between levels of irritability, behavioral changes in responsivity to stimuli, and measures of neurophysiological maturation in the first three months of life. The behavioral data consist of: (1) systematic evaluations of the infant's level of irritability in the naturalistic setting as reported by the mother, (2) assessment of changes in the infant's responsivity to a standardized schedule of visual, auditory and social stimuli, and (3) tabulation of somatic manifestations of changes other than irritability, e.g., illnesses. The indirect measures of changing neurophysiology consist of: (1) assessment of the developmental course of the transitory reflexes, and (2) developmental changes in serial electroencephalograms. Because the EEG analyses had not been completed at the time of this writing, EEG data will be presented in a separate communication.

Sixteen mothers of middle to upper-middle class were recruited from prenatal hospital clinics and discussion groups. Four cases were dropped from the final analyses, because of gaps in the data that resulted from irregularities in meeting the schedule.

Nine of the remaining mothers in the study were primiparas, three multiparous. The age range was 18 to 34 years. The only criteria for acceptance in the study were the mother's interest in observing developmental-like tests of her infant, and her willingness to bring the infant to the hospital biweekly for electroencephalographs.

The infants and mothers were seen in the hospital one or two days after delivery. All 12 infants had Apgar ratings of 8 or above. One infant of 37 weeks' gestation weighed 2240 grams, one weighed 4209 grams, and the remainder fell between 3100 and 3750. All the infants were considered normally healthy by the attending pediatrician.

Beginning in the second week, the mother and infant were seen in the home by two of three observers on a rotating schedule at biweekly intervals, until the infant was three and a half months of age. In a semi-structured interview the mother was asked about feeding, sleep, crying, soothing, smiling, illnesses, and routine care such as diapering and bathing, with particular care in detailing reports of fussiness and her handling of them. With the infant in an alert responsive state as far as possible, the schedule of tests was administered by one observer and recorded by the other. A complete process report of the interview and the tests was recorded independently by each observer. Data analysis was based entirely upon the written reports.

RESULTS [2]

Fussiness

From birth, all infants cry when hungry and in response to pain. For purposes of this study, fussiness was defined as a state of irritability not clearly related to physiologic need or specific externally caused discomfort, as determined by immediate termination of such crying when the precipitating cause was altered.

[2] The authors acknowledge with thanks the indispensable help of Dr. Donald Stilson as statistical consultant.

Behavioral manifestations of fussiness include crying, restlessness, muscular tension, or an inability to relax and fall asleep.

The mother was asked about all episodes of fussiness during the two weeks previous to the interview. Using the written reports of all three observers, each observer rated the fussiness level on a daily basis for each infant. The criteria for the six-point scale, taking intensity, frequency, and duration into account, were as follows: 0—fussiness (as defined above) absent for a 24-hour period; 1—intermittent or mild crying for five to 10 minutes, or tensing of bodily musculature and restlessness for 10 to 20 minutes; 2—intermittent crying or restlessness for several short periods, or one period lasting up to an hour (mainly an increase in frequency and duration over rating 1); 3—hard crying or extreme restlessness for periods of a half hour to an hour and a half (mainly an increase in intensity over 2); 4—hard crying or extreme restlessness for periods longer than an hour, or a number of shorter periods of such behavior in a 24-hour period; and 5—no alert state in a 24-hour period without fussiness. The rating of two agreeing judges was used as the final value. In only 29 of the 1122 days requiring ratings were the three judgments entirely disparate; these intervals were considered unrateable.

All the mothers in the study reported some episodes of fussiness that met our definition. When the infant cried during an interview, we asked the mother to describe the observed crying in comparison with episodes she had reported. It was apparent that there was some variation among mothers in the use of terms to describe intensity. Despite this discrepancy, there was clear differentiation between the infants who were generally content and the most fussy, particularly of the three at the extreme who were considered by both mothers and their pediatricians to have colic.

To examine the relationship between fussiness and chronological age, we used three methods of analysis. First, to establish peak days of fussiness without regard to absolute value, a mean rating was calculated for each infant and all days when fussiness was above his average were designated. The days of fussiness tended to cluster into intervals. A one-sample-runs test for each child indicated that the intervals of fussiness were not randomly distributed over the first three months (significant in all cases beyond the .001 level). Second, examination of the absolute ratings indicated that, for all infants in the study, fussinesss was rated 3 or above for at least three days among the least fussy, to as many as 55 days among the most fussy infants. A one-sample-runs test of these data indicated that, in three of the least fussy infants, single days of extreme fussiness did occur, in conformation to a random distribution during the three-month period. It would seem that some infants have an occasional day of extreme irritability, which may occur at any maturational or developmental age, but that days of more than usual fussiness for each infant cluster into fussy and non-fussy periods.

Third, to determine the longitudinal course of fussiness for the group as a whole, mean ratings for each individual were computed by weekly intervals and summarized by mean values for the group as a whole. These results are given in Table 1.

Table 1 MEAN VALUES OF FUSSINESS RATINGS BY WEEKLY INTERVALS

						Weeks							
	1	2	3	4	5	6	7	8	9	10	11	12	13
Mean rating	.17	.86	1.62	1.81	1.59	1.55	1.55	1.58	1.54	1.58	1.71	1.39	1.15
s.d.	.30	.82	.96	.79	.70	.84	.91	.75	1.13	1.36	1.50	1.09	.94
N	10	12	12	12	12	12	12	12	12	12	12	10	10

The mean values show an increment through the fourth week, a slight drop in the fifth week, and maintain approximately the same level until the thirteenth week when it declines. The significance of the difference between means, comparing each week with every other (Table 2), is consistent with this initial increase followed by a plateau. The significance of the difference between the means of week 4 and week 13 is beyond the .01 level.

Beyond the ninth week, the means remain large but are not significantly different from those of week 2. As indicated by the standard deviations, there is an increase in variability at nine weeks and beyond. In order to describe in more gross terms the differences in variability at the different ages, the number of infants were counted with ratings within each of the six units of the scale. A comparison of these ratings levels, as shown in Table 3, indicates that median values predominate in the fourth week, whereas in the tenth week the distribution is bimodal. The infants with high values in the tenth week were the three considered to have colic.

These data are in accord with Benjamin's observations of an increase in fussiness at four weeks for the majority of infants, but are discrepant with his observation of an abrupt decline at eight to 10 weeks. Rather, there is a plateau until seven weeks, and a gradual decline thereafter until 13 weeks in the majority of infants, but in a few of the infants there is an increase in fussiness after eight weeks. Stated in terms of the hypothesis, the findings are compatible with the concept of a passive stimulus barrier before four weeks; but they fail to give evidence for the hypothesized abrupt maturation of inhibitory mechanisms at eight to 10 weeks, providing the infant with the ability to shut out stimuli actively.

With regard to individual variability, Benjamin had suggested that the degree of irritability manifest during the vulnerable period would be in part a function of the mother's ability to meet the child's needs. Expert mothering would tend to mask the phenomenon. If such a single environmental factor were responsible for individual variability in fussiness, we would have expected it to have a more continuous effect, decreasing fussiness not only at eight to 10 weeks but also at the onset of fussiness and throughout the vulnerable period. Rather, our data suggest that there is a maturational factor, common to most infants, causing an increase in fussiness at three to four weeks, and thereafter the basic maturational pattern is one of gradual decline to termination of fussy episodes by the fourteenth week, with a few infants a marked exception to the group trend.

Table 2 T VALUES OF DIFFERENCE IN FUSSINESS MEANS

Weeks	1	2	3	4	5	6	7	8	9	10	11	12	13
1		3.14*	3.83*	5.34*	5.67*	5.37*	4.61*	4.31*	3.36*	2.71	2.49	2.18	1.85
2			2.08	2.91*	2.36	2.19	2.00	2.00	1.64	1.47	1.40	.86	.46
3				.62	−.09	−.17	−.14	−.66	−.33	−.11	.13	−1.11	−1.89
4					−1.15	−.77	−.64	−1.32	−.74	−.60	−.62	−2.18	−3.21*
5						−.21	−.14	−.39	−.13	−.02	.09	−.81	−1.69
6							.04	.16	−.01	.07	.34	−.27	−.77
7								.28	−.02	.06	.44	−.11	−.62
8									−.63	.58	.38	−.58	−1.35
9										.20	.07	−1.06	−1.66
10											.13	−1.65	−1.82
11												−1.67	−1.73
12													−1.40

* Significant beyond .01 level

Table 3 COMPARISON OF DISTRIBUTION OF FUSSINESS RATINGS AT 4 AND 10
WEEKS BY NUMBER OF INFANTS IN EACH INTERVAL

	Fussiness Ratings				
	0–.99	1–1.99	2–2.99	3–3.99	4–4.99
4 weeks	1	3	7	1	0
10 weeks	5	4	0	2	1

Visual Responsivity

Among the various parameters of visual development during the first three
months of life, the sequence of changes in fixation times was considered to be a
suitable measure of an increase in responsivity and subsequent control over
input. On many tests of infant development (Bayley, 1969; Gesell, 1942; Griffiths,
1954; and others), three successive steps in visual fixation behavior in infants
describe a reliable developmental course: momentary fixation on an object at
one month of age, steady fixation at two months, and eye movements alternating
between two objects, or between the object and the environment at three
months.

This developmental course is consonant with our hypothesized increase in
responsivity in the second month and with the presence of an active mechanism
for limiting stimulus input in the third month.

Fantz (1965) found that, among a number of different targets, a bull's-eye
was the most provocative of infants' visual attention over the entire first six
months of life; that a striped pattern was significantly preferred by infants under
two months of age, whereas the bull's-eye was more strongly preferred after this
age. In two infants studied longitudinally from birth, Stechler (1966) reported
that, between 10 to 15 days of age, fixation and unremitting staring at a target
continued for as long as 35 minutes, terminating not with sleep but with crying
and distress. He called this phenomenon "obligatory attention."

In this study, a six-inch black and white bull's-eye with half-inch concentric
circles and a six-inch square of half-inch stripes were used to measure the established stages in the infant's visual development. Each stimulus was held in the
infant's line of vision for three minutes with the infant in an alert state. We
recorded the length of the infant's fixation on the stimulus, his motor activity,
facial expression and any alterations in state.

The simplest measure of changes in visual responsivity was the longest
interval during the three-minute presentation when the infant remained fixated
on the target, with less than a 10-second glance away. Our interest was in the
assessment of optimal fixation times.

The frequency of fixations of one, two and three minute intervals by two-
week periods is shown in Table 4.

All the infants responded to the bull's-eye and/or the stripes with a steady
fixation for the full three minutes at some time during the period of the study.

Table 4 LENGTH OF FIXATION TIMES TO VISUAL TARGETS

				Weeks				
Seconds	2–3	4–5	6–7	8–9	10–11	12–13	14–15	16–17
0–59	7	5	2	2	1	1	5	4
60–119	1	2	2	2	1	1	2	0
120–180	2	3	6	8	8	7	4	1
Number of infants	10	10	10	12	10	9	11	5

Between two and five weeks of age the majority of infants fixated for less than a minute; between six and 13 weeks, fixations of more than two minutes occurred with highest frequency; after 14 weeks, there was again a trend to fixations of less than a minute.

One infant was an exception to the group. He fixated for the full 180 seconds to both targets between two and six weeks of age, but at 8 weeks responded very differently to the bull's-eye and to the stripes. When presented with the bull's-eye, he glanced at it briefly for 10 seconds or less, and then moved his head from side to side as if in avoidance of the target. In response to the stripes, he maintained a steady fixation for 180 seconds until he was 16 weeks old. His mother, an unusually sensitive observer, reported that he likes to look at the edges of things. This infant had severe internal strabismus, not apparent until six weeks; it was later corrected surgically.

It is reasonable to assume that these data reflect the three successive steps in visual development—i.e., momentary fixation, steady fixation, and alternating eye movements—as given on infant development scales. Descriptively, the short fixations during the early and late periods are quite different. During the early period, the infants fixate most often for 20 to 30 seconds, with some movement of the eyes from one part of the stimulus to another; the eyes then slide off and do not return to the stimulus. In order to reinstate the stimulus, it must be moved into the infant's line of vision. The infant fixates again for a similar period of time before again roving off. During the 14- to 17-week period, the infant fixates the stimulus for, on the average, 10 seconds; then, with a definite movement, he looks at the examiner or at the environment for approximately 10 seconds and returns to the stimulus. He continues the alternating movements, which sometimes involve only the eyes but more frequently also turning of the head. By contrast, during prolonged fixations the infant may glance away for one to two seconds but returns his gaze spontaneously, as if compelled to look at the target or as if "stimulus-bound."

For the group as a whole, the increased incidence of obligatory looking occurs two weeks later (six weeks) than the marked increase in fussiness (four weeks). When we compared onset of increased fussiness with onset of obligatory looking in each infant, we found that in nine cases obligatory looking occurred after the onset of fussiness, five of these instances having a difference of three to six weeks.

Alternating eye movements were observed in nine of the 12 infants; in one it developed at 12 weeks of age, in six at 14–15 weeks and in two at 16–17 weeks; it was not yet present at 17 weeks in the infant with strabismus. (One infant could not be tested after 12 weeks.) In all nine cases, alternating eye movements occurred after the decline of fussiness; but there was no relationship in time between the decrease in fussiness and the onset of alternating vision.

Our conclusion is that prolonged fixation times in infants, as a measure of increased visual responsivity, with the accompanying stimulus-bound quality of obligatory looking, is not specifically related to either an increase in fussiness or its decline. The two phenomena overlap in time, because the onset of obligatory looking occurs during heightened fussiness and lasts from six to 14 weeks.

Length of fixation times was the most objective measure feasible for assessing the infant's visual development, but it represents only one aspect of the behavior. Behaviors accompanying fixations on the targets were categorized as follows: (1) motor activity—inactive, increasing, waxing and waning; (2) vocalizations—cooing or babbling, fussing, crying; (3) facial expression—pleasant, pre-cry face, smile. In addition, the total effect of the three-minute presentation was judged as either pleasurable or displeasurable. Only tests administered when the infant was in a stable alert-responsive state were thus categorized (55 out of 77 tests).

At two weeks of age, the infants responded to the visual stimuli with inactivity. Not only is the capacity for sustained attention limited, but our evidence suggests that when such attention is activated, it has an inhibitory effect on motor activity. In three infants who were in a drowsy state when the stimulus was presented, this quieting effect was also observed, but the data are not included in the above analysis. These infants fixated the visual stimulus, were motorically inactive, their eyes drooped closed and reopened with fixation several times before they went to sleep. The stimulus appeared to have a soporific effect in a drowsy infant.

At four to five weeks of age, there was an initial reduction in activity (approximately 10 to 30 seconds), followed by increasing activity, and accompanied by fussiness and finally by hard crying. The increase in activity resulted in the infant's turning away from the stimulus without a return; the crying sometimes terminated the fixation interval, because the eyes closed as the result of facial distortion. Both these responses resulted in less than maximal fixation times. Two infants who responded for long fixation times without evidence of displeasure were both delayed two to three weeks, as compared with the group as a whole, in the onset of increased fussiness.

These findings suggest that using only length of fixation time as a measure of response can lead to inaccuracies and severely limits the assessment of visual responsivity. The crucial change at four weeks appears to be in the link between visual input and motor response—a change from a quieting effect to a negative response. In addition, the infant in the early period does not have the activation of motor activity in response to visual stimulation that he will have later, and hence he does not have feedback from motor discharge. With the maturation of prolonged visual attentiveness, motor responses are activated and the infant appears to be "overwhelmed" not only by the visual stimulus but by an accelerating motor response as well.

With the increase in duration of compelling fixation on the visual stimuli in the ensuing weeks, displeasurable responses were replaced by pleasurable reactions, though motor activity continued to be high. In half the subjects, on one occasion in each, motor activity alternated with periods of inactivity, each lasting approximately 30 seconds—a waxing and waning effect. During the inactive phase, the infant maintained steady visual attention to the stimulus; during the burst of motor activity, there were also vocalizations, occasional smiles, and brief glances away from the target, but the infant was "stimulus-bound." This waxing and waning marked the onset of pleasurable responses and in successive observations it was followed by high and continuous motor activity. It represents a modulation of motor activity and of gazing, each preempting the other in alternation.

After eight weeks of age, pleasurable responses predominate. Out of 22 presentations between eight and 11 weeks, three infants responded with displeasure on one occasion only. However, only one of these infants was in a period of above-average fussiness. Comparison of above-average periods of fussiness with pleasurable and displeasurable responses to the visual stimuli indicates that it is not predictable that infants who are fussy in the second and third months will respond with displeasure to prolonged fixations; they may respond with cooing and smiles. Nor do the non-fussy infants always respond with pleasure. In addition, some infants responded with both smiling and frowning to the same stimulus presentation. Therefore, the change denotes a marked increase in the pleasurable response, which is, however, not yet entirely stable.

These findings permit a reformulation of the relationship between increased irritability and changing visual responsivity in infancy. Before four weeks of age, obligatory looking is relatively absent and what visual attention is activated results in a cessation of motor activity. Obligatory looking is a behavioral manifestation of binding to a stimulus, in the absence of the ability to shut out or terminate the stimulus. In this study, when this stimulus-bound property first began to develop at around four weeks in the majority of infants, it characteristically led to distress, but in the next few weeks it lost this property and was accompanied instead by pleasurable behaviors. It would seem that the capacity for pleasure can mitigate the overwhelming effect of stimulation. This finding may partially account for the gradual decline in fussiness after seven weeks of age. This leads to a further revision of the original hypothesis. The increased responsivity to stimulation results in irritability, but the concomitantly occurring increased coordination between sensorimotor systems increases the capacity to sustain more stimulation over longer periods of time without distress. As links between visual input and motor action develop, the infant becomes equipped with a means of dealing with stimulation, before a specific means of turning away or avoiding visual stimulation has developed.

The nature of the neurophysiological maturation taking place in the visual system cannot be deduced from the behavioral data; nor can the behavioral activity be understood from anatomical and physiological descriptions of the mature organism. If the developmental course of such neuronal activity as the excitatory and inhibitory functioning of the visual receptive fields into "on," "off," and "on-off" zones were known (Kuffler, 1952), it might have explanatory value for the development of the stimulus-bound period.

Auditory Responsivity

Currently there are a number of investigations of response to auditory stimuli in early infancy that rigorously control the stimulus variables and use objective measures of response, such as heart rate. The infant's response is known to vary with pitch, intensity, repetition, and duration of the sound, as well as with the infant's state and chronological age. One such study (by Clifton and Meyers, 1969) used rigorously controlled auditory stimuli and measured heart rate as the response; its results indicate that newborns respond with cardiac acceleration, whereas four-month-old infants respond with deceleration. The investigators hypothesize that this difference may signify the development of the orienting response, indicating that a fundamental neurophysiologic change occurs, but their data did not permit them to say precisely when and how the change takes place.

In our multiple variable study, with observations conducted in the homes, such carefully controlled experimental procedures did not seem feasible. Two auditory stimuli, novel to the infant, were included in our testing sequence: (1) a resonant metallic bell was rung approximately 24 inches from each side of the infant's head and (2) a loud blast on a toy horn was administered six times at five-second intervals.

Responses to a bell, similar to the one used in this study, are included in a number of infant development scales (Bayley, 1969; Griffiths, 1954; Gesell, 1942). In the first month the infant is expected to indicate by a motor response that the bell has been heard; at around three months of age he turns his head, and looks toward the sound, or locates it visually. Wolff reported that a smiling response to such a bell precedes a predictable social smile (Wolff, 1963).

In this study the infants' responses to the bell were observed in 63 of the 86 observation sessions. Descriptions of responses included changes in motor activity, visual attentiveness, head turning, and change in facial expression. When we rang the bell, only two infants were entirely unresponsive (one at two weeks and the other at two and at six weeks). A simple startle or blink was observed in four infants at two to four weeks. The most common response (28 of 63) was a decrease in activity and/or visual attentiveness without a startle, smile, or head turning. There was no significant difference in the proportion of infants responding in this manner at any age between two and 14 weeks. All infants responded with head turning at least once, with the mode at eight to 10 weeks, but again there was no significant increase or decrease in frequency of the response at any age level. Four infants responded with a smile (one infant at six, eight, and 10 weeks, one at 10 and 12 weeks and the other two at 10 and 12 weeks respectively).

Our conclusion was that while the bell elicited attention and did not cause fussiness, it yielded little definitive information about developmental changes in responsivity in the auditory modality.

The intermittent sounding of the toy horn was an item derived from the three-month level of the Hetzer-Wolf Development Scale. On the scale, the response necessary to pass the item is a consistent decrease or a consistent increase in the infant's reaction to successive sounds of the horn; i.e., the first sound may cause a startle or motor activity and, with each successive sound, the response is less until the last sound, when the infant is very quiet or completely inactive. Or the opposite: startle or motor activity to the first sound, which increases to each successive sound until by the sixth the infant is very active and may be crying hard. This item was included in the study because it seemed possible that the opposite reactions might occur in the same infant at different ages as a function of neurological maturation, the increasing response being a manifestation of the absence of a stimulus barrier and the decreasing response evidence of an active inhibitory process.

Categories for scoring responses to the horn were determined empirically. During the first month the responses consisted of a decrease in activity, a blink or slight startle to one or more of the sounds but inconsistent over the series, or no observable change in behavior. If the infant was fussy or tending toward drowsiness when the horn was sounded, it was not possible to determine that any change in responsivity, either an increase or decrease, was a specific response to the sounds. Between five and eight weeks, changes in motor activity occurred more frequently. Five of the infants responded similarly with variability in reactions, stopping activity in response to some of the sounds in the series and increasing activity to others without any patterning of responses. The sounds were not responded to as a unit, over the 30-second presentation, but with dissociation between sounds. Between nine and 12 weeks, all the infants responded with consistent increase in irritability, which terminated by the sixth sound in hard crying. The most common pattern (five infants) was a large startle to the initial sound, a decrease in activity to the second sound maintained until the third sound, when a turning down of the mouth or "pre-cry" face appeared, followed at the successive sounds by fussing and finally hard crying. Two other infants responded in this manner but without the initial startle. These responses were very striking in infants who had been alert, responsive, and smiling but became increasingly distressed and were finally shrieking by the sixth sound of the horn.

After 14 weeks, a different response occurred in three infants who had previously responded with crying. After an initial slight startle or decrease in activity, the infant averted his head and became visually attentive, in two cases looking at his hand and in the third focusing on his mother across the room. They maintained the visual regard without further response to the sounds of the horn.

These findings suggest that, in the first month, the series of loud sounds is responded to with indifference or, as was found with regard to the visual stimuli, with a decrease in motor activity. Also, as was found with visual stimuli, during the second month the sounds caused activation of a motor response, but the intermittent sounds were responded to as discrete stimuli, without a cumulative effect. In the third month the response to the sounds was maintained during the five-second interval between sounds, resulting in a cumulative and increasingly distressful response. By the fourth month there is some indication that infants can begin to shut out noxious sound by concentration of attention into the visual modality.

Comparison of individual fussiness ratings and peak periods of fussiness indicated no relationship between changing responsivity to auditory stimuli and fussiness levels. Both those infants who had declined in fussiness and those who were extremely fussy at eight to 10 weeks responded with the startle-to-cry response to the horn.

The changing responsivity to auditory stimuli suggests further revision of the observational basis of the hypothesis we are testing. First, there appears to be independence in the development of the various modalities, an increase in irritability in response to visual stimuli occurring at three to four weeks, but not until eight to 10 weeks in the auditory modality. Discrepancies in maturational level between sensory systems, anticipated by Benjamin, are to be expected from anatomical descriptions of neuromaturation. For example, Yakovlev and Lecours (1967) found that the visual system myelinates rapidly after birth in one short spurt which is completed at about four postnatal months, in contrast with myelinization of the cortical end of the auditory system, which is protracted beyond the first postnatal year. They regard myelinization as "a morphological criterion of the functional maturity of a conduction path" and suggest that the contrast in rate and timing of myelinization in the visual and acoustic systems both pre- and postnatally should correlate with the maturation of reflex and behavioral patterns in these spheres. Second, though the auditory findings are supportive of the two critical periods of maturation suggested by the hypothesis, the second critical period, at the beginning of the second month, is not characterized by the active avoidance of stimulation but by a heightening of capacity to sustain attention. The onset of the stimulus-bound quality in the auditory modality has a distressing effect on the infant, similar to stimulus-bound response to a continuous provocative visual stimulus at four weeks. The evidence suggests an abrupt maturation in the auditory modality at eight to 10 weeks, which permits sustained attention; but the capacity to divert attention to a different modality, an active inhibition in the presence of active receptivity, does not develop until the fourth month.

The Smile

Because of the importance of the smile during the first three months, not only as a psychosocial development but also as an indicator of an organized response to stimulation, a systematic test of the development of the smile was included in the study.

To elicit the smile, the examiner bent over the supine, alert infant and nodded silently. If the infant did not smile, the examiner talked as he nodded.

This item was most often administered first in a testing sequence and in addition intermittently during the course of testing.

All smiles occurring during the observation (social and non-social, spontaneous or elicited) were recorded. The infant's smiling responses were rated from the written descriptions by two judges on a four-point scale: (1) smile absent; (2) fleeting or minimal smiles; (3) a full smile, but infrequent and not easily elicited; and (4) a predictable response to the human face, easily elicited and frequent.

Ratings of 86 observations by two judges using the written descriptions resulted in 78 perfect agreements; the remaining eight were resolved by consensus.

The results of the ratings, grouped by two-week intervals, are shown in Table 5. The developmental course of the smile in this group of infants corresponds in general to reports in the literature (Ambrose, 1961; Polak, et al., 1964; Spitz and Wolf, 1946) when limited time samples were used (cf. Wolff, 1963). All the infants, except the infant with severe strabismus, had developed the predictable social smile by 13 weeks, the earliest at eight weeks.

Table 5 NUMBER OF INFANTS RESPONDING TO THE HUMAN FACE WITH A SMILE

| | | | | Weeks | | | |
Rating Category	2–3	4–5	6–7	8–9	10–11	12–13	14–15
1. Absent	12	8	5	1	1	0	1
2. Fleeting or minimal	0	2	3	3	0	1	1
3. Full but infrequent and hard to elicit	0	1	3	4	4	0	0
4. "Predictable," easily elicited and frequent	0	0	0	3	6	7	9
Number	12	11	11	11	11	8	11

Examination of relationships in individuals between fussiness ratings and smile ratings indicate that in six infants, within the two-week period of the development of the predictable smile, fussiness declined to ratings of zero or near zero. For these infants the presence of the predictable smile is coincident with the termination of fussy episodes. However, the infants who continued to be fussy in the third month also developed the predictable smile during this period. Of the three most fussy infants, two developed this level of smiling at nine weeks and one at 13 weeks.

The infant who developed the social smile earliest, at eight weeks, was also one of the earliest to respond with minimal or fleeting smiles at four weeks. This infant was not fussy between five and seven weeks, but at nine to 10 weeks, after the smile was well established, he had a recrudescence of marked fussiness.

These findings suggest that there is no simple reciprocal relationship between levels of fussiness and the development of the smile. Although an absence of irritability and a heightening of smiling are associated, a high level of irritability does not necessarily preclude the development of the smile.

The effectiveness of different kinds of stimuli in eliciting the smile changes during the course of its development. In this study, when the infants achieved a predictable social smile, the silent nodding face alone was sufficient to elicit the response. Minimal or infrequent smiles (ratings of 2 or 3) required the addition of the voice in nine cases; the nodding face alone was sufficient in only three. Even though the addition of the voice may enhance the smile, the predictable social smiling response is considered to be predominantly visual.

Obligatory looking was present in all infants before or concomitant with the predictable smile. However, the relatively early development of obligatory looking was not predictive of a relatively earlier onset of the smile. Prolonged visual fixations may be a prerequisite but not a determinant of the social smile.

The social smile is a specific motor response to a particular visual configuration. It is not an avoidance of stimulation but rather a signal that maintains continuation of stimulation and the most convincing behavioral manifestation of pleasure. The repetitive predictable social smile at eight to 10 weeks represents a culmination of the development of the association between steady visual attentiveness and an appropriate and adequate motor response. After this association has been well established, the infant apparently is able to make use of it as a means of avoiding stimuli that cause displeasure. For example, Bühler (1921) found that 75 per cent of infants between two and four months of age showed negative reactions to a falsetto voice or deep humming only if the experimenter could not be seen; and in naturalistic observations, Meili (1957) reported that the noise of a camera frequently produced negative reactions when the face of the photographer was hidden by the camera, but not when it was visible. We did not test the efficacy of a face in reducing the noxious effect of the horn at eight to 10 weeks. However, the absence of fussiness in half the infants, following the establishment of the predictable social smile, supports the contention that smiling modulates irritability. The fact that fussy infants also develop the social smile indicates that the maturation and learning involved in smiling are alone insufficient to provide the infant with reliably effective protection from distress.

By the fourth month, the majority of infants have the ability to use a motor movement to disengage a visual stimulus or to redirect attention in order to avoid stimuli. In her classic study of conditioning of the smiling response Brackbill (1958) reinforced smiling in three and a half- to four and a half-month-old infants by returning the smile and fondling the infant. During extinction, when she presented only the immobile face, not only did smiling decline, but the infants responded to her face by turning away. When she propped the infant's head so it could not turn, the infant persisted in avoiding fixation on her face by looking elsewhere.

These findings lend further support to the proposed revision of the behavioral basis of Benjamin's hypothesis. Restated, it is that: during the vulnerable period the infant is equipped with some means of reducing the negative effects of stimulation; and an active barrier to stimulation, as conceptualized by Benjamin, does not develop until the fourth month.

Reflexes

There are a number of reflex behaviors, present at birth or soon after, that decline or disappear by three to four months of age (Dekaban, 1959). As indicators of progressing central nervous system maturation, the following reflexes were included in the testing protocol—the Babkin, tonic-neck-reflex, palmar grasp, Moro, Landau, stepping and placing. Because of problems associated with reliability in data collection, data gaps and lack of sensitivity of rating methods, only results of the first two will be reported at this time.

BABKIN. The Babkin, or hand-mouth reflex is elicited by a sudden firm pressure on the infant's palms; the response consists predominantly of opening the mouth, with flexion or rotation of the head; closing eyes and flexion of the knees are additional but variable components in the response.

The reflex is reported to be strong in prematures (Parmalee, 1963), present in about 80 per cent of full-term newborns (Lippman, 1958), and disappears by the third or fourth month of life (Babkin, 1958; Lippman, 1958). It is absent during regular sleep, weak during irregular sleep, and strongest during alert unsatiated states (Lenard, et al., 1968; Lippman, 1958). Its absence is not unequivocally related to pathology, but its presence in the first month of life is compatible with an intact organism (Parmalee, 1963).

In this study an optimal testing consisted of three trials, with at least three minutes intervening between them, the infant being in an alert state. The responses were rated by the examiner and the observer on a five-point scale: (0) no response; (1) slight mouth movement; (2) moderate mouth opening; (3) marked mouth opening, plus one other component; and (4) mouth opening and other components strong. A tabulation of ratings for the group is given in Table 6.

These findings are similar to Lippman's report on 50 cases studied longitudinally at one-month intervals, in that the reflex is most active in the first month, declines in the second month, and virtually disappears by the third month. However, our measures, taken at biweekly intervals rather than monthly, further suggest that the decline of the reflex is not along a simple gradient. First, in seven out of 10 cases there is an abrupt suppression of the reflex at six to seven weeks. The Scheffé test of the difference in the values in the first month and at six to seven weeks would permit rejection of the null hypothesis at about the .10 level but not at the .05 (Hayes, 1963). The developmental course for the group suggests an abrupt change in the majority of infants, but the lack of statistical significance suggests replication of Lippman's findings. Two infants were exceptions to the group trend, each at one extreme. In one, the reflex could never be elicited (seven test sessions), and in the other all components were strongly present until 12 weeks, when the reflex abruptly disappeared. In seven infants,

Table 6 BABKIN REFLEX

				Weeks			
Rating	2–3	4–5	6–7	8–9	10–11	12–13	14–15
4. Mouth opening and other components strong	4	3	2	2	1	1	0
3. Marked mouth opening plus one other component	5	6	0	0	0	1	0
2. Moderate mouth opening	1	1	1	5	4	0	1
1. Slight mouth movement	0	1	4	2	3	0	1
0. No response	2	0	3	3	3	7	8
N	12	11	10	12	11	9	10
Mean	2.7	3.0	1.4	1.6	1.4	.7	.3

after the drop to minimal or absent, there was one observation between eight and 12 weeks when a more marked response occurred, followed at the next testing by minimal or no response.

These findings suggest that in the majority of cases, at about six weeks of age neurophysiological maturation takes place that suppresses, inhibits, or replaces the functioning of the reflex. This was after the first peak of fussiness and at the same time as obligatory looking was being maintained without causing irritability. Since it was suggested that the relationship between visual input and motor response (as manifested by activity without increasing distress) is in part responsible for the increasing capacity to maintain visual fixation, it may be reasonable to assume that an allied development occurs, which affects the primitive connection between pressure on the palm and the motor responses of the Babkin. That the two changes in behavior may have a common determinant is further suggested by the fact that the infant in whom the reflex remained high for 12 weeks did not engage in obligatory looking until the drop in the Babkin occurred.

There is no apparent relationship between the recrudescence of the Babkin in the third month and the fussiness level, in that the seven infants in whom it was seen included those with both above- and below-average levels of fussiness. The cry response to the intermittent horn occurs at the same time as the recrudescence of the Babkin in six cases, and with a two-week intervening interval in the seventh case. This auditory response, unlike the Babkin, sometimes occurred at more than one observation, but both are characteristic of the third month. A relationship to the smiling response may exist in that, for all seven cases, the recrudescence of the Babkin occurred at the same observation as the onset of the predictable social smile. This more precise relationship may be a function of maturation, affecting the area they have in common, the mouth.

In the absence of knowledge of the neuroanatomical pathways mediating the Babkin reflex, these findings are of limited value in elucidating the specific nature of the neuromaturation that takes place.

THE TONIC-NECK REFLEX.   The tonic-neck reflex consists of asymmetrical positioning of the extremities when the head is turned to the side, with extension on the side toward which the face is rotated and flexion on the side of the occiput.

There is some discrepancy in the literature in reports of the developmental course of the reflex, the result apparently of different methods of eliciting and observing the reflex behavior. It was found to be present in the fetus after four to five months gestational age (Minkowski, 1921; Gesell, 1938) and more strongly present in prematures (Pacella and Barrera, 1940) than in full-term infants. Reports of the frequency of its occurrence in full-term neonates vary from 8 per cent to 40 percent (Vassella and Karlson, 1962), but it is generally agreed that it is less active in the newborn than at four weeks, when it is found to be present in 80 per cent to 100 per cent of normal infants (Gesell, 1938; Paine et al., 1964). It becomes inactive in the first four months of life. A functioning tonic-neck reflex after four months of age is suggestive of motor pathology (Byers, 1938).

The reflex is usually believed to originate with proprioceptive impulses from the neck muscles, perhaps from the atlanto-occipital and atlantoaxial joints, and to have an afferent pathway through the upper cervical roots (McCough, 1951). It has been suggested that the absence of the reflex in the full-term newborn is due to the predominance of the flexed position, a function of the inhibition of the extensors at a subcortical level. The presence of the tonic-neck reflex marks the end of this inhibitory influence.

Infants assume the tonic-neck position spontaneously when supine in alert states; it is absent during sleep. It may be induced by having the infant visually pursue an object until the head is turned to an extreme position, or by forcibly turning the infant's head. In this study all three observational possibilities were used: (1) observation of tonic-neck positions assumed spontaneously while the infant was lying supine for presentation of test items; (2) when visual pursuit could be elicited, the examiner moved his face, while smiling, nodding, and talking, in a 180° arc above the infant, pausing in the extreme positions to allow sufficient time for the infant to make the motor adjustment; and (3) forcefully turning the infant's head to the extreme right and left. In some cases these were supplemented by the mother's report of how frequently she observed the position or the infant's preference for one side.

The responses were tabulated as present or absent for each observation. Criterion for "present" was: with head averted in either direction, both arms assume the classical position consistent with the head direction, if ever observed under any of the three conditions.

As is shown in Table 7 the reflex is most frequently observed at four to five weeks. The two infants in whom it was absent at this time were never observed to assume the position spontaneously nor could it be evoked. (In one infant in seven observation sessions and in the other in only four observations it

Table 7　TONIC-NECK REFLEX

	2–3	4–5	6–7	Weeks 8–9	10–11	12–13	14–16
Absent	5	2	4	5	5	5	7
Present	5	10	5	6	4	2	2
N	10	12	9	11	9	7	9

could be ruled out with certainty.) There was wide individual variability in the termination of the reflex from six to beyond 15 weeks of age.

A second assessment of the response was made by rating on a three-point scale: (1) absent or only one component (for example, averted head and contralateral arm flexed); (2) spontaneous or evoked responses occur, but not consistently or persistently, and (3) predominantly present spontaneously and easily evoked. These results, shown in Table 8, indicate that the optimal and persistent response does not occur after 10 weeks.

Table 8　TONIC-NECK REFLEX RATINGS

	2–3	4–5	6–7	Weeks 8–9	10–11	12–13	14–15
1. Absent or partial	5	3	4	5	4	6	7
2. Inconsistent	3	3	1	3	5	1	2
3. Persistent	2	6	4	3	0	0	0

Comparison of tonic-neck reflex ratings and fussiness levels suggests that those infants in whom the tonic-neck reflex was strong and of longer duration were among the least fussy infants, while those with absent or weak reflex postures were among the most fussy. This difference is most apparent at the extremes and is not statistically significant if the group is divided into half, using either fussiness or tonic-neck reflex ratings as the dependent variable. Gesell and Thompson made the clinical observation that tonic-neck reflexes are prominent phenomena in *placid* babies until about the twelfth week of life—a finding that supports the suggestions in this study that there is an inverse relationship between strength of the reflex and intensity of fussiness.

There was no consistent relationship between the strength or developmental course of the tonic-neck reflex and the indices of visual attention, auditory response, or the strength of the Babkin reflex.

Note was taken of the difficulty in turning the infant's head when the tonic-neck reflex was imposed by the examiner. This resistance varied from easy rotation to such high resistance that more force than the examiner was willing to exert would have been required to turn the head, particularly because such forcing caused the infant to cry hard. In some instances of high resistance, the infant rolled in the direction of the turn, lifting the shoulders and making the turn impossible. Paine et al. (1964) found that this "neck righting" reflex replaced the tonic-neck reflex at four months. In the first five weeks it was easy to turn the heads of all the infants regardless of the strength of the reflex. Beyond five weeks, head-turning remained easy only in infants with a persistently strong reflex. The active resistance to head turning and the onset of the neck-righting reflex indicate that the disappearance of the reflex after 10 weeks involves an actively supervening antagonistic development.

The presence of the tonic-neck reflex in the majority of infants at four weeks represents neurophysiologic maturation over the earlier predominantly flexed position. Whatever structures or function this maturation may involve, it is clear that the change does not contribute to the infant's increased vulnerability to stimulation. On the contrary, if the infant is in the tonic-neck position he receives less feedback from motor activity than if his activity prevents the assumption of this stable posture. The inverse relationship between fussiness and the strength of the reflex at the extremes suggests that an optimally functioning reflex tends to decrease the potential for overstimulation, and the corollary: an absent or weak reflex increases the vulnerability to overstimulation through feedback from motor excitation. The tonic-neck reflex may serve as another adaptive mechanism that accounts in part for individual variability in the reduction of fussiness between six and 10 weeks.

Illness

At each interview the mother was asked whether the infant had had any major or minor ailments. There were no serious illnesses in the group, but for all the subjects there were occasional reports of vomiting, diarrhea, or upper respiratory infection (stuffy nose), all generally very mild and of short duration. In 10 cases there were reports of skin eruptions, either diaper rash or rash on the face, neck, arms, or back, which were confirmed by our observations. The incidence of rash has a developmental pattern shown in Table 9.

Table 9 INCIDENCE OF RASH

				Weeks			
	2–3	4–5	6–7	8–9	10–11	12–13	14–15
Diaper rash	3	5	2	1	2	1	0
Rash on face, neck, arms, or back	0	7	6	4	3	2	3
No rash	9	2	5	8	7	9	9
N	12	12	12	12	12	12	12

There is an abrupt increase in rash, most often on the face, at four to five weeks of age. Some infants had both face and diaper rash. The incidence decreases after eight weeks. Between four and eight weeks, the rashes were more severe and of longer duration than they were after eight weeks.

There was considerable individual variability in the susceptibility to rash, two infants never having the slightest sign of skin eruptions, and the most severe case having intermittent face or diaper rash persisting from 21 to 81 days. Only in this most severe case was there a family history of allergy.

The role of contact or food sensitivity in precipitating rashes needs to be considered. Diaper rash may be in part a function of the mother's method of washing diapers. Its early appearance and later absence may be due to her experience, or lack of it, with various brands of detergent and bleaches used in the wash. Examination of the relationships between face and body rash with food intake indicates that it is unrelated to breast or bottle feeding, or to such supplements as fruit juices or solid foods.

There was a sex difference in tendency to rash on the face. All six of the girls had face rash; in one it occurred at four weeks, lasted only a few days and was mild. The most severe case was a girl. The infants who were completely free of any skin eruption were boys and only one boy had severe face rash. It would be of interest to examine this apparent sex difference in a larger number of infants.

Skin eruptions occur concomitantly with the increase in fussiness at four weeks and are relatively rare after the third month. There is no relationship between continued irritability or colic and the presence or absence of rash in the third month.

Mother Ratings

At each interview an attempt was made to gain a clinical impression of the mother and her manner of handling the infant. In order to focus attention on certain aspects of her behavior and provide a means of comparing the impressions of the three interviewers, a rating scale containing eight items was constructed. A priori criteria were agreed upon for a 5-step scale on each item and each observer independently rated the mother after the interview, omitting any items on which he did not feel confident.

The eight items rated were: (1) the mother's overall ability to reduce tension or induce quieting in the infant; (2) the mother's sensitivity to the infant's cues—i.e., recognition of the infant's state and responding appropriately to his needs, or its opposite: an imposition of her own wishes and needs, with disregard of signs from the infant; (3) frequency of tactile expressions of affection, kissing, stroking, fondling; (4) the mother's motoric skill and smoothness in handling the infant, judged during routine care, such as diaper changing; (5) "kinesthetic unity" between mother and infant, or the degree to which the mother's posture and the infant's position when held by her blend into an esthetically harmonious unit; or, at the other end of the scale, holding the infant in awkward positions or apart from her body; (6) anxious response to infant's crying; (7) use of passive motion such as rocking, swaying, or walking to quiet the infant; and (8) length of time the mother waited to attend the crying infant.

In addition to the well-known inaccuracies of such rating scales, the judges expressed reservations about the precision of their ratings. Despite these weaknesses, a tabulation of the ratings using the mode of all judgments permitted a rank ordering of the infants on each of the scales. A Spearman rank-order correlation coefficient of these items with the rank order of mean fussiness ratings for each infant suggests some relationships between fussiness levels and mother's handling.

As Table 10 indicates, the mothers of the most fussy infants were poorer in the overall ability to reduce tension—a relationship of questionable causality since it has a high probability of being circular. A similar objection may be raised to the correlation between the infant's fussiness and the mother's response of anxiety to crying, particularly since it was noted that some of the mothers of moderately or less fussy infants were judged to respond with equally high anxiety on occasions when the infant became fussy. The highest correlations involved parameters describing the mother's physical handling of the infant—i.e., her skill in manipulating and ease in holding the infant, and her inclination to engage in affectionate play. The mothers of least fussy infants were distinguished by a tendency to wait longer before attending the crying infant.

Table 10 SPEARMAN RANK-ORDER CORRELATIONS OF FUSSINESS WITH RATINGS OF MOTHERS

	Scale		
	1	5	
Fussiness	*Least*	*Most*	
1. Overall ability to reduce tension	best	poorest	.54*
2. Sensitivity to infant's cues	best	poorest	.45
3. Fondling	most	least	.68*
4. Skill in motor handling	best	poorest	.68*
5. Kinesthetic unity	most	least	.61*
6. Anxiety to crying	least	most	.64*
7. Use of rocking motions	least	most	.46
8. Time waits to attend	shortest	longest	−.61*

* Significance $p < .05$

These findings suggest that, for the most fussy infants, the mother's manner of handling was such as to increase stimulation levels, and also to interrupt or to be unresponsive to the development of the infant's attentiveness and pleasurable responses. It seems likely that those infants who develop colic or have a period of intense fussiness during the second month are responding to a different ratio of pleasurable-displeasurable stimulation, which prolongs irritability but does not interfere with maturational processes.

This leads to a revision of Benjamin's original statement that a high level of irritability from three to 10 weeks of age was a basic state that might be masked by skillful handling, to the suggestion that, as a result of the development of attention and pleasure in responsivity, irritability will normally decline—except when these developments are hindered by maternal insensitivity.

DISCUSSION

If the differences in our observations from those originally made by Benjamin are valid, the propositions derived from them need reexamination.

The first proposition, as we stated it, was: *Between birth and three to four weeks, the lack of functional neuroconnections in the central nervous system limits the processing of sensory input, with a resultant relative lack of responsivity.*

The behavioral observations are in general accord with this hypothesis. The concept of a passive stimulus barrier is appropriate to the extent that prolonged receptivity to external stimulation does not occur. Also during the first month, there appear to be some inhibitory mechanisms functioning, possibly subcortical, as manifested in the absence of the tonic-neck reflex and the cessation of motor activity in response to visual stimuli. There is neither an absolute barrier to stimulation nor an absolute lack of functional inhibitory mechanisms. However, this interpretation of the findings does not lead to any reformulation of the proposition.

The proposition addressed to the second age period, the so-called vulnerable period, as we stated it was: There is an intervening period, between three to four and eight to 10 weeks, during which the infant is without autonomous means of protection from the environment. Neuromaturation suddenly increases the infant's capacity to process stimuli at three to four weeks, but maturation of those mechanisms involved in inhibiting or regulating input is delayed until eight to 10 weeks.

The increase in irritability at three to four weeks is in accord with the hypothesized neuromaturation at that time. Furthermore, during the vulnerable period, there was no behavioral evidence of the inhibitory or regulatory mechanisms that make possible the active avoidance of stimulation. However, the findings are interpreted as indicating that the infant is equipped with a developing means of responding positively to stimulation, through sensorimotor coordination and learned associations to familiar need-fulfilling objects. The effectiveness of this capacity to respond favorably to stimulation, in the absence of the ability to avoid it, is variable among individuals, apparently because of such factors as the strength of the tonic-neck reflex or reinforcement from the environment of the pleasure-displeasure dichotomy.

On the basis of these findings, the proposition may be modified as follows: *At three to four weeks neuromaturation suddenly increases, without a comparable increase in functioning of inhibitory or regulatory mechanisms. Between three to four weeks and about four months sensory input and motor responses become increasingly coordinated, providing the infant with a means of pleasurable discharge. The infant is still without autonomous means of protection against stimulation but it does become equipped with a relatively more integrated means of processing it.*

The finding that in many infants there is an abrupt decline in the Babkin reflex at around six weeks may be viewed as evidence of an inhibitory, suppressing, or supervening development occurring during this period. Some such developments may occur concomitantly, but the weight of the evidence is in accord with the revision.

The proposition pertaining to the third period as we stated it is: Beginning at eight to 10 weeks of age, and rapidly thereafter, inhibitory or regulatory mechanisms mature, providing the infant with the ability to shut out stimuli.

The behavioral evidence is in accord with the hypothesized beginning of a major neuromaturational change at eight to 10 weeks, but there is no clear evidence that the inception of the ability actively to shut out stimuli takes place at this time. Such findings as the increase in auditory responsivity, the presence of the social smile, the recrudescence of the Babkin, the decline in strength of the tonic-neck reflex, and the reduction in rash are in part compatible with and in part discrepant with an increase in central nervous system inhibition. They are more readily interpreted as representing a major reorganization in neuro-functioning. Furthermore, the results of the study suggest that an active stimulus barrier, as manifested in diverted attention or in motor actions, does not become effective until well into the fourth month. If our study had extended into the fifth month, these behavioral correlates of an active stimulus barrier would probably have been better elucidated.

Therefore the third proposition is modified as: *At eight to 10 weeks, complex neuromaturation, effecting diverse changes in responsivity, occurs, followed in about a month by the emergence of functioning inhibitory or regulatory mechanisms that are utilizable for reducing the impact of stimulation.*

The contribution of this study to psychoanalytic developmental theory other than the main theme is limited. Some of the findings may pertain to a very early ego function, extensively discussed by psychoanalytic theoreticians: the distinction of the "outside" from the "inside." From the quality of the infant's response as well as the reported findings, it was suggested that the onset of the stage in development when the infant can distinguish external from internal sensations occurs at around four weeks through vision, and may be delayed until eight weeks in the auditory modality; in either case the distinction appears to be facilitated at its inception by a negative emotional response. It seems likely that changing reactions also occur in the kinesthetic and tactile modalities, areas in which we were unable to design discriminating tests.

Further research would be required to investigate the predictive value of individual variability in the nature and timing of these behavioral findings and later developing ego functions. For example, if a study were extended beyond three and a half months, when the infant begins to avoid stimulation, it might be possible to differentiate those infants who, in avoiding stimulation, use motor actions predominantly and those who do so by focusing attention on a familiar person. Such distinctions might represent early precursors to later personality styles or choice of defense.

The validation or refutation of the hypothesis will depend upon more knowledge of neuroanatomical and neurophysiological development during the first three months of life than is available at present. Changes in central nervous system functioning as reflected indirectly by the EEG correlates may be of value in this regard.

REFERENCES

Ambrose, J. (1961). The Development of the Smiling Response in Early Infancy. In: *Determinants of Infant Behavior,* Vol. 1, ed. B. Foss. New York: Wiley, pp. 179–201.

Babkin, P. (1958). The Establishment of Reflex Activity in Early Postnatal Life. *Fiziologicheskii Zhurnal SSSR,* 44:922–927.

Bayley, N. (1969). *Manual for the Bayley Scales of Infant Development.* New York: Psychological Corporation.

Benjamin, J. (1961a). Some Developmental Observations Relating to the Theory of Anxiety. *Journal of the American Psychoanalytic Association,* 9:652–668.

———— (1961b). The Innate and the Experiential in Development. In: *Lectures in Experimental Psychiatry,* ed. H. Brosin. Pittsburgh: University of Pittsburgh Press, pp. 19–42.

———— (1963). Further Comments on Some Developmental Aspects of Anxiety. In: *Counterpoint: Libidinal Object and Subject,* ed. H. Gaskill. New York: International Universities Press, pp. 121–153.

———— (1965). Developmental Biology and Psychoanalysis. In: *Psychoanalysis and Current Biological Thought,* ed. N. Greenfield and W. Lewis. Madison: University of Wisconsin Press, pp. 57–80.

Bergman, P., and Escalona, S. K. (1949). Unusual Sensitivities in Very Young Children. *Psychoanalytic Study of the Child,* 3/4:333–352. New York: International Universities Press.

Brackbill, Y. (1958). Extinction of the Smiling Response in Infants as a Function of Reinforcement Schedule. *Child Development,* 29:114–124.

Brazelton, T. B. (1962). Crying in Infancy. *Pediatrics,* 29:579–588.

Bühler, C. (1921). *Kindheit und Jugend.* Leipzig: Hirzel.

Byers, R. K. (1938). Tonic Neck Reflexes in Children. *American Journal of Diseases of Children,* 55:696–742.

Clifton, R., and Meyers, W. (1969). The Heart-Rate Response of Four-Month-Old Infants to Auditory Stimuli. *Journal of Experimental Child Psychology,* 7:122–134.

Dekaban, A. (1959). *Neurology of Infancy.* Baltimore: Williams and Wilkins.

Erikson, E. (1950). *Childhood and Society.* New York: Norton.

Fantz, R. (1965). Visual Perception from Birth as Shown by Pattern Selectivity. *Annals of the New York Academy of Sciences,* 118:793–814.

Freud, S. (1915). Instincts and Their Vicissitudes. *Standard Edition,* 14:166–204. London: Hogarth Press, 1957.

———— (1920). Beyond the Pleasure Principle. *Standard Edition,* 28:7–64. London: Hogarth Press, 1955.

———— (1925). A Note upon the "Mystic Writing-Pad." *Standard Edition,* 19:227–232. London: Hogarth Press, 1961.

———— (1930). Civilization and Its Discontents. *Standard Edition,* 21:64–145. London: Hogarth Press, 1961.

Gesell, A. (1938). The Tonic-Neck Reflex in the Human Infant. *Journal of Pediatrics,* 13:455–464.

———— (1942). *The First Five Years of Life.* London: Methuen.

Greenacre, P. (1958). Toward an Understanding of the Physical Nucleus of Some Defence Reactions. *International Journal of Psycho-Analysis,* 39:69–76.

Griffiths, R. (1954). *The Abilities of Babies.* New York: McGraw-Hill.

Hartmann, H. (1950). Psychoanalysis and Developmental Psychology. *Psychoanalytic Study of the Child,* 5:7–17. New York: International Universities Press.

Hayes, W. (1963). *Statistics for Psychologists.* New York: Holt, Rinehart and Winston.

Kuffler, S. (1952). Neurons in the Retina: Organization, Inhibition and Excitation Problems. *Symposium on Quantitative Biology,* 27:281–292.

Lenard, H., Bernuth, H. von, and Prechtl, H. (1968). Reflexes and Their Relationship to Behavioral State in the Newborn. *Acta Paediatrica Scandinavica,* 57:177–185.

Lippman, K. (1958). Über der Babkinschen Reflex. *Archiv für Kinderheilkunde,* 157:234–238.

McCough, G. P., Deering, I. D., and Ling, T. H. (1951). Location of Receptors for Tonic-Neck Reflexes. *Journal of Neurophysiology,* 14:191–195.

Meili, R. (1957). *Anfänge der Charakterentwicklung.* Bern and Stuttgart: Huber.

Minkowski, M. (1921). Sur les Mouvements les Réflexes et les Réactions musculaires du Foetus humain de 2 à 5 Mois et leurs Relations avec le Système nerveux foetal. *Revue Neurologique,* 1105–1118, 1235–1250.

Pacella, B., and Barrera, S. (1940). Postural Reflexes and Grasp Phenomena in Infants. *Journal of Neurophysiology,* 3:213–218.

Paine, R., et al. (1964). The Evolution of Postural Reflexes in Normal Infants and in the Presence of Chronic Brain Syndromes. *Neurology,* 14:1036–1048.

Paradise, J. (1966). Maternal and Other Factors in the Etiology of Infantile Colic. *Journal of the American Medical Association,* 197:191–199.

Parmalee, A. (1963). The Hand-Mouth Reflex of Babkin in Premature Infants. *Pediatrics,* 31:734–740.

Pierce, P. (1948). Delayed Onset of "Three Months" Colic in Premature Infants. *American Journal of Diseases of Children,* 75:190–192.

Polak, P., Emde, R., and Spitz, R. (1964). The Smiling Response to the Human Face: I. Methodology, Quantification and Natural History. *Journal of Nervous and Mental Disease,* 139:103–109.

Spitz, R. A. (1957). *No and Yes: On the Genesis of Human Communication.* New York: International Universities Press.

———— (1961). Some Early Prototypes of Ego Defenses. *Journal of the American Psychoanalytic Association,* 9:626–651.

———— and Wolf, K. (1946). The Smiling Response: A Contribution to the Ontogenesis of Social Relations. *Genetic Psychology Monographs,* 34:57–125.

Stechler, S., and Latz, E. (1966). Some Observations on Attention and Arousal in the Human Infant. *Journal of the American Academy of Child Psychiatry,* 5:517–525.

Stewart, A., et al. (1953). Excessive Infant Crying in Relation to Parent Behavior. *American Journal of Psychiatry,* 110:687–694.

Vassella, F., and Karlson, B. (1962). Asymmetric Tonic-Neck Reflex. *Developmental Medicine and Child Neurology,* 4:363–369.

Wessel, M., et al. (1954). Paroxysmal Fussing in Infancy, Sometimes Called Colic. *Pediatrics,* 15:421–434.

White, B., and Held, R. (1966). Plasticity of Sensorimotor Development. In: *The Causes of Behavior: Readings in Child Development and Educational Psychology,* 2nd ed., ed. J. Rosenblith and W. Allinsmith. Boston: Allyn and Bacon, pp. 60–70.

Wolff, P. (1963). Observations on the Early Development of Smiling. In: *Determinants of Infant Behavior,* Vol. 2, ed. B. Foss. London: Methuen, pp. 113–167.

———— (1969). The Natural History of Crying and Other Vocalizations in Early Infancy. In: *Determinants of Infant Behavior,* Vol. 4, ed. B. Foss. London: Methuen, pp. 81–110.

Yakovlev, P., and Lecours, A. (1967). The Myelogenetic Cycles of Regional Maturation of the Brain. In: *Regional Development of the Brain in Early Life,* ed. A. Minkowski. Oxford: Blackwell, pp. 3–70.

4

CLINICAL AND QUANTITATIVE

A QUANTITATIVE STUDY
OF A PSYCHOANALYSIS

Hartvig Dahl, M.D.[1]

The widespread uneasiness among psychoanalysts about the current status and the future of our profession is largely based, I believe, on our failure to redeem the promise of psychoanalysis as a science. We must start fulfilling that promise in a more basic way than we have generally recognized, by revising our very methods of collecting data. I am convinced that we must begin by audio-recording psychoanalyses, to eliminate the unsystematic and unspecified selection procedures involved in note-taking, as well as the errors resulting from our fallible memories. Moreover, I assume that we need to make our data public, in the sense that analysts other than ourselves can have access to the fine details of what each has heard and responded to in private. I cannot accept Meissner's (1966) position that this is a pointless task because the real data are by nature private—that is, subjective experiences of analysands and analysts. If it is really true that the words used by analyst and patient do not significantly inform us about the analytic process, then we might as well forget about our scientific development. Gill et al. (1968) have cogently stated the important arguments for recording.

But recording alone is only a beginning. What we need even more is a whole new approach to the study of analyses. We cannot live off the genius of Freud forever, nor off the second generation of truly gifted and creative clinicians upon whose insights we still feed but whom we have begun to lose. All current signs point to a steady decline in creative innovation and fresh clinical insights. In short, it can be said, and I believe most analysts would agree, that there is a powerful need for new life, new blood, new students with fire and creative imagination. By all the signs, this hope is forlorn unless the field of psychoanalysis is reinvigorated by some fundamentally new feature that will attract creative men and women.

[1] Preparation of this paper was supported by a United States Public Health Service Research Scientist Development Award (5-KO1-MH 23108) from the National Institute of Mental Health. This is a preliminary report of part of a larger study of one case.

Such an innovation is at hand, for progress in science is made not only by gifted individuals; it is also made by new technologies. One such technology awaits us and offers a whole new order of possibilities for restoring the investigative spirit to analysis, for enabling younger analysts to accumulate relevant experience earlier, and for bringing a whole set of new disciplines to bear on our field. I refer to the possibilities of content-analysis techniques that computers have provided. Few analysts know about the enormous strides in recent years in the ability of computers to process text. New programming languages have made such processing practical, and the latest computers combine the necessary speed, memory capacity, and economy.

One of the basic problems in studying analyses has always been the enormous reduction of data required. Computers are marvelously reliable, tenacious and dutiful, when properly told what to do. Given correct protocols from tape recordings, a properly programmed computer can search for and count words, alone or in context, can assign them to conceptual categories, and can give us the frequency of occurrence of each category.

I wish I could say that the study I am about to report utilized computers to the full extent currently possible. It did not. Moreover, there are various technical issues and certain problems of a detailed nature that I must skip for lack of space. All these matters will be covered in a detailed publication when the studies on this case are complete.

Here I report on three of the ways in which I studied data from 363 tape-recorded psychoanalytic sessions. First, I factor-analyzed a correlation matrix of 53 variables of interest to psychoanalysts, produced estimates of the amount of each factor in each hour, and plotted these factor scores over time. Second, I selected 25 hours having certain types of factor score profiles and, using a computer content-analysis dictionary, compared frequency counts of 83 different categories with the factor scores for each hour. Third, I had analysts rate eight of these hours for the predominance of analytic work or of resistance to such work.

The data are from the case of a young woman whose analysis was begun by a male analyst, Dr. A, a number of years ago. It was specifically a research case and was recorded with the patient's consent. After 102 hours, Dr. A became ill and had to stop the analysis. About five months later a female analyst, Dr. B, was able to take over the case and continue the recording. Dr. A had made a list of some 58 subjects and processes that interested him. This list was subsequently revised by Dr. B. She then regularly read a somewhat abbreviated transcript of each hour and simply counted the presence of any of the 58 categories. At the time I learned of these data and obtained Dr. B's permission to analyze them, 363 hours were available. The analysis continued for some time afterward, was eventually changed to psychotherapy, and then terminated. I shall describe the patient and the story of the analysis later.

After preliminary examination, I eliminated several variables that had too few entries to be useful, and added as variables the day of the week and the hour number, ending up with 53 variables. Table 1 lists these variables, together

Table 1

Variable No.	Variable Name, Hour Number, and Examples
1	*Fear of Insanity*
	113 Just now I was recalling the topic of losing my mind. There seems to be a constellation between homosexuality, going crazy, and these kind of paranoiac fears I am subject to. The specific thought about losing my mind slightly before we began, I had a dream I was losing my mind. It wasn't that I was going crazy, but my intelligence was unable to function.
2	*Fear of Hurting Children*
	162 Before the sessions broke off for you to have the baby, I was experiencing anxiety about feelings that might well up in me, that I couldn't control. Anxiety of pushing a child or anyone off the train platform. When I was here I tried to express what I might be feeling and I experienced anxiety with shortness of breath.
3	*Compulsive Eating*
	191 She couldn't imagine herself losing control or being afraid of her own desires, where I can. Times I gain weight overeating in an attempt to lose it. Some faint idea of the whole cycle of indulgence.
4	*Angry Feelings*
	465 I was angry.
	463 Was feeling very irritated.
	441 If your judgment about things like this is an issue I'm going to resent it . . . I don't know if I then have to.
5	*Thoughts of Doing Violence*
	249 On the train I thought of pushing or being pushed off.
6	*Depression*
	450 I'm in a depressed mood.
7	*Thoughts of Suicide*
	450 The point about suicide was that they felt she's got so much feelings—frustrations and very low toleration for handling difficulties, that if she tried to control it, maybe she would end up committing suicide.
	450 Was thinking about suicide yesterday.
8	*Anxiety*
	113 I woke up this morning tense and apprehensive, as though everything was vaguely threatening.
9	*Guilt and Punishment*
	450 Tied up in my mind, I was reading *The New Statesman,* which is a Left paper. I was being punished.
	450 Punished by peers in school and by my parents. Sense that I will suffer if I don't watch my feelings.
	249 Yes, I think that's close to it, because I think, how should I put it, that you feel guilty to the extent that you withdraw here or run away or what have you. (Analyst)
10	*Homosexuality*
	113 That's an association both with the expression of hostility and also with some homosexual impulses.
11	*Heterosexuality*
	113 There's a young man at R who is a writer. It's his first year out

Table 1 (*continued*)

Variable No.	Variable Name, Hour Number, and Examples

there, and he is very attractive and very responsive. Although he's married and I know that, yet there is a fantasied thing I've got going.

12   *Positive Oedipal Feelings*

217   The fantasies of a man, which doesn't describe my father well. It's in exaggerated form. Experience doesn't describe my father. I magically admit the attitude I have for him by labeling him in that way or seeking a person like him. Magically transforming him in reference to me so I have an exaggerated reality and a wish fulfillment at the same time.

13   *Penis Envy and Castration*

249   It came up in relation to thoughts of having a penis. Could it be a wish? I would have been discovered to have the disease and isolated, shamed, humiliated. If I was aware of a fantasy of having a penis and afraid of being discovered and knowing it was wrong for a girl to have one, I would be scorned or rejected very violently.

14   *Other References to Genitals*

249   Like some forcefulness on—like being a penis entering a vagina.

15   *Having a Baby*

113   I don't know why this makes me feel like crying, but . . . that I . . . er . . . that I won't, that I won't, I won't marry or have children.

113   I see that problem at this point that means . . . I don't know, that I . . . er . . . want to have a child too.

16   *Masturbation*

249   That summer some children talked about the word masturbation, or maybe homosexuality. (CC-10)*

17   *Anality*

249   I can't believe I would ever understand the composite image of breast and penis and the association to feces or remember anything more about the two memories I mentioned yesterday.

18   *Domination-Submission*

441   Although it seems that way I think I just feel you are using your power and you are going to defend this situation and then it seems to me a kind of a very circumstantial thing.

441   I did sense again how it could not be resolved very well because how it turned out it's like a power struggle.

19   *Involvement-Separation*

463   I was to meet you somewhere or—anyway, something about unexpected informality or contact.

450   After I left here Wednesday, thought about this reaction I'm having, drawing back, that fear of closeness, only manifests itself in a conscious way to me with women.

465   L and I are not going to see each other any more.

441   That doesn't invite me to develop a need for you, and that I will see the end as something painful as if I'd been rejected and I don't see what the point is in doing this.

* CC means cross-coded.

Table 1 (*continued*)

Variable No.	Variable Name, Hour Number, and Examples
20	*Mother*
	113 I associate that she's from the past and that it's related to my talking about mother in here yesterday.
21	*Father*
	249 To my knowledge I never saw my father naked.
22	*Sister*
	249 I asked out of the same general feeling that she's going to have a difficult life like my sister and myself.
23	*Parents*
	113 I associate, I have a thought that you must be wondering about this, from that to my parent's concern with nail-biting when I was a child.
24	*Mother Role*
	113 Now it occurs to me that last night, I think I was wondering how it could be, if it can be, that somehow understanding my relationship to you, since I see you almost entirely as a mother figure, how that's going to help me establish better relationships with men.
25	*Negroes*
	463 One thing I remember specifically, that in the dream there was something about the children looking part Negro. Very light skin, but clearly part Negro. Then I realized in the dream you were part Negro too.
26	*Political Interests*
	441 Well, I think that I shouldn't have to think about whether you approve of my doing things about Vietnam.
	462 About an incident that happened last week at school, about the military recruitment on campus.
27	*Paranoia*
	450 Something happened on the bus that bothered me. Was sitting down, the buses were still crowded. There was a Negro boy who was standing in front of me. He sat down beside me. I had two papers, a morning and *The New Statesman*. Was reading one and the other was on my lap. He took the paper off my lap. I said, that is my paper. He said, I just want to look at it. I told him, you didn't ask me, I'd rather you didn't. I took it back. It was strange. When he got off, he stepped on my foot. Don't know if it was deliberate or not. Thought he might hit me before he got out. When I took the paper he didn't try to insist on it. He had no reaction. (CC-25)
28	*Color in Dreams*
	113 The other fragment of a dream I remember involves—I don't know exactly the situation but I was talking to another girl, C who I knew in S and now she comes down from time to time and lives in S. There were two cats lying curled like the top of a stoop, like on a pillar or something. One was black and the other pink. (CC-51)
29	*Performance Material*
	180 I'm not unwilling to talk if you encourage me. Maybe I have to

Table 1 (*continued*)

Variable No.	Variable Name, Hour Number, and Examples

say those things and get them off my mind. Declined to speak at the teach-in. I had nothing to say. To get up before all those people not having anything to say, a vacuum inside me. I don't get to talk to people. I've stopped thinking about things or having ideas.

30 *Moving or Details of Dwelling*
    202 In the dream where the boys attack outside of the apartment. There was a wall and the couch like in this room, like the wall between my living room and bedroom which is a partition with a couch against it. In today's dream I was afraid to go into the living room.

31 *Fair Play and Justice*
    463 And that it's much easier for you to have a rule that you can say is unjust or just or whatever. (Analyst)

32 *Childhood Memories*
    249 The summer I was 11 at the beach, some kids put on a show and I wore a dress like that.
    249 It reminds me of one of my small stock of memories, playing dentist, putting rocks in my mouth.
    113 It was recalling that sometime, I guess it was about age 4 or 5 but maybe later, I recollect trying to urinate like a boy.

33 *Report of Major Affect in Dream or Reality*
    225 Not that I am on exhibition. I'm self-conscious because there's no conversation. I can't stand sitting waiting for the food. I had no reason to say that I felt very bad together with what I said to A. I began to think I was awful. In the middle of the day I was in tears. Felt no one could care for me because I'm a horrible person.

34 *Masochistic Wish*
    462 The fact that you're not pulling away, that what I think you see as a self-destructive piece of behavior, trying to understand, trying to sort it out. (Analyst, CC-19)

35 *Negative Feelings Toward Analyst*
    113 What comes to mind is that somehow I think, I don't know if I can fully explain this, but I'm envious of you.

36 *Genetic Interpretations*
    173 Some of the apprehensions is the fear that I will intervene and the thought that I am controlling your bowel movement, giving you enemas, etc., by requiring you to speak your thoughts, making you lose control of your thoughts, making you do something at a different time, in a different way from what you want. (Analyst)

37 *Other Interpretations*
    463 Don't you think it's likely to do with what went on between us?
    463 Is it that your going away was an effort to make distance and saying OK meant I was willing? And if it wasn't I'd say no?
    463 I hope I can make this clear to you because it's very clear to me now. I think you're freer when there is a rule that you can defy than when there's an opportunity for negotiation. In other words, I think I made it harder for you to leave by saying OK.

Table 1 (continued)

Variable No.	Variable Name, Hour Number, and Examples
	249 You can see the reason for some of the hesitation you have had, the thought that you would be crazy, homosexual, if you began to really associate in the analysis. (All analyst)
38	*Response to Interventions as Interaction*
	463 (Analyst) Yes. The last escape hatch from it being you and me. You can't say it's the convention of the analysis. I wonder whether that too doesn't serve that purpose. (Patient) Don't have any thoughts about that. Not thinking about my reaction to what you said. Didn't tell me. Thinking you haven't confirmed or denied. Assumed you wouldn't.
39	*Transference Phenomena*
	163 It didn't seem I was feeling angry about you having a child. The way it came to mind was about there being another child, so maybe I do feel that (patient's voice fell away for the last few words).
40	*Other References to Analyst*
	249 Some memory recreating earlier anger and I would scream and flail in here. You would be around to control. (CC-4)
	249 Whether I am preoccupied with it because of having such impulses myself, specifically in relationship to you.
	249 Probably doing better today in the analysis. You must be approving. (CC-43)
	249 Maybe you understand about the breast-penis-feces collocation. Would you tell me? Maybe at some time you would. If you did you would leave me question that, leave me to unravel it myself.
41	*Research*
	463 The second thing, probably more important, I said I was someone's research patient and it cost me little money. He mentioned that he had a cousin who had been a research patient, who had a woman doctor and that this woman doctor had told him after two and a half years that she couldn't do anything for him and let him go.
42	*Non-verbal Behavior on Couch Which Is Discussed in the Analysis*
	462 But there have been, even in the last week, plenty of sessions where you were silent for a long time, where you have yourself reported you felt extremely withdrawn and you weren't saying what you were thinking or what you were feeling. (Analyst)
	113 That reference to taillessness in the dream brought to mind that during the hour yesterday, I was conscious of my genitals . . . my female genitals, that is, and so am I now . . . and partly why I stopped.
	113 Anyway, just now, I have the need to urinate and that may be related to the question of control.
43	*Reflections on Quality of Associations*
	113 I see that yesterday and in the beginning today, the subject matter was my feelings about you and about my mother as females few minutes, I'm talking about my male proclivities. I don't know who provide warmth and perhaps nourishment. Now, in the last the nature of the connection between those two subjects.

Table 1 *(concluded)*

Variable No.	Variable Name, Hour Number, and Examples
44	*Major Affect in Analysis*
	465 If I say he can't hurt me, nobody can hurt me (speech broken, crying). The reason he gave or continues to handle things in the way, even though I told him I didn't like it, was that I should be less unhappy. Indicated there was no unhappiness for him. He could manage. That was very insulting to me (crying).
45	*Major Speech Disturbances*
	465 He didn't have anything to say. Suppose he could see the contradictions. (Disrupted speech.) I have many feelings.
46	*Momentary or Immediate Forgetting*
	459 I meant to say I don't do it out of selfishness. In a way it's—part of those feelings have to do with my feeling superior. Partly it's just easier (silence)—forgot what I was going to say.
47	*Discussion of Arrangements*
	462 May have to go to a meeting in school tomorrow.
48	*Instructions about Associations*
	462 If we could understand, it might be more valuable in getting over it, so to speak, than not feeling it.
	463 There is still something in the relationship we have to work on.
	463 I don't mean you're purposely not doing what you should or even that you could change overnight. I want you to notice it. (All analyst)
49	*Other References to Analysis*
	229 I saw downstairs one of the people that I recognize from the other building. Made me think again, I don't want anyone else in on this analysis.
	229 Just a general feeling, you're not. Everything else except the analysis feels transient.
	463 Yes. And we know you've complained bitterly of the conventions of the analysis. (Analyst)
(50	*Analyst Speaks* [frequency per hour])
51	*Dream Report*
	113 I remember two fragments of a dream.
	463 Dreamed about you last night.
(52	*Day of the Week*)
(53	*Hour Number*)

with one or more examples of text (chosen unsystematically from what happened to be available) which was coded for each.

There are several features to be noted. Many, but not all, of the categories lend themselves to coding with minimal or no inference. For example, categories such as *Mother* and *Father* are simply manifest references to them. Categories such as *Depression, Anxiety, Angry Feelings,* or *Guilt and Punishment* were coded when the patient or analyst manifestly spoke of such feelings: the patient would have to say she was tense or anxious or nervous; it was not an inference on the part of the analyst. Other categories, such as *Paranoia* and *Response to Intervention as Interaction,* clearly require a judgment on the part of the analyst, as does *Reflections on the Quality of Associations*. Others are coded from comments in the transcript as in *Major Affect in Analysis,* which was almost always crying, and *Major Speech Disturbances.*

But 53 variables are a lot to keep in mind all at once, and experience has shown that there is usually a lot of redundancy in psychological variables. Factor analysis is basically a procedure for removing redundancy, for picking out relatively non-redundant variables and systematically grouping those that go together. Normally, it is applied to variables measured on many people, but it can also be applied to variables measured on one person over many time units. The latter is called P-technique Factor Analysis; Lester Luborsky (1953) was among the very first to use it, in the early 1950's. The P-technique was then nearly abandoned until very recently. This is its first application to extensive psychoanalytic data. Table 2 shows the six factors derived from a matrix of intercorrelations of the 53 variables I have just described.

Thirty-one of the 53 variables are grouped into six factors. The variables that are most important in determining each factor are listed along with their factor loadings. Factors do not come out of the computer labeled. It is necessary to look at the variables that define a factor and decide what concept or construct they represent. Factors 2, 3, 4, and 5 are very easily understood. Factor 2, I have labeled a *Family* factor for obvious reasons. Factor 3, a *Sex* factor, is of special interest to analysts because the variables of *heterosexuality, having a baby, thoughts of doing violence, masochistic wishes, penis envy and castration, positive oedipal feelings,* and *guilt and punishment* are here grouped together. Factor 4 is a *Dream* factor. Factor 5, labeled *Anxiety,* is of interest because it includes not only *anxiety, fear of insanity,* and *fear of hurting children,* but *anality* and a measure of obsessive thinking, namely, *reflections on the quality of associations.*

I thought about Factors 1 and 6 for some time before deciding to call them *Resistance* factors. You will notice that the highest-loading variable on Factor 1 is *analyst speaks*. This is simply a count of the number of times the analyst spoke during an hour. It is highly correlated with the hour number, which means that the analyst spoke more and more often as the analysis went on. I then noted the other variables that loaded on this factor: *other interpretations, other references to the analyst, involvement-separation, major speech disturbances,* and *paranoia.* It occurred to me that what must have been happening was that the analyst was encountering severe resistance and making an increasingly active effort to deal with it. Factor 6 then appeared to be another type of resistance. It includes the analyst's *instructions about associations, other references to the analysis, discussion of arrangements* (such as money and time), and *response to interventions as interaction* (the patient's focus is not upon the content of the intervention, but upon its interpersonal significance).

The results in Table 2 are based upon the frequency of occurrence of these variables. But it is not necessarily true that because a particular matter is mentioned 10 times it is more important than a matter that is mentioned only once.

I decided to find out whether there would be any difference if the data

Table 2. FACTORS BASED ON FREQUENCY DATA*

Variables	Factor Loadings
Factor I (Resistance I)	
Analyst Speaks	.82
Other Interpretations	.75
Involvement-Separation	.66
Other References to the Analyst	.62
Major Speech Disturbances	.48
Paranoia	.35
Factor II (Family-Genetic)	
Mother	.72
Father	.56
Childhood Memories	.46
Sister	.44
Genetic Interpretations	.37
Factor III (Sexuality)	
Heterosexuality	.58
Having a Baby	.46
Thoughts of Doing Violence	.44
Masochistic Wish	.36
Penis Envy and Castration	.35
Positive Oedipal Feelings	.31
Guilt and Punishment	.30
Factor IV (Dreams)	
Dream Report	.55
Color in Dreams	.45
Moving or Details of Dwelling	.37
Report of Major Affect in Dream or Reality	.30
Factor V (Anxiety)	
Anxiety	.45
Reflections on the Quality of Associations	.37
Anality	.35
Fear of Insanity	.33
Fear of Hurting Children	.28
Factor VI (Interaction—Resistance II)	
Instructions about Associations	.37
Response to Interventions as Interaction	.30
Other References to the Analysis	.30
Discussion of Arrangements	.28

* Square root transformation of frequencies (f), ($x = \sqrt{f} + \sqrt{f+1}$). With two exceptions, variables chosen to represent a factor had factor loadings $\geq.30$. The correlation matrix was factored by principal components method with a Varimax (orthogonal) rotation. Six factors accounted for 78 per cent of the variance.

were treated as though any number of occurrences is equivalent to one occurrence. For example, if the patient said she was tense several times during an hour and it had been so tabulated, I now counted this as 1, and if the variable was not found at all it was counted zero. I then repeated the whole procedure; the results are shown in Table 3. The striking thing is the similarity in results from

Table 3. FACTORS BASED ON ALL-OR-NONE DATA*

Variables	Factor Loadings
Factor I (Analyst Speaks—Resistance I)	
Analyst Speaks	.59
Paranoia	.45
Major Speech Disturbances	.40
Momentary Forgetting	−.30
Mother Role	−.30
Other Interpretations	.27
Factor II (Family—Genetic)	
Mother	.64
Father	.48
Childhood Memories	.44
Sister	.43
Genetic Interpretations	.31
Factor III (Sexuality)	
Heterosexuality	.48
Having a Baby	.42
Negative Feelings toward Analyst	−.40
Penis Envy and Castration	.35
Masochistic Wish	.27
Positive Oedipal Feelings	.26
Factor IV (Dreams)	
Color in Dreams	.49
Dream Report	.48
Moving or Details of Dwelling	.35
Report of Major Affect in Dream or Reality	.31
Factor V (Anxiety)	
Anxiety	.36
Thoughts of Doing Violence	.36
Anality	.31
Reflections on Quality of Associations	.31
Fear of Hurting Children	.23
Factor VI (Interaction—Resistance II)	
Instructions about Associations	.37
Response to Interventions as Interaction	.36
Involvement-Separation	.30

* All-or-none transformation of frequencies (f) (when $f > 1$, $x = 1$). With two exceptions, variables chosen to represent a factor had factor loadings $\geq .27$. Principal components solution with Varimax rotation. Six factors accounted for 73 per cent of the variance.

the two procedures. Although there are a number of relatively minor differences, the main one consists in the shifting of the variable *involvement-separation* from Factor 1 to Factor 6. For reasons that will become clear later on, the *involvement-separation* theme is of major importance in the case. For technical reasons we can see its contribution more effectively when it is grouped with Factor 6 rather than with Factor 1. The rest of this report is based on the all-or-none data.

After we have reduced the variables in number and have grouped them by factor analysis, it then becomes possible to get a measure of the amount of each factor that is present during each of the 363 hours. Estimates of these amounts are called factor scores.[2] Since it is very difficult to look at long columns of numbers—363 in all—I obtained averages for each week and plotted the amounts of each of these factors for each of the 108 weeks. Figure 1 is a graph of these plots. There are a number of things to be noted about these plots. For each factor the central line is the mean value; up is more, and down is less. The striking characteristic of Factor 1, which I have called *Resistance 1,* is its practically linear

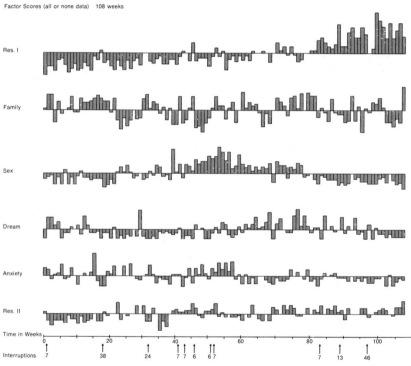

Figure 1. Each vertical bar represents the average factor score for a week, standardized over the entire 108 weeks. The center line is zero; above the line is a positive score and below the line is a negative score. The numbers under the arrows at the bottom represent the numbers of days of an interruption in the analysis.

[2] These factor scores were estimated by treating the variables that were chosen to represent the factor as predictors of a dependent variable, the factor, and computing beta weights for a linear combination of the variables.

increase over the 108 weeks. Factor 2, the *Family* factor, has some kind of cycle, but it is very hard to relate it systematically to other factors. For about the first 20 weeks most of the values are above the mean. Factor 3 is the *Sexuality* factor. Most of its values are low until about the 40th week; then it sharply increases to about the 54th week, then gradually drops off to about the 80th week, and finally returns to low values. Factor 4, the *Dream* factor, shows some dreams in the early weeks, but is generally low until about the 60th week. There is then a rising and descending curve of dreams until the 100th week, with a peak at about 80. Factor 5, the *Anxiety* factor, is intermittently above the mean in the first 40 weeks, but the striking thing is a steady increase after the 40th week until about the 59th week, when it drops sharply and remains less than the mean during the rest of the period. And Factor 6, the second *Resistance* factor, including *involvement-separation*, is consistently negative until the 18th week; then it suddenly shifts upward, where it remains for pretty much the rest of the 108-week period.

By this time I had done what is known as a second-order factor analysis in my head; that is, I had reduced these six factors to two. I combined the two resistance factors into one (R). Then I combined the other four factors into one factor which represented both content and conflict (C). Let me now briefly explain the main reason for reducing everything to these two measures. What I really wanted was an overall measure of "analytic work." This is a key concept for understanding the psychoanalytic process, but we have had no way to measure its viscissitudes over time. My thinking ran something like this: during periods when the patient is doing what we call analytic work she will, on the average, tend to talk about her conflicts; she will refer to sexual topics, to her family and childhood, to her anxieties and symptoms, and she will tend to report dreams. It is true that we cannot define a typical pattern of the way these topics will alternate over time, and it is also true that talking about these matters may sometimes be in the service of resistance. Nonetheless, if conflicts are to be resolved, they must be dealt with, and it therefore seems reasonable, for the time being, to adopt the simplifying assumption that these topics will be most evident during periods of "work" and least evident during periods of "resistance" and less productive work.

It therefore occurred to me that it would be possible to get a rough overall measure of analytic work by summing the four conflict factors and subtracting the resistance factors from them. If my reasoning is correct, then the probability of "work" will tend to be greatest when C is high and R is low; conversely, the probability of "work" will tend to be lowest when C is low and R is high.[3] Thus I began to think of C minus R as a rough measure of analytic work. I am quite aware that this idea involves a number of difficulties; but its merit is that it turned out to be useful. Figure 2 shows plots of the sum of the conflict factors (C), the sum of the resistance factors (R), and the difference between them (C − R).

In Figure 2 the top graph (C) represents the sum of the four conflict

---

[3] Much later I actually did a second-order factor analysis and the results were consistent with the intuitive grouping.

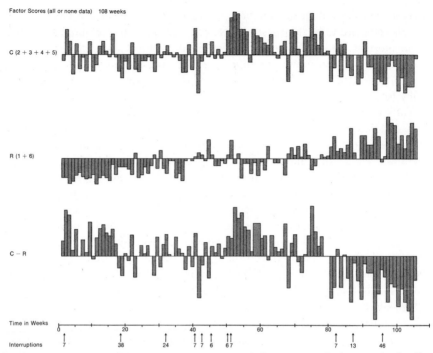

Figure 2. Each vertical bar represents a sum of the average factor scores for the indicated factors. *C* is the sum of the factor scores for factors 2, 3, 4, and 5; *R* is the sum of factors 1 and 6; *C* − *R* is *C* minus *R*. The center line is zero; above the line is a positive score and below the line is a negative score.

factors, the middle graph (*R*) represents the sum of the two resistance factors, and the bottom graph (*C* − *R*) shows the difference between the two. As before, each vertical bar represents one week. The features I want to call attention to here show up most clearly in the *C* minus *R* or, if you will, the "analytic-work" time plot. Notice that in the first 18 weeks the scores are above the mean. Then there is a sudden drop and a good deal of variability up and down, until after the 45th week; next there is a great rise to about the 54th week, and from there to the 108th week there is a very pronounced downward trend, with only one exception.

THE COURSE OF THE ANALYSIS

In order to demonstrate the striking correlation between these time plots and some of the main events of the analysis it is necessary to describe something about the patient and the course of the analysis. The patient was a young, unmarried, professional woman. At the time she began her analysis with Dr. A, two of her express hopes were that she would be able to change her relationships with men in such a way that she could get married, and that she would be able to have children. During the early months of the analysis with Dr. A, it seemed quite clear that she was developing a positive transference—perhaps it might even be called a working alliance. Then, suddenly and unexpectedly, Dr. A became ill. The patient was given little or no information about the circumstances, and was finally told that he would not be able to return. Our time plots begin with the first session with Dr. B, who was herself five months pregnant at the time of taking on this patient. The vertical arrows at the bottom of the time plot show all the major interruptions in the analysis and the number of days of inter- ruption. The first major interruption of 38 days came after 18 weeks, when the analyst left to have her baby. This event coincides with the sudden shift in the C minus R score (Fig. 2). This shift is the result of abrupt changes in both the C and the R scores. The Resistance scores increase and the Content-Conflict scores decrease. Shortly after the 40th week, during the summer when there were several short holidays, the patient met a married man with whom she quickly began an affair. She promptly got pregnant, and then during the 53rd week had an abortion, with the approval of her lover. Following this, with the single excep- tion of some events betwen the 70th and 80th weeks, our measure shows a steady decline.

It seems reasonable to assume that this young lady, who wanted among other things to get married and to have a child of her own, began her analysis with the expectation that she would indeed find these things. I believe that she also expected to find in her male analyst someone who would not threaten her with desertion by getting ill, as her father frequently had with threats of heart attacks. When Dr. A did become ill, her wish was thwarted and her fear confirmed. Five months later, she began analysis with a woman who was pregnant, and the signs, it seems to me, are quite clear that there was a pronounced change in the analysis following the analyst's leaving to have her baby. There seems little doubt that the patient viewed this event with great envy and jealousy. About half a year later, when she met the married man, she decided to have an affair, to get pregnant and to have a baby; but no sooner did she become pregnant "accidentally" than she decided to have an abortion. It is evident from an inde- pendent summary of the case that the patient took the fact that the man readily agreed to the abortion and was very supportive during it as a sign that nothing could come of her relationship with him. The abortion occurred just before the peak of C (53rd week); the course from there on was downhill with a single exception. Notice the increase in talk about sexual matters during the affair as well as the steady increase in anxiety during the affair, the abortion, and imme- diately afterwards.

But there is another striking finding. The increase in dreams coincides with the decrease in anxiety and the decrease in sexual topics. The content of these dreams is often violent and destructive; associations went to powerful feelings of jealousy and anger at the birth of a sister when she was two or three years old. It seems reasonable to assume that her wish to have a baby was now being fulfilled only in her dreams; that what had begun as a conscious wish had been abandoned under the combined influence of her own childhood conflicts and the fortuitous events of the analyses; that her jealousy, her ill-fated (predestined to be so) affair, pregnancy, and subsequent abortion had conspired to destroy all hope of realistic fulfillment. The independent summary of the analysis during this period (80th to 108th week) is replete with comments about the stalemate, the stagnation, the difficult resistance, and the analyst's nearly futile efforts to do something successful about it.

COMPUTER CONTENT ANALYSIS

A second way of studying this analysis was through a simple form of computer content-analysis. This approach is based on two simplifying assumptions. The first is that words alone, independent of grammar, carry significant information. The second is that words and ideas that occur together belong together—the principle of association by contiguity. Since it was not practical at the time to keypunch all 363 hours, I had to have a criterion for selecting a much smaller number of hours. In view of the striking relationship between the course of the analysis and the graphic representation of it by factor scores, I decided to use the factor scores as a basis for selecting certain hours in which analytic work (insofar as the factor scores might indeed measure this) was predominant, and other hours in which resistance to analytic work was predominant. Accordingly, I selected hours with low scores on factors 1 and 6 and high scores on factors 2, 3, 4, and 5 as "work" hours, and hours with high scores on 1 and 6 and low scores on 2, 3, 4 and 5 as "resistance" hours. Hours with scores in the middle on all six factors were selected to represent the middle. Figure 3 shows what these profiles look like.

I then searched the text of the patient's portion of 25 hours (10 "work," 10 "resistance," and five "middle") for words from the Harvard III Psychosociological Dictionary. In this dictionary, each of about 3200 words is defined by assigning it to one of 55 denotative categories and to one or more of 28 connotative categories. Thus a word is defined by the categories to which it is assigned. A category is in turn defined by the words that are assigned to it. Details of this dictionary are described in The General Inquirer by Stone et al. (1966). A computer program reads in the text of the hour from IBM cards, looks up each word, counts the number of times each concept is found in each hour, and converts these to percentages.

Figure 4 shows the results in graphic form. With 17 dictionary categories, the highest percentages occurred in the "work" hours, intermediate percentages occurred in the "middle" hours, and the lowest percentages occurred in the "resistance" hours. Three dictionary categories show just the reverse, with their highest values occurring in the "resistance hours" and their lowest values in the "work" hours. Table 4 summarizes the results as correlations between the percentages of each of the dictionary categories and the overall "analytic work" measure, $C - R$, over the 25 hours. The results are clear: the analysis of the content of the patient's speech reveals sharp differences between the hours with different factor-score profiles.

Of the many interesting details of these differences, I shall mention only

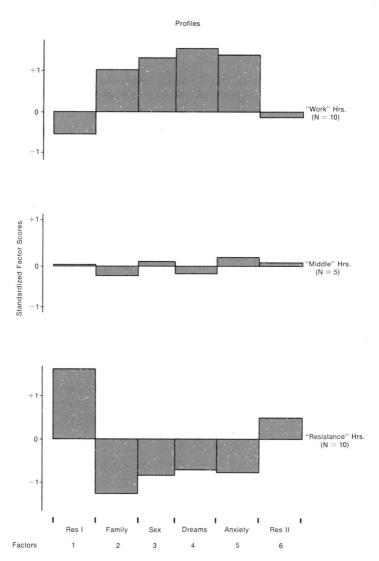

Figure 3. In each profile, the bars represent the average factor scores (of N hours) for each of the six factors.

three. There are more Self references (*mine, my, myself, self*) during the "work" hours. There are more references to Others (*you, your, yourself, they, them, their, themselves*) during "resistance" hours. There are many more Non-specific Object references during "resistance" hours. This category includes such words as *anything, characteristic, component, everything, it, that, thing, sort, what,* etc. With the addition of a few verbs, prepositions, and articles it is possible, using this list, to talk endlessly and say nothing. (This category would, I am certain, dominate a great many political speeches.)

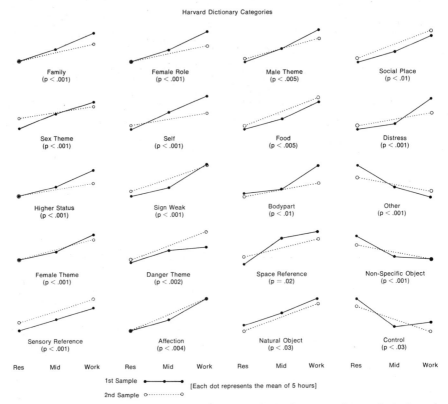

Figure 4. For illustrative purposes, all slopes have been made equivalent and numerical axes omitted. The *p* values, based on linear trend analyses, indicate the significance of the linearity of the relationship between the dictionary category score (plotted vertically) and the three different types of hours (plotted horizontally).

But it was still not demonstrated that my use of the concept of work as measured by the factor scores was related to the concept as used by analysts. Accordingly, I asked several analysts to act as judges. First I asked each of them to read an example of each of the two types of hours. Then I asked them to read transcripts of eight other hours and to judge whether analytic work or resistance to analytic work was predominant, and also to give a confidence rating for each judgment. The two ratings were combined into a 6-point scale. The coefficient of reliability for the mean of the three analysts who completed the ratings was .90. Their mean ratings correlated with the factor score criterion $(C - R)$ .93.

Some of the deficiencies in the measure of analytic work will be intuitively apparent to experienced clinicians. Moreover, since it was a measure derived from the clustering of variables specifically chosen for this particular case, we simply do not know whether the same clusters would occur in the next case, or whether, if they did, they would measure the same thing. Nonetheless it is encouraging to have found systematic relationships among the three different kinds of measures—the 53 analyst-coded variables, the computer-dictionary cate-

Table 4. PRODUCT-MOMENT CORRELATIONS (*r*) BETWEEN THE HARVARD DICTIONARY CATEGORY SCORE (PERCENTAGE OF OC-CURRENCE) FOR EACH HOUR AND THE FACTOR SCORE CRITERION ($C - R$) FOR EACH HOUR*

Dictionary Category	r
Family	.80
Sex Theme	.78
Higher Status	.77
Female Theme	.72
Distress	.69
Self	.68
Other	−.67
Non-Specific Object	−.67
Female Role	.66
Sensory Reference	.66
Sign Weak	.64
Danger Theme	.60
Affection	.59
Food	.55
Male Theme	.53
Body Part	.51
Social Place	.51
Space Reference	..50
Control	−.49
Natural Object	.42

* $N = 25$ hours. For $p = .05$, $r = .40$; for $p = .01$, $r = .51$; for $p = .001$, $r = .62$.

gories, and the clinician's judgments. These relationships show that large amounts of psychoanalytic material can be quantitatively described in a way that does not lose clinical meaning. Indeed, in this case the time plots may have enhanced our understanding of the course of the analysis. More important, however, is the demonstration that a simple computer content-analysis procedure, using simple frequency counts of words and a dictionary not particularly suited to the purpose, can discriminate among qualitatively different kinds of hours.

FUTURE RESEARCH NEEDS

In order to continue this kind of research, we need to take certain steps. First, we need to establish a library of recorded psychoanalyses, characteristic cases, analyzed by the best and most gifted analysts. Thirty completed cases might be a suitable initial goal. What will we do with these? We have already learned that it is possible to transcribe tape recordings directly onto IBM cards, without inter-mediate typescripts. All the text is then stored on computer tape by an editing program, and can be retrieved in various ways by appropriate and simple requests. For example, we can ask for and get print-outs of the complete text of all hours that contain a dream report, or we can get a Key Word in Context index output of any word or set of words, so that we can examine the context and then decide whether we have found what we want. In effect, this is an instant indexing system based on the actual words used by analyst and patient. At the same time, if the analyst dictates notes about the hour and includes in these notes his own first classifications of the material, these notes can be stored and retrieved in a similar way. I am now doing this with the notes I dictate after each hour of an analytic case I am recording.

Second, we need to develop computer content-analysis dictionaries specifically for psychoanalytic concepts. Initially, these would be constructed like the Harvard III Psychosociological Dictionary to which I have referred. But we will soon be discontented with something so gross and error-prone. We will want contextual dictionaries, which will allow us to label and count concepts only when a number of several sub-concepts or words have been found in a specified segment of material. In developing the basic conceptual categories and the words that define them, we will need to apply the most sophisticated techniques of current psychometric theory, so that we can know something about the reliabilities of our measuring instruments. At the same time, we need to construct other content-analysis measuring instruments, such as the Gottschalk (1969) scales, and we need to try specifying the judgments in these instruments with sufficient precision so that we can write computer programs to do the ratings.

Third, we need vastly increased mathematical and statistical sophistication. We need to learn a great deal about the expected frequencies of the words that are actually used by people on the couch. From the economists we must borrow knowledge of the application of the mathematics for multiple time series. And to do these things means that we must analyze our own resistances to numbers and computers.

The consequences of getting reliable data through recording, of using computer-based content-analysis procedure, and of applying sophisticated statistical and mathematical analyses to our data will be, I believe, a revitalization of our field. It will force us to formulate our clinical theories in ways that will allow us to specify the kind of evidence we need to answer particular questions, and then permit us to return to the data, make our counts, and determine the probabilities that our results support or refute our expectations.

I know this must seem fanciful after so brief an exposure to these quite primitive and tentative demonstrations of a few possibilities. Nonetheless, I believe that what I have suggested is essential to attract to psychoanalysis the kind of imaginative and research-oriented young candidates that our field needs. And even if in the end these approaches fail, we will have had an exciting time along the way.

REFERENCES

Gill, M. M., et al. (1968). Studies in Audio-Recorded Psychoanalysis. I. General Considerations. *Journal of the American Psychoanalytic Association,* 16:230–244.

Gottschalk, L. A., and Gleser, G. C. (1969). *The Measurement of Psychological States through the Content Analysis of Verbal Behavior.* Berkeley: University of California Press.

Luborsky, L. (1953). Intraindividual Repetitive Measurements (P Technique) in Understanding Psychotherapeutic Change. In: *Psychotherapy Theory and Research,* ed. O. H. Mowrer. New York: Ronald Press, pp. 389–413.

Meissner, W. W. (1966). The Operational Principle and Meaning in Psychoanalysis. *Psychoanalytic Quarterly,* 35:233–255.

Stone, P. J., et al. (1966). *The General Inquirer: A Computer Approach to Content Analysis.* Cambridge: M.I.T. Press, pp. 170–186.

COGNITIVE RESPONSE TO STRESS:
Experimental Studies of a "Compulsion to Repeat Trauma" [1]

Mardi J. Horowitz, M.D., and Stephanie Scharf Becker, M.A.

Any discussion of human response to stress must include the topic of cognitive mediation. Most investigators agree that adaptation and accommodation to stress depend on cognitive processes, but the meagerness of available methods has impeded a systematic study of cognitive hypotheses. The research scientist interested in stress response faces a series of hurdles: he must find clinically relevant hypotheses; he must operationalize these hypotheses into an acceptable experimental methodology; and he must obtain reliable results. While this three-step process is the research "ideal" in the area of response to stress, it has been difficult to accomplish.

A particular problem has been in operationalizing clinical hypotheses and choosing measures appropriate for drawing inferences about thought processes. Traditionally, in laboratory studies of stress response, physiological variables have been most easily quantified and most reliable. Psychological variables, such as those derived from conscious experience and performance levels, have seldom been successful because they do not reach statistical significance, and, if they are significant in one experiment, they are seldom replicated in a second. Yet changes in conscious experience must not be neglected if we are to develop a scientific model of cognitive mediation of stress. Physiological data can add richness and depth to cognitive theory, but they can be interpreted only in the light of psychological episodes. To study the nature of psychological stress requires reliable and valid cognitive measures.

This paper presents a theory of cognitive response to stress that is supported by cognitive data from experimental studies. The theory, derived from

[1] This work was supported by grants from the United States Public Health Service (MH-17373) and Mount Zion Medical Center, San Francisco. Dr. Horowitz is supported by a Research Career Development Award (II) from the National Institute of Mental Health (MH-22573-07). The authors thank Robert Wallerstein, Harold Sampson, Jack Block, Jacob Cohen, and Leonard Horowitz for methodological consultation. Marilyn Jones, Ellen Mason, and Ann Miller also helped with technical preparation of this paper.

psychoanalytic observations of compulsive repetition of traumatic experiences in psychiatric patients, predicts that intrusive and stimulus-repetitive thought will tend to follow mild to moderate as well as major forms of stress, and it also predicts the appearance of this response in persons without any psychiatric diagnosis. In experimental tests of these predictions we used films to induce stress and non-stress conditions, and content-analysis techniques to quantify intrusive and repetitive thought in cognitive reports. The results supported our predictions and are summarized in this paper.

We begin with a brief review of the clinical observations that led to the research. A set of terms, a theoretical model, and an experimental paradigm are then described, together with a condensed outline of five interrelated experiments. After summary and discussion of the experimental results, we conclude with a detailed elaboration and generalization of the theoretical model of cognitive response to stress.

THE BACKGROUND OF CLINICAL OBSERVATION

Breuer and Freud (1893–95) concluded that hysterical symptoms, such as aberrant expressive behaviors and involuntary thoughts or images, were re-enactments of traumatic events. For example, Freud traced the recurrent hallucinations of an angry face, in the case of Katherin, to an earlier frightening perception of her uncle's rage-filled face when he threatened her because she had revealed his illicit sexual acts. Observations of the psychological effects of combat on World War I veterans moved Freud (1920) to re-emphasize the clinical importance of terrifyingly vivid recollections of traumatic experiences, and of their repetition, in spite of the patient's terror and desire to avoid such painful memories. Clinical observations by other analysts and psychiatrists confirmed and supplemented those of Freud. Post-traumatic syndromes, described and consensually validated by various clinicians, include many varieties of compulsive repetition (Bibring, 1943; Fenichel, 1945; Furst, 1967).

Observations of various cognitive and behavioral repetitions have not been limited solely to psychiatric patients. Similar syndromes have been found in general populations after war experiences (Grinker and Spiegel, 1945; Kardiner, 1959), natural disasters (Cobb and Lindemann, 1943; Friedman and Linn, 1957), accidents (Keiser, 1968), and in survivors of concentration camps (Niederland, 1968). Traumatic scenes tend to return in subsequent thought as obsessive ruminations, unbidden images, hallucinations, or nightmares. Repetitive emotional states, symbolic actions, and patterns of behavioral re-enactment have also been noted.

These repetitions in thought include an overt expression of some elements of the traumatic scene, even though these elements may be embedded within a disguising format or symbolic structure (Freud, 1937; Greenacre, 1952; Sachs, 1967; Stern, 1961). The form taken by compulsive repetitiveness after traumas has been related to personality factors such as a person's habitual style of thought representation, his cognitive defensive and controlling strategies, and his array of other motives, fantasies, memories, and representational schemata (Greenacre, 1952; Murphy, 1961). Thus, as psychoanalytic clinicians studied the phenomenology of repetition after trauma in greater depth, they not only confirmed Freud's observations, but found that the repetition itself could be used for defensive purposes—as a way of expressing, screening, or transforming other currently dangerous and powerful ideas and feelings (Glover, 1929; Horowitz, 1970; Malev, 1969; Reider, 1960).

Although persons who have been exposed to the inciting events may manifest these response patterns with different styles, sequences, durations, and intensities, there are certain common elements in their response patterns. Prominent among these general response tendencies are compulsive and repeated verbalizations about the events, recurrent obsessive ideas, images, and nightmares. The converse—amnesia, or avoidance of speaking of the event—may also occur (Davis, 1966). What interests us about these observations is that they indicate a particular cognitive response to stress. The recollections are a product of thought processes and yet are subjectively experienced as non-volitional, or "alien to the self"—a seemingly paradoxical combination of lower-level and higher-level cognitive functioning. We believe that attention to these observations can lead to a theoretical model of cognitive responses to stress which can, in turn, generate predictions for experimental examination.

Our interest in cognitive responses focuses on the apparent outcomes of such cognitive processes as perception, organization, memory, and recall. Thus, our focus will be on the subjective experience that evolves from cognitive processes outside of subjective experience. A model of cognitive processes and experiences, together with appropriate experiments, would fill a need in stress research, since cognitive responses in general have been largely neglected as experimental variables. Instead the focus has been on emotional responses, defensive strategies, performance and behavioral patterns, and physiological changes (see Lazarus, 1964, and Janis and Leventhal, 1968, for reviews).

Before advancing our theoretical model, hypotheses, and experiments, we shall consider some of the explanations of compulsive repetition in psychoanalytic theory that are relevant to a cognitive point of view.

Psychoanalytic Explanations

Psychoanalytic metapsychology examines any phenomenon from multiple points of view, with several levels of explanatory principles and assignments of meaning within each point of view. Review of these explanations of compulsive repetitions in thought is beyond the scope of this paper (see Bibring, 1943; Furst, 1967; Rangell, 1967; Schur, 1966, for such reviews). For clarity and focus we shall discuss cognitive operations, leaving aside a discussion of the complex motives and emotions that emerge within and influence cognitive operations.

Early in his theoretical formulations, Freud (1893) postulated that the usually vivid and peremptory images that are formed in recollection of traumatic perceptions occur because of a need for further discharge or abreaction of emotional responses that had been activated by an external event, but incompletely expressed at that time. While this theory focused on emotional rather than ideational responses, it contained the important concept that *symptoms persist until some type of mental process is completed.* In his "Project for a Scientific Psychology" (1895), Freud outlined a provisional program for neuronal processing of perceptions which, leaving aside the neurophysiological speculations, is essentially a model of *sequential cognitive processes.* These processes, in his terms, "tamed memories," so that they could be stored and remain relatively dormant. "Untamed memories" retained a peremptory quality; whenever they were activated, they tended to be represented with unusual, even hallucinatory, vividness, and to evoke strong emotional responses (see Klein, 1967, for a contemporary theoretical model of the ideational operations involved in peremptory ideation).

Freud (1917) went on to define trauma theoretically as "an experience which within a short period of time presents the mind with an increase of stimulus too powerful to be dealt with or worked off in the usual way, and this must result in permanent disturbances in the manner in which energy operates" (p. 275).[2] Such unusually high incursions of excitations represented a "breach in an otherwise efficacious barrier against stimuli" (Freud, 1920, p. 29). This internal situation activated various motives, each of which might favor a cognitive repetition of the traumatic event: a wish to discharge emotions through abreaction; a need to increase retroactively the cathexes that compose the stimulus barrier, through generation of signal anxiety; and a desire to gain mastery over the events by repeated reconceptualization, including such manuevers as familiarization through repetition and conversion of passivity into activity.

But Freud believed such motives were insufficient to account for the seemingly inexorable repetitions seen after some traumas. He speculated that the unusual incursion of stimuli might activate a repetition compulsion, which functioned as a drive. While he linked the repetition compulsion to the largely unaccepted theory of a death instinct, the concept did include the idea that repetitiousness might be a fundamental and primitive property of the mind that is inhibited by the adequate functioning of higher cognitive processes. Later analysts, such as Bibring (1943) and Greenacre (1967), amplified this concept when they suggested that the excessive incursions of excitation that are characteristic of traumatic perceptions might lead to a regression to primitive modes of coding perceptual stimuli, which might in turn have the intrinsic property of compulsive emergence as subsequent images.

Many post-Freudian theoreticians, as reviewed by Schur (1966), tended to diminish the importance of the repetition compulsion as a primary drive, and to explain compulsive repetitions as efforts to achieve mastery over ideas and emo-

---

[2] Freud (1917) considered this economic point of view "one of the most important, but unluckily also one of the most obscure, regions of psychoanalysis" (p. 356). The central problem, as he saw it, was finding out how the mind processes stimuli so that arousal levels remain within tolerable or desirable limits. A model of cognitive processing of stimuli may help our understanding of this problem, since the emotions that contribute to arousal levels are not reflex responses to stimuli but rather the results of cognitive mediation of stimuli.

tions that seem overwhelming. These efforts might achieve adaptation through "discharges of excessive energy" in emotional abreactions, and through "binding excitations" by way of such cognitive processes as establishing word representations, associational connections, and ideational transformations. *Ideational transformation included both defensive maneuvers (e.g., denial, reversal, reaction formation, projection, identification with the aggressor, etc.) and coping maneuvers, as in adaptation through assimilation and accommodation* (Piaget, 1937).

In summary, clinicians are in agreement on the observation of compulsive cognitive repetitions after traumas (and a variety of other post-traumatic symptoms) and many explanations for them have been proffered. We shall consider compulsive repetitions within a cognitive model of stress response. While we must leave undiscussed the important theories of anxiety and emotional conflict related to trauma, our cognitive model will be compatible with such explanations.

DEVELOPING A THEORY OF COGNITIVE RESPONSE TO STRESS

An important first step is careful and consistent definition of terms. At present, the term "trauma" has so many diffuse meanings that it is infelicitous for research. We will use the broader term "stress," which is also variously defined in the psychological literature (Janis and Leventhal, 1968). The *locus* of the stress is what varies the most. For example, the phrase "he was stressed" can be interpreted as "he was in a *state* of stress," i.e., stress is inside him, is a function of his own internal processes; or "stress was *applied* to him" from outside, by the environment or by another person.

To define the locus and nature of a given stress, we use the terms *stress event, stress state, modulation, stretch, strain, strengthen,* and *adaptation,* depending on what we wish to describe. The term *stress event* describes situational factors and an event structure that is a potential source of stress for the average person in a representative sample. The event may be external or internal. An *external stress event* is thus descriptive of the environment surrounding the person; it implies a change from the usual or homeostatic level of stimuli, sufficient to challenge the average person.

External events are recorded in modified form as internal representations. Even with cessation of the external event, these internal representations persist and can induce a state of stress. Activation of these internal representations—including memory responses to previous external stress events, as well as memories of psychic responses (emotions, fantasies, appraisals, associations, action plans—thus constitutes an *internal stress event.* External (stress) events activate internal stress events. Persons with easily activated internal stress events will tend to enter a stress state sooner or more intensely than persons with fewer or less readily activated propensities for internal stress events.

A *stress event* is not necessarily a situation that is unpleasant or dangerous. Any event that increased stimuli to the point of stress (for the average person) would be labeled a stress event, even though the content might evoke pleasurable affects. Thus, very erotic situations might be termed stress events. The term *stress event* is used to describe situations in general ("roller coaster rides are stress events," "death wishes are stress events") and the word *event* can be replaced by more specific nouns, e.g. "it was a stress film," "he had a stress fantasy."

We can then define a *stress state* as a condition in which an external and/or internal stress event is affecting the active functioning of the person, to the extent that an unusually high demand is being imposed on some process or structure. For a stress event to affect an individual, there must be some form of perception or representation, which may or may not be regulated. Freud designated this process of stimulus regulation as "the stimulus barrier," but while the term "stimulus barrier" is commonly used in psychoanalytic literature, we do not advocate its use in a cognitive model of stress response, since that function would be performed by many different processes, at various levels of stimulus processing. The concept of regulation of perception, representation, and information-processing of stress events is relevant to the concept of stress states, however; to avoid the concrete metaphor of "barrier," we will use the term *"modulation* of stimulus input."

Stress event, modulation, and *stress state* stand in the following relationship. *Stress event* refers to the pressure of stimuli in the surrounding environment, in recorded memory, or in predispositions to cognitive processes; *modulation* refers to a functional capacity for resisting or modifying perception or representation of stress events. A *stress state* is the result of the interaction between a stress event (external and/or internal) and modulation, and refers to a relatively high entry of stimuli into the psychic system by comparison with available processes of assimilation. A person with a high capacity for modulation of a stress event may not enter a state of stress; conversely, a person with a low capacity for inhibition or modulation will have a lower threshold for entering a state of stress (in conditions of increasing intensity of stress events).

We have defined a *stress state* as a condition in which an unusually high demand is placed upon processes or structures. This demand may not necessarily exceed the functional *capacity* of given processes or structures, because these processes or structures may *increase* their levels of performance; in such a case, the effect of the high demand state will be to alter the processes or structures. We will term this alteration a *stretch*. A *stress state* will be affected both by *modulation* of entry of *stress events* into the psychic system and by the capacity for maximum *stretch*. A process or structure that is *stretched* during a stress state may return to baseline levels of functional capacity, or it may increase or decrease in functional capacity. We call an increase in functional capacity a *strengthening;* the reverse, a *strain*. The processes and structures referred to must be individually labeled and further described but, in general, they are the processes and structures that lead to *assimilation* and *accommodation* (Piaget, 1937) and thus to the termination of an internal stress event.

Adaptation is a less temporary change than stretch and involves relatively enduring changes in processes or "cognitive structures." Like strain and strengthening, the term *adaptation* is a judgment of outcome made on the basis of subsequent events and appraisals. We can observe and describe stress events and responses during or after the stress events themselves, but the intervening variables are more in the realm of inference. Terms such as internal stress event, stress state, stretch, strain, strengthening, and adaptation refer to these inferred processes. We have been somewhat lengthy in defining these terms because the language of description affects theory formation, just as theoretical models affect language choices.

Through the use of these definitions, the clinical observations of a tendency to repeat trauma compulsively can be reformulated into both a theory and predictions that can be experimentally tested. We shall state this theory briefly here, in order to develop the relevant hypotheses. Later, after describing the evidence that supported the hypotheses, we shall elaborate the theory in greater detail, to indicate its relevance for more generalized observations.

An external (stress) event may lead to activation of internal stress events. The combined stress events induce a state of stress that is characterized by stretch of the processes for assimilating and accommodating to new stimuli. Because immediate functional capacity may be exceeded by the stretch, programmatic sequences required for assimilation of stressful perceptions (and immediate reactions to perceptions) remain uncompleted. One property of programmatic sequences may be that they remain operative until terminal "switch-off" phases are reached; that is, they have a *tendency toward completion*. (The conditions that lead to completion will be considered further in the discussion section.) The completion tendency still remains after the cessation of an external stress event. Representations of the stress events, and of the initial responses to them, return to awareness whenever the programmatic sequence of processes involved in assimilation is resumed. Because the tendency to completion is automatic, it acts as an impulsive motive. When this motive results in representations, they are experienced subjectively as intrusive, event-repetitive, and/or unusually vivid or intense mental representations.

One reason why the process-completion effect results in conscious experience is that stress events, by definition, have high organismic relevance. Repetition of stress-related representations would have the same high place in vigilance hierarchies as stress-related perceptions; they would gain attention and acquire a conscious status in subjective experience.

Thus, *we hypothesize that, following incompletely processed stress events, there is an (impulsive) tendency toward completion of the cognitive sequences involved in the information-processing that leads eventually to assimilation and accommodation. A predicted result of this completion tendency is to repeat cognitive representations of the stress event and initial responses to the stress event until completion occurs.* If the initial perceptions that result in stretch are visual, there will be a tendency for the repetitions to be experienced as unbidden visual images. Since we also predict that these repetitions will tend to become conscious, the hypothesis, if correct, should be supported by systematic observations of subjective experience after stressful events. Since we hypothesize a general response tendency, *we predict that mild to moderate stress events, as well as major stress events, will tend to be followed by a subjective experience of intru-sive and repetitive thinking in normal persons.*[3]

We hypothesize this response as a general tendency, with different mani-festations in different persons, so that this prediction applies to groups, rather than to individuals. As is true of any impulsive cognitive motive, there may be a conflict between the impulsive aim for representation and completion, and the defensive or controlling aims for the inhibition of such expressions. Large degrees of conflict will retard the hypothesized completion process, leading to lengthy periods of stress response after a stress event. People vary not only in terms of their conflicts, but also in their patterns, styles, and capacity for defense and control. In general, however, if the impulse gets stronger (e.g., with associative priming in reaction to external events) or the defense gets weaker (e.g., with lowered inhibitory capacity), a usually inhibited representation may suddenly enter conscious experience. This experience will be subjectively regarded as an intrusive image or thought.

Restatement of Hypotheses in Terms of Experimental Variables

The preceding section described a theory from which we drew general hypoth-eses. Here, those hypotheses are translated into operational terms that reflect the different independent and dependent variables of the experimental work. Using a film as the experimental stress event, we predicted cognitive response to stress as follows:

1. After a stress film, subjects as a group will have more intrusive thought, more visual images, more thoughts repetitive of film content, and more negative affect, as compared with their baseline scores or scores after a neutral film.

Aware of the problems of control for experimental artifacts, we postulated that:

2. Stress film effects will be greater than such experimental treatment factors as change in experimenter demand, change in experimental instructions, change in order of film viewing, or change in subject population.

This second hypothesis is necessary because the main variables in the first hypothesis rely on cognitive response and introspective reports, which vary with such factors as social desirability and idiosyncratic response sets. We believe that our main hypothesis will lead to greater effect sizes than such factors, and that the variation of stress condition will override effects that are due to demand, temporal order, or subject selection.

[3] We shall consider the relationship between stress-related repetitions and "normal" repetitions in an expanded view of the theoretical model presented in the dis-cussion section.

We also predicted that:

3. Increases in dependent variables will not be simply a function of general increases in output of cognitive reports.
4. Thoughts that are irrelevant to an immediate performance task will increase after the stress film, but not as greatly as the increases in the specific sub-categories of intrusive thought, film-repetitive thought, and visual-image thought.

The last two predictions relate to the possibility that a stress film might increase general arousal, thereby leading to greater cognitive output or report size than after a neutral film. Content analysis for specific types of cognitive response might show an increase simply because there was a greater volume of reporting. To control for this possibility we predicted, as above, that the variables involved in our main hypotheses would increase more than other cognitive variables, such as number of words or number of task-irrelevant thoughts.

EXPERIMENTAL PARADIGM

All experiments had the same basic design. Variations were introduced only as a function of specific treatments. In each experiment, subjects participated at the same time and as a group. A motion picture was used as the independent stimulus variable, and all subjects saw both a stress film and a film with more neutral content. Before and after each film, measurements were taken of each subject to obtain baseline, neutral, and stress-condition scores.

We began an experiment by informing subjects of the general procedures, including the probability of seeing a film with stressful content, and obtaining subjects' informed consent. Following this introduction, the instructions for the experimental tasks and introspective reporting were given, after which subjects performed baseline measures. Next, a film was shown, after which subjects again did tasks and gave mental reports. After both films and the last tasks and mental reports, additional self-rating material was administered. A general "de-briefing" discussion followed the collection of data. Some subjects were also followed up through questionnaires, telephone calls, or interviews.

Selection of a Stress Film as the External Stress Event

Previous experimental studies have employed a range of techniques to induce stress, evoke fear, or create a threat situation. External stress events include electric shock (Dunn, 1968), tests for social desirability of personality characteristics (Miller, 1968), exposure to an audience (Terris and Rahhal, 1969), imagining a stressful event (Craig, 1968), to name a few. One of the principal and most effective methods for stress induction has been use of the motion picture (Lazarus, 1964; Alexander and Flagg, 1961). In our research there are good methodological reasons for selecting the film technique. A stimulus encoded on film remains unchanged after any number of viewings, and is reproducible for many subjects over long periods of time. Thus, as a medium for presenting an external stress event, film is easy to manipulate and facilitates replication studies. Moreover, the form and content of a film can be modified to test a particular hypothesis.

Another advantage of film is its familiarity. Threat of electric shock is an uncommon real-life event; exposure to movie or television events is part of ordinary life experience. This familiarity reduces the novelty and mysteriousness of experimental procedures and thus somewhat reduces their intrinsic threat potential independent of content.

One potential problem with film is that the stress event is vicarious. The subject witnesses other persons being acted upon or threatened; he is not directly acted upon or physically placed in a threat situation. Higbee (1969), in his review of 15 years of research on the effects of fear arousal and threat appeal, differentiates two basic situations:

"The first type, corresponding to neurotic anxiety or inhibitory fear, may be a nauseated, sick feeling aroused by gruesome, vivid descriptions and pictures of such scenes as automobile accidents . . . The second type of fear, perhaps corresponding to realistic fear or anticipation fear, appears to be somewhat more concerned with the likelihood of the subjects' experiencing the threat" (p. 434). According to Higbee, both types of situation affect subjects, although it remains unclear whether responses are similar under both conditions, as suggested by Alfert (1966), or different, as maintained by Higbee (1969). What is relevant here is that direct threat to subjects is not necessary to produce stress responses; a vicarious stimulus is sufficient and has ethical advantages. Another support for the use of films is that ample clinical experience indicates the stressful effects of some movies and television programs. The vicarious experience produces a complex internal stress event that acts directly upon the subject to produce a state of stress.

The stress film we used was "Subincision." It is a film widely used in stress film research, and has been shown to cause physiological and affective changes (Lazarus, 1964; Speisman et al., 1964).[4] "Subincision" depicts a gory operation on the penis as part of aboriginal puberty rites performed on adolescent boys by older men. The movie contains explicit scenes of cutting operations, young boys in pain and nudity, as well as other ceremonial rites. The most general theme is of bodily injury, but more specific and complex conflicts may be aroused (e.g., fear of castration). The film was edited to run about nine minutes.

The neutral film, "The Runner," depicts a man in track uniform running through the countryside and meeting old and young people along the way, suggesting a symbolic trip through life. The content is interesting, slightly wistful,

---

[4] We thank Richard Lazarus and Paul Ekman for advice in film selection, and for lending us films in our preliminary work.

slightly humorous, and may be mildly depressing. This film has no overtly stressful scenes. Both films are silent, black and white, and of the same length; both have repeated scenes, and show human groups as subject matter.

In each of three experiments, the order of film viewing was counterbalanced. Half the subjects saw the neutral film first and then the stress film; the other half of the subject sample saw the stress film first and then the neutral film. There is very little difference in scores attributable to order effects and, in this paper, order effects are discussed only if they vary from this general finding.

Measurements Obtained Before and After Films

The primary variables in this research are derived from methods that depend on introspective reports. In most of the experiments, the reports are interspersed between segments of a perceptual task performed by subjects at three different times in the experiments, to obtain baseline, post-neutral film and post-stress film measurements.

PERCEPTUAL TASK.   The perceptual task is like that developed by Antrobus, Singer, and Greenberg (1966). The subject judges whether a musical tone is higher, lower, or the same as a preceding tone. Each measurement period consists of four two-minute segments; each segment is composed of 23 tones. Five different tones, all produced by an electric organ, are used, and the successive tones are one and a half tonal intervals apart. To avoid patterning of alertness, the duration between tones is randomly three, four, or seven seconds.

The task is tedious, but in order to succeed at it the subject must attend continuously to the external environment and maintain an active short-term memory of the immediately preceding stimulus. Use of the task leads subjects to believe that an important measurement is success at matching tones, and deflects some concern from the mental reports.

At the end of each tone segment, there is a two-minute break. A tape-recorded instruction asks subjects to report (in writing) their mental contents from *during* the tone task. Mental contents are generally defined as "any thoughts, feelings, visual images, other images, observations, 'flashes,' memories or anything else that occurs in the mind." The instructions urge subjects to pay attention to the tones, and to rely on spontaneous recall in reporting what entered their awareness during the previous tone-task.

AFFECT SORT.   These ratings were a Q-sort of 12 adjectives: anxious, attentive, calm, cooperative, disgusted, evasive, friendly, in control, irritated, relaxed, sad, tired. Subjects were told to rank the four terms that were most applicable to them from 1 to 4, with 1 being the most applicable. Also, they were to rank the four adjectives least applicable to them from 9 to 12, with 12 being the least applicable. They were to disregard the four middle cards. (For statistical analysis, the four middle cards were given a ranking of 6.5.)

The ranking was to reflect how subjects had felt during the previous five minutes. The sort itself is done quickly and spontaneously and takes about one minute. After each sort, the subjects recorded the ranking order on a separate piece of paper, and then shuffled the cards so the order of the cards would not dictate the next sort.

The adjective sort was administered under five conditions: baseline, and immediately before and after the two films.

ENTRY SCALE. After both films and all tone task–mental report segments were completed, subjects were instructed about the Entry Scale. To use the scale, they went back over their protocols, and gave each visual image a rating on a 5-point scale:

1. I formed the image deliberately.
2. The image happened to occur in my stream of thought at the moment.
3. The image popped into mind unexpectedly.
4. The image seemed to force its way into my awareness.
5. I could not get the image out of my mind.

The scale gave an indication of how voluntary, spontaneous, or unbidden the images were; it provided both frequency data and a subject's rating of intrusiveness for visual images.

Operational Definitions of Cognitive Variables

We derived cognitive data by two methods: self-report and content analysis. The self-report data included the number of visual images rated for entry, the entry rating itself, and the affect Q-sort responses. Self-report data on number of images and intrusiveness of images were amenable to comparison with visual image frequency and number of intrusions determined by content analysis.

Judges content-analyzed the raw data from introspective mental reports for four variables: intrusive thought, film references, visual image frequency, and task-irrelevant thoughts. From clinical observation, we expected that, after visual perception of an external stress event, there may be repetitive and intrusive recollections in unusually vivid visual images. But this observation is a constellation of several attributes. As suggested by Nunnally (1967), it is preferable, when commencing investigation of a relatively new construct, to measure isolated attributes, each of which can be given an operational definition. Thus we developed operational definitions for four independent variables.

The content analysis is based on a manual (Horowitz, 1970) and is done independently by either two or three judges. Judges are blind as to treatment group and experimental condition. After the judges' scores are collated, a subject's score on a variable became the mean of the judges' analyses. Spearman-Brown reliability correlations for intrusions, film references, and task-irrelevant thoughts in the stress condition gave an idea of how well the judges correlate Definitions of the content analysis variables are, briefly, as follows:

An *intrusive* thought is any thought that:

1. Implies non-volitional entry into awareness ("I was startled to find myself thinking of my childhood").
2. Requires suppressive effort ("I can't get her out of my mind").
3. The mental event of having the thought is experienced as something to be avoided ("I don't want to think about that film again").
4. The identical thought recurs (only the repetition of the thought is scored).

A *film reference* is any thought that refers directly to the film, film setting, or film experience. A *task-irrelevant* thought is any thought other than those concerning the tone task. A *visual image* is any report that indicates that the subjective experience seemed as if it had visual sensory qualities, such as color, shape, spatial placement, or movement. Judges scored each variable separately. A unit of thought (perhaps a word or a phrase, or a sentence, or a short paragraph) could be scored as one, two, or all three variables, or not at all.

In addition to the self-report and content analysis variables, there were two directly scored measurements: number of errors on the tone task, and number of words in the self-report. Presumably error scores would give an indication of changes in ability to do perceptual cognitive tasks, and perhaps correlate with other stress effects. We scored the word output to see whether increases in cognitive variables occur with parallel increases in general reporting.

All experiments measured intrusions, film references, visual images by self-report, task-irrelevant thoughts, entry rating, error scores, and number of words in the mental reports. Almost every experiment also content-analyzed for visual images.

Subjects

Most subjects in this series were male or female college students. One sample consisted of enlisted naval medical corspmen. Subjects were screened to eliminate volunteers with psychiatric illness and those who used drugs extensively.

Data Analysis

We analyzed the data within most experiments using two-tailed statistical tests to determine the significance of differences in scores on a given variable. Occasionally we used non-parametric tests such as the sign, rank sums, Wilcoxson, or Mann-Whitney U tests. When we say a result was significant, we mean that the p value was less than .05, unless otherwise noted. After summarizing the series of Experiments 1 to 4, we consider all the data and present the results of analyses of variance for each variable.

INITIAL TEST OF THE HYPOTHESIS
AND REPLICATION STUDIES

The purpose of the first experiment (Experiment 1, Horowitz, 1969) in this series was to test the main hypothesis that intrusive thoughts, visual images, and film references would occur more frequently after a stress film than after a neutral film. The order of film viewing was counterbalanced as a control for that artifact. Subjects were randomly assigned to the order in which they saw the films. (The affect sort was not done for this experiment.) Twenty-one college students (18 male, three female) participated and received oral instructions about the nature of the stimuli and how to perform the required tasks. We assumed that this group would be good reporters and sensitive to their cognitive experiences. Instructions about the mental reports were very general and did not reveal the experimenter's specific interests.

The results supported the main hypotheses (see Figures 1–8). Content analysis indicated that the subjects had significantly more film references, intrusions, and visual images after the stress film than after the neutral film. On the Entry Scale, subjects rated their images as more intrusive and scored more visual images after the stress film than after the neutral film. However, the results on visual images were ambiguous: the scores showed a significant difference between the neutral and stress conditions, but not between the baseline and stress conditions. A similar but statistically non-significant trend was seen for task-irrelevant thoughts, where baseline and stress condition scores were about the same, while neutral scores lightly decreased. Visual images with contents depicting scenes of the film increased significantly between the neutral and stress conditions. Error scores on the tone task remained about the same throughout. In sum, then, the data supported the principal hypothesis, except in the case of task-irrelevant thoughts, which did not increase after the stress event. However, the stability of task-irrelevant thoughts and the number of words in the mental reports suggests that increases in the other cognitive variables were not a function of increased reporting or increased task-irrelevant thoughts.

To check the reliability of these findings, a replication experiment (*Experiment 2*) was run on a different population (Horowitz, Becker, and Moskowitz, 1971).[5] The subjects were 21 naval corpsmen, in training as psychiatric technicians. All were high school graduates, and none had gone on to college. We predicted that they would report less thought content in general, because they were presumably less verbal and less sophisticated about experimental procedures. However, as in Experiment 1, we predicted that, after the stress film, subjects would have more visual images, more film references, and more intrusive thoughts, but about the same error scores and task-irrelevant thoughts.

The experimental design was the same as in the initial experiment (Experiment 1), but a power failure immediately before the second film interrupted the

[5] Kenneth Rashid, M.D., helped run this experiment; the cooperation of the Clinical Investigations Center and Department of Psychiatry, U.S. Naval Hospital, Oakland, Calif., is gratefully acknowledged.

procedures. The experiment continued when power was restored, but to control for the long break between films, we did not analyze the data using each subject as his own control, as we had in Experiment 1. Instead, baseline scores were compared for both subgroups, and those who saw the stress film first did not differ much from those who saw the neutral film first. Then, scores from Film 1 were compared for differences between the two subgroups, in order to estimate the effect of the neutral film versus stress film.

Results (Figures 1–8) from this experiment showed that intrusive thinking (both by content analysis and self-report on images) and film references occurred significantly more frequently for the group that saw the stress film. There were no significant differences between the neutral and stress conditions for error scores, or frequency of visual images (either by content analysis or self-report). Task-irrelevant thoughts increased after both the neutral and stress films, but the stress condition had significantly higher scores than the neutral condition. The affect Q-sort showed that negative affect also increased after the stress film.

The results from Experiment 2 again supported the hypothesis about intrusive thought and recollections of film content. We knew, however, that data from introspective reports, both as reported and inferred, were highly vulnerable to factors other than specific experimental stimulus effects. Experiments 1 and 2, though confirming our main hypothesis about film references and intrusive thought, were not specifically designed to control for experimental or measurement error. In addition, the data on visual images—an important element of the clinical observations—were ambiguous because findings in Experiment 2 were not statistically significant, and in Experiment 1 only partial findings were significant.

Experiments 3 and 4 were, therefore, designed to test the effect of experimental changes in demand, or experimental changes in instructions on variables drawn from introspective reports. In both these experiments, the stress film effect was predicted to be greater than effects from changes in demand or instructions.

Experiment 3 replicated previous studies with controls for specificity of instructions about mental reports (Horowitz and Becker, 1971a). Thirty-one male college students were randomly divided into two groups: one received general instructions, the other received specific instructions about the experimenter's interest in visual images. The results showed significantly more intrusive thinking, film references, and negative affect after the stress film. Error scores and word output remained about the same throughout. The frequency of visual images did not vary with change in the film stimulus, but *did vary* with change in instructions. For visual image frequency, there were large discrepancies between the self-report data and the content analysis data: the number of images reported by subjects was far greater than the number of images judged by content analysis.

Experiment 4 tested the hypothesis that stress film effects are more powerful than effects due to an experimenter-imposed social desirability demand (Horowitz and Becker, 1971b). Thirty female subjects saw the films. At random, half the subjects received a demand set that made intrusive visual images after stress seem "normal," while the other 15 subjects received a demand set that made intrusive visual images seem "abnormal." Except for the sentence that conveyed the demand, all other experimental instructions and communications were identical.

In previous experiments, film order had been counterbalanced and significant order effects were not noted. There was, however, a non-significant tendency for the stress film to produce more intrusions if shown first and stress film images sometimes emerged even after the neutral (second) film. The converse was not noted. In this experiment, therefore, all subjects saw the neutral film first, and the stress film second. Before and after each film, subjects engaged in the affect sort, tone tasks, and mental reports.

Changes due to the stress film were considerably greater than any changes due to demand set. Indeed, the only measure that seemed to have any demand effect was that of visual images in the post-stress film period, and this result was of borderline significance ($p < .1$, two-tailed t-test).

The stress film produced significantly more intrusive thinking and film references. Task-irrelevant thoughts also increased. Error scores on the tone task remained about the same, and the mean word output remained almost the same in each condition. While subjects reported about the same *number* of visual images in the baseline, neutral, and stress conditions, they rated those images as significantly more intrusive after stress, and a greater proportion of these images were revisualizations of stressful scenes in the film. Along with these cognitive changes, subjects had increased negative affect after the stress film, and high scores for negative affect correlated significantly and positively with high frequencies of intrusive thoughts.

RESULTS BY VARIABLES

Figures 1–8 show the means in the baseline, neutral, and stress conditions for each variable. The data for each dependent variable from subjects in all four experiments were analyzed in a series of two-way analyses of variance for repeated measures. In general, there were six levels to the main treatment effect between subjects: Experiments 1, 2, the "general" (g) and "specific" (s) groups of Experiment 3 (3s and 3g), and the "normal" and "abnormal" groups of Experiment 4 (4n and 4a). There were two levels to the main experimental effect within subjects: neutral-baseline and stress-baseline change scores. The total number of subjects was 103. Table 1 shows the F statistics, the mean change scores between conditions, and the eta coefficients for the F statistics.

Intrusive Thought

Two types of data indicated significant increases in intrusive thought after stress—the content analysis for intrusions (Figure 1) and subjects' ratings of images on

Table 1 **TABLE F's, MEAN DIFFERENCE SCORES, AND CORRELATION RATIOS**

Condition Effect: Neutral vs. Stress Conditions

Variable:	df	Mean Difference Scores		F	Correlation Ratio (eta)[d]
		N-B	S-B		
Intrusions	1,97	.3	1.8	67.39**	.64
Film References	1,97	1.4	3.0	29.50**	.48
Visual Images—Content Analyzed	1,69[b]	0	.5	13.28**	.39
Entry Rating	1,77[a]	.4	1.0	12.78**	.36
Task-Irrelevant Thoughts	1,97	1.4	2.6	14.60**	.35
Visual Images—Self-Report	1,77[c]	.2	.6	2.50	.14
Error Scores	1,97	−1.0	.1	1.69	.08

Treatment Effect: Differences between Experimental Treatment Groups

Variable:	df	F	Correlation Ratio (eta)[d]
Film References	5,97	4.30**	.37
Task-Irrelevant Thoughts	5,97	3.80**	.35
Intrusions	5,97	3.61**	.34
Visual Images—Content Analyzed	3,69[b]	1.69	.17
Visual Images—Self-Report	4,77[c]	1.20	.10
Error Scores	5,97	.53	.0
Entry Rating	4,77[a]	.38	.0

Interaction Effect: Condition X Treatment

Variable:	df	F	Correlation Ratio (eta)[d]
Intrusions	5,97	5.10**	.41
Task-Irrelevant Thoughts	5,97	3.30**	.32
Film References	5,97	2.50*	.26
Entry Rating	4,77[a]	1.87	.20
Visual Images—Self-Report	4,77[c]	1.50	.16
Errors	5,97	.43	.0
Visual Images—Content Analyzed	3,69[b]	.34	.0

[a] Rating data from Experiment 1 are not exactly comparable
[b] Experiment 4 is not available
[c] Individuals' data from Experiment 1 are not available
[d] See Cohen (1965)
 * $p < .05$
** $p < .01$

the Entry Scale (Figure 2). (Judges scoring for intrusions had high interjudge reliability—.85 or above in the various experiments.) In the analysis of variance for intrusions (N = 103), both main effects and the interaction effect were significant well beyond the .01 level. The eta for conditions is very large and suggests a large stress-film effect. The eta statistics for the main effect due to variation in treatments and the interaction effect are much smaller. Newman-Keuls gaps tests for paired comparisons on the main effect due to experiments did not attribute the significance on the *F* tests to any particular pair of means. Tests for the interaction effects attributed differences to 4a and 4n (female subjects with specific instruc-

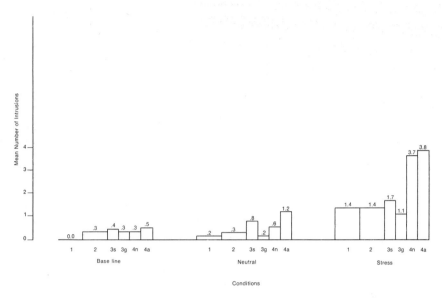

Figure 1. Summary graph of mean scores for content analysis data for intrusions for Experiments 1 through 4. The Specific (s) and General (g) subgroups of Experiment 3 and the Normal (n) and Abnormal (a) subgroups of Experiment 4 are shown separately.

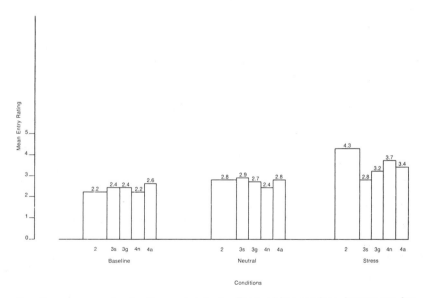

Figure 2. Summary graph of self-report data for Entry of Images into Awareness for Experiments 2 through 4.

tions) in the stress condition, versus 3g (male subjects with general instructions) in the neutral condition.

The analysis of variance for mean entry ratings (N = 82) [6] shows a similar pattern. In this analysis, the only significant F was on the mean square for conditions (F = 12.78) and the eta coefficient was .36. The mean squares due to variation in experiments and the interaction were not significant. It is of interest to note that subjects were comfortable using the Entry Scale; the low percentage of subjects who did not use the scale (5 per cent) may be due to an absence of imagery among them. This percentage of non-users of the Entry Scale corresponds to Singer's (1966) figures on the percentage of people who do not experience visual images.

The content analysis and entry ratings were different procedures for the assessment of intrusive thought. Both variables significantly increased after the stress film in each experiment. In Experiments 3 and 4, entry ratings and intrusion scores after the stress film are significantly and positively correlated, $r_3 = +.39$ and $r_4 = +.56$ (Experiment 2 had a positive but non-significant correlation of +.22). The immediate implications of these results are that subjects, after the stress film, (a) rate their visual images as more intrusive, surprising, forceful, "against the will," and (b) are rated by content analysts, using four operational criteria, as having more intrusive thoughts. *The agreement between two forms of measurement (self-report and content analysis), the high interjudge correlations, and significant findings in a variety of replication studies support the validity of the finding that there is an intrusion effect after stress.*

The content analysis variable "intrusions" is based on four criteria for judgment, which are operationally defined in the content-analysis manual for judging how thought enters subjective experience. These criteria for scoring an intrusion are distinctly different from those for scoring other cognitive variables. But significant positive correlations were noted between intrusions and film references (range of r was .55 to .70) and between intrusions and task-irrelevant thoughts (range of r was .21 to .50).

Are intrusions simply a contaminated version of film references or task-irrelevant thoughts? Ideally, these variables should be as independent and uni-dimensional as possible, so that we can best identify the exact nature of dependent variables and their relationship to independent variables. In general, the data we have on correlations of cognitive variables show that there is both overlap and independence. That is, there are units scored as intrusions but not as film references, units scored as both, and units scored as film references but not as intrusions. The data suggest, however, that the variables reflect different constructs.

For example, the data from Experiment 3 have the following distribution of intrusions, film references, and intrusive film references (those film references also scored as intrusions) after the neutral and stress films:

---

[6] Experiment 1 is not included in the graph for Entry Rating, because at that time the Entry Rating was a 7-point scale and not comparable with the later 5-point scale.

Table 2 DISTRIBUTION OF INTRUSIONS AND FILM REFERENCES

Experiment 3	Total Number of Intrusions		Total Units Scored as Both Intrusions and Film References		Total Number of Film References	
	Neutral	*Stress*	*Neutral*	*Stress*	*Neutral*	*Stress*
Specific N = 16	12	27	8	20	29	42
General N = 15	3	16	1	13	16	33
All Subjects N = 31	14	43	9	33	45	75

These data show that after the stress film about 75 per cent of the intrusions are film references, but less than half of the film references are intrusive. Thus, many intrusions did focus on the film's content, but references to the film were not necessarily intrusive.

Another issue has to do with the relationship between task-irrelevant thoughts and intrusions. That is, it is possible that intrusions increase merely as a function of a general increase in task-irrelevant thoughts. We can use the point-biserial correlation (r_{pb}) as a comparative index of effect size for dependent variables (Cohen, 1965). If we compare changes between the neutral and stress conditions, the increase in intrusions is much greater than the increase in task-irrelevant thoughts. For example, in Experiment 4, where task-irrelevant thoughts do increase after stress, the r_{pb} for the difference between post-neutral and post-stress conditions was .73 for intrusions, as compared with .50 for task-irrelevant thoughts. Also the differences in the magnitude of eta statistics for condition effect suggest a difference in effect size between intrusions and task-irrelevant thoughts. Such differences are found in every experiment, and suggest that intrusions increase above and beyond any increase in task-irrelevant thoughts.

Visual Images

A major prediction was that a stress event presented in a visual medium would induce increased visual images, as measured by (1) self-report and (2) content analysis. Originally, we had conceived of the content-analysis variable as the main variable, with convergent validation to be obtained with self-report ratings. Results from individual experiments and from pooled data show the measurement of frequency of visual images to be less reliable and less valid than is desirable for dependent experimental variables. In Experiments 1 and 2, while visual images were significantly more frequent after the stress film, the difference between the baseline and stress conditions was not significant (see Figure 3). In Experiment 3, the frequency of visual images by content analysis did not differ significantly between the neutral and stress conditions. Considering all experiments together, the analysis of variance showed a significant F for the main effect due to condition, but the eta coefficient (.39) was much lower than that for intrusions (.64) and film references (.48).

The number of self-reported visual images was obtained by counting the number of entry ratings applied in each condition. This figure did not change

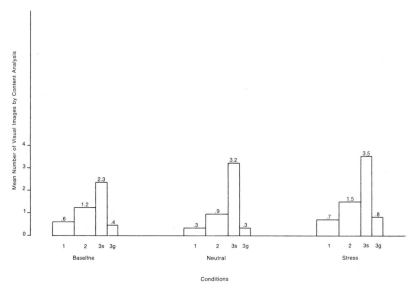

Figure 3. Summary graph of content analysis data for Visual Images for Experiments 1 through 3.

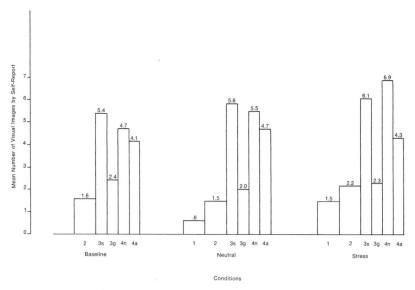

Figure 4. Summary graph of self-report data for Visual Images for Experiments 1 through 4. Baseline data for Experiment 1 are missing.

between experimental conditions (baseline, neutral, stress), considering all experiments together (see Figure 4). While the F for the differences between experiments did not reach the critical level, t tests on data in Experiment 4 showed that subjects who received instructions specifying the experimenter's interest in images reported significantly more visual images in every condition than subjects whose instructions did not specify a focus on images.

Content analysts invariably scored far fewer visual images than subjects scored for themselves (compare Figures 3 and 4). We believe that judges required some detail in order to arrive at a score, and that subjects reported only vivid or intense images in sufficient detail for judges to note a visual quality in the cognitive experience. Also, a judge would score a given description as one image although the subject may have actually experienced (and rated the experience as) more than one image.

Even though the frequency of images by both self-report and content analysis measures did not uniformly change after the stress film, a larger proportion of image content was devoted to film recollections in the post-stress film condition than in the post-neutral film condition.

Film References

Data from all the experiments showed that there were significantly more repetitions of the film in thought after the stress film than after the neutral film (Figure 5). In the ANOVA, the F for condition differences was 29.50 and eta was .48.

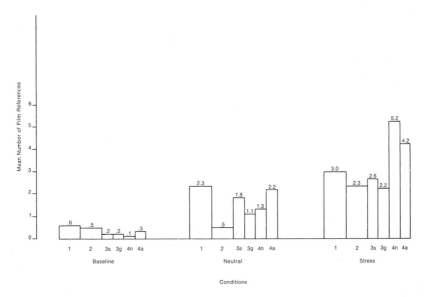

Figure 5. Summary graph of content analysis data for Film References for Experiments 1 through 4.

Interjudge correlations ranged from .90 to .95 in the various experiments. The counterbalanced designs indicate that the additional film references were not due to the passage of time, but were a stress-film effect. In addition, while differences between treatments had a small but significant F (4.30), the Newman-Keuls test did not attribute these differences to any particular pairs of means.

Task-Irrelevant Thoughts

In counterbalanced experiments (Experiments 1 and 3), the number of task-irrelevant thoughts after the neutral film did not differ significantly from those after the stress film, nor was there a significant order effect on this variable. In the independent-groups design (Experiment 2), task-irrelevant thoughts were significantly more frequent after the stress film. In the uncounterbalanced study (Experiment 4, involving females only), a significant increase in task-irrelevant thoughts occurred in each experimental condition (see Figure 6). This signifi-

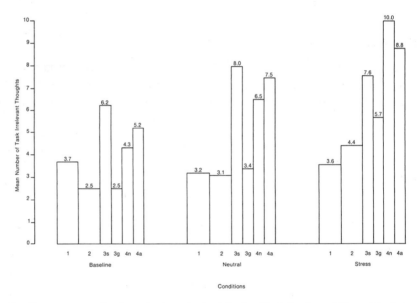

Figure 6. Summary graph of content analysis data for Task-Irrelevant Thoughts for Experiments 1 through 4.

cant increase may be due to two factors: a tendency to more task-irrelevant thoughts after the stress film (the third condition), and a tendency to more task-irrelevant thoughts with the onset of fatigue.

As mentioned earlier, a distinction between task-irrelevant thoughts and other content analysis variables, especially intrusions and film references, is suggested by the inconsistency of the task-irrelevant thought data across experiments, and large differences in the size of the *F* and eta statistics.

Error Scores

Error scores remained remarkably uniform across experimental conditions (Figure 7). Although the mean scores between experimental groups differed, the standard deviations were large, suggesting marked individual differences on the tone task. (The *F* test for treatments ($df = 5,97$) was not significant.) The similarity of these data strongly suggests at least that this particular cognitive task does not pick up decrements in cognitive performance after stress. A more inferential conclusion is that performance on cognitive tasks such as these shows no decrement at mild-to-moderate levels of stress, and that changes in subjective experience are more reliable indices of these levels of stress.

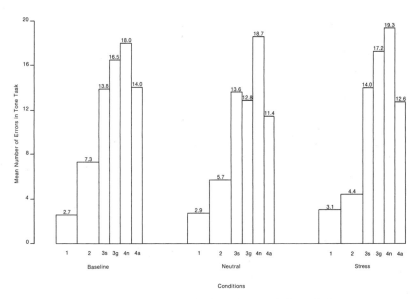

Figure 7. Summary graph of Error scores for Experiments 1 through 4.

Number of Words

The number of words recorded by subjects in the mental-contents reports, while varying between experiments and subjects, was relatively constant within each experiment and subject (see Figure 8). This stability suggests that increases in variables derived from mental reports are not artifacts of increases in mental reporting, since such increases were not observed. We transformed data on the content-analysis variables into mean per 100 words and, as expected, this transformation did not affect the direction or significance of the findings.

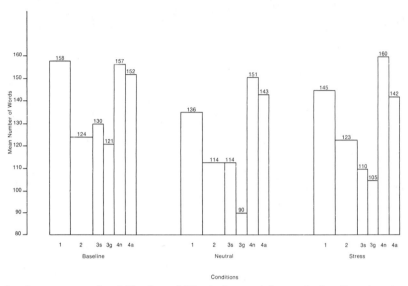

Figure 8. Summary graph of Number of Words in mental reports for Experiments 1 through 4.

Affect Rankings

The affect Q-sort was used in Experiments 2, 3, and 4, and the Q-sort rankings were treated as ordinal data. In all three experiments, subjects' ranking of affect adjectives after the stress film showed a decrease in positive affect and an increase in negative affect.

One of our principal interests in the affect scores was to see what affects might correlate with high scores in content-analysis categories, task performance, and self-report variables. Data from Experiments 3 and 4 were analyzed. Directly after the stress film, if a subject reports himself as relatively less friendly, less in control, more irritated, and more sad, then he is more likely to report later mental contents that will be judged by content analysis as being high in intrusive thinking. Similarly, after the stress film, if the subject reports himself as relatively less attentive, less in control, less relaxed, and more sad, then he will be likely to rate his own subsequent visual images as intrusive. These results are from significant correlations among two subject samples, regardless of sex, demand or instruction group. For each treatment group, this same general trend was evident, although the same specific affect adjective did not always correlate with intrusiveness in each. Again, subjects who report negative affect after the stress film tend to have intrusive thinking during the tone task. Among the possible interpretations of these data, we feel that one is most plausible: subjects who experience affective strain also experience cognitive strain, particularly intrusive thinking.

One interesting comparison was done between male and female college students in Experiments 3 and 4. Rankings on positive affects and negative affects were compared (Table 3). In the baseline condition, the positive and negative affects

Table 3 COMPARISON OF AFFECT RANKINGS FOR MALES AND FEMALES

	BASELINE CONDITION			POST-STRESS EVENT		
	Ranked Higher by Men (N = 31)	Ranked Higher by Women (N = 30)	Ranked the Same	Ranked Higher by Men	Ranked Higher by Women	Ranked the Same
Positive Affects	Relaxed Cooperative In control	Calm Attentive	Friendly	Attentive In control Cooperative Friendly Calm Relaxed	None	None
Negative Affects	Irritated	Sad Tired	Disgusted Evasive Anxiety	Anxiety	Sad Disgusted Irritated Tired Evasive	None

283

are distributed about equally between men and women. After the stress film, the men gave the positive affects higher rankings than the women, but, except for anxiety, the women gave the negative affects higher rankings than the men. The female subjects also had a non-significant trend toward higher levels of intrusions per person and a higher percentage (100 per cent versus 61 per cent) of female subjects had at least one score for intrusions on content analysis.

EXPERIMENT 5: CHANGE IN EXPERIMENTAL TASK TO CONTROL FOR TASK-INDUCED INTRUSIONS

From the previous four experiments, variables related to intrusive and film-repetitive thinking consistently increased in frequency after exposure to a stressful film. These observations harmonized with clinical observations and confirmed our experimental hypotheses. We felt that the confirmation would be strengthened if similar results could be obtained from an experiment involving a different task.

In past work we had used a signal-detection task and had periodically obtained introspective reports of mental contents to assess intrusive thinking. In order to succeed at the signal-detection task, the subject must pay close attention to the external stimulus, as well as maintain a short-term memory of it. Thus the task severely limits the amount of time subjects have for thoughts that are not relevant to external stimuli; a task-irrelevant thought can be experienced as intrusive solely because it may be dysfunctional and distracting to the subject's wish to succeed in performing the task. Although in past experiments intrusive thoughts emerged during signal detection, we still questioned the possible interaction between this particular task and the intrusion rating. Suppose the subject felt that he ought to pay exclusive attention to the external signals—an attitude the instructions deliberately impart. He might then regard any thought unrelated to the task as intrusive, describe his thoughts as intrusive, and then have them rated by a content analyst as intrusive.

Experiment 5 (Horowitz and Becker, 1971c) was designed to obtain introspective data in which any kind of thought content was permissible. During this task, the subject's single responsibility is to form thought images. Unlike the signal-detection task, this design encourages attention to internal thoughts. The subject can form any thought without necessarily forming an intrusion or role-alien product. If in this freer context subjects experience intrusive thinking, then there is greater assurance in regarding intrusive thinking, as measured in these experiments, as an intrapsychic rather than role-related process.

The task is based on that developed by Kafka and Reiser (1967) and related also to the sequential image-formation tasks of Corman, Escalona, and Reiser (1964) and Horowitz (1965). It is designed for use with individual subjects, and elicits verbal, graphic, and scale responses. The experimenter asks the subject to form spontaneously a visual image within 20 seconds. At the end of 20 seconds, the experimenter asks the subject to describe the image contents, and then to draw his mental image, trying to depict the form as experienced rather than artistically. After drawing, the process is repeated. There were three Image-

Describe-Draw (IDD) periods before the film, and six IDD's after the first film. At the end of each series, subjects rated their images for visual vividness and for quality of entry into awareness on two 5-point scales.

In pilot work (Horowitz, 1970), 10 subjects were shown two stress films and one neutral film on different days. In addition to "Subincision" and "The Runner," another stress film, "It Didn't Have to Happen," was shown. This film also depicted themes of bodily injury—three accidents in a wood shop setting—and has shown stress effects on physiological measures (Lazarus and Opton, 1966). Intrusive images occurred significantly more frequently after both stress films than after the neutral film. Thus, data with this varied experimental task and varied experimental stimuli complemented data from the first four experiments.

Since this procedure seemed workable, Experiment 5 was designed with a subject sample of 20. In this experiment only the stress film "It Didn't Have to Happen" was used. Three IDD's were administered before and six IDD's after the stress film. The hypothesis again was an increase in intrusive images and film references after the stress film. Experiment 5 was also used as pilot work to study the effect of an experimental intervention on stress responses. Our hypothetical model of cognitive response posits stress-specific responses that eventually decrease and return to baseline levels. It would be useful to see when and how cognitive responses return to the baseline and thus to learn more about the durability of such responses.

The 20 subjects were randomly distributed between two subgroups that saw the same film, underwent the same assessment procedures, but were treated differently after the stress film. In one group, an experienced social work interviewer, who was a different person from the female experimenter, conducted a five-minute discussion which focused on the subject's description of film content and her feelings during and after the film. The interviewer offered no interpretations, value judgments, or probing questions; the discussion was conducted after the stress film and before the IDD task. At the end of this five-minute discussion, the interviewer left and experimental procedures resumed. Individuals in the second group continued with IDD immediately after the stress film. In each group there were 10 female nursing students.

The two main questions in this study were:

1. How does a different experimental task affect the dependent cognitive variables?
2. What are the different effects, if any, of short differences in post-stress treatment on the dependent variables?

The mean content analysis scores for all 20 subjects showed significantly more intrusions, film references, and negative affect in the first three IDD reports after the stress film, as compared with the three IDD reports of the baseline, which for all 20 subjects were very similar. Thus, even with a change in experimental task, but using the same content-analysis criteria, the stress film caused increases in these dependent variables.

After the stress film, scores by treatment group show the "No Discussion" group to have significantly more intrusions, more negative affect, and more film references (in the six IDD reports) than the "Discussion" group. Entry and Vividness for both groups remained about the same, both before and after the stress film. These results suggest that the discussion may have an effect in decreasing responses to the stress film. However, in this experiment there was no control group for passage of time (five-minute wait–no discussion), so that the results are merely suggestive.

PHYSIOLOGICAL MEASUREMENT: GALVANIC SKIN RESPONSE

In developing a phenomenology of stress, it would be useful to describe eventually the relationship between physiological changes and cognitive responses. Past work on physiological response to stress (Lazarus, Speisman, Mordkoff, and Davison, 1962) shows that galvanic skin response (GSR has been the variable that most consistently showed a significant change after exposure to a stressful film. During Experiment 5 we continually recorded the GSR. We were also interested in how subjects might adapt to a second film viewing of the same stress film, after one of the two treatment conditions and after the image-forming tasks. Thus, after the cognitive tasks were completed, subjects again saw the same stress film. We intended to compare GSR during the first and second film periods and to see whether the changes related in any obvious way to treatment group, or to an idiosyncratic tendency to intrusive repetitive thought.

To analyze the GSR, subjects' raw resistance scores were transformed into log conductance scores. For each subject, there were four scores for each film. (Only 14 subjects had GSR records good enough for data analysis.) The scores corresponded to skin resistance measured at four time periods in the film: one minute into film, before any stressful events, then during accidents 1, 2, and 3.

For one three-way analysis of variance on these data, there was no F test significant at the .05 level (between factor = treatment; within factors = film; time periods). These data from our small sample indicated that having a five-minute discussion did not affect GSR on repetition of the film. A second analysis of variance was done, comparing subjects with more versus subjects with fewer intrusive thoughts. Only the interaction between intrusions, film, and time period was marginally significant ($p < .06$). The mean scores are plotted in Figure 9.

This near-significant finding was in a direction contrary to expectation. Subjects who had higher levels of intrusive thought had lower levels of skin conductance (believed to indicate less physiological arousal during the film), although they reported more negative affect after both the first and second films. Whatever the explanation, the interrelationship between cognitive and affective response, on the one hand, and physiological response, on the other hand, is not clear-cut.

We also examined the log conductance scores and the *number* of non-specific GSR responses ("GSR's") during the "silent formation" period, when subjects silently formed images that were later scored by judges as intrusive. The

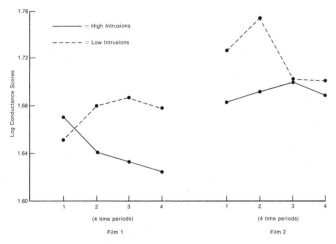

Figure 9. GSR data from Experiment 5, comparing subjects high on intrusions (n = 7) to subjects low on intrusions (n = 7). Points plotted are mean scores.

latter scores were contrasted with GSR scores, during periods when non-intrusive images were formed by the same subjects. No pattern of differences was noted. We tentatively concluded that no large, obvious, direct correlation exists between intrusive repetitive thought and skin conductance.

DISCUSSION

The hypotheses of increased intrusive and stimulus-repetitive thought after stress were confirmed in these experimental studies. In what follows we reconsider the reliability and validity of these findings and their theoretical implications.

Considerations of Reliability and Validity

Two factors support the reliability of the experimental results. First, the predicted significant effects were present throughout a series of interrelated experiments. Subject populations varied with differences in sex and educational status; instructions were varied from spoken to written, from general to specific, and from a "normal" set to an "abnormal" set; the context of cognition changed from vigilance outwards to vigilance inwards, and more than one stress film was used. With many experimental variations—in subject samples, instructions, experiments, experimental task, and stress films—intrusions and film references still consistently increased after the stress film in the predicted direction. Second, independent judges, some unaware of the hypotheses, scored in similar ranges and had very good levels of correlation. In later review conferences, judges generally found that disagreements were due to oversight and *under*scoring rather than to excessive scoring. Thus, the variety of replication studies, with changes in independent variables and judges, indicated that the responses we measured were not idiosyncratic to a particular subject group or set of experimental conditions.

The research identified two cognitive concepts of central importance: intrusive thought, and repetition in thought of a previously external stimulus. Because these concepts refer to subjective experience, some discussion should center on the measurement issues, and our methods of measurement. Subjective cognitive experience is so private that conclusive and direct verification of it is impossible. Often even the person who experiences cognitive events may find them difficult to describe or relate. An assessment of subjective experience necessarily relies on indirect measurement, because it finally depends on a subject's self-report, even if the report is as simple as merely indicating the presence or absence of a mental event. Ultimately, the issue of indirect measurement questions the *knowing* of another person's experience, as well as the limitations, both in the subject and the experimenter, of adequately describing or translating subjective experience so that it may be understood by another person. Because of the presumed difference between experience and report and the notorious susceptibility of subjective experience to experimental demand, it becomes very important, when studying introspective experience, to demonstrate replicated results, in a variety of experimental situations, with a variety of measurement techniques.

The labels used to describe a given type of subjective experience may be applied according to highly personal definitions of meaning. Thus, while different persons may have quite similar experiences, they may describe them with different labels, just as they may use the same label to designate dissimilar experiences. Quantification of subjective experience requires finding some way for different persons to use the same labels consistently.

A partial solution is to ask a subject to label his own subjective experience but to supply him with a given set of terms, as in our Entry Scale. But the observer can never be sure how appropriately a subject applies the labels that were given to him. We know that a subject may still label according to his idiosyncratic response set and his sense of what is socially desirable, as well as on the basis of other motives, conscious or unconscious, for disguise or distortion (Rosenthal and Rosnow, 1969).

The content-analysis method, used to quantify our principal data, takes the labeling process away from the subject, and places it with an observer who can be trained and checked for consistency. Removal of the labeling process reduces a source of subject bias, because the subject only describes his thought; he no longer has to deal with the awareness of or responsibility for labeling and categorizing it. We believe that this separation of "responsibilities"—the subject reports and observers' label—reduces somewhat the hazards of using introspective reports of subjective experience. By defining constructs operationally, and by training judges in applying these criteria reliably, we feel it is possible to quantify cognitive responses to stress, even when these cognitive responses are forms of subjective experience.

As methodologically useful or successful as content analysis may be, the variables it defines must be similar to the experiences that exist for subjects in real life. At this point we can reexamine our three main content-analysis variables—film references, intrusions, and visual images—and consider their validity as concepts.

Film references were defined as overt inclusions of content specifically contained in the film stimulus. Two great advantages of the film method are that the repetition of stimulus content has good face validity and involves simple operational criteria. On the other hand, *intrusions* are described as a form rather than a content of thought. They are, therefore, harder to identify and require closer evaluation for validity.

First, the operational definitions used in the content-analysis manual follow closely the guidelines of clinical experience: thought experiences are scored as intrusive if they have a non-volitional entry into awareness, evoke suppressive efforts, lead to wishes to avoid further repetition, or if the same thought recurs non-deliberately. These criteria are not esoteric or exotic; their everyday clinical familiarity supports the validity of the intrusion concept. Second, we used two different methods of measurement to assess intrusions: content analysis gave positive and significant results, with an extremely large effect; self-report on the entry scale also gave positive and significant results, although not as large an effect. The different methods of measurement were correlated significantly and positively in several experiments. We conclude that our content-analysis procedure for measurement of intrusive thought is a useful and valid tool for cognitive research—one that could be used in the assessment of any type of cognitive report.

Like intrusions, a third content-analysis variable—visual images—consisted of criteria for labeling the form rather than the content of a subjective experience. Measurement of this variable led to results that were less stable across experiments than the film-reference and intrusion variables. In some, but not all experiments, significantly more visual images were found after the stress film than after the neutral film. Although the overall analysis of variance for all experiments together showed a significant condition effect on content analysis of image frequency (more images after stress), the overall results using self-report of image frequency were not significant. In addition, in Experiment 3, the number of visual images scored shifted significantly with a shift in instructions from general to specific. Even those subjects with specific instructions to report any visual or spatial sensory quality in subjective experience invariably indicated on self-report many more images than judges scored using the criteria of the content-analysis manual.

These findings led us to reconsider the idea that visual images are mental events that have "frequency" and can be counted. Image formation is not like a series of still photographs, slides, or a movie. The images may move or remain stationary; they may be enlarged or collapsed; there may be many different images at the same time, with constantly changing levels of intensity or vividness. Also, people vary widely in their style of cognitive representation. Although almost all subjects formed visual images, some did so with greater intensity or clarity than others. Some subjects reported rapidly flickering images, others durable ones; some reported several images at once, others, one at a time. Thus, frequency is difficult to report for any subject and hard to generalize across subjects. The concept of frequency itself may be less valid than such constructs as prevalence of image formation, and clarity, intensity, and controllability of imagery. While we believe the findings support the reliability and validity of the film-content repetition and the intrusion variables, we are less secure in our belief in the reliability and validity of image frequency, even though significant findings did emerge.

THEORETICAL IMPLICATIONS

The findings support the hypothesis that in persons without psychiatric illness there is a tendency toward intrusive thought and repetition, even after mild to moderately stressful stimuli. These findings are based on a circumscribed type of stress event and a limited assessment of the range of possible cognitive responses. One basic issue for further study concerns the relationship between the nature of a stress event and the nature of a cognitive response. This relationship can be considered in terms of four clarifying questions:

1. Is the response (e.g. intrusive and repetitive thinking) proportional to the *quantity* of the external stress event? If so, as external stress events increase in magnitude (along different operational dimensions), individuals would respond with more episodes or more intense instances of intrusive and repetitive thinking (all else being held constant).
2. Is the response based on the *quality* of the stress event? If so, some types of stress evoke more intrusions (or other types of cognitive response) than others.
3. Is the response limited to stress states, or may it also be elicited in non-stress states? If the response is found to be limited to stress states, and if increasing the magnitude of stress events led to increasing levels of response, then the response could be used as an index of the presence and degree of a stress state.
4. Is the response keyed to what Lazarus (1969) calls "dispositional variables," i.e., to habitual personal responses to a given type of stress? If so, some persons might have intrusive repetitions, others might not. We would like to know: (a) how general the phenomenon is, and (b) who responds in this way, in terms of other response characteristics and personality variables.

We shall briefly review where this research stands in relation to each question and consider the theoretical issues and experimental plans that are relevant to each question.

1. Does the magnitude of response relate to the magnitude of a stress event?

Approaching this question requires clarification of different dimensions of response and event, as well as operational definitions of what is meant by "magnitude." In the present series of experiments, there are no clear answers because magnitude of stress was not systematically varied. There are a few clues, if we consider magnitude of stress to be related to the increase in negative affect reported by subjects immediately after the stress film—i.e., magnitude along a dimension of intensity, as experienced by a subject.

The frequency of intrusive thought was positively correlated in several experiments with higher reports of negative affect immediately after the stress film. Also, a higher percentage of female subjects had intrusive thoughts, and females ranked negative affects at a higher level, than did comparable male subjects (Experiment 3 versus Experiment 4). A third clue is found in Experiment 5 where more intrusions occurred in subjects who did not take part in the brief discussion period. Although these data were from experiments that took care *not* to vary *external stress events,* they do suggest the possibility that the frequency of intrusive thinking may increase as the magnitude of the *stress state* increases.

These clues and this theoretical consideration generate a hypothesis for future experimental testing. It should be possible to have one group of subjects rate various films as external stress events, using scales or semantic differential methods. The films would then be ranked from most to least stressful, in terms of these criteria. We could then compare the level of intrusive thought after each film, in different subject groups drawn from the same population. We would predict that the film ranked as most stressful on independent criteria would lead to the highest level of intrusions and stimulus-repetitive thinking.

In such an experiment, the operational definition of "magnitude of stress event" would be based on: (a) selecting a variety of films intuitively, according to estimated differences in stressfulness of content (for example, a film showing a minor injury would be predicted to be less stressful than one depicting major bodily harm); and (b) rank-ordering the films selected, according to the averaged responses of a group of sample subjects. Thus, variations in "magnitude of stress" would be due to variations in film content in such an experiment.

But content variation is not the sole determinant of the magnitude of an external stress event. The speed of onset—sudden or gradual—the formal organization, and the duration of the external stress event are also important. The film method would allow systematic investigation of the effect of such changes in each factor on cognitive response.

To determine the effect of duration of *external stress events* on intrusive repetitiveness in cognitive response, we have edited a stress film to present the same content in scenes of differing length. According to psychoanalytic theory, we could predict an inverted "U"-shaped effect (Janis and Leventhal, 1968). As the duration of an external stress event increases, there may be greater internal registration of stimuli, along with greater arousal or priming of ideational and affective associates. To the degree that the associates are involved in conflict, an *internal stress event* of increasing magnitude will be evoked. Also, increasing external event duration may lead to some type of overloading of assimilative, coping, and defensive processes, resulting in what Freud termed the "breach of the stimulus barrier" and what we would re-term "relatively inadequate *modulation* of perception." We might thus predict increasing levels of intrusiveness and/or repetitiveness of thought.

On the other hand, a declining slope of the inverted "U" effect could also be predicted. Increased duration of an external stress event might allow time for primary and secondary reappraisal of the threat and coping resources, as defined by Lazarus (1966) in his theory of coping with stress. The result might be decreasing levels of *stretch,* with time to review the stress event and, in cognitive response, decreasing levels of intrusion as time passes. Finally, we might predict no results because some persons within a group were on the ascending slope of increasing stress response, while others were on the descending slope of increased adaptation, at any given length of external stress event.

While theory does not allow us to choose among the three predicted outcomes, since we cannot estimate in advance the relative strengths of impulses and defenses, empirical studies may contribute information. In collaboration with Daniel Greenson, M.D., we have conducted one pilot study to determine the subjective effects of the films with increasing durations of the same content. Five males and five females watched an automobile accident film, edited into five clips, so that each clip showed speeding cars, a crash in slow motion, and injured victims. As they saw successive repetitions of this same theme in different film footages (different cars, people, injuries, etc.), they reported increasing levels of affective disturbance. No subject reported reduction in experienced stress with increasing duration of the external stress event. Next we plan to select independent subject groups from the same population sample, show each group varying lengths of this specially edited film, and see whether intrusions and/or film references increase as duration increases.

2. Is the response of intrusive repetitiveness associated with certain qualities of stress events, or is it a general response tendency during stress states, whatever the quality of the inciting events?

To work on this extremely interesting and complex question of stress quality would require exacting operational definitions of qualitative variations. The most obvious ways of defining quality involve description of the themes and contents of stress events. But the quality of a stress event is not limited to its content themes; it may include the sensory mode of presentation, the vicarious or real-life context, the degree of realistic or fantastic organization, and the clarity or obscurity of stimuli.

In the present series of experiments, two films of differing specific content were used, but both films had similar theme content (bodily injury), had victims and aggressors, and showed scenes of bleeding and pain. Conceivably, the cognitive responses of intrusive and stimulus-repetitive thinking could be greater after such perceptions of violence and injury than after perceptions of other types of stress event. One way to find out would be to contrast cognitive responses to injury films and to films depicting themes such as separation, loss, or injustice. Some evidence suggests that we might predict these same two cognitive responses after stresses that vary in quality. Cartwright, Bernick, Borowitz, and Kling (1969) found penetration of themes of erotic films into subsequent dreams, although intrusiveness of thought was not measured.

In general social observation, persons sometimes do describe intrusive rumination after depressing films that do not depict injuries or violence. In mourning, intrusive revisualizations of the lost person are commonplace and may reach hallucinatory intensity. Intrusive thoughts and hallucinations, sometimes of recurrent themes, are also reported in natural or experimental episodes of social isolation.

The quality of stress events can also be studied in terms of formal characteristics rather than content characteristics. If the external stress event takes place in a largely visual mode of presentation, will the cognitive responses repeat the visual quality in image representation? If the stress event were presented in auditory form, would cognitive responses include intrusive auditory images? These questions can be approached using the present basic experimental paradigm and comparing the effects of audio tapes, silent films, and sound films of similar content on subsequent cognitive responses.

3. Do intrusive-repetitive forms of cognitive response occur only in stress states?

Clinical and experimental observations indicate that intrusive repetitions occur in situations other than recent exposure to an *external stress event*. The affected persons are not "the average persons" hypothesized as responding to an external stress event; they have idiosyncratic susceptibilities toward the triggering of an internal stress event through associative priming. For example, one male subject in a pilot study had recurrent intrusive images of the wistful glance of a young woman in the neutral film; the scene reminded him of a conflictual personal event, a girl friend's unwanted pregnancy. The non-stressful external event evoked a stress state for him because it evoked an internal stress event, revival of conflicted thoughts and feelings. In the internal stress event, the image of the woman's glance carried the meaning of an accusation.

The effects of an external stress event can also be associatively primed and re-evoked at later times. For example, after one experiment a subject passed a construction site, where he saw wood shavings. Glancing at these shavings led to an intrusive recollection of the most frightening scene of the woodshop accident film, in which a worker is impaled on a shaft of wood.

Internal associative processes may also trigger intrusive repetitions after these responses have "worn off" as spontaneous events. For example, one subject went to a party after having "forgotten all about the film." While watching a pretty girl cross her legs, he had a fantasy of reaching over and touching her legs. To his surprise, a painful scene from the "Subincision" film came vividly to mind.

These examples could all be regarded as neutral external events that activate an *internal stress event*—in these instances *internal stress events* based on recent *external stress events*. Of course, *any* heightened drive states may lead to intrusive and repetitive thinking. For example, a starving man may have repeated intrusive images of food. We could still regard the hunger state as an *internal stress event* (an internal situation that would put the average person in a state of stress). These observations, together with a great many clinical observations of obsessive ruminations and unbidden images, indicate that this type of cognitive response is not restricted to conjunction with an external stress event.

So far, we have assumed that external stress events, in order to evoke a stress state within a given person, must evoke an internal stress event composed of representations. The above discussion led to the assumption that intrusive-repetitive thinking is not restricted to conjunction with internal stress events responsive to external stress events, but may occur in response to internal stress events alone. The question then follows, does intrusive repetitive thinking always occur when there is an internal stress event, or an internal stress state?

Intrusive repetitions are noted phenomenologically where there is no evidence for an *external stress event* and no subjective experiential evidence for an internal stress event. (Theoretical grounds for inferring an *internal stress state* will be discussed subsequently.) Two examples are available from common experience. Sometimes a catchy commercial jingle will emerge repeatedly in awareness, in spite of one's irritation and wish to suppress or avoid such repetitions. This is an intrusive repetition of an auditory image.

Similar intrusive repetitions occur in visual images in microscopists who have intrusive images of cells after many hours of such perceptual stimuli. Skiers report a similar event in kinesthetic images: while resting after a day's bodily patterning, they have intrusive sensations of kinesthetic maneuvering as a subjective experience, with or without bodily micromovements. Presumably this may happen to persons who have no psychological conflict about their work or sport, and who have not found their day's perceptual experience subjectively stressful during the actual events.

Even the intrusive repetitions in images of the microscopist at rest may, however, relate to a stress state. This is because stress is not defined as a state restricted to unpleasant configurations, but is rather extended to overloading of processes for assimilating stimuli. In the seemingly neutral content of counting white blood cells for several hours, there may be a stimulus overload due to repetition of form. That is, the schema-forming, schema-holding, and schema-matching processes involved in perceptual recognition may be placed in a state of *stretch* by perceptual repetition. This state of *stretch* may be regarded as a localized *stress state*. The repetition during subsequent rest periods may be a result of this *stretch* of schema-formation, perhaps even a form of discharge or working-off of the encodings. If this line of reasoning is correct, it seems that intrusive repetitions are related to *stress states,* although different stress states must be individually defined by *specifying their relationship to internal and external events and the cognitive processes involved.*

If intrusive repetitiveness were demonstrated to be a cognitive response highly indicative of stress states, as this line of reasoning has suggested, then it would be possible to measure this variable as one index of how stressed a person was in a given context. Various treatments could then be compared in terms of their effectiveness in reducing the frequency of intrusions and repetitions. Thus, various theories about stress or stretch-reduction could be tested empirically.

4. How general is the cognitive response of intrusive repetitiveness across persons? Do only certain persons respond in this manner to stress? Does this response characteristic, if more prevalent in some persons than others, correlate with other attributes of personality or cognitive style?

The number of persons scored as having at least one intrusion after the stress films ranges from a high of 100 per cent of subjects in Experiment 4a and 4n to a low of 53 per cent of subjects in Experiment 3g. This high percentage of response suggests that experiencing intrusions after stress is a general tendency. But individuals may vary widely and consistently in terms of the degree of manifestation of a general response tendency.

In pilot studies of individual subjects, studied intensively but unsystematically across varied conditions, it is our distinct impression that persons do differ in their propensity toward intrusive-repetitive responses and that these differences are not simply ascribable to variations in degree of stress experienced by subjects. A typology of subjects began to impress itself upon us, although we have not yet operationally defined characteristics for quantification.

In unstructured times after a stress film, some subjects seemed to embark on a strategy of cognitive review of the film (and the experiment also), while others attempted to put the film out of mind. Some subjects were relatively successful with their self-selected strategy: they could think of the film without experiencing intrusive associations or repetitions, or they could entirely put it out of mind.

Either strategy might also fail. The most striking intrusive repetitive events occurred in a group of subjects we found ourselves calling "weak or brittle repressors." They favored a strategy of putting the stress event out of mind, but many intrusive breakthroughs did occur. When such intrusive breakthroughs occurred, these subjects repeated their strategy, in that they avoided further conceptualization and used denial, splitting, evasion, and suppression as auxiliary defensive operations. Clinically, this resembles the hysterical cognitive style (Shapiro, 1965).

Other experiments to study these questions of individual differences should include study of the same subjects across repeated conditions to see whether some persons consistently rate highest on intrusive repetitiveness. Additional studies should measure cognitive style variables, such as leveling–sharpening and repression–sensitization, to see whether there is correlation between this type of cognitive response to stress and such dispositional variables.

These dispositional variables should include, eventually, examinations of "syndromes" of stress response as suggested by Lazarus et al. (1969). For example, our "successful repressors" appear to be persons who ward off repetition of ideas. Is it possible that they respond with some type of physiological or affective pattern that is different from that of subjects who do not completely ward off cognitive responses after stress? This question would have to be deferred to a much later experimental series. Not only is there much more to work out within the sphere of cognitive response, but existing research physiological variables, themselves, are found to be idiosyncratic, nonspecific, and mysterious in their correlations (Lacey and Lacey, 1958; Johnson, 1970; Lazarus et al., 1969).

THEORETICAL MODEL

We have suggested that intrusive and stimulus repetitive thought are general tendencies in cognitive response to stress that would be more or less present in different persons and after different types of stress. We present here a more detailed and generalized provisional model than that described in the introduction. These elaborations were developed during the course of this work, and they are consistent with our experimental findings. This tentative model is also consistent with the definitional model of stress presented in the introduction, the clinical observations upon which it is based, and the hypotheses for future study developed so far in this discussion. Following Miller, Galanter, and Pribram (1960), Klein (1967), and Neisser (1967), the model is one of processes rather than structures and is thus a programmatic sequence for information processing.

The model must begin as a simple statement of the course of a perception. Perception is an active process with feedback and regulatory operations. In the present model, we shall assume that, once perceptual processes are initiated, they set in motion a programmatic sequence that has a place of entry and a place of exit. A property of the programmatic sequence will be a tendency for directional processing to the point of exit. In other words starting the program carries with it a *tendency to completion*.

Assumption of a completion tendency inherent in plans or programs is not new. Mandler (1964) has observed a completion tendency in complex series of behavioral responses that are interrupted. After an organized response has been interrupted, this tendency to completion persists as long as the situation remains essentially unchanged. Mandler avoids attributing energies to the tendency for completion; he follows Miller, Galanter, and Pribram (1960) in attributing this effect to a built-in tendency to execute successive steps. If a task plan is interrupted, the uncompleted portion automatically remains stored in working memory. The problem is shifted from explaining the source of energy pressing for completion, to explaining how and when a given plan is terminated or "switched off" (Mandler, 1964; Miller, 1963). Lewin (1935), for example, theorized that any intention to reach a goal (initiation of a plan) produces a tension system that is preserved until a goal is reached, at which point it is released. It was this theory that led to prediction of the Zeigarnik effect—the improved memory for uncompleted tasks. Mandler (1964) suggests that, in addition to the completion tendency of initiated plans, interruption may lead to a state of increased arousal, which is distressing and yet maintained until completion occurs. The organism then favors completion in order to terminate this distress.

Klein (1967) has developed further this concept of the completion tendency and the distress-reduction tendency of plans or programs in his theoretical model of peremptory ideation. Klein adds the concept of conscious and unconscious plans for processing thought, and also the concept of defense mechanisms as sources of interruption of programmatic sequences. When repressive capacity (inhibition) is lessened, or when motives (what Klein calls primary regions of imbalance) increase, the ideomotor cycle resumes operations again, follows the interrupted and repressed plan, and the result may be an episode of peremptory ideation.

In the following model, we enlarge upon the general cognitive models suggested by Miller, Galanter, and Pribram, Mandler, Neisser, and Klein. Our specific contribution will be to specify the fate of stressful perceptions and images and also to explain the occurrence of intrusive subjective experiences. We shall indicate that intrusive subjective experiences occur when three conditions are met: when there is a content of high priority; when the programmatic sequence for processing that content is in a state of non-completion; and when there is opposition to the continued processing of that programmatic sequence.

We presume that cognitive processes have a finite capacity and that information for processing may exceed that capacity. Some perceptions are not completely processed during the availability of the external stimulus configuration. The completion of processing in such instances relies on internal retention of information contained in the stimulus and in initial reactions to the stimulus. We will call this internal encoding of stimulus information an *image*. Thus, with perception, a series of images is formed as a (usually) short-term memory (or Neisser's *iconic* memory) and, in later phases of assimilation and accommodation, these image representations become the referent at the time when review and revision of information takes place. These images are internal models deriving configuration from both perceptual programs, expectancy programs, and memory review programs. There are probably many images, some based more on feature recognition, some more on topographic representation of retinal patterns, some more on expectancy. Comparisons between images leads to rejection of minor or unduplicated formats, and to the accentuation or sharpening of reduplicated or highly relevant formats. These selected images will be held, we assume, until further processing is completed, when the other images—the rejected "possibilities"—will be released from the image-holding process.

The images in the holding operation will, as the next step in the program to be completed, be matched with other representations. The new formation or activation of representations will extend the interpretation of meaning; it will include activation of other images in various sensory modes plus, importantly, word representations. The visual-image representations also undergo progressive changes, are held at various stages of development, and are compared back and forth. Neisser (1967) would term the representational processes closer to the beginning of the program (perception) *iconic images;* those later in the programmatic sequence he would call *symbolic images,* and the checking and rechecking between held images he would refer to as *analysis by synthesis.*

This extension of meaning through transformation into multiple representation will be part of another programmatic step—the appraisal of implications of the perceptions, and the images that are the encoded form of the perceptual

process. This appraisal would follow many branching routes of associational connections. These branching routes would include assessment of threat, appraisal
of coping capacity and coping alternatives, and reappraisal of threat based on
the flow of events and reflection (Lazarus, 1966). Assessments of information
would include checking and rechecking of new self- and world-schemata, suggested by the novel information, against more established self- and world-
schemata. There would be revision of enduring self- and world-schemata, as
necessitated by the new information. There would also be working out of relevant action plans and perceptual expectancies. At the final phases of the program
(that is, at the periphery of the various branching components of the program),
there would be storage of memories of the various representations and codifica-
tions, according to the multiple markers, organizations, and associational connections established during the earlier phases of the program.

Extending the program analogy further, we can presume an operation that
functions as a question: "Are the above processes complete?" If this "question"
is "answered" affirmatively (the "test" part of Miller, Galanter, and Pribram's
(1960) "TOTE" model), the images in the holding stations are released, and there
is exit from the program aroused initially by the perceptual process.

In simple or unconflicted assimilation of perception, the entire programmatic sequence would rapidly reach completion. We need not necessarily assume
any subjective experience—the program could be executed without consciousness
or a subjective sense of mental activity. With complex, novel, or threatening images,
the processes that extend representation in time and appraise multiple implications are in a state of stress, in that their capacities for processing are stretched
(or their limits exceeded). One consequence is maintenance of the overall program in a state of "on-ness" or non-completion. Under these situations, the
images or encodings of images remain in the holding operation.

While the overall program is in operation, a "higher" program assesses the
urgency of the program in relation to other programs, ones that might require
use of the same processing channels. A relatively low priority also leaves the
program "on" and the images in holding. Programs of high priority that are
difficult to complete may occupy the processing channels for extended periods.
This creates a situation of *stretch*, in that there is a backlog of non-terminated
programs that are "on," with information held in encoded form. There may also
be stretch, in the sense of an expansion of processing channels, perhaps at the
expense of other processing channels.

Suppose that assessing implications activates ideational and emotional
conflicts. Running the program creates a danger situation because of responses
such as anxiety, guilt, shame, or other emotions. Generation of such affective
states may lead to reciprocal inhibition of the program at various sites. Or, in
other terms, defensive motives may lead to alteration of programmatic hierarchies
through intensified inhibition of some programmatic sequences, or facilitation of
less dangerous programmatic sequences (e.g., reaction formation, reversal).

For example, translation of visual images into word representations may be blocked. Such inhibitions leave the program in an unconsummated state; and this "on" state acts as a continuous tendency to go on to the next step of the program. If there were a shift in priorities or a reduction in inhibitory capacity, the images encoded in the holding operation might be reactivated for further processing. If the image formation involved led to a "danger state," the process of transformation into verbal meaning might again be inhibited and, until processing is completed, the images might be periodically re-formed. As Klein (1967) pointed out for peremptory ideation in general, repression (inhibition) carries with it the preservation of that which is repressed in a "fresh" or *unmodulated* form. Such unmodulated forms of encoding tend toward episodic "repressive breakthroughs."

This state of prolonged extension of a non-terminated programmatic sequence can constitute a *strain,* in that it introduces distortions into the establishment of programmatic hierarchies, necessitates prolonged use of active inhibition, and leads to disruption of processing other information through the episodic breakthroughs of undesired mental contents.

So far we have not dealt directly with the problem of conscious experience, except to suggest that conscious experience was not necessary for the sequential and programmatic encoding and processing outlined in the model. In the following considerations of how encoded images gain conscious status in subjective experience, let us assume, as is consistent with modern neurophysiology, that there is a sequential development in the percept-registration, image-forming, and image-holding apparatus. The "lower" cognitive functions form images by the schemata-to-signal comparisons involved in perception. The "higher" cognitive functions form images that represent categories of meaning and significant object relationships. Simultaneously, in other systems of representational holding, from lower to higher functions,[7] there are related words, as well as images of other modes of representation. At any level of representation, there might be several superimposed images, any one of which could be enlarged or reduplicated. Let us assume, further, that the more intensely an image is encoded at any level (the more reduplicated, larger, detailed, or deeply etched), the more likely it is to become conscious.

As the implications of images are appraised, another "higher-order" program, overseeing many simultaneous assimilation programs, asks, in effect, "Is it important?" If an image is appraised as important, it is enlarged (in whatever way) and becomes conscious. Hierarchically, stressful *perceptions* will become

---

[7] "Higher" and "lower" are clumsy terms to apply to cognitive functions but they are the terms most frequently used in the literature. In general, the "lower" functions are more automatic, "earlier," less voluntary, and ordinarily not accessible to conscious experience. In contrast, the "higher" functions are less automatized, "later," more readily accessible to conscious experience, and hence more "voluntary" in terms of the order of control processes. In the course from perception to thought about a perception, the lower cognitive functions would be those involved in signal detection, recognition, construction, and codification, while the higher cognitive functions would be those involved in applying symbolic labels as well as in comparisons and manipulations of information according to varieties of conceptual meaning.

conscious because they are, by the definition of stress, important. This hierarchy will hold true, we presume, for *images* held for some time, due to non-completion of the program. Thus, when a stymied program is disinhibited, the program resumes its sequence. As it does so, the image encoded in the holding operation is re-formed. Because of its importance, it is attended to in that special way called consciousness.

Because of the previous state of inhibition and the relatively sudden reversal in dynamics, the conscious image will be unrelated to the previous organization of conscious subjective experience. The result will be the subjective experience of intrusive thinking that we have measured in our experiments. If the program is repeatedly interrupted, if it is hard to complete because of the complex appraisals necessary (again, the definition of stress), then there will be repetitions of the same content (which we also measured).

So far, it has been suggested that an image may be enlarged to consciousness whenever it has a high place on a hierarchy of organismic relevance, and that images related to stress events would, by definition, be placed high on such a hierarchy. Images might also be enlarged to consciousness whenever nonconscious automatic processes were insufficient to complete a phase within the overall programmatic sequence.

Suppose there is an evaluative aspect of programmatic sequences that assesses the effectiveness of any given phase. If simpler, less differentiated, automatized processes were insufficient to complete a given step, then higher level, more complex, and more differentiated processes might be activated. If the impasse continued, the highest order of cognitive function, conscious thought, might be used to solve the problem. Conscious reasoning might lead to an appropriate solution and thus resolve the impasse reached by habitual modes of reaction. The revision in appraisals, attitudes, and reactions achieved by conscious cognitive processing might lead to revision of previous automatic types of assimilation and accommodation in favor of new ones. Thus strengthening would be accomplished. Since events impose stress when automatic solutions are insufficient, representations of stress events are likely to be repeated in conscious experience as they are processed. Since the stress images may give rise to emotional responses that are unpleasant, the conscious experiences may seem unwelcome or they may be suppressed. Thus, displeasure may occur even if the conscious experience proves adaptational.

To summarize, the model explains a general tendency toward intrusive repetitiveness after stressful perception. It also permits eventual descriptions of individual variations in how this general response tendency will be manifested. *The general cognitive response tendency is a property of both the program and the nature of the stress.* In effect, the program outlined is turned "on" by perception; it also influences perception. Once "on," it tends toward completion at a greater or lesser pace, depending on its status in a system of priorities involving other programs. Because stress is a relative overload of capacities for completing various phases of the program, stress-related images are encoded and are re-formed for further processing whenever possible.

SUPPLEMENTARY CONSIDERATIONS

While we speculate that the model program is a general state of affairs, individuals will differ in specific format styles and, especially, in their patterns of *regulating* programs, singly and in competition. Some persons will characteristically inhibit such review programs or assign them low priority. Some persons will have effective inhibitory operations at selective sites. Other persons will have less effective inhibitory operations, or inhibit programmatic sequences at other sites. For example, some persons ("hysterics") may habitually tend to inhibit translation of conflictual or dreaded images into word meanings. Other persons ("obsessives") might be unable to prevent such translation, but instead might habitually facilitate the formation of counter-ideas, or contrasting emotions, to counterbalance the dangerous ideas or feelings.

The model is a detailed theory of one aspect of ego functioning. It allows designation, in theoretical discussion, of what inferred processes are stretched since the model is a sequential program for multiple and interrelated processes. In intrusive repetitions after external stress events (such as films), the plan-sequences involved are the higher cognitive functions, those that deal with meaning and emotional implications. The impasse of the programmatic sequence at these later phases leads also to a state of *stretch* for all earlier phases, such as image retention.

The neutral stimulus events, such as seeing images of blood cells after a long day at the microscope, involve lower cognitive functions—the earlier phases of the overall program. Such processes as schemata retention and the matching process of schemata and perception are stretched, with relatively no "stress state" involving later programmatic sequences or "higher" cognitive functions. The involuntary revisualizations would be due to the processes involved in clearing the image-retention and schemata-retention processes. The massive, dense, or reduplicated image schemata in this instance result from the repetition and automatization of a highly circumscribed perceptual process (rather than the relatively single, unique, and broadly important process of an emotionally stressful perception). When the schemata of blood cells are represented for appraisal and memory storage (to complete the program), the images are so dense, large, or reduplicated in representation that they achieve consciousness.

The model can also be extended to include internal stress events. Vivid images of entirely internal origin may be formed during fantasy or dreaming. This image formation process could use some of the same process channels as perception. The stressful internal images could be held for assimilation and accommodation, and could initiate the same programmatic sequences as stressful perceptual images derived from external stimulation.

Finally, the model is consistent with both gestalt feature-detection and associationist models of perception. The stepwise program includes a more or less stepwise development of associations and appraisals. It also includes a dimension of image holding and revision that goes from unclear to clear, as competing image models are refined and some rejected in favor of some central image.

The programmatic sequences suggested in our model result in a hierarchy of image encodings that are "held" at various levels of information processing. Images that are held in encoded form may be activated and an image formed when programs are in active operation; or they may be held between episodes of image formation, when the program is inhibited. The encodings are, thus, the patterns of information that can be transformed into image representation. This model of cognitive sequences conforms to a neurophysiological model of image formation recently proposed by Pribram (1971). He bases his model on the concept of the holographic representation, which contains all information about an entire image in every "piece" of the holograph.

The larger the holographic representation, the more redundant the information and the more detailed the image that can be formed on the basis of the holograph (itself not an image but a system of encoded information that can be used to re-form an image). Images in holding operations could be stored as holographically recorded information through a microstructure of slow potentials at the junctures or synapses of neural elements. Pribram suggests that slow wave fronts could move across these neural interfaces to check the status of the microstructure. Such a process could check the image-forming apparatus to see whether it is cleared and ready for new information. Conceivably, these waves could activate encoded images that were not released, cleared, or reduced in size because they were not fully processed. The resultant subjective experience would be formation of an image. The wider the area of holographic representation, the more likelihood there is of a conscious experience and the more indication there might be for further processing. At any rate, the activation of the image would turn the latent program sequence "on" and lead to further cognitive processing.

The schema of a blood cell, as discussed earlier, would occupy a wide area of holographic representation after a day's repetitive and automatized perception. Every time a wave front activated the encoding during a rest period, an intrusive image of the cells might be experienced subjectively. With each repetition during later rest periods, the area might decrease somewhat, as the information was recorded more economically and less widely, and the intrusive revisualizations would eventually cease. This excursion into metaneurology is meant only to indicate that the programmatic sequence model of a sector of ego functioning was not inconsistent with current neurophysiological speculation on image formation.

SUMMARY

We have formulated theoretical and experimental predictions of intrusive and repetitive thoughts after stressful events. These predictions were based on clinical psychoanalytic observations of compulsive repetitions of traumatic events. We tested the predictions in a series of interrelated experiments, which embodied controls for common sources of artifactual results in research on cognitive processes. The results of these experiments strongly supported the hypothesis of a tendency toward intrusive repetitive thought after mild or moderate, as well as major, stresses in persons without psychiatric illness. A set of useful definitions and a theoretical cognitive model of response to stress were presented. Our method of measuring intrusive repetitive thought appears to be reliable and valid, and we suggest its use in stress and cognitive research. We also suggest that our tentative cognitive model of response to stress describes one sector of ego functioning more precisely and contributes to the metapsychology of psychic trauma and problems of adaptation to stress.

REFERENCES

Alexander, F., et al. (1961). Experimental Studies of Emotional Stress: I. Hyperthyroidism. *Psychosomatic Medicine,* 23:104–114.

Alfert, E. (1966). Comparison of Responses to a Vicarious and a Direct Threat. *Journal of Experimental Research in Personality,* 1:179–186.

Antrobus, J. S., Singer, J. L., and Greenberg, S. (1966). Studies in the Stream of Consciousness; Experimental Enhancement and Suppression of Spontaneous Cognitive Processes. *Perceptual and Motor Skills,* 23:399–417.

Bibring, E. (1943). The Conception of the Repetition Compulsion. *Psychoanalytic Quarterly,* 12:486–519.

Breuer, J., and Freud, S. (1893–95) Studies on Hysteria. *Standard Edition,* 2. London: Hogarth Press, 1955.

Cartwright, R. D., Bernick, N., Borowitz, G., and Kling, A. (1969). Effect of an Erotic Movie on the Sleep and Dreams of Young Men. *Archives of General Psychiatry,* 20:262–271.

Cobb, S., and Lindemann, E. (1943). Neuropsychiatric Observation after the Coconut Grove Fire. *Annals of Surgery,* 117:814–824.

Cohen, J. (1965). Some Statistical Issues in Psychological Research. In: *Handbook of Clinical Psychology,* ed. B. B. Wolman. New York: McGraw-Hill, pp. 95–121.

Corman, H. H., Escalona, S. K., and Reiser, M. F. (1964). Visual Imagery and Preconscious Thought Processes. *Archives of General Psychiatry,* 10:160–172.

Craig, K. D. (1968). Physiological Arousal as a Function of Imagined, Vicarious, and Direct Stress Experience. *Journal of Abnormal Psychology,* 73:513–520.

Davis, D. R. (1966). *An Introduction to Psychopathology,* 2nd ed. London: Oxford University Press.

Dunn, R. F. (1968). Anxiety and Verbal Concept Learning. *Journal of Experimental Psychology,* 76:286–290.

Fenichel, O. (1945). *The Psychoanalytic Theory of Neurosis.* New York: W. W. Norton.

———— (1954). The Concept of Trauma. In: *Collected Papers,* Vol. 2. New York: W. W. Norton, pp. 49–69.

Freud, S. (1893). On the Psychical Mechanism of Hysterical Phenomena: A Lecture. *Standard Edition,* 3:25–39. London: Hogarth Press, 1962.

———— (1895). Project for a Scientific Psychology. *Standard Edition,* 1:281–387. London: Hogarth Press, 1966.

———— (1917). Introductory Lectures on Psycho-Analysis. *Standard Edition.* 16:243–464. London: Hogarth Press, 1963.

———— (1920). Beyond the Pleasure Principle. *Standard Edition,* 18:7–64. London: Hogarth Press, 1953.

———— (1937). Constructions in Analysis. *Standard Edition,* 23:255–269. London: Hogarth Press, 1964.

Friedman, P., and Linn, L. (1957). Some Psychiatric Notes on the Andrea Doria. *American Journal of Psychiatry,* 114:426–432.

Furst, S. S. (1967). Psychic Trauma: A Survey. In: *Psychic Trauma,* ed. S. S. Furst. New York: Basic Books.

Glover, E. (1929). The "Screening" Function of Traumatic Memories. *International Journal of Psycho-Analysis,* 10: 90–93.

Goldstein, M. J., et al. (1965). Coping Style as a Factor in Psychophysiological Response to a Tension Arousing Film. *Journal of Personality and Social Psychology,* 1:290–302.

Greenacre, P. (1952). *Trauma, Growth and Personality.* New York: W. W. Norton.

———— (1967). The Influence of Infantile Trauma on Genetic Patterns. In: *Psychic Trauma,* ed. S. S. Furst. New York: Basic Books, pp. 108–153.

Grinker, R. R., and Spiegel, J. P. (1945). *Men under Stress.* Philadelphia: Blakiston.

Higbee, K. L. (1969). Fifteen Years of Fear Arousal: Research on Threat Appeals: 1953–1969. *Psychological Bulletin,* 72:426–444.

Holt, R. R. (1964). Imagery . . . the Return of the Ostracized. *American Psychologist,* 19:254–264.

Horowitz, M. J. (1965). Visual Imagery: A Study of Pictorial Cognition Using the Dot-Image Sequence. *Journal of Nervous and Mental Disease,* 141:615–622.

———— (1969). Psychic Trauma: Return of Images after a Stress Film. *Archives of General Psychiatry,* 20:552–559.

———— (1970). *Image Formation and Cognition.* New York: Appleton-Century-Crofts.

————, and Becker, S. S. (1971a). Intrusive Thinking after Stress. *Journal of Nervous and Mental Disease,* 153:32–40.

————, ———— (1971b). Cognitive Response to Stress and Experimental Demand. *Journal of Abnormal Psychology,* 78:86–92.

————, ———— (1971c). Cognitive Response to Stressful Stimuli. *Archives of General Psychiatry,* 25:419–428.

————, ————, and Moskowitz, M. L. (1971). Cognitive Response to Stress: A Replication Study. *Psychological Reports,* 29:763–767.

Janis, I. L., and Leventhal, H. (1968). Human Reactions to Stress. In: *Handbook of Personality Theory and Research,* ed. E. F. Borgatta and W. W. Lambert. Chicago: Rand McNally, pp. 1041–1085.

Johnson, L. C. (1970). A Psychophysiology for All States. *Psychophysiology,* 6:501–516.

Kafka, E., and Reiser, M. (1967). Defensive and Adaptive Ego Processes: Their Relationships to GSR Activity in Free Imagery Experiments. *Archives of General Psychiatry,* 16:34–40.

Kardiner, A. (1959). Traumatic Neuroses of War. In: *American Handbook of Psychiatry,* Vol. 1, ed. S. Arieti. New York: Basic Books, pp. 245–257.

Katkin, E. S. (1965). Relationship between Manifest Anxiety and Two Indices of Autonomic Response to Stress. *Journal of Personality and Social Psychology,* 2:324–333.

Keiser, L. (1968). *The Traumatic Neurosis.* Philadelphia: Lippincott.

Klein, G. (1967). Peremptory Ideation: Structure and Force in Motivated Ideas. In: *Motives and Thought,* ed. R. R. Holt. *Psychological Issues,* Monograph No. 18/19:80–128. New York: International Universities Press.

Lacey, J. I., and Lacey, B. C. (1958). Verification and Extension of the Principle of Autonomic Response Stereotypy. *American Journal of Psychology,* 71:50–73.

Lazarus, R. S. (1964). A Laboratory Approach to the Dynamics of Psychological Stress. *American Psychologist,* 19:400–411.

———— (1966). *Psychological Stress and the Coping Process.* New York: McGraw-Hill.

———— Averill, J. R., and Opton, E. M., Jr. (1969). The Psychology of Coping: Issues of Research and Assessment. Paper given at conference on Coping and Adaptation, Stanford University.

———— and Opton, E. M. (1966). The Use of Motion Picture Films in the Study of Psychological Stress: A Summary of Experimental Studies and Theoretical Formulations. In: *Anxiety and Behavior,* ed. C. Spielberger. New York: Academic Press.

———— Speisman, J. C., Mordkoff, A. M., Davison, L. A. (1962). A Laboratory Study of

Psychological Stress Produced by a Motion Picture Film. *Psychological Monographs,* 76: No. 34 (Whole No. 553).

Lewin, K. (1935). *A Dynamic Theory of Personality.* New York: McGraw-Hill.

Malev, M. (1969). Use of the Repetition Compulsion by the Ego. *Psychoanalytic Quarterly,* 38:52–71.

Mandler, G. (1964). The Interruption of Behavior. In: *Nebraska Symposium on Motivation,* ed. D. Levine. Lincoln: University of Nebraska Press, pp. 163–219.

Miller, A. G. (1968). Psychological Stress as a Determinant of Cognitive Complexity. *Psychological Reports,* 23:635–639.

Miller, G. A., Galanter, E., and Pribram, K. H. (1960). *Plans and the Structure of Behavior.* New York: Holt.

Miller, N. E. (1963). Some Reflections on the Law of Effect Produce a New Alternative to Drive Reduction. In: *Nebraska Symposium on Motivation,* ed. M. R. Jones. Lincoln: University of Nebraska Press, pp. 65–112.

Murphy, W. F. (1961). A Note on Trauma and Loss. *Journal of the American Psychoanalytic Association.* 9:519–532.

Neisser, U. (1967). *Cognitive Psychology.* New York: Appleton-Century-Crofts.

Niederland, W. G. (1968). Clinical Observations on the "Survivor Syndrome." *International Journal of Psychiatry,* 49:313–315.

Nomikos, M. S., Averill, J. R., Lazarus, R. S., and Opton, E. M., Jr. (1968). Surprise versus Suspense in the Production of Stress Reaction. *Journal of Personality and Social Psychology,* 8:204–208.

Nunnally, J. (1967). *Psychometric Theory.* New York: McGraw-Hill.

Piaget, J. (1937) *The Construction of Reality in the Child.* New York: Basic Books, 1954.

Pribram, K. H. (1971). *The Language of the Brain.* Englewood Cliffs, N.J.: Prentice-Hall.

Rangell, L. (1967). The Metapsychology of Psychic Trauma. In: *Psychic Trauma,* ed. S. S. Furst. New York: Basic Books.

Rapaport, D., and Gill, M. (1959). The Points of View and Assumptions of Metapsychology. *International Journal of Psycho-Analysis,* 40:153–162.

Reider, N. (1960). Percept as a Screen: Economic and Structural Aspects. *Journal of the American Psychoanalytic Association,* 8:82–99.

Rosenthal, R., and Rosnow, R. L., eds. (1969). *Artifact in Behavioral Research.* New York: Academic Press.

Sachs, O. (1967). Distinctions between Fantasy and Reality Elements in Memory and Reconstruction. *International Journal of Psycho-Analysis* 48:416–423.

Schur, M. (1966). *The Id and the Regulatory Principles of Mental Functioning.* New York: International Universities Press.

Shapiro, D. (1965). *Neurotic Styles.* New York: Basic Books.

Singer, J. S. (1966). *Daydreaming.* New York: Random House.

Speisman, J. C., Davison, L., Lazarus, R. S., and Mordkoff, A. M. (1964). Experimental Analysis of a Film Used as a Threatening Stimulus. *Journal of Consulting Psychology,* 28:23–33.

Stern, M. M. (1961). Blank Hallucinations: Remarks about Trauma and Perceptual Disturbances. *International Journal of Psycho-Analysis,* 42:205–215.

Terris, W., and Rahhal, D. (1969). Generalized Resistance to the Effects of Psychological Stressors. *Journal of Personality and Social Psychology,* 13:93–97.

DRIVE STIMULATION AND PSYCHOPATHOLOGY:
On the Conditions Under Which Drive-Related External Events Evoke Pathological Reactions [1]

Lloyd H. Silverman, Ph.D.

INTRODUCTION

As psychoanalytic thinking has evolved through the years, there has developed an increasing concern with the role of the environment as a co-determiner of personality and behavior, a trend perhaps best exemplified in the writings of Erikson. However, unlike those from the so-called "culturalist" and "interpersonalist" schools, psychoanalysts like Erikson have taken pains to make it clear that a concern with environmental considerations should not mean a neglect or de-emphasis of biological and intrapsychic processes. Rather, according to what one can consider the contemporary psychoanalytic position, both biological and environmental variables are important in terms of their acting on and being mediated by intrapsychic processes.

This paper will concern itself with a particular class of environmental-intrapsychic interactions: those in which an external event evokes a psychopathological reaction. Under this heading I include both those events that precipitate the initial emergence of pathological expression and those that stimulate the reappearance or intensification of such expressions after they have first appeared.

Psychoanalytic theory views psychopathology as involving a response to and an expression of unconscious conflict. Our current understanding is that such pathology appears when an individual experiences a libidinal or aggressive drive as threatening. Unable to utilize a more expressive form of regulatory control, he attempts to ward off the drive by invoking one or more defensive operations. Sometimes these defenses are successful, and have no, or minimal, maladaptive consequences. On other occasions, they are unsuccessful in that drive derivatives or anxiety appear, or the more complex phenomena emerge that we call symptoms, the latter being viewed as compromise formations, expressing

[1] I wish to thank Drs. William I. Grossman, Tupper F. Pettit, and Doris K. Silverman for their criticisms and suggestions.

simultaneously the demands of the drive, defensive and adaptive needs of the individual, and sometimes a need for punishment as well.[2]

What then is the role of the environment in the appearance of psychopathology? Here one must differentiate, as Freud (1912) did, between *predisposing* and *precipitating* events; this paper is limited to the second; the first is vastly more complex and difficult. With respect to precipitating events, it is consonant with psychoanalytic thinking (see Fenichel, 1945, pp. 454–457) to view external events as capable of eliciting a psychopathological reaction in any of three ways: (1) by stimulating a threatening drive; (2) by stimulating the fear that the person associates with a threatening drive (castration, abandonment, or loss of love); (3) by affecting a defense that has until then been used adaptively, leading either to the maladaptive use of the same defense or to "compelling" the use of a new, less adaptively employed defense. In any of these circumstances, psychopathology can appear or become intensified. In the current paper, I shall deal only with the first of these types of precipitating events, this being, I believe, the most common. On the basis of both experimental laboratory data and clinical illustrations, I shall attempt to specify the conditions under which drive-related events, or what I shall call "drive stimuli," evoke psychopathology.

LABORATORY EXPERIMENTS UTILIZING SUBLIMINAL DRIVE STIMULI

Let me begin by calling attention to a series of experiments in which a particular experimental technique, developed in our laboratory, has been utilized for studying the effects of drive stimulation on psychopathology. The technique consists of the tachistoscopic presentation of drive-related pictorial and verbal stimuli to subjects at a subliminal level, and observing their effects on different forms of psychopathology. In each of 18 studies concluded to date, this manipulation, when contrasted with the subliminal presentation of neutral (i.e., non-drive-related) stimuli, has proven capable of evoking pathological manifestations. The changes that have taken place in the subjects who have participated in these studies have typically been small and have lasted for only a brief duration; yet they have been sufficiently clear and measurable to constitute a large body of experimental evidence, demonstrating the link between drive stimulation and psychopathology. Before discussing the relevance of these investigations for the topic under consideration, let me describe the experimental procedure that has been employed and review the results obtained.[3]

[2] For a much fuller account of the contemporary psychoanalytic position, see Rangell (1963). It is to be noted that while there is a clear consensus among psychoanalytic clinicians on the applicability of the above model for understanding neurotic pathology, its applicability to psychotic phenomena is controversial (see Arlow and Brenner, 1964, Chap. 10).

[3] Fuller descriptions of the procedures and results can be found in the following original reports: L. H. Silverman and D. K. Silverman (1964); L. H. Silverman (1965a, 1966); L. H. Silverman and Goldweber (1966); L. H. Silverman and S. E. Silverman (1967); L. H. Silverman and Spiro (1967a, 1968); Buchholz (1968); Antell (1969); Lomangino (1969); L. H. Silverman, Spiro, Weisberg, and Candell (1969); S. E. Silverman (1969); Spiro

In each of the experiments that have been carried out, subjects were seen individually for at least two sessions, one for a drive condition and one for a control. In each session, after rapport was established, a baseline measure of the subject's propensity for the pathology under study was obtained by administering one or more psychological procedures, as these might be given in a clinical situation in which a psychodiagnostic assessment was being made. These procedures have included the Rorschach, Thematic Apperception Test (TAT), word association test, story recall test, mood adjective check list, etc. Each subject was then asked to look through the eyepiece of the tachistoscope next to which he was sitting, and was told he would be shown a few flashes of light that he was to describe. Either the stimulus with drive-related content or the one with relatively neutral content was then exposed, each exposure lasting for four milliseconds, a period during which conscious recognition of any content of the stimulus is not possible. After these exposures, there followed a "critical" series of the same procedures that were given in the baseline series, allowing for a determination of how the individual had been affected by the particular subliminal stimulus that had been exposed.[4]

The procedure for the other session was identical with that just described, except that a different stimulus was exposed before the critical series. Subjects exposed to the stimulus with drive-related content in the first session were shown a neutral stimulus in the later session, and vice versa. In each session, an assistant inserted the slide with the stimulus on it into the tachistoscope before the experimenter entered the room. Thus, the experimenter who worked the tachistoscope and administered the psychological procedure never knew which stimulus was being exposed. Since the subject was also unaware of the nature of the stimulus (because it was subliminal), the procedure can be described as "double blind," in the same sense as are drug studies in which neither the patient nor the person administering the capsule knows whether a drug or a placebo has been ingested. A final precaution taken to rule out the possibility that bias might influence the results was that the material obtained during the psychological procedures was evaluated "blind" by other psychologists.

The studies that were carried out with this procedure were designed to investigate specific relationships between particular drives (assumed to be already active in the individual and simply "triggered" by the drive stimuli) and particular pathological expressions. These relationships can be grouped under three

---

and Silverman (1969); Ellman (1970); Rutstein (1970); L. H. Silverman and Candell (1970); L. H. Silverman, Klinger, Lustbader, and Farrell (in press); L. H. Silverman, Candell, Pettit, and Blum (1971).

[4] The following are examples of the drive and neutral stimuli that have been utilized: When the effects of triggering the aggressive drive have been studied, such pictures have been used as a tiger attacking a monkey vs. two playful beagles and a snarling man with a knife in his upraised hand vs. a man waving pleasantly. Also, such verbal messages have been employed as *"destroy mother"* vs. *"men talking"* and *"cannibal eats person"* vs. *"friend greets man."* When the effects of stimulating different libidinal drives have been investigated, stimuli have included pictures of a nude woman vs. a clothed man; a nude man in a homosexually compromising position vs. a dressed man reading a newspaper; a dog defecating vs. a butterfly flying, etc.

headings: first, experiments testing dynamic propositions that enjoy a high degree of consensus among psychoanalytic clinicians, but have not previously been supported by experimental research. Included here was an experiment with two groups of stutterers (L. H. Silverman, Klinger, Lustbader, and Farrell, in press), in which a stimulus designed to trigger anal derivatives intensified their speech disturbance to a statistically significant extent.[5] Also there are two investigations (Rutstein, 1970; L. H. Silverman, Candell, Pettit, and Blum, 1971) in which psychiatric inpatients, with depression as one of their symptoms, reported an intensification of depressive feelings and experiences after the subliminal exposure of stimuli with aggressive content.

A second group of studies have provided data relevant to an ongoing controversy within the psychoanalytic community on the role of conflict over drive in such ego pathology in schizophrenics as regressive thinking and behavior. Twelve experiments have been carried out—ten in our laboratory (summarized in L. H. Silverman, 1971)—and two in independent replications elsewhere (Buchholz, 1968; Lomangino, 1969), in which a great deal of evidence has been adduced that this kind of pathology in schizophrenics emerges in response to the eliciting of aggressive drive derivatives. As I discuss in detail elsewhere (L. H. Silverman, 1970) these findings are consonant with one of the two conflicting positions that are being debated by psychoanalytic clinicians as to how this type of pathology should be understood.[6]

In a final group of experiments, psychopathology has been studied in "normal" populations—i.e., in non-psychiatric groups—for whom clinical psychoanalytic data have been largely lacking. Several studies come under this heading: (1) experiments demonstrating that regressive ego pathology (of the kind discussed above in the studies of schizophrenics), when appearing in certain kinds of non-schizophrenics in the milder form that they often take, are also in response to the stirring of aggressive drive derivatives (L. H. Silverman, 1965a; L. H. Silverman and Goldweber, 1966); (2) an investigation of college students, in which it was found that the triggering of both aggressive and libidinal drive derivatives interfered with "creative thinking" on a task requiring the composing of metaphors (Antell, 1969); (3) a study of college women, in which the stirring of ideas related to menstruation led to psychological changes, involving mood changes and attitudes toward men, which psychoanalytic clinicians have described as part

---

[5] In all subsequent reports of experimental findings in this paper, "statistical significance" is to be understood, although I shall omit explicit reference to it.

[6] In several of these experiments (L. H. Silverman et al., 1969; L. H. Silverman and Candell, 1970; L. H. Silverman, Candell, et al., 1971) a second major finding bearing on the motivation of schizophrenics has emerged. For each of four groups of patients with this diagnosis, a stimulus designed to trigger fantasies of symbiotic union with mother—the object toward whom the schizophrenics' aggression presumably is primarily directed—has *reduced* the same kind of ego pathology that the aggressive stimuli have intensified, a finding that has led to a formulation of the function and meaning served by this kind of pathology (L. H. Silverman, 1970). This "symbiosis stimulus" is different in some crucial respects from the drive stimuli that are dealt with in this paper, but the complexities involved necessitate the postponement for a future publication of consideration of this stimulus in relation to the subject matter under discussion.

of the female castration complex (Ellman, 1970); (4) a study of college men, indicating that for a group of them who were heterosexually blocked, the stimulation of heterosexual drive derivatives led to defensive psychological changes of the kind psychoanalytic clinicians have described as characterizing male homosexuals (L. H. Silverman and D. K. Silverman, 1964).

In the original reports of each of the investigations reviewed above, the relationship between the findings and relevant psychoanalytic formulations has been detailed; and elsewhere (L. H. Silverman, 1967, 1970) I have discussed more generally the role that experiments such as these can play in the testing, refining, and expanding of psychoanalytic dynamic propositions. In the current paper, I shall limit myself to the bearing these results have on the goal outlined earlier: the specification of the conditions under which drive stimuli evoke psycho-pathology. In order to proceed with such a discussion, I must first call attention to one additional finding from several of the studies cited. In six of the experiments (L. H. Silverman and Goldweber, 1966; L. H. Silverman and Spiro, 1968; Lomangino, 1969; Rutstein, 1970; L. H. Silverman and Candell, 1970; L. H. Silverman, Klinger, et. al., in press) the positive results obtained seemed dependent on *subliminal* drive stimuli as the decisive factor. For, in each of these, there was a third condition in which the same drive stimulus was *presented supraliminally,* with subjects aware of its drive content, and in none of these was any intensification of pathology evidenced.

REAL-LIFE ANALOGUES TO LABORATORY SUBLIMINAL MANIPULATIONS

Before discussing the implications of these findings, as well as additional data, let me first describe the kinds of real-life situations that evoke psychopathology and are analogous to the condition of subliminal drive stimulation we have created in the laboratory. I am referring here to situations in which *the drive relevance of the impinging stimulus is hidden,* for any of several reasons, only one of which is that the stimulus itself registers without awareness. Let me begin with a real-life example of subliminal perception and then turn to two other kinds of situations—ones with which I believe clinicians are more familiar—in whicn drive relevance is hidden even though the stimulus is *not* subliminal.

The patient was a 25-year-old man who had been in psychoanalytic treatment for several years. His wife had recently become pregnant, an event about which both of them were consciously ambivalent; so much so that they were considering abortion. The material emerging in treatment at the time centered on the patient's view of the fetus as an unwanted rival for his wife's affection and attention, a feeling that related rather clearly to the anger and jealousy that beset him when, at age nine, he learned that his mother was pregnant with his brother, his only sibling. The abortion under contemplation had, as an important unconscious meaning, the venting of death wishes directed most immediately toward his prospective child, but more basically toward his sibling; and the symptom this conflict gave rise to was an anxious obsessive preoccupation with his wife's situation. It was during a period of treatment when the meaning of all this had been interpreted to him, but not yet worked through, that the following event took place. The analysand reported at the beginning of one session something "interesting" that had happened during the day. He was walking in the street feeling at ease when suddenly he became anxiously preoccupied. While so beset, he looked up and noted a sign on a building that he was passing that read "floor scraping." He experienced a sudden insight, and with that the anxiety symptom remitted. The understanding that he reported was that "floor scraping" symbolized the contemplated abortion and thus stirred up in him his angry and guilty feelings toward his surrogate and real sibling.

It would hardly be possible to estimate how frequently subliminal stimuli elicit psychopathology in real life, as seemed to happen in the above example. In the instance reported, the linking of his anxious preoccupation with the stimulus depended on the unusual combination of the man's having a "feel" for symbols, knowing about the subliminal concept, and then "recovering" the stimulus after the symptom appeared. It seems reasonable to suppose, however, that at least some of those instances in which there is the appearance or intensification of pathology *without* apparent external stimulation are attributable to the impingement of a subliminal drive stimulus.[7]

We now can turn to the more familiar kinds of analogue to the subliminal laboratory situation, in which a drive stimulus impinges on a person well above threshold, but its drive relevance is hidden. First, there are those situations in which there is a symbolic or otherwise disguised associative link between the drive that is triggered and the situation in which the pathology emerges. As one example, consider a 30-year-old male analysand who regularly reported bodily discomfort, restlessness, and somnolence while watching movies and plays. As might be expected, his analysis revealed an intensely strong and much conflicted voyeuristic drive and many derivatives of primal-scene memories. This drive and the related memories were understood as becoming stimulated whenever he found himself in the role of the "viewer." The hypothesis that these events required the drive relevance of the stimuli to be out of his awareness in order for them to be pathogenic was rather interestingly supported in this case. The analysand reported that the most notable exception to the appearance of these

---

[7] It should be apparent from the example cited above that I have implicitly defined "subliminality" much more loosely for real-life analogues than for laboratory experiments. For the former, it simply refers to the absence of evidence that the individual is aware of the impinging stimulus before its effect is felt; for the latter it refers, in addition, to the subject's inability to recognize content aspects of a stimulus, even when his attention is directed to the attainment of such recognition. Moreover, in our laboratory experiments, for the great majority of subjects, not only was there no recognition, but they were unable to differentiate the experimental stimuli from the control in a "discrimination task" administered after the experimental procedure proper. For a discussion of how these experimental results support the concept of subliminal registration, more strictly defined, see L. H. Silverman and Spiro (1967b), and L. H. Silverman (1968).

symptoms was when the movie or play had an explicitly sexual theme; at such times, he observed, he was symptom-free.

In the same category, let me now offer another example. In the illustration above, the associative link resided in the unconscious meaning of the *activity* the individual was engaged in (viewing a performance); in this example the link resided in the unconscious meaning of the *content of the stimulus*. A 24-year-old unmarried woman in analysis, who felt exceedingly frustrated over the fact that she was childless, received a birth announcement from an old friend toward whom she had always felt rivalry. She reacted to the announcement with an intensified longing for a child of her own and jealous feelings toward her rival, although not symptomatically. Some time later, however, while reading a book during a train ride, she suddenly, and at the time inexplicably, felt depersonalized. This was a symptom from which she had suffered in the past but which, at that point in analysis, no longer plagued her. She reported that the symptom came on when she began to read a particular article, but she could see no relationship between the article itself and her conflicts and symptom. Suddenly, in the session, she remembered with a laugh that the name of the author of the article was "Rothschild," to which she instantly associated the married name—Roth— of the friend who had sent her the birth announcement a few weeks before. She felt convinced that she was unwittingly reminded of "the child of Roth" and that it was the unconscious hostility this "silently" aroused that brought back her symptom. In this case, as in the previous one, it was possible to contrast her reaction to the situation in which the drive relevance of the stimulus was hidden to that of a related situation in which she was aware of this relevance. I am referring here to the woman's initial response when she received the birth announcement from her friend and consciously experienced feelings of jealousy and longing, but no symptoms.

The other category of pathology-evoking situations in which the stimulus is supraliminal but its drive relevance is hidden is one that Freud (1912) characterized as "the most easily discoverable . . . cause of an onset of neurosis . . . described in general terms as *frustration*." Let us note the way Freud traced a frustrating situation as leading to the emergence of pathology.

[A person is] healthy so long as his need for love [is] satisfied by a real object in the external world; he becomes neurotic as soon as this object is withdrawn from him without a substitute taking its place . . . the immediate effect of the frustration lies in its bringing into play the dispositional factors which have hitherto been inoperative. . . . The libido . . . may follow the path of regression along infantile lines and strive after aims that correspond with them. If these strivings, which are incompatible with the subject's present-day individuality, acquire enough intensity, a conflict must result between them and the other portion of his personality, which has maintained its relation to reality. This conflict is resolved by the formation of symptoms, and is followed by the onset of manifest illness (pp. 231–233).

The type of situation Freud described qualifies under the current heading, since the person, while aware that the situation is frustrating his genital impulses, is not aware that it is serving as a stimulus for pregenital drives. That is, the reactive pregenital "pull" of the situation remains hidden. If one updates Freud's account, so that it is in keeping with the dual instinct theory and contemporary understanding of the relationship between frustration and aggression, a parallel train of events could be described in which aggressive as well as pregenital libidinal drives are silently elicited by the loss of a love object, and pathology results. Most prominent here are the oft-described situations in which neurotic or psychotic depressions are evoked by a death, a rebuff, or a disappointment. Our usual understanding of these situations is that aggression had been stimulated by the "loss" and then turned against the self; typically, the situation in which this takes place is one in which the aggression-stimulating implications of the event are hidden from the person's awareness.[8]

I have thus described the following three types of real-life situations in which pathology is evoked by a drive stimulus, the drive relevance of which is hidden: (1) where the stimulus is subliminal; (2) where the stimulus is supraliminal, its link to drive being symbolic or otherwise disguised; (3) where the stimulus is supraliminal with it frustrating one drive, and thereby reactively and silently arousing another. For some of the case illustrations I was also able to describe parallel events in which the drive relevance of the stimulus was not hidden, and in these instances there was no pathological outcome. Here, then, we have analogues to the experimental results reported earlier, in which subliminally presented drive stimuli intensified psychopathology, but the supraliminal presentation of the same stimuli with their drive relevance visible did *not* have this effect. It must now be pointed out, however, that, although in the *great majority* of situations in which a drive stimulus elicits pathology, the drive relevance of the stimulus is hidden (and some evidence that this kind of situation is predominant will be presented shortly), this is *not* a necessary condition for the emergence of pathology. Instances can be cited from both laboratory experiments and real life, in which the drive relevance of the stimulus was visible, yet a pathological outcome still ensued. An examination of the conditions prevailing in these instances will now be undertaken, since the contrast between them and the conditions of the non-pathogenic experimental and real-life illus-

[8] In 1917, Freud pointed out that sometimes it is not the loss of an object that constitutes the frustrating event precipitating a pathological reaction, but a "narcissistic frustration." In discussing the "wolf-man" he wrote: "He broke down after an organic affection to the genitals had revived his fear of castration, shattered his narcissism, and compelled him to abandon his hope of being personally favored by destiny" (p. 118). In terms of the categories that have been suggested here, to the extent that the pathology that emerged could be attributed to an aggressive drive that was reactively mobilized by the frustration, I would include it in the above category. To the extent that the narcissistic "injury" directly activated castration fears, it would no longer be classified under the "stimulation of drive" heading, but would be considered instead in the category of "stimulation of fears" referred to earlier. It is apparent from Freud's example that the same external event can bring on pathology for more than one reason.

trations already offered will enable us to specify one of the necessary conditions for the emergence of pathology.

LABORATORY EXPERIMENTS UTILIZING
SUPRALIMINAL DRIVE STIMULI

I shall begin with a discussion of the laboratory data since, not surprisingly, this will allow us to see more clearly just what the differences between the two situations are. Consider first the supraliminal condition for the six experiments cited earlier (L. H. Silverman and Goldweber, 1966; L. H. Silverman and Spiro, 1968; Lomangino, 1969; L. H. Silverman and Candell, 1970; Rutstein, 1970; L. H. Silverman, Klinger, et. al., in press) in which *no* intensification of pathology followed the exposure of the drive stimulus. The instructions in each of these experiments was for the subject simply to "look at" the stimulus. Little or no verbalization was required; the subject was generally asked simply to say "yes" if he saw a picture or "no" if he did not, without any demand for a further cognitive response.

Contrast four experiments—one carried out in our laboratory and three elsewhere—in which a supraliminal presentation of a drive stimulus *did* intensify pathology; in each of these, *a cognitive demand was made of the subject while he was confronting the stimulus.* One of these experiments (L. H. Silverman and Spiro, 1968) was mentioned in the earlier listing since there was a cognitively "non-demanding" supraliminal condition that had no pathological effect. But we used another condition in this experiment, in which the same drive stimulus was presented supraliminally, but this time the subject was instructed, while viewing it, "to describe it [the picture] as fully as you can." Under this condition, pathological reactions in the schizophrenics intensified significantly, just as they had in the subliminal drive condition. Similarly, in a study by Sarnoff (1959), the supraliminal presentation of drive-related stimuli (pictures of nude women) to college males was accompanied by the instruction that the subject was to write a detailed account of his esthetic judgment of each picture. Here, the experimental manipulation was found to intensify the form of psychopathology under study ("fears of death") in those who were judged, a priori, to be most vulnerable to it ("high castration anxiety Ss"). Finally, in two other experiments mentioned earlier (Buchholz, 1968; Ellman, 1970), in which a subliminal condition intensified pathology, there was also a supraliminal condition that had the same effect. In both of these, this latter condition consisted of the reading of a drive-related passage, with the subject instructed to commit to memory the material that he heard, this too qualifying as cognitively demanding instructions.

Why should there be such a consistent difference in outcome between those studies in which the supraliminal presentation of drive stimuli was accompanied by a cognitive demand and those in which no such demand was made? In order to help make this determination, I first put myself through the two kinds of procedures and then did the same with several psychiatric patients and non-patients, encouraging each to report, immediately afterward, his experiences.

The differences I experienced were also reported by a number of the others: in contrast to the cognitively demanding instructions, the non-demanding instructions made for a considerably more relaxed atmosphere and provided "unfilled" time. Both these factors encouraged frequent fantasy experiences, such as seldom, if at all, occurred after the other instructions. These fantasy experiences, while sometimes more elaborate, usually took the form of repeatedly completing the action the figure in the picture was engaged in. Thus, for a picture depicting a roaring lion charging, there were reports of the lion completing his attack; and for a picture showing one person attacking another with a knife, the subject experienced a "follow-through" of the attack. This kind of reaction is particularly understandable when one considers that the supraliminal condition both in the original experiments and in the procedures here described called for many exposures of the same stimulus, with each exposure lasting for ten seconds, a rather lengthy period of time to gaze at a picture completely passively, i.e., without any fantasy activity.

In keeping with the contemporary psychoanalytic understanding of psychopathology, the differential effect that the two kinds of supraliminal conditions had on intensifying pathology in the experiments cited earlier can be explained as follows. Whereas under both conditions, drive derivatives were stirred, under the cognitively demanding conditions, for the reasons mentioned above, there was no invitation for, or sanctioning of, drive gratification. Consequently, it became more likely that the drive stirrings would be reacted to with intensified defensive efforts and thus new pathological manifestations. Under the non-demanding conditions, on the other hand, there was an implicit sanction for drive gratification via fantasy atcivity. This made it unnecessary to invoke fresh defensive efforts, and therefore no increased expressions of pathology resulted.[9]

The results of one other experiment should be discussed in this context— a study by Sarnoff (1960) in which the experimental condition provided much greater sanction of drive expression than was the case under the non-demanding supraliminal conditions that have been described. Sarnoff was investigating the character trait of cynicism "as a reaction formation against feelings of affection." In order to stir up these feelings, he had subjects view a version of the William Saroyan play *Hello Out There*, in which there was "a tender portrayal of spontaneous and unequivocal trust, warmth, and affection." "Before" and "after" measures of cynicism were obtained for both the experimental subjects and a control group, with the time interval between test and retest the same for both groups. Sarnoff reported a number of interesting results, mainly involving interactions between the experimental effect and pre-experimental measures that had been obtained on the degree to which each subject *generally* tended to use reaction formation as a defense against affectionate feelings. But the result that

[9] The above explanation is quite different from one offered earlier (L. H. Silverman and Spiro, 1968), which was based on considerably less data. It would further follow from the current explanation that, for those subjects who do not avail themselves of the opportunity to fantasize under supraliminal non-demanding conditions, there will be just as much intensification of pathology as under cognitively demanding conditions. I plan to test this hypothesis in a future experiment.

interests us here was not predicted nor discussed: the experimental subjects as a total group responded to the Saroyan play by feeling *less* cynical. In other words, the experimental manipulation here did more than it did under the supraliminal, cognitively non-demanding condition of the experiments already cited. In the Sarnoff experiment, the much greater opportunity for socially approved fantasy gratification apparently not only made it unnecessary for subjects to invoke defenses against the libidinal drive derivatives that the manipulation stirred up, but also allowed for expression of derivatives that had been defended against prior to the subjects' participation in the experiment. Thus, there was *less* defensiveness against affectionate feelings than was usually the case, and consequently less cynicism.[10]

LABORATORY EXPERIMENTS UTILIZING AGGRESSIVE PROVOCATIONS

The experimental results presented thus far are consistent with the proposition that a drive-related stimulus will *not* elicit psychopathology if the conditions under which it is introduced are experienced by the individual as sanctioning some form of drive gratification. On the other hand, pathology *will* be evoked if such sanction is absent (assuming the presence of the other necessary conditions, a matter I shall come to presently). Thus, the subliminal manipulations in which subjects were unaware of the drive stimulus and thus could hardly have experienced sanction for drive expression, and the cognitively demanding supraliminal manipulations both led to the latter outcome, whereas the non-demanding supraliminal manipulations led to the former. One other group of published studies has to do with attempts to elicit psychopathology experimentally, although in a different way from that described, and their results are also in keeping with this proposition.

In these experiments, all of which have investigated the effects of stimulating the aggressive drive, gross behavioral manipulations have been employed, rather than the presentation of material with drive-related contents. More specifically, the intervention consisted of insulting and otherwise provoking subjects, with measures taken before and after of different aspects of ego functioning. In two of these studies, subjects were given varying instructions in terms of whether they sanctioned, as a form of drive gratification, expressions of anger toward the provoker, the dependent variable being the amount of cognitive impairment that followed each condition. Thus, in an experiment by Worchel (1957), college students were divided into several groups, three of which were encouraged after the provocation to express their angry feelings prior to the crucial cognitive assessment, while the other two groups were given no such encouragement. Cognitive impairment was greater for each of the latter groups

---

[10] I have observed clinical instances in which symptoms diminish after the viewing of a movie or play. Kris' (1952) discussion of the esthetic illusion is most relevant here (particularly pp. 43–46).

than for each of the former. The other study, reported by Horwitz (1963), yielded similar results. Here, *gradations of sanction* were compared, with one group encouraged to express hostile feelings and actions toward the provoker; the second group was encouraged only to express hostile feelings; a third group was given no opportunity for expression of either hostile feelings or actions, but no attempt was made to discourage their having hostile thoughts; and for the fourth group, influence was brought to bear on the subjects so that hostile thoughts were *discouraged*. Group four displayed the most impairment, group three the next most, group two next to the least impairment, and group one the least. Thus there was a perfect correspondence between the amount of aggressive expression sanctioned and the ability to stave off cognitive impairment.

At this point, a clarification is in order. The discussion thus far may have made it sound as if the question of whether an individual will respond to drive stimulation with drive expression depends *only* on the objective conditions that prevail. Everyday observation clearly contradicts such an assumption and makes it apparent that what serves as permission for one individual may not do so for another. Studies now will be cited that demonstrate that, when different people are confronted with a drive stimulus under identical conditions, with some blocking drive gratification while others feel free to gratify the drive, it is the former for whom there is an emergence of pathological responses. In one of these (Feldstein and Jaffe, 1962, with additional data reported in L. H. Silverman, 1965b), verbalizations of college students were taped during a pre-experimental interview, and then again after an intervention in which subjects were provoked by being insulted and demeaned. The verbal productions were assessed for various kinds of impairments of thinking and speech, and at the end of the experiment, subjects were asked to describe what they had experienced in response to the provocations. For those who reported feeling angry, there was no indication of increased ego impairment from the first to the second interview, but for the subjects who did not report anger there was a significant increase in such impairment. A second study of this sort was carried out by Rosenwald (1961), who utilized high school students as subjects. He first assessed them for their need to avoid expressions of hostility by giving them a projective technique in which each subject was asked to complete a series of stories in which there was an aggressive provocation of the main character. The subjects were then divided into two groups; those who felt free to give aggressive responses to the provocations, and those who did not. Both groups were given anagrams to solve before and after an "insult manipulation," and only for the latter (blocked) group was there a significant impairment in cognitive ability after the manipulation.

Finally, mention should be made of results from two of the studies that were cited earlier as having been carried out in our laboratory, in which there was a supraliminal, cognitively non-demanding condition (L. H. Silverman and Goldweber, 1967; L. H. Silverman and Spiro, 1968). As already has been stated, for the groups as a whole, there was *no* increase in pathological expressions; nevertheless, for a small subgroup of subjects in each study who gave evidence of *blocking awareness* of the supraliminal drive stimuli, there *was* an increase in pathology. Since someone who does not even allow himself to perceive accurately a drive stimulus that most people have no difficulty perceiving can hardly be expected in such a situation to allow himself drive gratification, these results can be viewed as providing further evidence for the proposition under consideration.

REAL-LIFE ANALOGUES TO LABORATORY PROVOCATIONS

How do clinical data fit in with the experimental results just presented? First, with respect to the expression of aggression that usually takes place when an individual is attacked and the prophylactic function the expression serves, Hartmann, Kris, and Loewenstein (1949), on the basis of their clinical observations, drew a very similar conclusion to that drawn from the experimental results. They wrote: "Objective danger is one situation that allows for and invites discharge of aggression . . . and . . . hence . . . is less likely to lead to pathological responses" (p. 23).

Second, it has been clinically observed that the permission for gratifying aggressive impulses that one usually experiences upon being attacked, and the prophylactic effect this has, can be negated by external prohibitions against gratification, as it was for Horwitz's (1963) experimental group, which showed the most pathology after being discouraged from having angry thoughts. Bettelheim (1960) presented an extreme example in real life in his description of concentration camp prisoners. He graphically described how the reign of terror carried out by the Nazi captors so intimidated the prisoners that all forms of aggressive expression against their tormentors were blocked, and this led to widespread pathological reactions, including paranoid projections, displacement of aggression against weaker prisoners, and personality disintegration.

Finally, there are instances in which, even in the absence of external prohibitions, a particular individual does not experience the permission for aggressive expression that most people would when faced with the same provocation, and a pathological response follows. The usual psychoanalytic understanding of such instances is that the objectively warranted gratification (and this may be only verbal aggression, an affective experience of anger, or even an aggressive fantasy) is disallowed because of the unconscious meaning it has for the person in that particular situation. (This is what I would assume prevented the inhibited subgroups of subjects in the studies of Feldstein and Jaffe [1962] and Rosenwald [1960] from expressing aggression, since these subgroups then manifested cognitive impairment.) A recent clinical example of this kind occurred in the analysis of a 35-year-old male, who had significant problems stemming from unconscious death wishes toward his father. In the face of aggressive provocations, he *was* usually able to react with appropriate anger and would, at these times, show no intensification of symptoms. However, on one occasion he reacted, instead, symptomatically. Analysis of the situation revealed that the particular person involved had characteristics that allowed the patient to identify him unconsciously with his father and to equate any aggressive expression toward him with patricide.

It has been my clinical impression, however, that it is relatively rare for pathology to be evoked by the kinds of real-life situations described above, in which the drive relevance of the stimulus is visible. Much more often, it has seemed to me, the drive relevance has been hidden, as it was in the clinical illustrations cited earlier. In order to check this impression, a co-worker (Elizabeth A. Blum) and I systematically examined the case material appearing in the first book of published psychoanalytic case reports (Breuer and Freud, 1893–95). Twenty instances could be found in which we agreed that a drive-related external event could be inferred as the stimulus for a pathological reaction, and in 15 of these the drive relevance of the stimulus could clearly be classified as "hidden." [11]

THEORETICAL FORMULATION

The experimental and clinical data presented thus far support the following summarizing formulation: someone who is in conflict over a particular drive will react to an external stimulus that stirs that drive by attempting to block its expression in any of the following situations: (1) when the drive relevance of the stimulus is hidden, because (a) it is subliminal; (b) it is supraliminal with its link to drive symbolic or otherwise disguised; or (c) it is supraliminal with it frustrating one drive, thus reactively and silently arousing another; (2) when the external circumstances in which the stimulation takes place explicitly or implicitly prohibit the appropriate expression; (3) when, even in the absence of conditions 1 and 2, the particular characteristics of the situation have an unconscious meaning for the individual that makes even a warranted expression taboo. In any of these situations, if particular defenses are then employed, the outcome will be a pathological one.[12]

The specification "if particular defenses are then employed" is necessary, since it is a generally accepted assumption among contemporary psychoanalytic

[11] These instances can be found on the following pages: 37, 40, 50, 51, 52, 55, 59, 112 (footnote), 114, 119, 146, 151, 155, 172, 213. In some of the material, one can note a parallel event cited that was similar to those described in the illustrations given earlier, in which the drive stimulus was visible and no pathological reaction followed. For example: "A girl of seventeen had her first hysterical attack . . . when a cat jumped on her shoulder in the dark . . . a few days before, a young man had attacked her on the same dark staircase" (p. 213). Here we can see, side by side, an instance where the drive relevance of the stimulus was hidden and an instance where it was visible, with the pathological reaction occurring only in the former case.

[12] It is interesting to compare the above formulation with the early psychoanalytic view of the way in which external events evoke psychopathology. In their classic *Studies on Hysteria*, Breuer and Freud (1893–1895) described, as pathogenic events, emotion-arousing traumas that had not been sufficiently abreacted. This insufficient abreaction was seen as occurring under two sets of conditions: "In the first group [are] those cases in which the patients have not reacted to a psychical trauma because the nature of the trauma excluded a reaction as in the case of the apparently irreparable loss of a loved person; or because social circumstances made reaction impossible; or because it was a question of things which the patient wished to forget. . . . The second group of conditions are determined not by the content of the [experience] but by the

clinicians that some defenses have no pathological consequences. Moreover, it should be noted that by putting the burden of the outcome on the *kind of defense* employed, rather than on the warding off of gratification per se, the formulation allows one to account for those relatively rare instances in which pathological reactions are accompanied by drive expression. This is understandable if one remembers that drive expression does not *always* mean the absence or relaxation of defensive efforts, but at times occurs *despite* these efforts, thus reflecting defensive failure. Such instances need not embarrass our formulation, so long as one can maintain that the persons in whom this phenomenon occurs have defensive resources that are less adequate than usual. In my experience, these instances have been limited to psychotics and children, two groups for whom the above claim would be warranted. With regard to psychotics, I have observed instances in which expressions of anger or even rage were accompanied by disturbed and even delusional thinking or gross disturbances in other ego functions.[13] Similarly, with young children one also can observe drive gratification

---

psychical states in which the patient received the experience in question. . . . They originated during the prevalence of severely paralyzing affects such as fright or during positively abnormal states such as the semi-hypnotic twilight state of day-dreaming, autohypnoses and so on. In such cases it is the nature of the state that makes a reaction to the event impossible" (pp. 10–11).

In the current formulation, pathogenic events are those that stimulate drive derivatives of any kind, not only those that would qualify as emotion-arousing; and correspondingly, it is not only the absence of emotional abreaction at the time of the event that allows it to be pathogenic, but the absence of other drive-gratifying reactions as well, such as (conscious) fantasy expression. Furthermore, while according to the early view a pathological outcome is a direct result of the warding off of an expressive reaction (Breuer and Freud's "strangulation of affect"), in the current formulation, as elaborated above, pathogenicity depends on the *type* of defense employed in fending off, rather than the fending off per se. Finally, with regard to the circumstances under which an expressive reaction is averted, the three conditions that Breuer and Freud cite in their first group can be put under categories 1c, 2, and 3, respectively, as proposed above. Although I believe a consensus could be reached among contemporary psychoanalytic clinicians on the validity of these conditions as favoring a pathological outcome, the second set of conditions that these same authors proposed would be considered much more equivocal. The "hypnoidal" conditions in the second set, which are the ones Breuer and Freud focus on in the rest of their discussion, are seldom, if ever, mentioned in current clinical writings; and even in a later section of the same publication, Freud himself voiced skepticism about their pathogenicity (p. 286). It can be added, however, that to the degree that this early hypothesis *does* have validity, in the context of the current formulation, it can be considered akin to the subliminal condition listed under 1a above. That is, the impingement of a drive stimulus during a hypnoidal state (or what would today be referred to as an altered state of consciousness) disallows awareness (or at least focal awareness) of the stimulus, thus acting against a drive-expressive reaction.

[13] Opposite instances, in which aggressive expression is followed by a temporary remission of symptoms, are no doubt the more common, and it is these that have led some clinicians (e.g., Bak, 1954; Cohen, 1954) to formulate that schizophrenic symptoms are motivated by defensive needs against hostility, a view that is clearly supported by our experimental results. But the rarer instances described above can also be accommodated within this formulation, by assuming that sometimes these defensive needs, while still operating and therefore contributing to the schizophrenic's pathological state, are not successful in warding off expression of the aggressive drive.

side by side with the emergence of pathology. One such example has been cited by Erikson (1950). In the case of Sam, a boy of three who suffered from epileptic attacks, which Erikson understood to involve conflict over aggression, the following interaction is reported:

We [therapist and patient] have played dominoes, and in order to test his threshold, I have made him lose consistently, which was by no means easy. He grew very pale and all his sparkle dimmed out. Suddenly he stood up, took a rubber doll, and hit me in the face, hard. Then his glance turned into an aimless stare, he gagged as if about to vomit, and swooned slightly (1950, p. 29).

In line with the thesis presented here, it is interesting to contrast Sam with an adult neurotic analysand whom I have been treating for three years, who also suffers from *petit mal* attacks, which I understand as involving determinants very similar to those described by Erikson. For Sam, instances like the one cited above, in which an epileptic attack followed some gratification of the aggressive drive, were described as frequent (p. 29). For the adult neurotic, on the other hand, my treatment notes reveal that, while epileptic attacks occurred in several sessions after aggression could be inferred to have been stirred up, they were never preceded by aggressive expression, despite such expressions (i.e., angry verbalizations) at many other times.

NECESSARY CONDITIONS FOR A PSYCHOPATHOLOGICAL REACTION

In the formulation outlined above, I cited the various kinds of situations in which people attempt to block expression of a drive that has been stimulated, with a resultant pathological outcome. Since the available data indicate that this outcome requires one of these circumstances, I can speak here of a *necessary condition* for a pathological response, one that I shall term the "environmental condition." This could hardly be considered a *sufficient condition* for a pathological outcome, however. What then are the other necessary conditions?

Embedded in the same formulation are two others that refer to the individual rather than to the environment. These, which can be designated as the "superego condition" and "ego condition" respectively, are hardly new in psychoanalytic thinking; they have usually been at least implicit in discussions of pathogenesis: (1) that the drive the stimulus makes contact with is one that is unacceptable to the individual, thus producing a conflict: (2) that the individual lacks the "ego strength" [14] to handle this conflict in a non-pathological manner.

---

[14] What I view "ego strength" as referring to in this context is the inherent adaptiveness or maladaptiveness of the particular defenses employed, in interaction with the vulnerability of particular executive ego functions—i.e., thinking, perception, memory, motoric activity, etc.

Although I can report no research data attesting to the validity of these as necessary conditions, I believe that clinical data, if not everyday observations, offer abundant support for including them in the formulation; accordingly, they have been recognized in prior psychoanalytic conceptualizations.

Research data have, however, elucidated a fourth necessary condition that makes for a pathological outcome. This is one I believe clinicians are much less cognizant of than the preceding two; it can be termed the "id condition." The drive with which the stimulus makes contact has to have attained a certain minimal level of activation at the time the stimulus impinges. One cannot say in quantitative terms just what this minimal level must be, but the general validity of this proposition is supported by the following kinds of research data: In one of the subliminal studies cited earlier (L. H. Silverman, 1965a) in which aggressive stimulation led to the emergence of ego pathology in a non-psychiatric population, subjects had been randomly divided into two groups. For one, they were "primed" for aggression at the beginning of both the experimental and control sessions. That is, a highly charged aggressive passage was read to them at that time, presented as a memory task, and intended to activate aggressive drive derivatives *before* the aggressive subliminal stimulus was presented. The other group received no priming. Pathological responses to the aggressive subliminal stimulus were found only for the primed subjects.[15]

The relevance of activation level also emerged from another finding from the study just cited. The primed subjects were subdivided into two groups, one of which was characterized in their "baseline" Rorschachs (i.e., the Rorschach given *before* subliminal aggressive stimulation, but *after* priming) by a relatively large amount of aggressive imagery; the other group was characterized by relatively little imagery of this kind. The pathological effect of subliminal aggressive stimulation found for the total group was carried only by the former subgroup. In a second study with a non-psychiatric population (L. H. Silverman and Goldweber, 1966), this finding was replicated. Since the number of aggressive images can be viewed as reflecting the degree to which aggression was activated prior to the experimental manipulation, the findings from both these studies can be viewed as offering further support for the proposition.

The results from one of the subliminal experiments already cited provides further support. In Ellman's (1970) study of college women, in which she investigated the effects of a stimulus concerning menstruation on the female castration complex, she selected two groups of women as subjects. In Rorschachs administered *prior* to the experimental manipulation, one group had given a large number of responses reflecting this complex; the other group gave few such responses. Only the first group was affected by the experimental manipulation.

---

[15] In the various studies of the effects of aggressive stimulation on ego pathology in schizophrenics, the positive results reported were *not* dependent on prior priming. Considering these two sets of results together, we have postulated that, in schizophrenics, their aggressive drive under usual circumstances has attained this minimal level, whereas in most non-schizophrenics this is not the case.

The three studies cited in this section, demonstrating that the prior amount of drive-related Rorschach responses predicts whether pathological reactions will follow impingement by a drive stimulus, also allow us to restate this fourth necessary condition for pathological outcome in more conventional psychoanalytic terminology. One can say that the drive stimulus will have pathological consequences only when sufficient drive derivatives are available to consciousness (the number of Rorschach images reflecting the particular drive can provide an operational measure of this).[16] This view can be thought of as a counterpart to the clinical psychoanalytic axiom that only when derivatives of a drive come into an analysand's productions in sufficient quantity is it likely that an interpretation of the drive will be therapeutically effective. Apparently it is only when the quantitative criterion for drive derivatives is satisfied that an externally instigated, drive-related event can move an individual in either direction—toward "mental health" or toward "mental illness."

SUMMARY AND CONCLUSIONS

In this paper an attempt has been made to outline the conditions under which a drive-related external event evokes a psychopathological reaction. It has long been recognized by psychoanalytic writers that two of the necessary conditions are: (1) that the drive the stimulus makes contact with be one that is to some degree unacceptable to the individual; and (2) that the degree of "ego strength" present be insufficient to allow for adaptive handling of the unacceptable drive derivatives that are stirred. These can be referred to as the "superego" and "ego" conditions for a pathological outcome. On the basis of experimental and clinical data that have been presented the following necessary conditions can be added: (3) "id condition"—that sufficient drive derivatives related to the drive stimulus be available to consciousness at the time the stimulus impinges; (4) "environmental condition"—that the situation in which the drive stimulation occurs discourage drive gratification. This latter condition is fulfilled when any of the following circumstances prevail: (a) when the drive relevance of the stimulus is hidden; (b) when the external circumstances in which the stimulation takes place explicitly or implicitly prohibit gratification; (c) when the particular characteristics of the situation have, for the person involved, an unconscious meaning that makes any drive expression taboo.

The first of these environmental circumstances seems by far the most usual, and most of our experimental efforts have been directed toward studying it. In everyday life, drive relevance is usually hidden either because the link between the stimulus and the related drive is symbolic or otherwise disguised, or because the frustration of one drive reactively and silently arouses another. However, sometimes drive relevance is hidden in that a drive stimulus registers subliminally. This last state of affairs can most easily and practicably be simulated in

---

[16] A method for scoring drive content of Rorschach responses is provided in Holt's (1969) primary-process manual.

the laboratory and can thus be employed to provide data on the effects that stimuli with hidden drive relevance have on psychopathology.

REFERENCES

Antell, M. (1969). The Effect of Subliminal Activation of Sexual and Aggressive Drive Derivatives on Literary Creativity. Unpublished doctoral dissertation, New York University.

Arlow, J. A., and Brenner, C. (1964). *Psychoanalytic Concepts and the Structural Theory.* New York: International Universities Press.

Bak, R. C. (1954). The Schizophrenic Defense against Aggression. *International Journal of Psycho-Analysis,* 35:129–134.

Bettelheim, B. (1960). *The Informed Heart—Autonomy in a Mass Age.* New York: Free Press.

Breuer, J., and Freud, S. (1893–95). Studies on Hysteria. *Standard Edition,* 2. London: Hogarth Press, 1953.

Buchholz, E. S. (1968). A Study in the Management of Aggression by Schizophrenics; The Effects of Aggressive Stimuli on Cognition in Schizophrenics and Normals. Unpublished doctoral dissertation, New York University.

Cohen, F. (1954). Hostility and Psychotic Symptoms. *Psychiatric Quarterly,* 28:264–278.

Ellman, C. (1970). An Experimental Study of the Female Castration Complex. Unpublished doctoral dissertation, New York University.

Erikson, E. H. (1950). *Childhood and Society,* rev. ed. New York: Norton, 1963.

Feldstein, S., and Jaffe, J. (1962). The Relationship of Speech Disruption to the Experience of Anger. *Journal of Consulting Psychology,* 26:505–509.

Fenichel, O. (1945). *The Psychoanalytic Theory of Neurosis.* New York: Norton.

Freud, S. (1912). Types of Onset of Neurosis. *Standard Edition,* 12:231–238. London: Hogarth Press, 1958.

———— (1917). From the History of an Infantile Neurosis. *Standard Edition,* 17:7–122. London: Hogarth Press, 1955.

Hartmann, H., Kris, E., and Loewenstein, R. M. (1949). Notes on the Theory of Aggression. *Psychoanalytic Study of the Child,* 3/4:9–36. New York: International Universities Press.

Holt, R. R. (1969). Manual for the Scoring of Primary-Process Manifestations in Rorschach Responses: Draft 10. New York University, Research Center for Mental Health (mimeographed).

Horwitz, M. (1963). Hostility and Its Management in Classroom Groups. In: *Readings in the Social Psychology of Education,* ed. W. W. Charters and N. L. Gage. Boston: Allyn and Bacon, pp. 196–211.

Kris, E. (1952). *Psychoanalytic Explorations in Art.* New York: International Universities Press.

Lomangino, L. (1969). The Depiction of Subliminally and Supraliminally Presented Aggressive Stimuli and Its Effect on the Cognitive Function of Schizophrenics. Unpublished doctoral dissertation, Fordham University.

Rangell, L. (1963). The Scope of Intrapsychic Conflict: Microscopic and Macroscopic Considerations. *Psychoanalytic Study of the Child,* 18:75–102. New York: International Universities Press.

Rosenwald, G. C. (1961). The Assessment of Anxiety in Psychological Experimentation: A Theoretical Reformulation and Test. *Journal of Abnormal and Social Psychology,* 62:666–673.

Rutstein, E. (1970). The Effects of Aggressive Stimulation on Suicidal Patients: An Experimental Study of the Psychoanalytic Theory of Suicide. Unpublished doctoral dissertation, New York University.

Sarnoff, I. (1960). Reaction Formation and Cynicism. *Journal of Personality,* 28:129–143.

—— and Corwin, S. M. (1959). Castration Anxiety and the Fear of Death. *Journal of Personality,* 27:374–385.

Silverman, L. H. (1965a). A Study of the Effects of Subliminally Presented Aggressive Stimuli on the Production of Pathological Thinking in a Non-psychiatric Population. *Journal of Nervous and Mental Disease,* 141:443–455.

—— (1965b). Further Data on the Relationship between Aggressive Drive Activation and Impairments in Thinking: The Effects of the Blocking of Aggressive Discharge on the Thought Processes. *Journal of Nervous and Mental Disease,* 141:61–67.

—— (1966). A Technique for the Study of Psychodynamic Relationships: The Effects of Subliminally Presented Aggressive Stimuli on the Production of Pathological Thinking in a Schizophrenic Population. *Journal of Consulting Psychology,* 30:103–111.

—— (1967). An Experimental Approach to the Study of Dynamic Propositions in Psychoanalysis: The Relationship between the Aggressive Drive and Ego Regression—Initial Studies. *Journal of the American Psychoanalytic Association,* 15:376–403.

—— (1968). Further Comments on Matters Relevant to Investigations of Subliminal Phenomena: A Reply. *Perceptual and Motor Skills,* 27:1343–1350.

—— (1970). Further Experimental Studies of Dynamic Propositions in Psychoanalysis: On the Function and Meaning of Regressive Thinking. *Journal of the American Psychoanalytic Association,* 18:102–125.

—— (1971). An Experimental Technique for the Study of Unconscious Conflict. *British Journal of Medical Psychology,* 44:17–25.

——, and Candell, P. (1970). On the Relationship between Aggressive Activation, Symbiotic Merging, Intactness of Body Boundaries and Manifest Pathology in Schizophrenics. *Journal of Nervous and Mental Disease,* 150:387–399.

——, ——, Pettit, T. F., Blum, E. (1971). Further Data on the Effects of Aggressive Activation and Symbiotic Merging on the Ego Functioning of Schizophrenics. *Perceptual and Motor Skills,* 32:93–94.

——, and Goldweber, A. M. (1966). A Further Study of the Effects of Subliminal Aggressive Stimulation on Thinking. *Journal of Nervous and Mental Disease,* 143:463–472.

——, Klinger, H., Lustbader, L., and Farrell, J. (in press). The Effects of Subliminal Drive Stimulation on the Speech of Stutterers. *Journal of Nervous and Mental Disease.*

—— and Silverman, D. K. (1964). A Clinical-Experimental Approach to the Study of Subliminal Stimulation: The Effects of a Drive-Related Stimulus upon Rorschach Responses. *Journal of Abnormal and Social Psychology,* 69:158–172.

—— and Silverman, S. E. (1967). The Effects of Subliminally Presented Drive Stimuli on the Cognitive Functioning of Schizophrenics. *Journal of Projective Techniques,* 31:78–85.

—— and Spiro, R. H. (1967a). Further Investigation of the Effects of Subliminal Aggressive Stimulation on the Ego Functioning of Schizophrenics. *Journal of Consulting Psychology,* 31:225–272.

——, —— (1967b). Some Comments and Data on the Partial Cue Controversy and Other Matters Relevant to Investigations of Subliminal Phenomena. *Perceptual and Motor Skills,* 25:325–338.

——, —— (1968). The Effects of Subliminal, Supraliminal and Vocalized Aggression on the Ego Functioning of Schizophrenics. *Journal of Nervous and Mental Disease,* 146:50–61.

——, ——, Weisberg, J. S., and Candell, P. (1969). The Effects of Aggressive Activation and the Need to Merge on Pathological Thinking in Schizophrenics. *Journal of Nervous and Mental Disease,* 149:39–51.

Silverman, S. E. (1969). The Effects of Subliminally Induced Drive Derivatives on Ego Functioning in Schizophrenics. Unpublished doctoral dissertation, New York University.

Spiro, R. H., and Silverman, L. H. (1969). Effects of Body Awareness and Aggressive Activation on Ego Functioning of Schizophrenics. *Perceptual and Motor Skills,* 28:575–585.

Worchel, P. (1957). Catharsis and the Relief of Hostility. *Journal of Abnormal and Social Psychology,* 55:238–243.

DEPRESSION AS AFFECT, CHARACTER STYLE, AND SYMPTOM FORMATION [1]

Arthur H. Schmale, M.D.

Much has been written about depression and its psychological and somatic characteristics. There is general acceptance that the feeling reactions of depression are not the same as the clinical syndromes of depression, although both may occur in response to a loss; that the process of mourning is different from that of depression; that the role of the superego in the turning of aggression in on the self precludes the occurrence of melancholia in childhood; and that some depressed patients also have episodes of mania. Frequently, however, it is difficult to distinguish whether an author is describing depression as an affect, a character style, or a disease syndrome. The following approach emphasizes the differentiating characteristics, as well as the importance of an underlying somatic adaptive mechanism of withdrawal for all depressive reactions.

The approach begins with what Engel has called the "conservation-withdrawal" reaction (Engel and Reichsman, 1956; Engel, 1962b); proceeds in developmental time to the differentiation of two affects of depression, called helplessness and hopelessness (Schmale, 1958, 1964), and their signal functions; then goes on to the depressive character defenses; and concludes with the syndromes of depression, which include symptom formations that defend against repressed infantile conflicts over deprivation.

BACKGROUND

The approach to depression to be presented not only parallels Freud's 1926 formulation about the affect of anxiety and how it may be related to a neurotic syndrome formation, but extends his ideas about separation and castration from the threat of loss to loss itself.

[1] Presented in part at the Annual Meeting of the American Psychoanalytic Association, May 8, 1970, in San Francisco, California. Work reported on in this paper was supported by Grants MH-11668, MH-7521, and MH-07228 from the National Institute of Mental Health.

Abraham (1911) was the first to consider that the affect of depression in neurosis and psychosis was as prevalent as the affect of anxiety. He also emphasized the independent origins of depression and anxiety and stated, "The two affects are often present together or successively in one individual; so that a patient suffering from an anxiety-neurosis will be subject to states of mental depression, and a melancholic will complain of having anxiety" (1924). Others more recently, beginning with a paper by Bibring in 1953, have come to appreciate the importance of the affect of depression as an expression of the functioning of the autonomous mental apparatus that is equal in importance to that of the affect of anxiety (Frank, 1954; Greenson, 1959; Engel and Reichsman, 1956; Zetzel, 1960; Sandler and Joffe, 1965; Malerstein, 1968).

Engel (1962a, 1962b) proposed that the central nervous system is organized to respond to a mounting need by two different patterns: one pattern involves activity in an attempt to overcome or defend against the need; the other pattern is one of inhibition and inactivity, related to a heightened stimulus barrier, in an attempt to conserve resources in the face of continuing need. These patterns are not only built into the human nervous system, but are probably properties of all living cells. Schneirla (1965) demonstrated that even the simplest biological organisms have the capacity to approach a stimulus or to increase in activity in response to a change in environment, as well as to withdraw from a stimulus when an increasing need from within or from the environment becomes too consistently stimulating or depriving in relation to the needs of the organism. In this regard, Schur (1970) referred to Schneirla's evolutionary and developmental theory of approach and withdrawal as providing the biphasic biological processes underlying Freud's pleasure and unpleasure principles. In addition, Schur stated that Freud was struggling with the concept of withdrawal when he wrote about the principle of inertia (1895) and the death instinct (1920). In this respect, Freud's ideas about inertia and the death instinct are more appropriately related to the inactive, passively experienced conservation-withdrawal process proposed here rather than what Schur, Schneirla, and others have referred to as the active process of withdrawal.

Just as the biological trauma of birth includes a general, sudden increase in tension, with crying as the identifiable indicator of discomfort, which can then become the prototype for the affect of anxiety, so it is possible to postulate that the quiet sleep that occurs with the prolonged continuation of stimulation or the absence of stimulation, i.e., pain, cold, hunger, etc., becomes an identifiable characteristic for the withdrawal reaction and for what will become associated with the affect of depression. Quiet, slow-wave sleep, as identified by the electroencephalogram, may be the earliest global manifestation of the adaptive process of the neonate's detaching himself from his environment at the end of a period of activity when nothing more is needed or can be tolerated from the external environment (Emde, 1970). In such withdrawal as quiet sleep, there is a turning away from the external environment, with the organism functioning in close to a resting or refractory state—at least in the systems that are most directly related to perceiving or reacting to the external environment. Then, in time, as a result of internal need and/or level of external stimulation, there will again be an increasing awareness and activity, directed toward the external environment. This process of cyclical changing sensitivity and changing need for external relationships also helps to explain how, in both animals and man, a stimulus at one point in an activity-inactivity cycle may not be perceived, whereas at another it not only may be perceived, but may be perceived as dangerous or as more than can be tolerated.

Spitz postulated that the sleep of the neonate may be regarded as the prototype of all ego defenses (1961). "Perhaps sleep can be referred to as an ideal defense, or even better, as the earliest defense. It is an anaclitic defense, for as a defense it leans onto the physiological function of sleep." Hartmann (1950) indicated, ". . . it is tempting to consider very early processes in the autonomous area as forestages of later defense against both inner and outer dangers" (p. 125). He himself suggested that the neonate's closing of the eyelids when exposed to light could serve as a model for later defense.

Thus, the biological threshold mechanisms for dealing with excessive stimulation or prolonged deprivation are present in fetal and neonatal life as undifferentiated organismic processes. During infancy, the conservation-withdrawal reactions acquire psychic representation and then evolve, as the individual grows and matures, into a process that may become predominantly intrapsychic. Freud (1926) stated in reference to anxiety, "Affective states have become incorporated in the mind as precipitates of primeval traumatic experiences, and when a similar situation occurs, they are revived like mnemic symbols" (p. 93). "It is true that, as the development of the ego goes on, the earlier danger-situations tend to lose their force and to be set aside, so that we might say that each period of the individual's life has its appropriate determinant of anxiety" (p. 142). Zetzel (1966) extended Freud's consideration and emphasized the importance of understanding the developmental perspective for depression as well as anxiety. "Like anxiety, depression may by understood as an affective ego response to internal or external events. In both, recognition, tolerance, and mastery of painful affect appears to be a necessary precursor of and concomitant to adaptive progressive moves towards greater psychic maturity" (p. 239).

Although they will not be discussed here, it is important to recognize that genic and constitutional factors will determine, along with what is available in the environment, how much stimulation or deprivation is experienced, tolerated, and mastered at various points in developmental time.

THE PREPSYCHIC ORIGINS OF DEPRESSION (CONSERVATION-WITHDRAWAL REACTION)

As mentioned above, the conservation-withdrawal reaction is an automatic, adaptive response to prolonged somatic deprivation, which may include excessive sensory stimulation. The conversation-withdrawal reaction remains a global process during the first few months of life, and its most easily observed characteristic may be that of quiet or deep sleep. Spitz (1946) described a state in young children who were deprived of mothering and experienced a limited perceptual environment in a foundling home setting: behavior went from weepiness to frozen expressionless rigidity. He called this reaction "anaclitic depression."

Engel and Reichsman (1956) observed that the infant, Monica, rather than exhibiting anxiety and crying in the presence of a stranger, became limp and fell asleep. (During these periods, her stomach did not secrete gastric acid, even when stimulated with histamine.) They referred to this reaction as being one of "depression-withdrawal." Of special note in this study was the demonstration that this "depression-withdrawal" reaction would occur virtually instantaneously in response to a stimulus that could not be mastered, and the expected crying response simply did not take place. As they put it, Monica behaved as if she had learned that the crying reaction would bring no relief and, hence, directly activated the depression-withdrawal pattern instead.

Kehoe and Ironside (1963), using an hypnotic technique, were able to induce a depression-withdrawal response in healthy adult subjects and demonstrated an inhibition of gastric secretion comparable to the response observed in Monica, thus indicating that the response can also occur in healthy adults. Such somatic withdrawal reactions in adult life have been described as responses to unexpected bad news, report of a loss of a loved one, as well as at times of injury, pain, illness, or starvation. These reactions have at various times been included under the headings of asthenia, shock, exhaustive state, brain syndrome, massive regression, etc. (Hinkle, 1961; Oswald, 1962; Gellhorn and Loofbourrow, 1963. See also section on psychophysiological disorders of depression for the complications that may occur when the conservation-withdrawal reaction is resisted, or attempts are made to oppose the reaction actively.)

The biochemistry and physiology of the conservation-withdrawal reaction involves understanding feedback controls from the level of the cell to the most complex level of psychic organization. Engel (1970) suggested that the physiology of the conservation-withdrawal reaction may be linked to what Hess (1957) identified as the trophotropoic zone of the diencephalon and mesencephalon, which discharges over the parasympathetic nervous outflow system. Recent studies of autonomic nervous system and hormonal functioning add neurochemical support to the idea of a trophotropoic regulatory mechanism and perhaps control centers in the midbrain, for withdrawal, as well as deep, quiet sleep (Jouvet, 1969; Gellhorn, 1967).

THE AFFECTS OF DEPRESSION (HELPLESSNESS AND HOPELESSNESS)

Helplessness and hopelessness have been proposed as the primary affects of depression.[2] These two affects are related to the developmental traumas Freud

[2] A more detailed description of these two affects along with a number of other affects that are involved in early psychic differentiation can be found elsewhere (Schmale, 1964; Sweeney et al., 1970).

called separation and castration, but he dealt with these traumas mainly in terms of anxiety. Although the initial reaction in the situation of abandonment or castration may be one of anxiety, Freud himself said, "We know what the affective reactions to a separation are: They are pain and mourning, not anxiety" (Freud, 1926). The affect of anxiety thus involves the anticipation and desire to avoid the trauma, while the two affects of depression indicate that the trauma has already occurred or is considered to be inevitable.

Helplessness, as used in this presentation, refers to that affect of depression that is associated with the separation experience. It is first experienced during the latter part of the first year of life, when the child becomes aware of his dependence on a specific, external-world, mother-object for protection and gratification. Helplessness reflects the intrapsychic awareness of the conservation-withdrawal reaction associated with the child's feeling of incompleteness when the mother-object is not present and gratification is not forthcoming. Furthermore, it is likely that the child is aware that there is nothing he can do to get the desired gratification, yet he cannot conceive of his existence without the mothering gratification.

With the repeated experience of being helped after feeling helpless, the child learns to tolerate the feeling of helplessness in the absence of the gratifying object. He develops "trust" (Erikson) and "confidence" (Benedek) that he will find a replacement. (In terms of intrapsychic development, this is the phase of the beginning recognition of objects as separate and distinct from the self. If gratification can be consistently identified as coming from specific objects, representations of these objects will develop in the memory traces. Extended deprivation or overprotection may create a refusion of self and object images, with a consequent inability to test reality, as described by Jacobson [1964].)

The feeling of helplessness may recur at various times in life. Even in adult life, the affect may be experienced when there is the loss of an object upon which the individual has become dependent for specific kinds of help (gratification)—e.g., wife's solicitude, co-worker's assistance, salary increment, automobile's dependability, etc. The feeling of helplessness may persist for varying lengths of time, depending on the reappearance of the missing gratification or on something symbolically equal becoming available; or else the individual must accept that there will be no replacement, that he must give up the desired gratification and look for a new type of gratification.

Zetzel (1966) emphasizes the importance of being able to tolerate the passivity associated with the feeling of helplessness as a beginning recognition of reality and an awareness of the need to act oneself in order to master deprivation.

Hopelessness, as the other primary affect of depression, is associated with the castration experience. It is first experienced, in the process of normal development, somewhere between the ages of three and six years of life.[3] At this stage

---

[3] Mahler (1966) now feels that this stage may begin somewhat earlier, particularly for girls. She emphasizes the importance of the double trauma of toilet training and the discovery of the anatomical sexual difference between boys and girls as con-

of development, the child is forced to accept that he cannot have or achieve what he wants because of his own inadequacies. The limitations placed on him as a result of his sexual, intellectual, and physical immaturity and position in the family force him to defend against the wished-for gratification or relationships that he sees, or fantasies, mother, father, and others are having. The feeling of hopelessness is associated with an awareness of unachievable acceptance. There must be a giving up of the wished-for relationships, or the oedipal wish must be kept out of consciousness. The latter course leads to repression of the unresolved threat of castration, as the period of latency begins (Freud, 1924). The repressed unresolved oedipal strivings will once again increase in intensity during ado-lescence, at the time of major biological changes, which include an intrapsychic remodeling of the self-concept and a further development of the ego ideal. If there has been a premature internalization of very ambitious parental standards and demands during the earlier stages of self- and ego-ideal development, severely masochistic trends may develop and an inadequate sense of self may result. If delay in gratification can be tolerated, and more realistic and achiev-able goals set, then there is hope for the future.

When the individual is unable to achieve a goal that is important or neces-sary for his own esteem and as proof of self-worth in adult life—such as achieving specific social, business, or family recognition, or getting others to accept his standards, etc.—the feeling of hopelessness will recur. It will be replaced by a feeling of hope, however, if the individual can accept the passivity that comes with the feeling of hopelessness, and can recognize the impossibility of achieve-ment being associated with his continued pursuit of the old goal.

I wish to hypothesize that throughout life all major changes in self-worth or esteem require giving up an old object or a self-expectation or both, before new and hopefully more realistic relationships and goals can be actively pursued. (Freud's unpleasure principle [1900] was modeled on the awareness of the neces-sity to withdraw from excessive external stimulation and to re-establish con-stancy, says Schur [1970].)

SIGNAL FUNCTIONS OF THE AFFECTS OF DEPRESSION

As Freud stated in his 1926 paper, there is first the reflex or automatic response of anxiety, related to the earliest perceptions of trauma. With such experience, and as the capacity to conceptualize and remember is acquired, the danger of specific traumas can be anticipated. One can postulate a similar developmental progression for depression, beginning with the conservation-withdrawal response and proceeding to the affects of helplessness and hopelessness, as related to specific types of deprivation. When the occurrence of such deprivational trauma

tributing factors to the predisposition to a depressive mood in girls. This may mean that the phallic phase, in terms of absence of the penis for the girl, is experienced more purely in terms of its unresolvable deprivation and feelings of hopelessness, while the anticipation of the danger of castration for the boy may lead to a more prolonged reaction of anxiety before hopelessness is experienced.

can be anticipated in the future, it is possible through thoughts and actions to find ways of defending against the complete re-experiencing of the original deprivation.

The signal reactions of helplessness or hopelessness are acknowledgments of a psychic awareness that current activities may lead to the re-experiencing of deprivation or failure and warnings that a change in activities or a defense is in order. The signal may be experienced subjectively as an ill-defined loss of interest and energy, or as an awareness of being a little "down" or sad. The perception of these signals may be associated with the activation of various ego mechanisms that defend against the conscious idea of possible deprivation or failure. If such defenses are ineffective in protecting the individual, the feelings of helplessness or hopelessness may recur. But these defenses, if highly effective or readily available, may be mobilized without the signal's being consciously perceived. Luborsky (1967) demonstrated that sudden momentary lapses in thought during therapy come when the patient is on the verge of a new attitude that he has not expressed in therapy before. An attitude that is linked to a past conflict over not living up to superego or ego standards is momentarily forgotten "as part of an increase in defense against the threat of the associated repressed thoughts' coming into awareness" (p. 215). I interpret this as an example of signal hopelessness, related to a past experience when the individual thought he had not lived up to his ideal. Various forms of aggressive acting out—including delinquent behavior (particularly in adolescents), overeating, excesses of drugs, and alcohol—may all serve as defensive reactions to signal helplessness. These behavioral and somatic consequences of the signal reactions of depression are included in what at times are called "depressive equivalents."

Clinically, the experiencing of the signal affects of helplessness and hopelessness are frequently associated in time with the apparent onset of a wide variety of somatic and psychic disease states in the adult (Schmale, 1958; Adamson and Schmale, 1965; Schmale and Engel, 1967). Luborsky (1969) observed, in a more precise way, episodic stomach pains and migraine headache as two types of somatic symptoms that had their onset during specific therapy sessions, at a time in the session when the patient's speech content had just expressed feelings of helplessness.

These two affects of depression and associated changes in somatic health also may be experienced, following the actual loss of a loved one, during the process of mourning (Schmale, 1970).[4] As will be illustrated shortly, the experiencing of the two affects of depression is not equivalent to the clinical syndromes of depression. Rather, the experiencing of either of these affects, with their associated loss of ego autonomy and postulated concomitant somatic changes in thresholds, may allow whatever potential for somatic or psychic disease that is present in the individual or the environment to become manifest at that time. The clinical syndromes of depression are only several among many possible

---

[4] Studies delineating the phases of normal grief work and the role of the affects of helplessness and hopelessness in the process of giving up highly valued objects are now in progress.

consequences of, or reactions to, the affective or signal reactions of helplessness or hopelessness.

The possibility that the somatic vulnerability associated with the affect of helplessness or with its more primitive antecedent, the conservation-withdrawal reaction, is yet another area for study.

Much of what Bibring (1953) described in his "Mechanisms of Depression" paper and Rapaport (1967a) enlarged upon as an extension of Bibring's theory of depression fits with what I have called the affective reactions of helplessness or hopelessness. To say that the affective reactions discussed up to this point in the paper are experienced as reactivations of a structured infantile ego state of help-lessness (or hopelessness), which are not created *de novo* in repression, is in agreement with Bibring's theory of depression (1953). I disagree with Bibring and Rapaport, however, when they state, "*All* depressions are affective states and as such are reactivations of a structured infantile ego state of helplessness." The extent and reasons for this disagreement will become apparent in the section on clinical syndromes of depression.

By way of a brief review, the affects of depression—helplessness and hope-lessness—are important for updating intrapsychic concepts of the self and the external world as the individual grows and experiences. These affects are experi-enced and re-experienced, however, at times of vulnerability; and rather than progression to new ideas, new relationships, more confidence, and a greater sense of reality, they may result in fixations, inhibitions, and repression, which are the consequence of an inability to find more realistic ways of dealing with the awareness of continuing loss of gratification. It is at such times that the instinctual needs and superego demands may become more prominent, and intrapsychic reactions may go beyond that of an affective reaction of the ego: a neurotic symptom formation may be the result.

PSYCHOPHYSIOLOGICAL DISORDERS RELATED TO SIGNALS OF DEPRESSION

Following the development of signal helplessness or hopelessness, the anticipa-tion of deprivation may not reach conscious awareness before the somatic response of conservation-withdrawal occurs. In such circumstances, the indivi-dual may not consciously appreciate what is happening; or, even if he does, he may be forced by prior commitments to struggle to remain active. The resulting awareness of the struggle that occurs when the somatic activity associated with the conservation-withdrawal reaction is opposed by the individual's attempts to remain active comes under the heading of psychophysiological reactions. This is a counterpart to the psychophysiological reactions that occur during the struggle when bodily preparation for "fight or flight" is ignored by the individual, who has decided he has to remain inactive and actually cannot either fight or flee. These psychophysiological reactions may be brief, or they can become chronic and lead to somatic dysfunction or organ damage. Such reactions have been included under various headings in the past—for example, vegetative or organ neuroses (Alexander, 1950) and protective reaction patterns (Wolff, 1953). In physiological terms, instead of reciprocal innervation of one or the other divisions of the autonomic nervous system associated with arousal or conservation, there is a simultaneous activation of the two, even though the functioning of the one usually predominates over the other. Such reactions have been experimentally produced in animals by means of conditioning techniques wherein positive and negative conditional stimuli are made progressively more similar (Gellhorn, 1965).

Schur's idea (1953) of a secondary anxiety, which arouses a sense of danger that the initial experiencing of anxiety itself creates, can be applied to feelings of depression as a secondary reaction, particularly in response to the somatic withdrawal symptoms that may accompany the initial affect of depression. To extend this idea another step (this, too, is an extension of the ideas expressed above about psychophysiological reactions), the initial somatic response associated with the signal affect of depression may lead to the experiencing of anxiety; secondarily, and in a similar and more commonly experienced sequence, the initial signal of anxiety, if it persists, may lead to a secondary feeling of depression.

DEPRESSIVE CHARACTER STYLES

Persons who are unable to learn to trust others or unable to have confidence in themselves may grow up with a strong predisposition for experiencing helplessness or hopelessness. Many of them, however, acquire personality features that provide some protection against the frequent re-experiencing of the feelings of either helplessness or hopelessness.

One character defense against a strong predisposition to *helplessness* attempts to deal with the repeated perception of a threat of loss of dependent forms of gratification. Persons who develop this defense react to changes perceived within themselves with projection—that is, they make the external environment responsible for their discomfort or lack of gratification. They have a limited range of activities and only a few objects to whom they can relate for their narcissistic gratification. Their "sticky," demanding relationships are marked by a suddenly shifting but predominantly pessimistic outlook on the world and what it provides. Such persons are usually thought of as having an orally aggressive, orally dependent, or narcissistic character structure. A pathological form of this character type is called "the exception" (Freud, 1916). These are the people who think the world owes them something; however, when they get what they want, even if only occasionally or fleetingly, they are able to feel at one with the world. Kernberg's (1970) discussion of the narcissistic personality emphasizes the inadequacy of the superego organization, the pathological fusion of ideal self, ideal object and actual self-image, and the infrequency of the experience of guilt or shame.

Individuals with a character structure defending against a strong predisposition to *hopelessness* tend to have the idea that selfless persistence in working toward a goal provides satisfaction, irrespective of whether or not the goal is reached. They take on responsibility for everything that happens to them and all those around them, and their exaggerated sense of responsibility leads to rigidly held, unachievable goals as well as a preoccupation with the well-being and the needs of others, frequently to the exclusion of their own realistic needs. Anna Freud's (1946) concept of "altruistic surrender" as a character defense applies to this group. Most of what they experience is in terms of thoughts; there is little evidence of affective expression. Occasionally, however, there will be hints of pride and goodness while they are pursuing their impossible goals, and fleeting guilt and shame when the goals elude them. People with this character structure are frequently called masochistic, pseudo-independent, or obsessive. Those who have been described as "wrecked by success" (Freud, 1916) are included in this category of character formation.

DEPRESSIONS AS CLINICAL SYNDROMES

The clinical syndromes of depression are frequently categorized into one of two types; however, the choice of labels and the theoretical formulation associated with the two groups vary. Some speak of neurotic and psychotic depression, others of exogenous (reactive) and endogenous depression. There are some who think all clinical depressions can be identified as belonging to one quantitative spectrum of reactions, related to object loss, loss of self-esteem, or fear of abandonment. Many regard the patients' symptoms as representing complete intrapsychic breakdown, with little or no capacity left for reparation or defensive action. In the latter formulation, the syndromes of depression are thought to reflect the intensity of the experienced feelings of depression. Furthermore, in most of the psychoanalytic literature, the term "melancholia" is used synonymously with the term "depression" in speaking of a clinical syndrome of depression. Of major psychoanalytic concern over the years has been the question of whether aggression is primary or secondary, as well as how the aggression is expressed, and whether there is evidence for conscious or unconscious guilt and an associated need for punishment (Freud, 1917; Bibring, 1953; Gaylin, 1968).

What I propose for the further understanding of the clinical syndromes of depression can be subsumed under the headings of exogenous and endogenous depression. The term "exogenous" usually implies that the process was precipitated by recent events in the individual's life. Of greater dynamic significance, however, is the awareness of disruption and immobility related to the loss (or threat of loss) of gratification provided by an external source upon which the individual has a feeling of dependence for his sense of stability and worth. The current loss is symbolically related to an unresolved infantile trauma of separation, which threatens to become conscious. However, rather than seeing the clinical syndrome of exogenous depression merely as a reawakening of the repressed infantile trauma with the re-experiencing of the affect of helplessness, I hypothesize that the process is one in which the threat of such an occurrence leads to the formation of a defensive compromise. The resulting symptom of depression, which is symbolically related to the unconscious conflict, protects the individual from re-experiencing the infantile trauma of separation from mother.

Endogenous depression, on the other hand, is usually depicted as a struggle between ego and superego, with a turning of aggression from ambivalently held objects in and onto the self, resulting in feelings of despair. Endogenous depression can also be conceptualized as involving more than a reawakening of unresolved deprivation associated with castration (Freud, 1917). Here, too, I propose that a defensive compromise occurs, which is symbolically related to the repressed idea of being inadequate and castrated. The resulting symptom of depression attempts symbolically to destroy the evidence of castration, while continuing to repress the actual memory of the castration trauma. As Freud wrote in 1924, in "The Dissolution of the Oedipus Complex": "If the ego has really not achieved much more than a repression of the complex, then this latter persists unconsciously in the id, and will express itself later on in some pathogenic effect." Also, in an earlier paper (1920) he stated, "Loss of love and failure leave behind them a permanent injury to self-regard in the form of a narcissistic scar, which in my opinion, . . . contributes more than anything to the 'sense of inferiority' which is so common in neurotics" (p. 20).

Zetzel (1964) has referred to the clinical state of depression in terms of symptom formations of an inhibiting and distressing nature, which result from serious ego regression because of an "incapacity to bear" the feelings of depression.

EXOGENOUS DEPRESSION AND THE ASSOCIATED SYMPTOM FORMATION OF THE "NEED TO PROVE NEGLECT"

In contrast to the individual who is able to recognize and tolerate deprivation from sources upon whom he has been dependent, we see the person who has a repressed, unresolved infantile fixation, involving the separation from mother or mothering objects, which threatens to become conscious. In order to avoid the reawakening of the memory of mother's absences and her inability to be as gratifying as desired, there is an attempt to detach himself from the current reality and the object about to be lost. This is done by means of a symptom formation that involves disavowal of the perception of the original loss; in its place, two contrary and independent ideas are fantasied in turn: (1) objects are available for specifically desired gratification; and (2) objects are unwilling (rather than unable) to provide such gratification.

The first idea represents the fantasied distortion of the repressed wish for gratification from mother. The second idea indicates the distortion of reality: it states that it is not an inability on the mother's part, but rather an unwillingness on the part of others, that keeps him from being gratified. When the first of the two ideas is prominent, the individual fantasies a symbiotic relationship with objects and the world. The behavior of such an individual may be identified in its extreme form as a primitive type of mania or delusion of grandeur. When the second idea takes precedence, the individual fantasies that everyone dislikes him. In its extreme form, this idea also may reach psychotic proportions and be identified as paranoid.

When the two conflicting ideas occur together, the individual actively seeks out objects who will help to confirm his fantasies of neglect. Thus, I have labeled this type of depressive symptom compromise, "the need to prove neglect." Stated in another way, what was passively experienced in infancy as abandonment in relation to mother is now actively sought by way of a neurotic symptom, with a need to prove the fantasied neglect not by mother but by others in the current environment. Freud (1920), Rapaport (1967b), Loevinger (1966), and others have commented on the process of turning passively experienced trauma into actively pursued activities, as a means of mastering or defending against the feeling of anxiety. Here the traumatic experience of separation has been repressed and in its place is substituted the neurotic compromise, which involves the active pursuit of the need to prove neglect in order to avoid the feeling of helplessness.

Frequently, these individuals have maintained close dependent relationships with a key object; they have a depressive character structure, which defends against the repressed and unresolved separation deprivation of infancy, as described above. Not until there is a threat or loss of such an object, however, does the symptom formation occur. Thus, instead of giving up at the time of deprivation, there is a continued repression of the memories associated with the earlier infantile deprivation and an active pursuit of new objects and situations, with the repeated denial that anything is good or lasting. There is a demandingness for more, which grows with each gift or demonstration of affection that is provided. Thus, having to prove that others are neglectful allows an aggressive pursuit of objects, while the relatively primitive and defective superego facilitates the selection of objects that are equally narcissistic and demanding, with whom the person first identifies and on whom he then projects his own demandingness. During the period of actively and repeatedly being disappointed by the object's efforts, the individual is at least reassured that the object has remained in contact and has not abandoned him. There is no storing up of gratification. Once the object stops providing gratification, it is a case of "out of sight, out of mind." When the object is not available, there may be a retreat to oral forms of self-administered gratification, such as food, alcohol, drugs, etc. The symptom formation rarely provides protection against the repressed unresolved infantile conflict over abandonment. The more ineffective the defense, the greater the experience of the affect of helplessness and its somatic concomitants; taken together, these account for the phenomenon of the syndrome called exogenous depression.

To illustrate the "need to prove neglect" symptom as part of an exogenous depression, material is taken from the treatment of a 22-year-old, single music teacher, who came into therapy because of a period of poor concentration, massive weight gain, and a desire to stay in bed. Her symptom, "need to prove neglect," began in the setting of her first teaching job. Her widowed father, with whom she lived, indicated that he was going to have an active social life, now that she was grown up and financially independent. Although the patient could say that her father needed his independence and that she was happy for him, she immediately found herself seeking the companionship of others, which she had not done previously. She encountered, among others, an older married teacher who had been teaching for some years, and now showed an interest in helping her get started. At his first sign of interest, she began asking for more advice and fantasied that his interest in her went beyond that of friendship. After several months of becoming more and more involved with her, in an effort to prove that he could be of help, he began to realize that no matter what he did, it was not going to be enough. He also recognized that she had in some way misperceived his intentions and had developed the idea that he was going to leave his wife and children for her. He therefore tried to correct her impression and indicated he could no longer be her friend. Her response to his open rejection was: "No one was ever interested in me."

Thus, when the threat of loss of father brought reality symbolically close to reactivating her repressed infantile separation conflict, she developed the symptom of the "need to prove neglect." With the rejection by the teacher she had picked out to mother her, this neurotic compromise became ineffective and the biological features of fatigue, loss of motivation, somnolence, excessive eating and weight gain, plus feelings of helplessness, were added to the picture. It was this that led to the diagnosis of depression and her referral for treatment.

The patient gave evidence of having been clinging and demanding from an early age. Mother was described as an inconsistent and unpredictable object of gratification, who left the patient feeling insecure; as a result, she was unwilling to let her mother out of her sight. The mother had threatened to leave father on several occasions and, when the mother felt the patient was making impossible demands, she told her that she, the patient, would "be the death of her yet." Her mother became ill when the patient was four years old, and remained so until she died of cancer, when the patient was eight. The patient's initial reaction was one of denying that the loss had happened; but the underlying feelings of being lost and alone were reinforced when she was sent to live with her mother's sister and family in another town.

It was at this time that the first period of "the need to prove neglect" and withdrawal occurred. After a number of weeks of her refusing to go to school, crying, and staying in bed, her aunt, at her wits' end, talked the father into taking his daughter back with him. The two then lived with her maternal grandparents for a period of time. This was what she wanted. She fantasied that, in spite of her mother's "mean" relatives, who wanted to take her away from her father, her father's wishes had prevailed. He, like the mother, however, was only an object for narcissistic gratification, from whom she could accept no real affection but from whose mere presence she did derive a sense of security.

When the patient was twelve years old, her father remarried; she felt betrayed and imagined that the new mother had schemed to take her father away from her. She was a "born loser"—why couldn't father see how wicked and mean his new wife was? The father's marriage lasted approximately one year, and it was likely that the patient's intolerable behavior and attitude forced it to come to an end. Thereafter, she and her father lived together in an apartment, up through the time she began therapy.

She had few girl friends and almost no relationships with boys through high school and college; instead, she concentrated on the success she was able to achieve through her academic work. In spite of her insistence that she should keep house for father, he ended up doing most of the housework and cooking. She was too busy, couldn't be bothered, and felt burdened by the chores of everyday life.

Even though she had a narcissistic character structure, which included oral-aggressive ways of relating to objects, she did not become symptomatic (with the one exception of the period at age eight) until the time when she took her first teaching job and her father indicated that he was now going to have a social life of his own. She became aware of her increasing tension in the class-room, particularly in setting limits and avoiding anger when dealing with the seven- and eight-year-old children who wanted their way. (After some months of treatment she could recall how the children's behavior reminded her of her reaction to her mother's death and of being sent away, which occurred at approxi-mately the same age.) The married teacher, along with a succession of others who started out as sympathetic listeners to her complaints, were very quickly caught up in running errands and helping her with her work. Even though she acknowledged their help, it never came exactly in the right form or at the time it was most wanted. The more she complained and at times got angry, the more they tried to find ways to please her.

It is interesting—and important to the diagnosis of exogenous depression and the accompanying symptom compromise of the "need to prove neglect"—that there was never any intense guilt or shame reported or expressed during the many years she was in and out of treatment; her reactions were always in terms of what she wanted *and needed*. She would have fleeting moments of feeling fascination or bliss, when everything seemed to be going according to her fantasied wishes and she could deny her sense of incompleteness. Many activities and relationships were pursued as she repressed the recognition that her fantasy of an all-giving and protective mother was not to be fulfilled in reality. As a defensive compromise, she would not accept the interests or activities of others as adequate to fulfill her needs, yet she was not discouraged from asking for more until she was rejected outright. Then she would feel resentful and stuff herself with food, compose soulful songs of neglect, and withdraw from the external world. Satisfaction lay in how much she could involve people in trying to please her, and then repeatedly prove to herself that they were inadequate as sources of supply and not to be depended upon. Thus, her self-esteem was protected by a primitive fusion of the self with the ego ideal, while external objects and object images were devalued. This exogenous depression and its symptom formation of a "need to prove neglect" was precipitated by the realistic situation of having to leave father and go out into the adult world; this related symbolically to the earlier trauma experienced in separating from mother, and included her inability to establish an independent self-identity.

In her relationship to the therapist, there were long silences during which she would wait for the therapist to "give to" her. When she was told that she was afraid to trust the therapist and that she didn't want him to have a separate identity, she would reply in a hostile, demeaning way that he was being presumptuous in assuming that she could or might have some feelings for him. There was aggressive acting out in her relationships at school and sexual acting out in her social relationships. She was repeatedly late for her hour, and her reaction was: "It's better for me to be late than my taking a chance that you will be late." The end of the hour found her unable to leave on her own, and when the therapist would indicate the time was up, it was an indication that he was trying to get rid of her. There were numerous interruptions and discontinuations of therapy. Each time she returned, however, she seemed to be more involved and less threatened by the therapeutic relationship. She gradually began to see how her expectations of others were unrealistic and how she was forcing others to reject her.

ENDOGENOUS DEPRESSION AND THE SYMPTOM FORMATION OF THE "NEED TO PROVE SELF-NEGLECT"

Individuals who become endogenously depressed have a character structure and an ego ideal that set standards impossible to achieve. They see themselves as responsible not only for their own gratification, but for that of others. When they are forced by circumstances to accept that they cannot fulfill their fantasied goals for themselves, feelings of hopelessness begin to reappear. The feeling of hopelessness is defended against, however, because of existing repressed infantile fixations, which involve the unfulfilled desire to love, to be stronger and superior in relation to competing oedipal objects. The reality of inadequacy as an oedipal object threatens to become conscious; in its place two contrary and independent ideas are fantasied, as was true with the previously discussed symptom formation of exogenous depression. Again, this involves what Freud called "splitting of the ego"; this is a universal characteristic of neuroses, involving a disavowal of reality, in this case related to a repressed castration trauma (Freud, 1940b). The contrary fantasied ideas are: (1) the individual thinks he has the capacity to satisfy everyone, including himself; (2) he thinks of himself as unwilling (rather than unable) to achieve such satisfaction. The first idea is related to the repressed infantile wish to be accepted as the fulfilling oedipal object, the second to the defense against the wish, which represents the introjected standards imposed by the ego ideal. If the first idea becomes predominant, thinking and actions are accelerated and may reach mania proportions; if the second idea is predominant, then the need for self-punishment may occur, together with the thought of suicide, as the ultimate in self-destruction. When the two conflicting ideas occur together, the individual seeks to prove to himself and others that he is completely and exclusively responsible for his failures. Thus, I have labeled this type of defensive compromise, "The need to prove self-neglect."

Thoughts and activities associated with the need to prove self-neglect are designed to prove the need to suffer,[5] not so much out of guilt but more out of shame for not trying harder; this in turn allows the individual to hold onto the fantasied wish for acceptance as an oedipal object. Expressed in another way, the active insistence on being worthless and unsuccessful is a counterphobic way of defending against the passive feeling of oedipal inadequacy and the need to give up these fantasied goals and aspirations.

Describing melancholia in 1917, Freud stated, "Finally, it must strike us that after all the melancholic does not behave in quite the same way as a person who is crushed by remorse and self-reproach in a normal fashion. Feelings of shame in front of other people, which would more than anything characterize this latter condition, are lacking in the melancholic or at least they are not prominent in him. One might emphasize the presence in him of an almost opposite trait of insistent communicativeness which finds satisfaction in self exposure" (p. 237). Thus, the patient is not experiencing worthlessness in the usual sense; instead, he has developed a counterphobic defense against the repressed awareness of his inadequacies as an oedipal love object. There is the obsessive thought that, no matter what he does, he does not deserve to be loved or to achieve goals. What he has accomplished is insignificant in his eyes, compared with the objects to whom he relates. The more others insist that they see him as good and worthy, the more he feels a failure. When the objects give up attempting to prove his worth to him, he feels they are justified in giving up on him and willingly suffers the consequences, which he thinks he deserves. When the symptom compromise becomes ineffective in repressing the underlying oedipal conflict, the feeling of hopelessness and its accompanying biological manifestations will become a part of the syndrome, which is identified as endogenous depression. As mentioned previously, some patients will also have features of earlier developmental problems related to the separation period; once regression takes place, there will be a mixture of symptoms, including both the "need to prove neglect" and the "need to prove self-neglect."

Material to illustrate the "need to prove self-neglect" symptom as a part of an endogenous depression is taken from the treatment of a 26-year-old married nurse who, from an early age, felt responsible for others and developed a life style of trying to please others in order to feel worthy and self-sufficient. She entered treatment because of an inability to carry a pregnancy to term after six years of repeated miscarriages and the final recognition that there was no somatic explanation for her difficulties in having a child. Her menses had stopped; she had no appetite and was losing weight. She was pushing herself to continue nursing, but she had no desire for work, husband, or life in general. She was

---

[5] The need to suffer and to be ill appeared in an earlier translation of Freud's *An Outline of Psychoanalysis*, but the first phrase was dropped in the *Standard Edition*, 1964, p. 181. As already stated, the sense of guilt does not apply here as well as does the sense of shame, which is related to excessive ego ideal standards.

The concept of holding onto both illness and suffering was retained in "Analysis, Terminable and Interminable" (1937), where Freud acknowledged that only one portion of this resistance could be explained as a sense of guilt bound by the superego and, "whether bound or free, [it] may be at work in other, unspecified places" (pp. 242f.).

becoming increasingly concerned about what others were thinking of her as a woman, a nurse, a wife, and with regard to her not being able to have a child.

After several weeks of therapy, in which she obviously was trying hard to convince the therapist of her inadequacies, an interpretation was made which touched on how much time she was spending trying to prove her unworthiness. She immediately became apologetic, and then silent: she had been doing the best she could, and again had failed. This was the story of her life: she wasn't strong and independent enough. Therapy was her last chance to have a baby; she couldn't understand what was happening to her—her sick, older sister had surpassed her, by virtue of having two children and a devoted husband. "I was the lucky, the active, the healthy one. Remember my sister would say, 'Why doesn't Jane have all the allergies, need braces, and get bad marks?' However, I was the mischievous one and got all the punishment." At this time in therapy, she experienced a period of "nothingness"; this continued for several weeks, during which time she reported periods of wanting to cry but being unable to. She also felt incapable of living, and unworthy of her husband and her station in life; she developed pains in her chest and breasts, and had fantasies of being sick and dying.

Her reported past behavior demonstrated a long-standing pattern of striving for perfection through trying to please others while denying her own needs. Upon her marriage to a man who was dominated by his mother but who wanted the patient to give him a child, she was threatened by thoughts of deprivation associated with early childhood experiences and fantasies. Her inability to conceive threatened to awaken her repressed castration conflict. The symptom of the "need to prove self-neglect" for not giving her husband a child led to her blaming herself for not conceiving and for never being the daughter, nurse, and wife she should have been. The dynamics of the underlying repressed infantile conflict were illustrated by her reactions to my interpretations, as well as by her reported reactions to a number of life events.

Early events included her mother's going back to a career in nursing when the patient was three years old. This she had interpreted to mean that something about her was not satisfying to the mother. She was her father's favorite, but he was away on business much of the time; he also referred to her as his "good guy," and this she took to mean that he would have liked her even more if she had been a boy. She recalled a childhood fantasy that she practiced in order to tolerate feeling inadequate. She would fantasy that she had been bad and father wouldn't bring her a gift but he would bring sister something. "I did it just to see what it would feel like . . . kind of punished myself, maybe I wished father would acknowledge my existence . . . wish I was never born."

The patient, upon becoming aware of the repetitious nature of her depressive reaction, had the first inkling of how much she expected of herself and how ashamed she was for not being able to overcome her "inadequacies." This led to a memory of a man who came into the house when she was home alone and sick with a cold at age eight. The stranger forced her to touch his penis, while he put a finger into her vagina. She responded by screaming and chasing him with a scissors, so that he was forced to leave the house. Up to the day she reported this incident in therapy, she had never discussed it with anyone. She felt too guilty to tell her mother; besides, she remembered a story one of the nuns had told in school about someone trying to do this to a saint, who killed herself rather than let it happen.

It was at this point in therapy that the patient began having a "flight of ideas" related to a fantasy of superiority. She became more aggressive at home: she began telling her husband about her desire to have him home more and that she was not going to stand aside for his mother. She also talked to his mother and told her, in essence, that she was not going to let her run their lives. For the first time, she felt she was ready to have a baby—ready because she felt that her husband needed and wanted her. He agreed that he needed her more than he did his mother. Her menstrual periods resumed and for the first time she felt her husband really wanted a family of his own. She was ready to show her parents, her sister, and her husband's parents and siblings that she deserved to have a baby. In this setting, she quit her job and within several months became pregnant. The patient continued to be accelerated in her thinking and actions during this period, as well as very self-confident and euphoric in mood—which suggested a swing to what could be interpreted as a mild form of mania. Her narcissistic triumph over all those around her represented a displaced fulfillment of her infantile fantasy, which was to achieve oedipal acceptance—i.e., to have either the penis or a baby.

During the first three months of pregnancy, she spent much of her time sleeping. She was preoccupied with an increased awareness of her heartbeat, malaise, headaches, and some breast tenderness. She interpreted these symptoms as a price she was having to pay for getting pregnant and getting too involved with others. There were occasional thoughts of her previous miscarriages and fantasies with dreams of becoming sick, having cancer, and dying (again, the themes of suffering and illness).

Her associations, which equated pregnancy with illness, were related to a series of experiences at age five, which she referred to as her big separation problem. Her father's mother, who was living with them, died. The patient could not comprehend the finality of the event. At the time of the funeral, she was sent to a stranger's house, and she remembered screaming at her parents for leaving her: she thought they were trying to get rid of her because she was defective and undesirable. Roughly four months after this experience, her father was hospitalized and had a parotid tumor removed, after which he had radiation treatment. She was sure her father was never going to come home and developed a phobia about leaving the house; this kept her from visiting her father in the hospital. Also, about this time her aunt, who lived next door, became noticeably pregnant. The patient became obsessed with the idea that the baby wouldn't know when it was time to stop growing and come out. She recalled that her aunt was visibly upset when she asked how the aunt knew it was a baby and not a tumor.

Even though at this time in therapy she was withdrawn and had little energy, along with fleeting thoughts of cancer or death, there was increasing hope that she was going to have a baby. At the end of the first trimester, her father was reported to need a "little operation on his face—nothing serious." This was the first difficulty he had had in years, yet she suspected the worst. She also learned, at about this time, that a close friend of her parents had died the same day his daughter had a baby. This then brought out all the fantasies about having to give a life for a life. She had the fear that, if she did have her baby, something would happen to her father. She felt she was doing something wrong: she was being "too inquisitive" in wanting to be an adult and a mother, and doing too much by getting pregnant. She recalled childhood fantasies of being afraid that she wouldn't know what to say or how to act when she became an adult. When she heard that what her father had was a recurrence of his tumor, she wasn't surprised. She then had several days of nose bleeds, and dreamed that she was bleeding from the uterus and protesting, "No, no, no," in a dream. During this period, there was an increased interest in intercourse. She became curious about the birth process and decided to take instructions on how to relax, in order to have the baby without an anesthetic. She was also concerned that she might be a bother or trouble to the hospital staff and the doctors; this was something she had to avoid.

The rest of the pregnancy passed uneventfully as she proceeded to unravel her fears of pregnancy. Throughout her adolescence, she had had a fear of losing sexual control and becoming pregnant. She had fantasies of not knowing how pregnancy occurred: she even considered the possibility that "it" might occur spontaneously from becoming too sexually aroused. Also, at this time in therapy, she began to understand why she had picked her husband as the man to marry: not only was he good-looking and self-possessed, but he had so much self-control that she would be safe with him. "He would act as a restraining force."

In her ninth month of pregnancy, she received a call from her mother, indicating that her father was hospitalized and not expected to live. She returned to her home town, and was able to spend three days at her father's bedside before he died. She was surprised at how well she got through the funeral. She thought it helped to see that there were others grieving there with her. An emptiness hit her three days after the funeral. She felt sick when she returned home and tried to call her therapist but couldn't reach him. When she found that he was away for the weekend, she busied herself with scrubbing walls, canning, and baking. In therapy, the following week, she described in detail the events of the last several days with her father, and her ambivalent feelings, while she was at his bedside, of wanting him to live and yet wanting him to hurry up and die. Although tearful and upset, she did not become immobilized and depressed, as she had on a number of previous occasions.

Delivery several weeks later of a full-term boy was met with pleasure and a new sense of confidence; however, within three weeks she became concerned with the baby's pattern of feeding and crying. She was breast-feeding him, and he took a long time at it: he needed at least an hour of nursing before she was able to put him down. Eventually, it got so she dreaded the whole routine because of his crying when she did put him down. She resented his crying after she had done everything she could for him; it brought back feelings of being inadequate. In therapy during this period, she recognized that part of her resentment toward her son was related to her not having been breast-fed, whereas her sister had been. She felt tied down with the baby, and imagined her mother must have felt this way when she, the patient, was a baby. She resented her husband for being able to come and go, while she had to exist for home, baby, and intercourse. She also resented his desire to resume intercourse as soon as he could. She became aware that the baby screamed more when she was tense and felt inadequate: "Seems he had to scream for the two of us." She enjoyed nursing the baby and was excited by having husband watch her nurse and recalled her mother's inability to let her touch her mother's breasts; this then led to her curiosity about the penis and wanting to see more.

At this point, she reported for the first time the events of her wedding night. She revealed that she was too anxious to be able to look at her husband with his clothes off and "begged off" from having intercourse on the pretext that she was too tired. The next day, she started menstruating and this gave her an excuse to avoid intercourse for the next two weeks. She used this excuse to avoid intercourse on many occasions during the first several years of marriage. At this point in therapy, many memories of sexual curiosity came to the surface, and she eagerly wanted to try new things in her lovemaking with her husband. She recalled wanting to be a boy and have a penis. This period was followed by one in which she wished that she could at least have given her father a son, as a substitute for the son that he had wanted her to have been.

When the baby was eight months old, her husband, after much deliberation, became dubious about his chances for advancement in his work and decided to change employment. The patient again had a return of her old feelings that it was she who was responsible for her husband's feeling he wasn't doing well enough, and fantasied that this was his way of indicating his disappointment in her. She also had a recurrence of the bodily preoccupations she had not had since early in therapy. She dreamed of having a tumor of the mouth like her father's, bumps on the legs (associations included the idea that she wasn't getting enough nourishment from her husband). In real life, her husband was insisting that she wean the baby, but she protested and decided that she wasn't ready. Nevertheless, she felt guilty about using the baby for her own pleasure: she needed it more than the baby did. She was reminded that she had a little lump in her mouth that the dentist had seen two weeks previously and had referred to as a plugged salivary duct. She then dreamed and had fantasies of cancer, pregnancy, and death. This continued over the next several weeks until she had a salivary duct cyst removed. She felt that the painful dreams, the cyst, and the pain related to the removal of the cyst were the price she had to pay for her increased self-esteem, getting sexually aroused, and wanting to be passive and receptive. She continued in therapy for another year, as she worked through her sexual identity, but with no further episodes of depression; in the termination phase of therapy, she again became pregnant.

Thus, an unresolved oedipal conflict, related to the mother's going to work, which she had seen as punishment for her not being what mother wanted; father's disappointment in her for not having been a boy; her own disappointment in not having a penis; and her inability to have her father's baby—all these led to ideas of inadequacy and feelings of hopelessness, which she both repressed and defended against by being acutely sensitive to the needs of others, even to the exclusion of her own needs. This style of relating had led to her becoming a nurse, marrying a man with many inhibitions (and a domineering mother), and not giving birth to a baby. When she was unable to give her husband a child, feelings of hopelessness and oedipal inadequacies threatened to become conscious.

This then was the setting in which the symptoms of the "need to prove self-neglect" and the fantasies of disease and death began. Along with the compromise symptom, she experienced the biological symptoms of conservation-withdrawal, when the intrapsychic symptom of the need to suffer did not completely bind the conflict. Therapy allowed her to re-experience the feelings of inadequacy and hopelessness repeatedly, with an increasing awareness of the unresolved oedipal fantasies that occurred in association with these feelings. Gradually, she was able to anticipate the situations that would give rise to feelings of hopelessness, and to see how she would actively try to undo magically her feelings of inadequacy. Finally, she found that, when feelings of failure or deprivation occurred, she was able to tolerate them and eventually to master them, by accepting help from others or by a shift in interests, which would include more realistic and available goals.

Since this paper was written to illustrate the relationship of the many forms of depression to each other and not as a review, there has been no attempt to integrate this approach with all that has been observed and considered important in the writing of others. One of the few areas of possible disagreement with Freud's classical concept has to do with the importance he attributed to the loss of object in the dynamics of melancholia. Both Abraham (1911) and Freud (1917) utilized mourning, and its associated loss of an object from the real world, as their model for melancholia. Freud acknowledged, however, that the loss in melancholia is of a more ideal kind than that of mourning. He questioned "whether a loss in the ego irrespective of the object—a purely narcissistic blow to the ego—may not suffice to produce the picture of melancholia" (p. 253). I agree with this latter formulation and to this I have added that, along with the narcissistic blow there is an unresolved infantile castration conflict, which is prevented from becoming conscious by the formation of a neurotic symptom. Freud also stated that the person with melancholia must surely be right in some way about all the self-accusations he makes—i.e., he is petty, egoistic, dishonest, lacking in independence, someone whose sole aim has been to hide the weaknesses of his own nature (p. 246). These are typical statments by patients who, I have indicated, manifest "the need to prove self-neglect." Their accusations represent the fantasied ideation of the symptom compromise associated with melancholia, which involves a disavowal of the unresolved castration conflict. Beck

(1967) systematically studied such ideas in depressed patients in therapy and labeled them "cognitive distortions." Freud also described the role of the object in terms of the "shadow of the object which fell across the ego and the ego, henceforth, would be judged by a special agency as though it were an object, the forsaken object." The forsaken object can now be understood in terms of the repressed infantile loss of mother's love, which underlies exogenous depression, or the inadequacy of the self as an oedipal object, as in endogenous depression.

SUMMARY

An attempt has been made to integrate in a dynamic schema the many types of depression. This perspective is similar to what Freud (1926), and more recently Rangell (1968), have proposed for the understanding of anxiety. Both the affects of anxiety and those of depression have their organismic origins in the regulatory mechanisms for arousal and conservation-withdrawal. Following intrapsychic differentiation of self and external world, there are two critical periods of deprivation, which lead to what Bibring has called "the ego's shocking awareness of its helplessness" (and I would add, or hopelessness). Then, again, in Freud's terms, the affect undergoes taming and becomes a signal reaction. Signal reactions of helplessness and hopelessness may lead to new activities; or, if the affects are actively opposed, they may give rise to a psychophysiological disorder; or, if there is an underlying repressed conflict of separation or castration, this may be defended against by character changes and then later in time by a symptom compromise, which may then become one part of a clinical syndrome of depression. The effectiveness of the shift in activities or the ensuing defenses will determine the degree of somatic withdrawal or the duration of the depressive affects. The more effective the defense or the new activity, the less will be the experience of a feeling of helplessness or hopelessness, and the somatic concomitants of withdrawal and inactivity. As Abraham stated in his 1911 paper, "If rather than affect alone we could consider depression a symptom which represents a compromise between a wish and a defense with elements of both expressed in the symptom complex we could then look at depressions as we did phobias, conversions and obsessions and again see that the symptom of depression as with these other neurotic symptoms can be found in the course of many neuroses in addition to a more pure form labelled neurotic depression."

In addition to or instead of the formation of symptoms, the ego, in its attempt to master, diminish, or contain the affects of depression, may utilize other forms of defense, such as distortion of character and severe inhibitions. As Arlow and Brenner (1969) have said, when the ego is forced to resort to extreme measures of defense, so extensive that they disrupt the patient's relationship with the world about him and his feelings about himself, the patient is said to be psychotic rather than neurotic.

When the "need to prove neglect" symptom formation reaches psychotic levels of ego disorganization, the behavior is similar to what Jacobson described in her 1966 paper as "schizophrenic depression." She indicated that, in this form of depression, there is an absence of moral worthlessness (guilt or shame), together with feelings of hostility and self-consciousness and fear of a loss of identity.

With the "need to prove self-neglect" symptom formation, ego disorganization may lead to self-destructive thoughts and actions, as has been well-documented by Abraham, Freud, and many others in their descriptions of melancholia.

Thus, from the point of view of therapy, it is important to distinguish which form of depression is being experienced, in order to know whether one is dealing primarily with a biological threshold phenomenon, an affect with somatic components, a character style, or a defensive symptom formation that protects, with varying success, against an unresolved deprivation with fixations related to repressed infantile separation or castration trauma.

REFERENCES

Abraham, K. (1911). Notes on the Psychoanalytic Investigation and Treatment of Manic-Depressive Insanity and Allied Conditions. In: *Selected Papers*. London: Hogarth Press, 1948.

—— (1924). A Short Study of the Development of the Libido Viewed in the Light of Mental Disorders. In: *Selected Papers*. London: Hogarth Press, 1948, p. 418.

Adamson, J. D., and Schmale, A. H. (1965). Object Loss, Giving Up, and the Onset of Psychiatric Disease. *Psychosomatic Medicine, 28*:557.

Alexander, F. (1950). *Psychosomatic Medicine*. New York: Norton.

Arlow, J. A., and Brenner, C. (1969). The Psychopathology of the Psychoses: A Proposed Revision. *International Journal of Psycho-Analysis, 50*:5.

Beck, A. (1967). *Depression: Clinical, Experimental, and Theoretical Aspects*. New York: Harper and Row.

Bibring, E. (1953). The Mechanism of Depression. In: *Affective Disorders: Psychoanalytic Contributions to Their Study*, ed. P. Greenacre. New York: International Universities Press, p. 13.

Emde, R. (1970). Stress and Neonatal Sleep. Unpublished manuscript.

Engel, G. L. (1962a). Anxiety and Depression-Withdrawal: The Primary Affects of Unpleasure. *International Journal of Psycho-Analysis, 43*:89.

—— (1962b). *Psychological Development in Health and Disease*. Philadelphia: Saunders, pp. 387–388.

—— (1970). Nervousness and Fatigue. In: *Signs and Symptoms: Applied Physiology and Clinical Interpretation*, 5th ed., ed. C. M. MacBride. Philadelphia: Lippincott.

—— and Reichsman, F. (1956). Spontaneous and Experimentally Induced Depression in an Infant with Gastric Fistula: A Contribution to the Problem of Depression. *Journal of the American Psychoanalytic Association, 4*:428.

Erikson, E. H. (1968). *Identity: Youth and Crisis*. New York: Norton.

Frank, R. L. (1954). The Organized Adaptive Aspect of the Depression-Elation Response. In: *Depression*, ed. P. Hoch and J. Zubin. New York: Grune and Stratton.

Freud, A. (1946). *The Ego and the Mechanisms of Defence*. New York: International Universities Press, p. 137.

Freud, S. (1895). Project for a Scientific Psychology. *Standard Edition,* 1:295–387. London: Hogarth Press, 1966.

—— (1900). The Interpretation of Dreams. *Standard Edition,* 4 & 5. London: Hogarth Press, 1953.

—— (1916). Some Character Types Met with in Psycho-Analytic Work. *Standard Edition,* 14:311–332. London: Hogarth Press, 1957.

—— (1917). Mourning and Melancholia. *Standard Edition,* 14:237–258. London: Hogarth Press, 1957.

—— (1920). Beyond the Pleasure Principle. *Standard Edition,* 18:7–64. London: Hogarth Press, 1955.

—— (1924). The Dissolution of the Oedipus Complex. *Standard Edition,* 19:173–179. London: Hogarth Press, 1961.

—— (1926). Inhibitions, Symptoms and Anxiety. *Standard Edition,* 20:87–172. London: Hogarth Press, 1959.

—— (1937). Analysis Terminable and Interminable. *Standard Edition,* 23:216–253. London: Hogarth Press, 1964.

—— (1940a). An Outline of Psycho-Analysis. *Standard Edition,* 23:144–207. London: Hogarth Press, 1964.

—— (1940b). Splitting of the Ego in the Process of Defense. *Standard Edition,* 23:275–278. London: Hogarth Press, 1964.

Gaylin, W. (1968). *The Meaning of Despair.* New York: Science House.

Gellhorn, E. (1965). The Neurophysiological Basis of Anxiety: A Hypothesis. B. Observations on Experimental Neuroses. *Perspectives in Biology and Medicine,* 8:488.

—— (1967). *Principles of Autonomic Somatic Integrations.* Minneapolis: University of Minnesota Press.

——, and Loofbourrow, G. N. (1963). Autonomic-Affective Syndrome. *Emotions and Emotional Disorders.* New York: Hoeber Medical Div., Harper and Row, pp. 293–300.

Greenson, R. R. (1959). Phobia, Anxiety, and Depression. *Journal of the American Psychoanalytic Association,* 7:663.

Hartmann, H. (1950). Comments on the Psychoanalytic Theory of the Ego. In: *Essays on Ego Psychology.* New York: International Universities Press, 1964, p. 113.

Hess, W. R. (1957). *The Functional Organization of the Diencephalon.* New York: Grune and Stratton.

Hinkle, L. E. (1961). Physiological State of the Interrogation Subject as It Affects Brain Function. In: *The Manipulation of Human Behavior,* ed. A. D. Biderman and H. Zimmer. New York: John Wiley, p. 24.

Jacobson, E. (1953). Contribution to the Metapsychology of Cyclothymic Depression. In: *Affective Disorders,* ed. P. Greenacre. New York: International Universities Press, p. 49.

—— (1964). *The Self and the Object World.* New York: International Universities Press.

—— (1966). Problems in the Differentiation between Schizophrenic and Melancholic States of Depression. In: *Psychoanalysis: A General Psychology,* ed. R. M. Loewenstein, L. M. Newman, M. Schur, and A. J. Solnit. New York: International Universities Press, p. 499.

Jouvet, M. (1969). Biogenic Amines and the States of Sleep. *Science,* 163:32.

Kehoe, M., and Ironside, W. (1963). Studies on the Experimental Evocation of Depressive Responses Using Hypnosis. *Psychosomatic Medicine* 25:403.

Kernberg, O. F. (1970). Factors in the Psychoanalytic Treatment of Narcissistic Personalities. *Journal of the American Psychoanalytic Association,* 18:51.

Loevinger, J. (1966). Three Principles for a Psychoanalytic Psychology. *Journal of Abnormal Psychology,* 71:432.

Luborsky, L. (1967). Momentary Forgetting during Psychotherapy and Psychoanalysis: A Theory and Research Method. In: Motives and Thought: Psychoanalytic Essays in

Honor of David Rapaport, ed. R. R. Holt. *Psychological Issues,* Monograph No. 18/19. New York: International Universities Press, pp. 175–217.

———— (1969). The Symptom-Context Method. *Journal of the American Psychoanalytic Association,* 17:68.

Mahler, M. S. (1966). Notes on the Development of Basic Moods: The Depressive Affect. In: *Psychoanalysis: A General Psychology,* ed. R. M. Loewenstein, L. M. Newman, M. Schur, and A. Solnit. New York: International Universities Press.

Malerstein, A. J. (1968). Depression as a Pivotal Affect. *American Journal of Psychotherapy,* 22:202.

Oswald, I. (1962). Sleep as a Provoked Response. In: *Sleeping and Waking: Physiology and Psychology.* New York: Elsevier Publishing Co., pp. 146–167.

Rangell, L. (1968). A Further Attempt to Resolve the Problem of Anxiety. *Journal of the American Psychoanalytic Association,* 16:371.

Rapaport, D. (1967a). Edward Bibring's Theory of Depression. In: *Collected Papers.* New York: Basic Books, p. 758.

———— (1967b). Some Metapsychological Considerations concerning Activity and Passivity. In: *Collected Papers.* New York: Basic Books, p. 530.

Sandler, J., and Joffe, W. G. (1965). Notes on Childhood Depression, *International Journal of Psycho-Analysis,* 46:88.

Schmale, A. H. (1958). Relationship of Separation and Depression to Disease. I. A Report on a Hospitalized Medical Population. *Psychosomatic Medicine,* 20:259.

———— (1964). A Genetic View of Affects: With Special Reference to the Genesis of Helplessness and Hopelessness. *Psychoanalytic Study of the Child,* 19:287. New York: International Universities Press.

———— (1970). Psychic Trauma during Bereavement. *International Psychiatric Clinic,* 8: 147–168.

————, and Engel, G. (1967). The "Giving Up-Given Up" Complex Illustrated on Film. *Archives of General Psychiatry,* 17:135.

Schneirla, T. C. (1965). Aspects of Stimulation and Organization in Approach/Withdrawal Processes Underlying Vertebrate Behavioral Development. In: *Advances in the Study of Behavior,* ed. D. S. Lehrman. New York and London: Academic Press.

Schur, M. (1953). The Ego in Anxiety. In: *Drives, Affects, Behavior,* Vol. 1, ed. R. M. Lowenstein. New York: International Universities Press, p. 95.

———— (1970). A Principle of Evolutionary Biology for Psychoanalysis. *Journal of the American Psychoanalytic Association,* 18:422.

Spitz, R. A. (1946). Anaclitic Depression: An Inquiry into the Genesis of Psychiatric Conditions in Early Childhood. *Psychoanalytic Study of the Child,* 2:313. New York: International Universities Press.

———— (1961). Some Early Prototypes of Ego Defenses. *Journal of the American Psychoanalytic Association,* 9:626.

Sweeney, D. R., Tinling, D. C., and Schmale, A. H. (1970). Dimensions of Affective Expression in Four Expressive Modes. *Behavioral Science,* 15:393.

Wolff, H. G. (1953). *Stress and Disease.* Springfield. Ill.: Charles C Thomas.

Zetzel, E. R. (1960). Depressive Illness. *International Journal of Psycho-Analysis,* 41:476.

———— (1964). Depression and the Incapacity to Bear It. In: *Drives, Affects, Behavior,* Vol. 2, ed. M. Schur. New York: International Universities Press.

———— (1966). The Predisposition to Depression. *Canadian Psychiatric Association Journal,* 11:236.

5

PSYCHOHISTORICAL AND
PSYCHOBIOGRAPHICAL

ON PSYCHOHISTORY

Robert Jay Lifton, M.D.

Granted that there is such a thing as a "psychohistorical approach," can we then speak of a "new psychohistory"? If so, we had best be tentative. Historians know well—and psychologists should know—that anything now new will soon be old, and that we often label as new (or New) that which does not yet quite exist. As for psychohistory, it is in one sense already old, and in another hardly born.

None can deny the logic of a marriage between psychology and history. Many writers from both traditions have emphasized their common concern with narrative sequence and with the nature of man's experience in the midst of that sequence. But a certain amount of skepticism about logical marriages (and their offspring) is always in order. And the greater one's commitment to this marriage, the more convinced one becomes of the impossibility—and undesirability—of an easy union.

THE PROBLEMS INHERENT IN THE "MARRIAGE"

Skepticism, in fact, is as good a principle as any for approaching psychohistory. Most of us who are involved in the project are not only critical of traditional psychoanalytic views of history, but skeptical of the kind of pristine cause and effect—and therefore of the kind of knowledge—claimed by any monocausal or hyper-reductive approach to history. Our simple commitment to an effort to develop a psychological framework that takes historical currents seriously is itself an act of skepticism toward what I shall soon identify as the ahistorical position of most psychological thought. But this kind of skepticism must be differentiated from the automatic dismissal of all psychological approaches to history—and even from the more subtle dismissal of psychological efforts by an insistence upon the inability to "really know" anything significant about the minds of men (great or ordinary) or the past, or about the ways in which current individual and collective ideas and emotions connect with wider historical currents.

We are dealing, then, with three levels of skepticism: immediate and total rejection (the assumption that the knowledge sought is unobtainable and the whole enterprise therefore futile); anticipated rejection (the attitude, "You have to show me"; implicitly, "I don't expect or wish to be shown"); and a sense (which I share with a number of colleagues in the enterprise) that the kind of knowledge we seek is extremely refractory, and our methods of seeking it highly vulnerable. This third stance turns out to be in many ways the most skeptical of all.

It is tempting, especially for those with clinical experience, to speak of the forms of skepticism that dismiss out-of-hand, or nearly so, as "resistances." For the term suggests the kind of psychological force and need that can accompany the rejection. But I think the temptation itself should be "resisted," because the word also implies—whether used by classical psychoanalysts or Protestant evangelists or Chinese thought-reformers—that there is a true direction or intention that is ultimately to be accepted, even embraced, once the "resistance" has been overcome. This last assumption, dubious enough when applied to the individual, could be disastrous when applied to history. Moreover, by invoking the term resistance, one could all too readily fall into the psychologistic fallacy of explaining away criticism by examining the critics' involvements and needs, thereby avoiding any consideration of the weaknesses of what is being criticized.

Yet the psychological approach to history does cause discomfort—because it entails formidable problems in method, and because, for many working in both traditions and in other branches of social thought, it threatens to undermine explicit concepts and implicit images about how men behave, why societies change, and what constitutes an acceptable professional discipline or "field." We are all, in other words, formatively bound by our own psychohistorical "place," and by our activity in that place. And so we should be, at least to a point, if our skepticism is to be rooted as well as fertile. But what are the impediments? Why is it so difficult for psychology and history to get together? Generally speaking, I would say that not only do the two traditions often work at cross-purposes; worse, each has something of an impulse to eliminate the other. And this is so even if we limit our observations to depth psychology and to man-centered history.

For instance, there is in classical psychoanalysis an implicit assumption that the larger historical universe is *nothing but* a manifestation of the projections or emanations of the individual psyche. Or if not that, then history is seen as a kind of featureless background for those projections and emanations—something "out there" which is "given," but which does not significantly influence what is "in here." The emergence, over the past few decades, of a more developed "ego psychology" has somewhat altered the situation, by directing our attention to the influence of the environment on the development of the self. But, as Erikson has pointed out, the grudging and impoverished terms used in the psychoanalytic approach to the environment reveal that the approach itself has remained grudging and impoverished. Moreover, ego psychology has had very little to say about shifts in social ethos that are central to historical change—especially those related to the new technological environment and its destructive capacities.

Neo-Freudian psychoanalysis has been ahistorical in other ways. More open to the influence of environment, it has for the most part failed to evolve compelling general principles in the social sphere. And where it has actively sought such principles, as in the work of Abram Kardiner, it has tended to view a culture or a society as a more or less cross-sectional entity within which one can study the relationship of social institutions and "basic personality," but not as evolving phenomena whose relationship is importantly defined by change.[1] Neo-Freudian psychoanalysis thus still finds itself, as much as or at times even more than the Freudian tradition it rebelled against, bound by certain limitations of the rationalistic and mechanistic imagery of the nineteenth-century world view. And when psychoanalysis has moved in a phenomenological or existential direction, its intrapsychic insights, however valuable, have tended to be insulated from historical issues.

Historical writing, about which I can speak with considerably less authority, seems (perhaps somewhat analogously) either to replace a psychological perspective with commonsense assumptions about human motivation, or else to drown psychological man—that is, the inner life of individual man—in a sea of collectivity.

And yet there is much evidence of a longing from both sides for some kind of union—a widely shared recognition that psychological man lives in a history extending beyond himself, and that history is bound up with conflicts and struggles in the minds of men. Indeed, these two simple principles form the basis for a contemporary psychohistory.

THE FREUDIAN MODEL OF PSYCHOHISTORY

I have suggested that the general idea of a psychological approach to history is by no means new. But rather than attempt to document comprehensively the various efforts that have been made in the name of that idea, I would like to focus upon four models (really paradigms) of psychohistory, all of which have emerged in some relationship to the psychoanalytic tradition. Two of them are Freudian, and the other two both draw upon Freud and move away from his historical assumptions.

Freud's most fundamental historical model is not really historical at all,

---

[1] Kardiner was aware of the problem, but precisely the historical complexities of advanced Western (specifically American) society proved refractory to the approach he had evolved in the study of primitive societies. Primitive societies too, of course, could have revealed very different insights had they themselves been approached more from the perspective of historical change. (See especially Kardiner, 1939, 1945.)

but is rather a *pre*-historical paradigm: the primeval encounter between father and sons, in which the sons rebel against the father's authority and kill him, with the entire encounter psychologically centered around the Oedipus complex. This model was first put forward in *Totem and Taboo* (1913) as an explanation for the origins of society itself; and then again in modified form, toward the end of Freud's life, in *Moses and Monotheism* (1938), to account for the origins of Jewish religion and Jewish identity—for how, as Freud put it, the "one man, the man Moses . . . created the Jews." Freud saw Moses as a kind of foster father, an Egyptian who "chose" the Jews as his people and gave to them the gift of monotheism, only to be eventually rejected and murdered by his "chosen people," his symbolic sons.

As Philip Rieff (1963) has pointed out, the model here is that of "a certain event, or events, necessarily in remote rather than near history—indeed, at the beginning—becom[ing] determinative of all that must follow." Rieff suggests that Freud was influenced by certain facets of Judeo-Christian millennial thought and of German historicism, according to which one crucial Event determines and explains all subsequent, and even previous, history. The principle is that of *Kairos*, of the "decisive moment," as opposed to that of *Chronos*, the more orderly sequence of qualitatively identical units of "mathematical time." Freud's historical Event can be said to be a mythical one—the primeval murder of the father, as allegedly reenacted in the Jews' murder of Moses. But it is also individual-psychological, in the sense of being a product of the Oedipus complex, which is seen as the ultimate source of these decisive occurrences. Indeed, one could view Freud's overall historical method as a kind of apologia for the Oedipal Event.[2]

Now there are powerful insights in the two books expressed around this pre-historical encounter, insights that center upon the psychological significance of the perceived historical past for both present and future, and for the movement of history itself. And I shall soon suggest ways in which this model has nourished more recent psychohistorical approaches. But since the model is a mythic one, which transcends history as such, it can be profoundly misleading when it is used to explain specific historical events. (I have in mind particularly a current vogue among psychoanalytic and psychoanalytically-minded observers of viewing recent student rebellions as little more than a repetition of the primeval rebellion of enraged sons against their fathers, as a rebellion explained by—and reducible to—the Oedipus complex. The explanation happens to be congenial to those in authority, the symbolic [or, as I prefer, formative] fathers involved. But it totally neglects the larger historical currents that so forcibly

[2] Discussions suggesting the significance of the Moses event for Freud himself can be found in the Jones biography (1957); in James Strachey's (1964) Introduction to *Moses and Monotheism;* in Freud's own elaborate series of introductory and prefatory notes and summaries interspersed throughout the study; and in Maryse Choisy (1963). Rieff, Erik Erikson, and Kenneth Keniston contributed directly to my understanding of these matters, in their comments following my presentation of much of this paper at our small working group in psychohistory.

intrude upon the psyches of young and old alike, and therefore misrepresents both the individual-psychological and the group processes at play.) For within Freud's prehistoric paradigm there is bequeathed to us an iron mold of psychological repetition (or "repetition compulsion"), enveloping indiscriminately the individual and the undifferentiated collectivity. When this principle of repetition is seen as the essence of historical experience there can be nothing new in history; indeed, if (in Rieff's paraphrase of Freud) "history is predestination," then there is no history at all.

The second Freudian paradigm is perhaps the most obvious one, the one most likely to come to mind when people think of a psychoanalytic approach to history: that of individual psychopathology. The best known example here is the Bullitt-Freud biography of Woodrow Wilson (1967) [3] a work that Bullitt almost certainly wrote but which exemplifies the Freudian approach to history more than many present-day followers of Freud would care to admit. In language and quality of thought, the Wilson biography is a vulgarization of the Freudian paradigm (Freud himself never wrote without elegance). But the idea of interpreting the outcomes of major historical events as expressions of the individual psychopathology of a particular national leader—in this case Wilson's struggles with masculinity and his need to fail—was prefigured in Freud's own work. I have in mind not only his treatment of men like Leonardo and Dostoevski (as great artists rather than political leaders) but also Freud's general focus upon individual psychopathology as existing more or less apart from history. When this second paradigm dominates, psychopathology becomes a substitute for the psychohistorical interface. The psychopathological idiom for individual development (so prominent in the literature of psychoanalysis) becomes extended to the point where it serves as the idiom for history, or psychohistory. When this happens there is, once more, no history.

These two Freudian paradigms—the prehistorical confrontation and the leader's individual psychopathology—come together in their assumption that, in one way or another, history represents the intrapsychic struggles of the individual writ large: the same intrapsychic struggles that can be observed by the psychoanalyst in his therapeutic work. For instance, the scenario of *Totem and Taboo* includes not only the murderous rebellion against the father and the consuming of the father in the totem feast, but the subsequent remorse and residual guilt of the sons, and of their sons and daughters ad infinitum, which then reasserts itself periodically in the phenomenon of the "return of the repressed." [4] The entire argument derives from an individual-psychological model; and precisely the "return of the repressed" becomes the basis for Freud's view of history as psychological recurrence. And in the individual-psychopathological

---

[3] Erik Erikson's review of the book (1967) is itself an important statement on psychohistorical method.

[4] I shall not discuss the question of *how* this guilt is transmitted through the generations, or the problems surrounding the Lamarckian position on the inheritance of acquired characteristics that Freud held to throughout his work.

model, it is the *aberration* of a specific person that is writ large as historical explanation.

No wonder, then, that Freudian models are frustrating to the historian: they interpret but avoid history. They are equally problematic for the historically-minded psychologist. On the one hand Freud's clinical method, as many have pointed out, is entirely historical: it works on the assumption that a man automatically reveals his personal history if he merely lets his mind wander freely—that is, if he engages in free association. And Freud's fundamental discoveries—of the significance of man's individual and collective past—provide the beginning basis for psychohistory. Yet, on the other hand, these same Freudian principles, when applied with closed-system finality, tend to reduce history to *nothing but recurrence,* and thereby to eliminate virtually all that is innovative, or even accumulative, in the story of man.

The Faustian intellectual temptation is to dismiss the paradox and make things simple—either by direct and uncritical application of classical Freudian terms to all manner of historical events, or else by pretending that neither Freud nor the emotional turmoil he described (and himself stimulated) have ever existed. We do better, I am certain, to embrace the paradox, for it can be energizing.

ERIKSON AND THE "GREAT MAN IN HISTORY"

Erik Erikson has done just that. He has retained a focus upon the individual—the great man—and upon the kinds of inner conflicts that are illuminated by the Freudian tradition. But he has placed the great man within a specific historical context: hence the model of *the great man in history.* And with his elaboration of this paradigm something approaching a new psychohistory began to take shape.

Erikson's *Young Man Luther* (1958),[5] a pivotal work for the psychohistorical enterprise, has a direct historical relationship to Freud's *Moses and Monotheism.* Apart from Erikson's connection as a young man with the Freudian circle in Vienna, and his continuing identification of himself as a Freudian, his title is meant to echo Freud's phrase (mentioned earlier), "the man Moses." Freud used that same phrase as his original title for the book he later called *Moses and Monotheism.* I might add that Freud's original subtitle was, "A Historical Novel," which suggests an interesting element of self-irony in relationship to a historical method we must now view as highly dubious (I refer to the kind of evidence Freud employed to develop his thesis that Moses was an Egyptian, and that he was killed by the Jews). That subtitle has also found another recent echo, probably less intentional—"History as a Novel, The Novel as History"—the subtitle chosen by a promising young existentialist psychohistorian named Norman Mailer for his much-awarded book, *Armies of the Night.* The self-irony in juxta-

[5] See also Erikson (1950, 1964, 1968a, 1969).

posing history and fiction does not necessarily suggest that either Freud or Mailer lacked belief in his own views, but rather that each felt himself to be dealing with a kind of truth that took him beyond conventional historical description. Rather than truth stranger than fiction, each was suggesting a form of fictionalized truth, or perhaps fiction truer than truth.

Returning to Erikson, there are other ways in which his concept of the great man parallels Freud's. At the end of *Moses,* Freud said that "The great man influences his contemporaries in two ways: through his personality and through the idea for which he stands"—an "idea" which may "lay stress on an old group of wishes in the masses, or point to a new aim for their wishes." Freud saw Moses as having taken the Jews to a "higher level of spirituality," largely by means of the "dematerializing" of God and the prohibiting of the worship of a visible form of God. Similarly, Erikson saw as Luther's fundamental achievement, his "new emphasis on man in *inner* conflict and his salvation through introspective perfection"—an achievement and an emphasis Erikson compared with Kierkegaard's existentialism and Freud's psychoanalysis. Freud and Erikson both depicted the great man as a spiritual hero, as a man who achieves an intrapsychic breakthrough.

But Erikson also took several crucial steps away from Freud. Instead of an instinctual idiom—Freud's view of the great man as appealing to instinctual wishes (particularly aggressive ones), and possessing the ability to bring about in the masses a form of "instinctual renunciation" (control of aggression and "subordinat[ion of] sense perception to an abstract idea")—Erikson has sought out more specifically *historical* ground, the intersection of individual and collective histories. Luther's achievement, then, depends not so much upon instinctual renunciation as upon a quality Erikson sees Luther, Gandhi, and Freud to have shared: "a grim willingness to do the dirty work of their ages."

That "dirty work," though clearly involved with psychological universals, is historically specific. "We cannot lift a case history out of history," Erikson tells us. And he feels constrained to ask of himself and of his readers the kind of immersion he imagines Luther to have had in such early sixteenth-century matters confronting the young German aspirant to the priesthood as: the contradictions between ideal Catholic spirituality and the "high spiritual finance" of monetary purchase of immortality via the practice of indulgences; the influence of Occamism in Catholic theology; the prevailing child-rearing practices and standards of family (especially father-son) relationships; the discipline of monastic training; and the complexities of the Catholic response to the Renaissance. In all this, we leave behind Freud's concept of the traumatic historical event, followed by repression, and then by the "return of the repressed" in the form of guilt and conflict. We concern ourselves instead with the great man's monumental struggles at the border between religion and politics, with his effort to remake himself and his world simultaneously. For Luther to emerge from his own identity crisis, he had to bring about a shift in the historical identity of his epoch. He had to engage in a desperate effort "to lift his individual patienthood to the level of the universal one, and to try to solve for all what he could not solve for himself alone."

By "patienthood" Erikson (here following Kierkegaard) means exemplar of ultimate alternatives. One of the extraordinary qualities of Erikson's rendition of the young Luther is the book's painstaking exploration of the very tenuous psychic boundaries between identity crisis, psychosis, theological innovation, and individual and historical revitalization. What Erikson has demonstrated—in this study of Luther as in his more recent book on Gandhi—is a combination of psychoanalytic sensitivity and historical imagination. The combination has been long in coming.

ONE MODEL: SHARED HISTORICAL THEMES

But the great man tends to be inaccessible, at least to direct interview; or if accessible, not yet great. One must usually approach him through records or, if he belongs to recent history, through interviews with surviving friends and followers. This does not mean that the psychohistorian cannot say useful things on the basis of careful observations from a distance. But when he is centuries removed from the individual he wishes to study in depth, problems of historical reconstruction are inevitable.

Freud (1938) faced these problems with the cavalier grandiosity of a genius —as one particularly memorable footnote in *Moses and Monotheism* makes clear:

> *I am very well aware that in dealing so autocratically and arbitrarily with Biblical tradition—bringing it up to confirm my views when it suits me and unhesitatingly rejecting it when it contradicts me—I am exposing myself to serious methodological criticism and weakening the convincing force of my arguments. But this is the only way in which one can treat material of which one knows definitely that its trustworthiness has been severely impaired by the distorting influence of tendentious purposes. It is to be hoped that I shall find some degree of justification later on, when I come upon the track of these secret motives. Certainty is in any case unattainable and moreover it may be said that every other writer on the subject has adopted the same procedure (p. 27).*

While one cannot but admire Freud's honesty and boldness, the method seems a somewhat dubious one for the aspiring psychohistorian.

Erikson is much more careful with his historical data, but he too runs into difficulties. For instance, he is forced to recreate certain psychological themes of Luther's early family life on the basis of very limited evidence. And problems have also been raised about events in Luther's adult life, notably his celebrated "fit in the choir" during which he made his dramatic statement of negation of identity: "I am *not!*" Erikson himself points out that it is not known whether "Martin roared in Latin or in German," and others have questioned whether he roared at all—that is, whether the episode actually took place.

Apart from specific problems of reconstruction, there is the larger question concerning the extent to which any individual person, great or otherwise, can exemplify an entire historical epoch—or even (as in Erikson's treatment of Luther) its major collective psychological struggles. The question takes on special force during our unprecedentedly diverse and fickle century, no less so if raised in connection with the past.

Hence the emergence of another recent approach: that of *shared psychohistorical themes,* as observed in men and women exposed to particular kinds of individual and collective experience. Examples here are Kenneth Keniston's (1965, 1968) studies of alienated, and then activist, American students; and Robert Coles' (1967) work with children and adults in the midst of racial antagonism and social change. I have been much concerned with the development of this method and ask indulgence for discussing it in relationship to my own work.

I have conducted interview studies of three specific groups of people whose historical exposures seemed to me to have bearing on important characteristics of our era: Chinese and Westerners who underwent Chinese thought-reform (or "brainwashing") (1961); Japanese university students during the early sixties (1970); and Hiroshima survivors of the atomic bomb (1968a). My focus has been upon themes, forms, and images that are in significant ways shared, rather than upon the life of a single person as such.

The shared-themes approach is based upon a psychoanalytically derived stress on what goes on inside of people. But, as compared with Erikson's great-man paradigm, it moves still further from classical analytic tradition. That is, it moves outward from the individual in the direction of collective historical experience. It explicitly rejects the nineteenth-century scientific model of man as a mechanism propelled by quantities of energy—energy internally generated by means of instinctual drives, partially held in check by certain defense mechanisms (notably repression), but eventually erupting in the form of various actions of the individual directed at his outer environment. This instinctual idiom (and, one may say, world view) gives way to a symbolic and formative one.

The shared-themes approach also requires considerable innovation in interview method. For more than fifteen years I have found myself struggling with modifications of the psychiatric and psychoanalytic interview, in order to approach and understand various kinds of people who have not sought therapeutic help but, on the contrary, have been sought out by me. And sought out not because of any form of psychological disturbance as such, but because of particular experiences they have undergone—experiences that may indeed be (and usually have been) disturbing, but which both they and I see as having wider significance than any individual incapacities incurred, psychological or otherwise. I found myself developing a much freer interview style than the one I was taught in my professional training. It remains probing, encouraging the widest range of associations, and includes detailed life histories and explorations of dreams. But it focuses upon the specific situation responsible for bringing the two of us (most of the interviews have been individual ones) together, and takes the form of something close to an open dialogue emerging from that situation.

The relationship we develop is neither that of doctor and patient nor of ordinary friends, though at moments it can seem to resemble either. It is more one of shared exploration—mostly of the world of the person sought out,[6] but including a great deal of give-and-take, and more than a little discussion of my own attitudes and interests. It requires, in other words, a combination of humane spontaneity and professional discipline. Needless to say, one's way of combining the two is always idiosyncratic, and always less than ideal.

The method I am describing is partly empirical (in its stress upon specific data from interviews); partly phenomenological, or, as I prefer, formative (in its stress upon forms and images that are simultaneously individual and collective); and partly speculative (in its use of interview data, together with many other observations, to posit relationships between man and his history, and to suggest concepts that eliminate the artificial separation of the two). In this speculation, the investigator has the advantage of beginning from concrete information that is a product of his own direct perceptions. While I recognize that subjective distortion can render the advantage a mixed one, I think it can be said that exaggerated concerns with detached objectivity have too often caused us to undervalue what can be learned about history from our direct perceptions.

Within this perspective, all shared behavior is seen as simultaneously involved in a trinity of universality (that which is related to the psychobiological quests of all men in all historical epochs), specific cultural emphasis and style (as evolved by a particular people over centuries), and recent and contemporary historical influences (the part of the trinity that is most likely to be neglected in psychological work). My point is that any shared event is all of these. The weighting of the components may vary, but nothing is *purely* universal, or cultural-historical, or contemporary-historical; everything is all three. The overall approach, or at least my sense of it, is most fundamentally influenced by Freud and Erikson, but it is also influenced by Susanne Langer and Ernst Cassirer, Otto Rank, Albert Camus, Lancelot Law Whyte, David Riesman, and R. G. Collingwood; and by Leslie Farber, Kenneth Keniston, Benjamin Schwartz, and Philip Rieff.

[6] We have no good term for the person in this situation. The traditional one, "research subject," seems increasingly unsatisfactory to me because it suggests someone merely "studied" or "investigated" in a more or less passive way. "Patient" is entirely inappropriate, and "client" is not much better. "Historical actor" and "pivotal person" come closer, but they have their own ambiguities. I believe there will be a number of new terms developed, and also new methods of investigation and interview (we already depend, to a much greater extent than my discussion indicates, upon group interviews and a host of other informal approaches), which capture, in *active ways,* lived history. I would go so far as to say that progress in psychohistory depends upon these innovations in method. Once they have been developed in the study of contemporary matters, such innovations could also become applicable to the study of the past, though mainly in relationship to the search for and interpretation of various kinds of records and documents.

THE TECHNIQUE OF THE SHARED-THEMES APPROACH

Let me describe my use of the shared-themes approach in six months of research in Hiroshima (in 1962) on the psychological effects of the atomic bomb, and in subsequent writings on that subject. The work centered mainly on intensive interviews with 75 atomic-bomb survivors, about half of them chosen at random from an official list, the other half specially selected because of their active involvement over the years in atomic-bomb problems. Most of the interviews were tape-recorded, and the book I wrote about the work took shape mainly from those interviews, making extensive use of direct quotations to illustrate the death-haunted responses I encountered. But in both the research and the book, I moved outward from interviews with individual survivors to groups they formed, leaders who emerged from among them, and social currents in Hiroshima that they both created and were affected by. This in turn required close attention to the post-atomic-bomb history of the city, and to the relationship of that special history to the rest of Japan and the world at large, as well as to the city's own earlier heritage. A significant part of that history consisted of creative struggles—of writers, painters, and film-makers both from within and outside the city—to come to terms with Hiroshima. And these historical and creative struggles were deeply bound up with issues of memorialization and commemoration, with efforts to move beyond the bomb while remaining true to its dead.

Finally, through a detailed elaboration of the ethos of the survivor, I was in some degree able to unite the individual-psychological and historical currents I had observed. I compared survival of the atomic bomb to survival of other massive death immersions—of Nazi persecutions in our time, and of the plagues in the Middle Ages (as the latter reveal themselves through records), as well as to survival of natural disasters, and of the "ordinary" deaths of close friends and family members. I could then (in this and subsequent studies) raise questions about the general importance of the survivor ethos for our age, of the degree to which we have become historically prone to the survivor's retained death imprint, to his death guilt and his psychic numbing (or desensitization to death-dominated images), and to his struggle for significance (or what I call, after Langer, his *formulation*). These questions now intrude into virtually all my work, and I do not think it is too much to say that they haunt the contemporary imagination.

Thus, in my more recent book, *Revolutionary Immortality*, I discuss Mao Tse-tung's relationship to the Chinese Cultural Revolution in terms of his many experiences of individual and revolutionary survival. I relate his creative use of the survivor state to his extraordinary accomplishments as a leader, and consider the general relevance of death symbolism, in its broadest historical perspective, to the present Chinese Cultural Revolution. By connecting certain psychological characteristics of Mao's personal and revolutionary style with the predominant themes of the Cultural Revolution, I attempt to combine the great-man and shared-themes approaches.

The central thesis of the book revolves around Mao's anticipation of his own impending death, as well as his and his followers' fear of the "death of the revolution." What I see as the overwhelming threat Mao faces is not so much death itself as the suggestion that his "revolutionary works" will not endure. By revolutionary immortality, then, I mean a shared sense of participating in permanent revolutionary ferment, and of transcending individual death by "living on" indefinitely within this continuing revolution. I point out that some such vision has been present in all revolutions, and was directly expressed in Trotsky's principle of "permanent revolution," but that it has taken on unprecedented intensity in present-day Chinese Communist experience. This quest for revolutionary immortality provides a general framework within which the political and economic struggles, as well as the anti-bureaucratic and anti-revisionist assaults of the Cultural Revolution can be examined, without being reduced to a particular psychological or psychopathological trait of any one person.

Also related to that quest is a pattern that reflects the excruciating Maoist struggles with technology. I call that pattern "psychism," by which I mean an exaggerated reliance upon psychic power as a means of controlling the external environment, an attempt to replace the requirements of technology with pure revolutionary will. Technology is sought desperately, but feelings are cultivated. In this pattern of psychism, there is once more a coming together of Mao's personal-revolutionary style—including what Chinese Communist commentators themselves refer to as his "revolutionary romanticism"—with a number of larger currents surrounding the Cultural Revolution. The concept of psychism, like that of revolutionary immortality, is an attempt to say something about precisely that psychohistorical interface.

The book was not based upon the kind of detailed interview approach I described in relationship to my Hiroshima work. Rather, it is a brief, interpretive essay, which draws heavily upon documents and observations by others of the Cultural Revolution, as well as upon the writings of Mao; it drew upon only a very limited number of interviews with participants and observers of the events described. As compared with the Hiroshima study, it is more tenuous and more vulnerable. But I wrote it because I was convinced that the themes and concepts I develop in it could shed light on a mysteriously explosive social upheaval—and because I thought it a useful experiment in the pursuit of psycho-history.

THE SEARCH FOR IMMORTALITY

Yet the post-Freudian paradigms, like the Freudian ones, do not make clear exactly what they "explain," and fall far short of providing coherent theories of historical causation. The Freudian paradigms, we recall, lean heavily upon instinctual energies and struggles, which inevitably reduce themselves to the Oedipal Event, whether in connection with a pre-historical generational conflict or with the psychopathology of a leading historical actor. Now, if broadened, this principle of the Oedipal Event could be made to connect with more inclusive versions of generational impasse, in keeping with Ortega y Gasset's (1960) belief that "the concept of the generation is the most important one in the whole of history." But Ortega had in mind the "three different and vital times" (or twenty-, forty-, and sixty-year-olds) "lodged together in a single external and chronological fragment of time," which in turn provide an "internal lack of equilibrium," because of which "history moves, changes, wheels, and flows" (pp. 32–39). Implicit in Ortega's view, then, is an examination of the precise nature of these "three different and vital times," of precisely the historical dimension which Freudian models have tended to ignore.

Erikson's great-man paradigm looks for historical causation in the leader's singular capacity, and absolute need, so to speak, to carry history with him as he breaks out from, and transcends, his own demonic intrapsychic conflicts. Since these conflicts are rooted in the leader's historical period, and his solution affects a great collectivity of his contemporaries as well as subsequent generations, the great-man approach is relatively more specific than the other paradigms in its causal explanations. But we still sense a theoretical gap between the individual and the collectivity that none of the paradigms has fully bridged.

The shared-themes approach is the most diffuse of the four paradigms, though in many ways the most attuned to historical complexity. Within it, effect can become virtually indistinguishable from cause. A group understood to be *created by* a particular historical Event (the Hiroshima survivors), or by an evolving set of historical vicissitudes (dissident Japanese or American youth), is also seen simultaneously to *act upon* and affect history—by epitomizing, exacerbating, and suggesting something beyond, the immediate conflicts and visions of large numbers of contemporaries. If this kind of explanation, strictly speaking, deals more with historical flow than it does with cause, at least it leaves open many possibilities for more subtle theoretical explorations that relate cause and effect to evolving patterns and directions. Among these future possibilities are additional combinations of the shared-themes and great-man approach; and new ways of conceptualizing radical historical shifts—the breakdown and re-creation of the forms of human culture (biological, experiential, institutional, technological, aesthetic, and interpretive)—or what I call a New History (1969, 1970).

In both of the post-Freudian paradigms, the social theory that is necessary to bridge the gap between individual and collectivity remains fragmented, implicit, unclear, or nonexistent. One solution would be to graft onto either of the two paradigms such relatively established and comprehensive social theory as the neo-Marxist concepts of alienation and overspecialization. Useful as that might be, my own view is that much of the necessary theory will have to be constructed anew. In approaching intellectual traditions of all kinds, we may do better to draw upon them partially and critically—sometimes even fragmentally—as we construct new combinations of ideas from our continuing investigation of shared psychohistorical themes. Most of all, we should avoid that form of professional territoriality that insists that psychological, sociological, and historical realms remain categorically discrete, with each holding fast to an explanatory principle that is claimed to subsume, or to exist independently of, all else.

PROTEAN MAN—A MODERN PHENOMENON

The concept of revolutionary immortality is part of a more general theory of symbolic immortality I have been attempting to develop,[7] which concerns man's need, in the face of inevitable biological death, to maintain an inner sense of continuity with what has gone on before, and what will go on after, his own individual existence. From this standpoint, the *sense* of immortality is much more than mere denial of death (though it can certainly be bound up with denial). Rather, it is part of the compelling, life-enhancing imagery that binds each individual person to significant groups and events that are removed from him in place and time. The sense of immortality may be expressed biologically, by living on through (or in) one's sons and daughters and their sons and daughters; theologically, in the idea of a life after death, or in other forms of spiritual conquest of death; creatively, or through "works" and influences perceived as persisting beyond biological death; through identification with nature and its infinite extension into time and space (the idea of "eternal nature"); or experientially, through a feeling-state—one I speak of as experiential transcendence—so intense that, at least temporarily, time and death are eliminated (the mode classically employed by mystics).

What I wish to suggest is that this sense of immortality serves as the individual's connection with man's general past and future, as the individual's inner perception of his involvement in what we call the historical process. Much of human history consists of the struggle to achieve, maintain, and reaffirm a shared or collective sense of immortality under constantly changing psychic and material conditions.

Generally speaking, imagery of immortality has shifted, over the course of history, from the magical, to the supernatural, to the natural and man-centered—from literal promise of eternal life to more *symbolic* expressions of human continuity. One must add, however, that the emerging discussion and practice of "cryonics," the freezing of bodies from the time of death in the hope of later restoring life, returns us to the most literal kind of quest for direct bodily immortality. In any case, the shifting and recombining of modes of immortality mark great turning points in human history. The Darwinian Revolution, for instance, epitomized the shift from the theological to the biological mode, and did so in relationship both to man's origins and to his destiny. A shift of this kind, of course, can be neither total nor unopposed, and we are still in the midst of its reverberations.

Hiroshima and the subsequent development of nuclear weapons can be viewed as another major shift, perhaps more in the undermining of existing modes of immortality than in any clear suggestion of new combinations. Indeed, one way of viewing our present world-wide crisis, in terms other than political,

---

[7] I introduced the concept of symbolic immortality in my essay, "On Death and Death Symbolism: The Hiroshima Disaster" (1964), refer to it in a number of subsequent writings, and discuss in detail its general (and especially historical) ramifications in a forthcoming volume. *The Broken Connection.*

is as a form of radical psychohistorical dislocation, associated with the breakdown of viable modes of symbolic immortality. What has broken down is the sense of connection men have long felt with the vital and nourishing symbols of their cultural traditions, the sense of connection with their own history. Our sense of historical continuity (or of symbolic immortality) is now being profoundly threatened: by simple historical velocity, which subverts the imagery—notably the theological imagery—in which it has been traditionally maintained; and by nuclear and other ultimate weapons which, by their very existence, call into question all modes of immortality. When we consider (more often unconsciously or preconsciously than with clear awareness) the possibility of nuclear or bacteriological warfare, we can hardly be certain of living on in our children or grandchildren, in our works or influences upon others, in some form of theological conquest of death, or even in nature, which we now know to be itself vulnerable to our weapons. The striking contemporary reliance upon the fifth mode of symbolic immortality mentioned earlier, that of experiential transcendence—whether through drugs or other forms of "turned-on" psychic states—may well be a reflection of precisely this decline in our belief in the other four modes. We hunger for both connection and transcendence, and we have need to experiment with the historical and anti-historical boundaries of both.

In America we feel this kind of dislocation profoundly, so much so that we may well be in the vanguard of two specific responses to it. The first, which can have highly malignant consequences, entails an embrace—even deification—of technology as a new mode of immortality through which we seek to perpetuate ourselves. This embrace of technology can be associated with great adventure, and with other forms of imaginative transcendence, as in the case of the space program. But it takes on grotesque contours when the technology involved is that of weaponry. We then witness the development, not only in America but throughout the world, of what I call "the religion of nuclearism," an attitude of worship toward weapons of destruction, and a dependence upon them to solve otherwise baffling human problems—ultimately, the investment in them of the sense of immortality that has been lost.

A second response to historical dislocation is the emergence of what I call Protean man (1968b)—by which I mean a relatively new life-style, characterized by interminable exploration and flux, by a self-process that is capable of relatively easy shifts in belief and identification—a life-style that is post-modern and in some ways post-Freudian. Protean man has been created not only by the dislocations I have mentioned, but by the revolution in mass media as well. I have in mind the flooding of imagery produced by the extraordinary flow of post-modern cultural influences over mass communication networks, so that each individual can be touched, and at times significantly affected, by virtually everything, and presented with endless partial alternatives in every sphere of life, whether superficial messages, undigested cultural elements, or moving evocations.

These two concepts—symbolic immortality and Protean man—provide me with a way of returning to where we began, to psychologists and historians in the midst of a difficult struggle to create a new psychohistory.

To be sure, the theory of symbolic immortality can hardly resolve the many-sided dilemmas of historical causation. But it does seem to me to be a potentially useful way of looking at man in history—most specifically as a framework for the study of revolutions and of a variety of related problems of historical continuity and discontinuity. The general point of view seems also to be given force by the death-dominated times in which it emerges; history itself does much to create the ways in which we, at any particular moment, decide to study it.

Concerning the Protean style, I bring it up not only as a way of epitomizing contemporary experience but for another reason as well. Since I believe that this style in some degree inhabits us all, I assume further that it affects our relationship to ideas—the ways in which we respond to them, believe them, and attach them to our sense of self. Protean man is continuously open to new ideas and can move among them rather freely; his difficulty lies in giving lasting allegiance to any particular idea or idea-system. I do not believe that scholars are immune from this pattern; hence the intellectual restlessness within most disciplines—the dissatisfaction with established concepts, together with the failure of newer concepts of equal authority to appear.

Those working in the area of psychohistory, where established concepts hardly exist, are especially likely to encounter such restlessness in both their readers and themselves. It will not be easy to discover, and then collectively maintain, the kind of authoritative conceptual principles we have come to expect and depend upon within an intellectual tradition. Moreover, there is a sense in which psychohistory adds to the burdens of a discipline already immersed in difficult struggles to replace no longer acceptable nineteenth-century versions of history as clear narrative, or epic, or inevitable destiny—struggles to come to grips with the convoluted, opaque, and deadly actualities of the twentieth century. Psychohistory, at least in the version I have been describing, tends to complexify rather than simplify, which I think is as it should be. And Protean tendencies among scholars can render them receptive to the new principles of psychohistory and yet cautious in granting them intellectual authority, which is also as it should be.

Within these uncertainties lie extraordinary possibilities. These too are Protean, and I think one can observe in contemporary man an increasing capacity for coming to what would have previously been viewed as impossible intellectual combinations and innovations. Compared with his predecessors, he is not only less bound by tradition, but much more fluid in his potential integration of very diverse conceptual elements. And the new psychohistory—having stated my reservations and qualifications, I think I can begin to call it that—emerges as itself a radical investigative response to a radically dislocated historical epoch.

Despite what I speak of as Protean possibilities, and what some perceive as an exotic aura surrounding the idea of psychohistory, all that I have said here and experienced in my investigations militates strongly against facile intellectual efforts or the creation of "instant psychohistorians." To the contrary, the approach seems to require not only a central commitment to one of the disciplines (or a related one) and a considerable knowledge of the other, but something more:

a considerable ethical concern with the problems being investigated. Erik Erikson has hardly been neutral in his feelings about Luther's achievements or about what Gandhi's legacy might still mean for the world. Nor has Keniston been neutral about student radicals, Coles about minority-group aspirations, nor I about Hiroshima and its legacy. Rather, all of us have been struggling toward ways of acknowledging our involvements and exploring their relationship to our findings, toward making conceptual use of these very involvements. (See Erikson, 1968b.)

The developments I have so far discussed have for the most part come from the psychological direction. This is not because historians have been totally aloof from psychohistory: they have in fact produced a number of important studies within it. But at this phase, beginning with Erikson, the focus seems to be upon concepts emerging from the psychoanalytic heritage, even if in great tension with that heritage. No one knows what will happen in the future, but one can be sure that things will change. Psychohistory could be an avenue toward the revitalization of psychoanalysis itself, through which the latter might rediscover its own history and thereby transform itself. Or psychohistory could develop more autonomously and, despite (partly because of) its profound debt to psychoanalysis, separate itself decisively from the ahistorical bias of that tradition.

In the end, psychohistory may turn out to be nothing more than a minor intellectual curiosity. Or—and I confess that this is my belief—it could develop into a significant body of thought, whose evolving ideas will be as compelling as they are difficult to establish. However things turn out, psychohistory will benefit from the disciplined, free spirits who, whatever their origin, bring their critical imaginations to bear upon it.

REFERENCES

Bullitt, W. C., and Freud, S. (1967). *Thomas Woodrow Wilson: Twenty-eighth President of the United States—A Psychological Study*. Boston: Houghton Mifflin.

Choisy, M. (1963). *Sigmund Freud: A New Appraisal*. New York: Philosophical Library.

Coles, R. (1967). *Children of Crisis*. New York: Harcourt, Brace.

Erikson, E. (1950). *Childhood and Society*. New York: Norton.

—— (1958). *Young Man Luther*. New York: Norton.

—— (1964). *Insight and Responsibility*. New York: Norton.

—— (1967). Review of *Thomas Woodrow Wilson: Twenty-eighth President of the United States—A Psychological Study*, by W. C. Bullitt and S. Freud. *International Journal of Psycho-Analysis*, 48:462–468.

—— (1968a). *Identity: Youth and Crisis*. New York: Norton.

—— (1968b). On the Nature of Psycho-historical Evidence: In Search of Ghandhi. *Daedalus*, Summer.

—— (1969). *Gandhi's Truth*. New York: Norton.

Freud, S. (1913). Totem and Taboo. *Standard Edition*, 13:1–161. London: Hogarth Press, 1955.

—— (1938). Moses and Monotheism. *Standard Edition*, 23:7–137. London: Hogarth Press, 1964.

Jones, E. (1957). *The Life and Work of Sigmund Freud*. New York: Basic Books.

Kardiner, A. (1939). *The Individual and His Society*. New York: Columbia University Press.

———— et al. (1945). *The Psychological Frontiers of Society*. New York: Columbia University Press.

Keniston, K. (1965). *The Uncommitted*. New York: Harcourt, Brace.

———— (1968). *Young Radicals*. Boston: Atlantic-Little Brown.

Lifton, R. J. (1961). *Thought Reform and the Psychology of Totalism*. New York: Norton.

———— (1964). On Death and Death Symbolism: The Hiroshima Disaster. *Psychiatry*, 27:191–210.

———— (1968a). *Death in Life: Survivors of Hiroshima*. New York: Random House.

———— (1968b). Protean Man. *Partisan Review*, 35 (1):13–27. Reprinted with further commentary on the concept in *History and Human Survival*. New York: Random House, 1970.

———— (1969). The Young and the Old—Notes on a New History. *Atlantic Monthly*, September and October.

———— (1970). *History and Human Survival*. New York: Random House.

Ortega y Gasset, J. (1960). *What Is Philosophy?* New York: Norton.

Rieff, P. (1963). The Meaning of History and Religion in Freud's Thought. In: *Psychoanalysis and History*, ed. B. Mazlish. Englewood Cliffs, N.J.: Prentice-Hall.

Strachey, J. (1964). Introduction to Moses and Monotheism. *Standard Edition, 23*:3–5. London: Hogarth Press, 1964.

SOME REFLECTIONS ON THE CONTRIBUTION OF PSYCHOANALYSIS TO BIOGRAPHY

Bernard C. Meyer, M.D.

To some extent the history of the application of psychoanalysis to biography has tended to reflect the historical evolution of psychoanalysis itself. A number of the earlier biographical works carry the clinical stamp of Freud's (1911) Schreber paper; intentionally or not, the objects of these inquiries were often viewed as "cases," and the entire enterprise bore the unfelicitous designation *pathography*, thereby emphasizing the basic concern with abnormality and leading to the conclusion that what psychoanalysis had to offer to an understanding of the lives of great men consisted mainly in a documentation and explication of their foibles and follies. Like much of the psychoanalytic thinking of the times, moreover, these studies were often preoccupied with drive and defense—a sort of *chassis-orientation*, wherein the engine and brakes are equated with the entire vehicle. Hitschmann's (1956) assertion, for instance, that the philosopher "reveals by his endless doubting, searching, struggling, that he has never done with the primary problems and 'suffers' from them all his life," represents a rather monocular view of some of the greatest thinkers in the history of mankind (p. 36). The same may be said of his characterization of the career of Albert Schweitzer as an expression of reaction-formation (p. 249), a formulation that is to be deplored, not because it is incorrect, but because it is restricted. Commenting on this same study, Kohut (1960) has reminded us that an awareness of the misery existing in the world and the determination to live a life devoted to the suffering are also manifestations of the autonomous attitudes of a mature ego.

These comments are especially appropriate to the biography of Woodrow Wilson by Freud and Bullitt, who, giving but passing attention to the fact that Wilson became a world leader and a figure of impressive importance in his time, appear to have dispensed an overdose of rather acrid criticism in demonstrating that "Little Tommy Wilson" was an emotionally disturbed and morally weak man. Bearing in mind that, despite its recent date of publication, the Wilson book was written many years ago, it is comforting to tell one's self that it is a work characteristic of its epoch. It is no less tempting to claim that, parallel with the development of an ego psychology, the application of psychoanalysis to the field of biography has been characterized by more sophisticated and comprehensive studies, and by a lessening of what Erikson has called "an almost obsessional preoccupation with 'the unconscious' and a . . . dogmatic emphasis on inner processes as the only true essence of things human." Indeed only when it is stripped of such reductionism and its attendant parochial limitations can psychoanalysis make good its potential and valuable contribution to biography. What this can be has been succinctly expressed by Herbert Muller (1952) who, speaking of the study of history, wrote: "The main problem is not so much to fill in the many gaps of our factual knowledge, as to make sense out of the vast deal that we do know. For a historical fact never speaks for itself" (pp. 34–35). In the interest of making sense out of the vast deal we know about the lives of great men, psychoanalysis can be a remarkably precise and useful tool.

Yet, like many scientific instruments, both its precision and its usefulness are contingent upon the aptitude, the knowledge, and the intelligence of the user, and among its practitioners these qualifications vary considerably both in the field of therapy and in that of psychoanalysis applied to biography. For some, despite the lack of a license or other qualifications, the latter field enjoys a sort of perpetual open season, during which a gaggle of sitting subjects may be peppered with analytic buckshot. An example of such "wild" analysis may be found in Binion's (1968) recent biography of Lou Andreas-Salomé, in which the author unhesitatingly announces the cause of his subject's unhappy childhood: "A craving for her father excited by excretion and attended by darkling visions of re-entering his bowel-womb to repossess his penis" (p. 6). Now, aside from wondering what this sentence might mean, the reader may justly ask by what route the author arrived there, for there is nothing in the text up to this point—31 lines of the book so far—that has paved the way for any conclusion whatever, let alone this somewhat extravagant one. Psychoanalysis is not an arcanum nor an exercise in revealed truth; neither is it in the nature of its methodology, nor in that of any scientific discipline, for that matter, to initiate a study or an experiment with an unproven conclusion.

Imagine what an analytic shooting party might be enjoyed with this earliest memory of a distinguished Frenchman! It concerned Sunday mornings in the town of E, when the subject was four or five years old and the town would be awakened by the bugles of the fire department.

They would come down our street once a week, wearing antiquated helmets and hauling a hand pump, in order to test the hydrant. They always played the same tune: "As-tu vu la casquette, la casquette . . ." but this martial reveille never failed to delight me. My father would come in, pick me up in his arms, wrapping my long nightgown around my bare feet, and find a place for me beside him at the window. The fire chief, recognizable by his red plume, would shout to us: "Bonjour, messieurs!" To see the hose being unrolled, the powerful jet of water that rose higher than the house, the frail ladder that was hoisted, section by section, to the roofs, seemed to me the finest spectacle in the world. Then the ladder would be slid back into place, the hose would be rolled up again on its drum, the chief with the copper helmet would order: "Fall in!", the firemen would form a column of two's, the bugler would play La Casquette, and the company would set off in tune to the music toward the next hydrant.

Who could read this charming vignette without finding in it a tempting morsel for "analytic" interpretation? Here indeed are "obvious" allusions to bed-wetting, fire-setting, screen memories of father's impressive genital, and perhaps of primal scenes, and finally the early sources of a later distinguished career in urology. All such speculations, however, must be viewed as guesswork, which may be as wide of the mark as the allusion to urology, for the passage comes from *I Remember, I Remember,* an autobiographical memoir by André Maurois. "But of course!" exclaims the intrepid enthusiast. "In this early memory of a scopophilic experience, one can discover the origins of Maurois' later curiosity about the lives of great men; this is the cradle of his career as a biographer. The fire chief with the red plume is clearly D'Artagnan, the creation of the elder Dumas, who, together with his father and his son, was the subject of one of Maurois' great works." How fortunate are we psychoanalytic biographers! We have an answer for nearly everything.

Aside from problems caused by inadequacies in training or by faulty methodology, serious difficulties in the application of psychoanalysis to biography result from emotional factors residing in the biographer and notably in his rela-tionship to his subject. In his *Leonardo* study, Freud (1910) cautioned the biog-rapher against idealizing his subject in order to gratify an infantile fantasy, of which the all-too-evident corollary would surely be the danger of utilizing biog-raphy as a vehicle for venting hostile sentiments; these too, carrying a strong charge of countertransference, may be rooted in the writer's remote past. It is indeed doubtful, however, whether any biographer, analytic or not, can remain entirely untouched by such influences; how otherwise could one account for the impulse to narrate the great man's life in the first place?

Kohut (1960) has suggested that the analyst who is drawn to biographical studies of the artist may belong to a particular group in which there has existed a greater than average need for artistic expression during adolescence and early adulthood (p. 585). If this is true, it would provide an additional determinant for the identification between the analyst-biographer and his artist subject; indeed, in the event of a felicitous endowment of the analyst with a literary gift, his own work may emerge as an artistic production in its own right. (Here we have a variation of the apochryphal story of the young man, who, bowing to parental pressure, forsook his theatrical ambitions to become a surgeon. Many years later, after completing a particularly brilliant brain operation, he responded to an out-burst of spontaneous applause in the gallery by removing the appendix as an encore.) "A good biography", wrote Julian Symons in the Introduction to his brother's life of Frederick Rolfe, *The Quest For Corvo* (1966),

. . . is prompted not by the inherent qualities of the subject, but by the biographer's consciously or unconsciously realized opportunity for self-expression.

Johnson is in some sort the creation of Boswell as Richard Savage was the creation of Johnson. . . . a biography can never be objectively true; that is what distinguishes it from a record of social or historical fact . . . The features in a biography are all distinct enough and they are recognizably the features of the subject, but the hunted eyes and the hunting nose, the wafer-thin mouth and the rocky chin are the biographer's own.

Clearly the emotional needs of any biographer will determine the nature of the created portrait, which, like some idealized paintings of royal personages, may be unrecognizable save to the prejudiced eye of the idolator. Such practitioners of what has been ingeniously termed the "cherry-tree school" of biography are inevitably obliged to sift and censor the more unpalatable realities of their subject's life in order to recreate a figure not only *sans peur et sans reproche* but also *sans* perverse instinctual drives and *sans* unconscious thought processes. In their illuminating study *Beethoven and His Nephew*, the Sterbas (1954) have called attention to the fact that Beethoven's first biographer, Anton Schindler, destroyed more than 250 of the 400-odd "conversation books" by means of which the deaf composer conversed with others, an action that was clearly designed to eliminate certain unsavory data from the life of the man whom Schindler repeatedly referred to as "our hero."

Not infrequently the process of mythmaking is abetted by the unseen complicity of the subject himself. Thus, despite rather persuasive evidence that a bullet wound in the chest suffered by Joseph Conrad in his younger days as a French sailor was self-inflicted, there is an eager coterie of biographers, who, taking their cue from Conrad's quasi-autobiographical *Arrow of Gold*, have engaged in somewhat tortured reasoning to prove that he was shot in a duel of honor. No less striking is the collaboration in mythmaking between the French aviator and writer, Antoine de Saint-Exupéry, and his biographers. Writing like a latter-day Saint Paul in a volume entitled *Passion et Mort de Saint-Exupéry*, Jules Roy (1964) likens his subject to a Knight of the Holy Grail or to Christ himself: "In his pilot's seat," writes Roy, "his face had already lost its earthly appearance acquiring a sort of supernatural virtue; at the controls . . . he suddenly became a God, and the most powerful of all, Jupiter thundering, his eye on the world and his hand on the thunderbolt." Roy compares Saint-Exupéry's final flight on July 31, 1944, from which he never returned, to Christ on the Cross, leaving for the faithful a rule and a gospel in the form of his writings. "He mounted to Calvary after having known the anguish, the solitude and the little betrayals of great men." Another biographer, a lady friend, who wrote under the pseudonym Pierre Chevrier (1949), spoke of the "unrivaled radiance" of this "solitary knight" and with what might be termed a scrotal approach, ripped into those critics who failed to recognize Saint-Exupéry's *Citadelle* as a masterpiece, claiming that they constituted a "conspiracy of the impotent."

Like those painters whose self-portraits were deliberately fashioned to resemble Christ, Saint-Exupéry did little to discourage this deification. Far removed from the modest charm and sweetness of *The Little Prince* is the final section of *Pilote de Guerre* (*Flight to Arras*) which was written in a style that has led to its designation as his *Credo* or *Breviary*. "As the inheritor of God," he wrote, "my civilization made men equal in Man. . . . I understand for the first time one of the mysteries of the religion from whence comes the civilization I claim as mine: To bear the sins of man. Each man bears the sins of all men." In the final pages of his first novel, *Courrier Sud* (*Southern Mail*), the murdered body of the hero is found on the desert sands in the attitude of the crucifixion.[1] As for the unfinished work *Citadelle*, it is a rambling exercise in narcissism and megalomania, which, together with its quasi-Biblical language, smacks of religious grandiosity. Hints of an identification with God permeate this work, which is designed to represent a colloquy between a Berber chieftain and his son: "I am life and I control . . . I re-arm man so that he may *be* . . . I, the architect, I step in and mold the clay, which is the raw material, into the likeness of the creative vision that comes to me from God . . ."

As stated above, it would be agreeable to claim that, because of his training and clinical experience, the psychoanalytic biographer is immune to such seductive blandishments of his subject—agreeable, but untrue. Surely Freud (1936) was not excluding the psychoanalytic biographer when he wrote, "Anyone turning biographer commits himself to lies, to concealment, to hypocrisy, to flattery, and even to hiding his own lack of understanding, for biographical truth is not to be had, and even if it were it couldn't be used." Caught in the enticing romance of mythmaking or in the equally alluring trough of muckraking, the psychoanalytic biographer may reveal himself to be all too ready to abandon his nice psychoanalytic methodology and to scuttle his strict criteria for psychoanalytic validation.

Surely Hitschmann (1956) must have forgotten to lower his psychoanalytic centerboard when he went out sailing in search of Goethe and wrote: "There is no need to speak of Goethe's mother. Her forthright, cheerful nature, her soul, receptive to everything beautiful and good, her delightful letters—all this is well known to every educated person" (p. 126). Well-known it may be; but, true or not, these are not the data on which psychoanalysts place great reliance. By the same token, surely it was the combined hostility of Freud and Bullitt that contaminated their study of Wilson with the prejudice and reductionism that robbed their work of a potential for scholarship and importance.

To take still another example, despite his insistence on his own "psychoanalytic neutrality" and his psychological position of "proper equidistance" between his two subjects, Zeligs' (1967) impressive study of Alger Hiss and Whittaker Chambers leaves little doubt that, far from sitting like a passive juror

---

[1] Parenthetically it should be noted that, under circumstances that will be mentioned later, during his adolescence Saint-Exupéry abandoned the Catholic faith in which he had been reared.

impartially weighing evidence, he, like many of his readers, was possessed of some very distinct prejudices concerning the issue of guilt and innocence with which this great American drama of our times is richly imbued. No doubt it was largely such—highly understandable—prejudices that permitted Zeligs to believe that, in his spending many hours conversing with Hiss, he was collecting "analytic" data. In point of fact, although he regretted the fact that he was never able to interview Chambers, it is the portrait of the latter that emerges as a person of flesh and blood with three-dimensional credibility, while Hiss appears as a silhouette crayoned on cardboard. It is as if his two subjects had been viewed through markedly dissimilar optical instruments: the image of Chambers is seen through the illuminated magnification of the psychoanalytic miscroscope; that of Hiss, through the dimly lit medium of the naked eye.

There are, of course, several reasons for this discrepancy. First of all, the very fact that Zeligs approached Hiss in a personal and conversational attitude precluded the emergence of the kind of data with which a psychoanalyst works. It was indeed the availability of such data that made the Chambers portrait so much more alive, for Chambers was a literary person who furnished his biographer with a rich legacy of creative work, laden with hints and clues of those latent thoughts and fantasies that are indispensable for any biographical study written in depth. Neither an avowed poet nor artist, Hiss supplied his biographer with no such materials for analytic scrutiny.[2] Considerations of confidentiality and other ethical issues, moreover, subjected Zeligs' study of Hiss to severe limitations. It is indeed impossible to imagine that he could have dealt otherwise with his living subject; but that is not the issue. The salient point here is his apparent belief that he has treated his two subjects not only fairly equally, i.e., with "psychoanalytic neutrality," but with fairly similar psychoanalytic methods.

The consequences of the several pitfalls awaiting the psychoanalytic biographer are errors not merely of commission but of omission. Binion's (1968) biography of Lou Andreas-Salomé, for instance, is not merely an exercise in "wild" analysis; in his preoccupation with her charged-up obsession with famous men, he quite overlooks or minimizes the role of maternal influences both in his subject and in those who moved about her. An example of his strikingly disabling scotoma in this matter is his designating as "far-fetched" the claim that the poet Richard Beer-Hofmann's tendency to depression was related to the death of his mother when he was five days old. Anyone who can so easily dismiss the pathogenic effect of a mother's postpartum death cannot be very sensitive to a mother's role in the developmental history of the child. Under the circum-

---

[2] Although the poet is apt to tell us more about his inner world than the orator or the man of action, Freud, Erikson, and others have demonstrated that the contribution of psychoanalysis to biography is by no means limited to the life of the creative artist—if indeed it were possible to separate the latter from the rest of mankind. In actuality, the distinction is rather arbitrary and even untenable in some instances, for the poet has not always been a poet: in an earlier moment he has sometimes been a sailor, a flyer or a physician, and a psychoanalytically informed inquiry into that phase of his life may be just as rewarding as a study of his later artistic career.

stances, it is not surprising that Binion paid scant attention to the circumstances immediately preceding the two occasions when the childless Lou became pregnant, albeit briefly—namely, immediately after she had sustained an object loss. This sequence not only escapes the author's notice but once again underscores the impression that, where the mother-child interaction is concerned, he is too busy looking elsewhere to notice it.

Hitschmann displays a similar blind spot. In his study of Samuel Johnson (1956) he quite ignores the latter's patent mental anguish concerning his mother—which will be discussed later on—and, in keeping with his uncritical comments about Goethe's mother, ascribes Johnson's emotional troubles solely to a hatred of his father, which he views as arising in the oedipus complex. It is indeed remarkable how Hitschmann succeeded in evading the very obvious problem of Johnson and his mother and other maternal figures. Thus, although it is asserted that as an infant he was infected with scrofula by a tuberculous nurse, it is the "miserly" father who is blamed for having hired her (p. 258).

Granted then that countertransference and other psychological booby traps may trip up the psychoanalytic biographer, when he can divest himself sufficiently of his private biases to view his subject with relative objectivity, he can indeed contribute significantly to the goal of "making sense out of the vast deal that we do know." Toward the attainment of this goal one of the most valued qualifications is the analyst's unusual aptitude for paying meticulous attention to what he sees and hears; a second is his habitual reluctance to accept what he sees and hears at face value.

Of the many biographers of Saint-Exupéry, for example, no one appears to have noticed or to have been much troubled by a slip of the pen in the text of *Pilote de Guerre* and in its English translation *Flight to Arras*. In his chilling account of his experiences as a reconnaissance flyer during the disastrous days of the French debacle in May 1940, Saint-Exupéry alluded to the death of his younger brother, François, many years before, stating that at that time he himself was fifteen years old. In actual fact, he had been seventeen; it was François who was fifteen. It was at about that time too that Saint-Exupéry forsook the Catholic faith. That a strong element of guilt was contained in this patent identification with a dead brother seems inescapable; it would go far to account for a number of striking personal characteristics—namely, a severe tendency toward depression and hypochondriasis, a marked penchant for self-destructiveness,[3] and recurring expressions of doubts about his right to live.

Nor have his biographers paid much heed to the early and largely unexplained death of his forty-year-old father when Antoine was but four years old. In the eyes of an analyst, it is not surprising that as he grew into manhood he was drawn to Nietzsche, and displayed a strong tendency toward hero worship and an attraction for the kind of powerful man whom he fashioned fictionally in

[3] "When the flight is normal," wrote one of his flying comrades, "St.-Ex. is dangerous; amid complications, he becomes brilliant" (Chevrier, 1949, p. 76).

the person of Rivière, the stern and autocratic chief of the airline service who is the hero of his novel *Vol de Nuit* (*Night Flight*): "Rivière the Great, Rivière the Conqueror." Anticipating by some years the megalomania of *Citadelle*, Rivière regards man as a mere lump of wax to be kneaded into shape. ". . . it was his task to furnish this dead matter with a soul, to inject will power into it . . . to raise (his men) above themselves." In contrast to André Gide, who signalized his high regard for *Vol de Nuit* by writing its foreword, Clifton Fadiman (1932) found it a dangerous book and saw Rivière as "a sick man, a rotting man, like all men who are fascinated by the spectacle of pure power and pure efficiency divorced from beneficial ends." It is not surprising that there were doubts from time to time about Saint-Exupéry's attitude toward totalitarianism and that he seems to have been a bit slow in making up his mind about Hitler. It seems equally plausible to conclude that his ambivalence toward the strong leader played at least a contributory role in his implacable hostility toward de Gaulle (Cate, 1970).

However much attention to such details may contribute to the artist's biography, no claim is advanced that they enhance or detract from an appreciation of his art. Beethoven's genius survives the Sterbas' informative study, and if Phyllis Greenacre's work on Lewis Carroll suggests that Alice was a sort of desexualized Lolita for the Reverend Dodgson, that does not lessen her appeal by one scintilla. As for the Reverend—it simply makes him a bit more human. "Psychoanalysis does not strive to blacken the radiant and to drag the sublime into the mire," wrote Freud (1910). "It finds no satisfaction in diminishing the distance between the perfection of the great and the inadequacy of ordinary objects. But it cannot help finding that everything is worthy of understanding that can be perceived through these prototypes, and it also believes that none is so big as to be ashamed of being subject to the laws which control normal and morbid actions with the same strictness."

On the subject of the contribution that psychoanalysis might make to an understanding of genius, Freud was equally unambiguous. Before the problem of the creative artist, he wrote, analysis must lay down its arms (1928). Such studies as Marie Bonaparte's *Life of Edgar Allan Poe*, he declared, were not "meant to explain the genius of a poet, but to show the motifs which have stirred it up, and the topics imposed upon it by fate" (1933). Put in a somewhat different way, it may be said that, while genius as such lies beyond the grasp of psychoanalytic understanding, those various forces that facilitate or hinder the emergence of that gift do not. It may be foolish to attempt to account for the phenomenon called Mozart, but surely it is not foolish to seek out those psychological influences that may have determined the vicissitudes of his creative life. It is about that flowering and wilting that I now wish to speak, for no one conversant with the history of art can ignore the fact that, despite the richness of their endowment, many creative persons have exhibited marked variations both in the quality and in the quantity of their productions.

It is generally acknowledged, for example, that after 1910 there was a pronounced decline in the literary artistry of Joseph Conrad, in spite of, or parallel with, the fact that from that moment on he became a commercial success. His deterioration has been variously ascribed to physical and mental fatigue, financial worries, isolation from his friends, a tendency for this Polish emigré to speak in broken English, his being married to a "lump of a wife" and so on. The most casual attention to any of these explanations, however, quickly reveals their inadequacy, for the conditions they describe were essentially the same during the period of Conrad's artistic zenith, which corresponded roughly with the previous decade—1900–1910. There was, however, one conspicuous difference in his life after 1910, and that concerned his relationship with Ford Madox Hueffer (Ford), which in that seemingly fateful year came to an abrupt halt, coincident with Hueffer's leaving his wife for another woman and with Conrad's suffering a serious mental breakdown. It was indeed the seemingly enriching influence that Hueffer bestowed upon Conrad, that, borrowing an expression from the latter, prompted me to refer to Hueffer as Conrad's "Secret Sharer." "The artist descends into himself," wrote Conrad, "and in that lonely region of stress and strife, if he be deserving and fortunate, he finds the terms of his appeal." Fortunate he had been before 1910, when, secure in the company of the "inseparable partner of his existence," he could make that descent and discover within the depths of his imagination a vein rich in the gold that he could transmute into literary masterpieces.

"It is a fact," wrote Conrad to Hueffer (Baines, 1960), "I work better in your home, in touch with your sympathy," and for all her undisguised hostility toward Hueffer, Conrad's wife Jessie (1935) freely acknowledged the importance of his influence in encouraging her husband to write. A biological cast to this "secret sharing" is suggested by her allusion to the novel *Romance*, one of the three collaborative works of her husband and Hueffer, as the "child of their joint fabrication." A similar meaning is implied in Hueffer's (1932) account of how he would coax Conrad to keep on writing: "I would manoeuvre him towards the writing as the drake manoeuvres the sitting duck back to the nest when she has abandoned her eggs." The force of the allusion to parturition is hardly lessened by the report (Mencken, 1925) that Mrs. Conrad responded to Hueffer's later claims by denouncing him "as a cuckoo, shamelessly laying eggs in her husband's nest."

Impressed both by the germinative effect that Hueffer seemingly exerted upon Conrad's creativity and by the biological metaphor in which it was expressed, I have sought for other examples of "secret sharing" among creative persons. A striking parallel to the Conrad-Hueffer partnership can be discerned in the relationship between Hawthorne and Melville, wherein among other similarities to the former pair there was also an age difference of about fifteen years. As was the case with Conrad, moreover, Melville's greatest work, *Moby-Dick*, was composed during the height of the period of "secret sharing." Especially noteworthy is the fact that, before the establishment of this acquaintanceship, Melville had written an earlier draft, which, utterly unlike the final tragic apocalytic drama, had been designed to be a simple whaling story (Vincent, 1949). The final version—what Melville called "an evil book"—was understandably dedicated to Hawthorne. Reminiscent too of Hueffer's drake-and-duck formulation of his influence on Conrad is Melville's astonishing account of Hawthorne's effect on him: "Already I feel that this Hawthorne has dropped germinous seeds into my soul. He expands and deepens down, the more I contemplate him; and further and further, shoots his strong New England roots into the hot soil of my Southern soul"[4] (Arvin, 1957).

Another remarkable example of secret sharing has been provided by Beres (1951) in his scholarly and sensitive essay on Coleridge, Wordsworth, and *The Rime of the Ancient Mariner*. Following the separate psychological skeins of the two poets, Beres demonstrates how, although the writing of the poem—save for two lines—was the work of Coleridge, the final tapestry was indeed woven of the thoughts and feelings of the two men. It was planned together during a walk, and although Coleridge supplied the greater part of the story, the idea of the albatross and its destruction—surely a key theme in the poem—was Wordsworth's. With especial clarity, moreover, Beres shows how this single poem, jointly conceived, served to convey the separate emotional needs of each contributor. Of the mutual relationship between the two men, perhaps the most compelling evidence is a poem, "Dejection, An Ode," written by Coleridge on the occasion of Wordsworth's marriage:[5]

> A grief without a pang, void, dark, and drear,
> A stifled, drowsy, unimpassioned grief,
> Which finds no natural outlet, no relief,
> In word, or sigh, or tear—

Indeed, once pursued, the impression grows that, secret or not, some sort of sharing plays a common if not invariable role in the creative process. "Though it is a commonplace that genius cannot be accounted for," wrote Steegmuller (1949) in his biography of Maupassant, "there is less wonder about the *flowering* of [his] genius than about many another." Conspicuous among the forces promoting that flowering was Gustave Flaubert, who supplied both personal and professional devotion. "Such circumstances," continued Steegmuller, "were a hot-house, a forcing-bed, for genius." It must not be supposed, moreover, that Maupassant took all and gave nothing in return. Thirty years younger, he provided the unmarried and childless Flaubert with a protégé and a disciple, filling a void at a time when Flaubert was suffering keenly over a succession of deaths of friends and literary colleagues.

Similar considerations surely apply to many creative persons whose names

---

[4] What prompted him to speak of his soul as "Southern" is a mystery. His family came from New England and from the Hudson Valley in New York.
[5] Coleridge's severe depression in these circumstances is reminiscent of Conrad's reaction to his friend Hueffer's similar defection, as noted above.

are habitually linked with another: Johnson-Boswell,[6] Gilbert-Sullivan. In my clinical practice I have been able to view members of such pairs at close range and I have been particularly struck by the elaborate activities of these ducks and drakes and the remarkable complementary quality of their interactions.

No less striking than the vicissitudes in the *quality* of the artist's work are the marked variations in the apparent *quantity* of his available creative energy. For some, the major source of inspiration is the monthly rent bill; for others it may be a deadline. "Wait until the eve of the performance," Rossini once advised a young composer on how to write an overture. "Nothing stimulates the inspiration more than sheer necessity, the presence of a copyist who is waiting for your work, and the insistence of a frantic impresario who is tearing out his hair" (Robinson). In other cases the problem seems more complicated. Except for two minor works, Paul Dukas, the composer of the world-famous *Sorcerer's Apprentice,* published nothing during the last 23 years of his life. Although he continued to compose, he destroyed virtually everything he wrote. On the other hand, there are composers and writers whose creative output resembles the steady flow of time and tide and who, in season and out, continue to produce great and sometimes even greater works, virtually until their day of death.

There are other instances, however, in which it seems possible to discern specific influences that have transformed a dormant creative potential into a sudden and irresistible burst of artistic activity.

Once again an example from Conrad is informative. For some four and a half years before the beginning of the year 1894, he had been intermittently at work, eking out in a limping, desultory fashion what was destined to be his first novel, *Almayer's Folly.* And then, quite suddenly it seemed, it became the focus of all his energies, prompting him to declare that he regretted every moment spent away from his writing. In the space of some eight short weeks, the work was completed, and on April 24 he wrote to a friend: "I have the painful duty of announcing to you the death of Mr. Kaspar Almayer, which took place at 3 o'clock this morning." What had wrought the change, suddenly furnishing him with this unaccustomed access of energy? Death, it would seem: for in February he had received word from Poland that his devoted Uncle, Thaddeus Bobrowski, brother of his dead mother, his guardian and sole surviving relative, had died. It affected him profoundly, he asserted, causing him to declare: "He seems to have taken my soul away with him." Yet, despite his melancholy, Conrad appears to have reacted to his loss as if it could be canceled out by an act of creation. Art, it would seem, had triumphed over death and, like the Taj Mahal, that architectural poem enveloping the dusty bones of an Oriental princess, served as a denial of the importance of corporeal death and as an affirmation of the enduring vitality of the creative human spirit. Surely it was no caprice that caused Conrad

---

[6] Boswell needed celebrities, observed Copeland (1949). "Nothing is clearer after reading the journal than the degree to which he distrusted his own moral and psychological strength and struggled to appropriate the strength of famous and powerful people." (These comments, incidentally, are equally applicable to Conrad.)

to dedicate this first work to his faithful uncle; in doing so, he linked both together to make it abundantly clear that, like a grateful monument, his book would serve as a *memento mori*.[7]

Somewhat similar circumstances accompanied the writing of *Rasselas*, one of the best-known fictional works of Samuel Johnson. Some 250 pages in length, it was written, according to the author's report (Krutch, 1944), in the nights of the single week that followed the death of his aged mother on January 23, 1759, allegedly to defray the costs of the funeral. Whether the latter was indeed the guiding factor is questionable. Apparently Johnson had had little difficulty in borrowing money on other occasions from time to time and, not long before his mother's death, he had paid off the mortgage on her home. Although the question must remain unanswered, it is only of academic interest, for the main issue is the fact that for one reason or another his mother's death had acted as a spur to this creative outburst.[8]

Johnson was plainly guilty about his conduct toward his mother, whom he had left in his native Lichfield in 1737, when he was 27 years old. Although she continued to live there for another 22 years, until she was about 90, he never saw her again. All this time he was living in London, a mere 120 miles away. A few days before her death, he sent her a sum of money and thanked her for her indulgence toward him, begging her forgiveness for "all [he had] done ill, and all [he had] omitted to do well" (Krutch, p. 172). Some years before, while turning the key to his chamber, he thought he had heard her calling him. One might assume that his need to do penance became even more urgent after her death, and that the sudden access of creative energy that became available to him provided him with the means of doing so. It is noteworthy that he began to visit Lichfield a year or so later and that thereafter he was to make a sort of annual pilgrimage to that place.

As for the literary work that followed so swiftly upon her death, it is a kind of philosophical fable, pervaded by a mood of melancholy and by allusions to separation, reunion, and death. Rasselas is an Abyssinian prince, who, like his predecessors, is obliged to live in a palace, which is situated in a region that, surrounded by lofty and impassable mountains, is cut off from the rest of the world. Known as *The Happy Valley*, it can be entered only by a secret passage traversing a cavern whose outlet is concealed by a thick wood, and whose mouth, opening into the valley, is closed with gates of iron. (To a friend Johnson announced his mother's death, stating that "the life which made my own pleasant is at an end, and the *gates are shut* upon my prospects.") From the mountains

---

[7] The antidotal function of the novel is further emphasized by the likelihood that Conrad's announcement of the death of Almayer was a paraphrase of the message he had received some weeks before from Poland.

[8] It was not the first time he had responded to death in this manner: in 1743, shortly after the death of his friend Richard Savage, Johnson set out to write the story of his life; according to his own account, he wrote 48 pages in one sitting, staying up all night long to do so. Savage, it should be observed, lived in the grip of a violent hatred of his mother, whose alleged maltreatment of her son was uncritically believed by Johnson (Krutch, p. 80).

on all sides "are rivulets that descended, filling all the valley with verdure and fertility, and formed a lake in the middle. This lake discharged its superfluities by a stream which entered a dark cleft of the mountain on the northern side and fell with dreadful noise from precipice to precipice till it was heard no more." As for the iron gate, it was opened but once a year when, to the sound of music, the emperor visited his children for a period of eight days.

Despite the seeming contentment of most of the inhabitants, the prince spends a good amount of time in solitude and, not long after his twenty-sixth year, he begins to plot his escape. Ultimately, after digging a tunnel, he, in the company of his philosopher friend Imlac, his sister, and her companion, succeeds in gaining the outside world. Unfortunately, here again all is melancholy and misery, and in their wanderings they are repeatedly confronted by reminders of death. They visit tombs and pyramids and catacombs, and they come upon a man in despair over the death of a daughter. Finally they return to the Happy Valley.

In light of the explicit allusion to a claustrum and to the highly suggestive gynecomorphous symbolisms of the Happy Valley, it is not to be wondered at that claustrophobic and claustrophilic manifestations, notably in relation to women, can be discovered both in *Rasselas* and in the mental make-up of its creator. Moreover, whatever philosophical or other meanings may reside in this romantic fable, neither the timing of its writing nor the nature of its content leave any doubt that *Rasselas* is a literary requiem for the mother whom he had long ago abandoned—at the same age, incidentally, as Prince Rasselas, when the latter escaped from the fertile confines of the Happy Valley.[9] It should be added that, not long before he left Lichfield and his mother, Johnson had married a widow nearly twice his age.

For another and in some respects a similar example of the influence of bereavement upon the creative act, I am indebted to Marcel Heiman's (1959) excellent study of *Rip Van Winkle*. Here again the death of the writer's mother appears to have provided an important stimulus for a creative work, although a period of psychic depression intervened between the death of Washington Irving's mother and the writing of the story. Like Johnson, Irving too had been away from his mother for an extended interval—two years—at the time of her death, and he would not return to his native America for another fifteen. It had been a "hard parting with [his] poor old mother," he wrote when he left New York for his long stay in Europe (Williams, 1935, p. 144). Like *Rasselas,* Irving's story deals obliquely with death and with rebirth too, with escape from a confining existence and with the attainment of an ultimate reunion.

That death and grief have inspired Requiems and other musical compositions needs no documentation. A particularly poignant example is provided by the writing of the violin concerto of Alban Berg, which had been commissioned

---

[9] Speaking in behalf of the fetus about to be born, Oliver Wendell Holmes wrote:
 Tired of the prison where his legs were curled,
 He pants, like Rasselas, for a wider world.
 Contrariwise, I have been told that in Hong Kong there is a cemetery named The Happy Valley. I daresay there may be others bearing the same name.

early in 1935, when the composer was still working on his opera *Lulu*. For some time he found himself unable to settle on the form the concerto was to take, and he found himself bogged down in that state of inertia that is all too well known among creative artists: Baudelaire called it *"les sterilités des ecrivains nerveux."* And then in April an event occurred that was deeply disturbing to him—the sudden death from poliomyelitis of Manon Gropius, the eighteen-year-old daughter of Alma Mahler. Remarkably beautiful, she was also a promising actress, whom Max Reinhardt had cast in the role of an angel in his *Grosses Welttheater* in Salzburg. Berg was overcome by grief; yet in a short while he suddenly found a unifying form of his concerto, which he plunged into at a feverish pitch unknown to him before.

In the work, which was dedicated to the "memory of an angel" and named "Requiem for Manon," he sought to depict a "musical vision" of the character of the dead girl (Reich, 1944). Early in August he told his friend Webern that he was writing "like a madman," in order to finish the work by the middle of the month. This indeed he did, but at about the same time he was attacked by wasps which, it is claimed, stung him some 20 to 30 times. Berg had suffered recurrently from furunculosis, and on this occasion he again developed an abscess and presumably blood poisoning. During the remainder of the year he underwent a number of surgical procedures, and on Christmas eve, one week after the last attempt to discover the source of the suppuration, he died. The opera *Lulu*, which he had set aside to write the Requiem, remained unfinished. For whom, indeed, was the Requiem-concerto written—for the young Manon, for himself, or was it to commemorate a kind of union attained by dying together? [10]

To be sure, there are innumerable instances wherein the seeming antinomy between creativity and death concerns the death of the creator himself. There may be more poetry than truth in the claim that Mozart composed his D Minor Requiem in anticipation of his impending death, writing in a frenzy night and day to complete it before the arrival of the "mysterious stranger" who had commissioned it; but something very akin to that apocryphal tale did occur during the fatal illness—leukemia—of the Hungarian composer Béla Bartók. As he languished despondently in a hospital bed, a sudden breath of energy was bestowed upon him by the unexpected visit, not of a mysterious stranger, but of Serge Koussevitzky, who offered him a commission to write a piece for the Boston Symphony Orchestra. The effect was electric: one day later, according to his biographer, he was home again and "an enormous change seemed to have taken place—as if the entire center of his being had been restored and reawakened" (Fassett, 1958).

This was not the only occasion when Bartók combatted the ravages of his illness with his creative power. Indeed, although it had been feared that his emigration to America in 1940 would spell the end of his career as a composer, matters turned out quite differently. During the last four disease-ridden years of

---

[10] It is not amiss to mention an attempted suicide by Berg at the age of eighteen, ostensibly following an unhappy love affair (Reich, 1963).

his life, besides the Concerto for Orchestra commissioned by Koussevitzky, Bartók completed two other major works and left sketches for a Viola Concerto. His last completed work, the Third Piano Concerto, was finally scored save for the last seventeen bars. "Bartók worked feverishly to the very last to complete the Concerto," wrote his friend and colleague Tibor Serly, "and it was touching to note that he had prematurely scrawled in pencil the Hungarian word vége—'the end'—on the last bar of his sketch copy, as though he were desperately aiming to reach it. On no other score had he ever written the word."

A clinical depiction of the way in which art may serve to stave off death was presented some years ago by Dr. Richard S. Blacher and me (Meyer and Blacher, 1960). Our patient was a young woman who had been admitted to the psychiatric service of the Mount Sinai Hospital because of a depression that appeared in the final weeks of a planned but out-of-wedlock pregnancy. This was the latest venture of this volatile, restless, impulsive, and often melancholic person, whose life had been marked by a series of short-lived artistic careers: modeling, painting, sculpture, acting, singing, writing poetry and fiction, and photography. Our suspicion that all these creative undertakings, including the pregnancy, were expressions of a struggle to combat an irresistible appeal of death, was supported by the plot of a short story—"The Long Journey"—she had sketched: *A lonely spinster decided to take her life, but before committing the final act she undertook to construct her own coffin. To her surprise she found herself remarkably skilled in cabinet work, and when it was finished she proceeded to carve the exterior. Once again she discovered an unsuspected talent, and, caught up in the excitement over her new found gift, she laid aside her thought of suicide and began to turn out one figure after another. Now her work was beginning to become known and plans were made to hold a "one-man" show. Alas, on the brink of success, as she went about feverishly making final arrangements, she took a fateful misstep: as she rushed to the gallery, she ran heedlessly into the street, where she was struck by a vehicle and killed.*

Like her fictional heroine, our patient too was but temporarily protected by her creative thrusts. With the approach of her confinement she became increasingly despondent and, when she believed she was about to go into labor, she cried out in desperation: "It's too soon! Too soon! I'll be empty!"

Her words carry a familiar ring. "At present I am undergoing the depression which always follows publication," wrote Frederick Rolfe, after he had concluded *Hadrian the Seventh* (A. J. A. Symons, 1966). "A piece of Me has been taken from me. I have the limpness of a brand new mother. After the usual interval, Nature will enable me to replace what I have exuded" (p. 175). And although it has probably rarely been formulated in such patently biological and gynecological terms, the occurrence of a "post-(p)artum depression" is an exceedingly common experience among creative artists.

In contrast, those who have been literally or figuratively bereft of "a piece of themselves" are sometimes seized by a driving passion to recreate or replace it. I am indebted to a colleague for telling me the story of a man in his mid-eighties who, for the first time in his life, became a creative artist. Like the

Phoenix rising from the ashes, this man's art was born in a cradle of gangrene and dismemberment, for he was afflicted by a circulatory disturbance that necessitated a succession of amputations, beginning with his great toe and ultimately involving the entire limb below the hip. Not surprisingly, he reacted to this progressive scuttling of his body with melancholy and a sense of hopelessness that made caring for him exceedingly burdensome. One day, in desperation, his daughter offered him some drawing and coloring materials and, miraculously, he became a painter, and a good one too. Stylistically primitive, like Grandma Moses, he possessed much of the same liveliness and charm, but instead of New England his pictures were scenes from the Old Testament and recollections of his Polish childhood. The quantity of his output was phenomenal, and not a few of his works were acquired by first-rate museums and galleries. It was asserted that during his brief but meteoric artistic career—he died in his late eighties—despite the physical mutilation, he had experienced a *joie de vivre* he had never known before.[11]

Just as trees are planted in memory of the dead, so may men convalescing from a life-threatening condition, say, coronary thrombosis, unexpectedly impregnate their wives and strongly resist any suggestion that this unplanned-for reaffirmation of life be aborted. All psychoanalysts are familiar with the frequency with which impregnation of hitherto childless women may follow upon the death of a parent or a parent of the spouse. And like Conrad's first literary creation, the children conceived in this atmosphere of grief and bereavement are often named for, that is to say, dedicated to, the person whose death has given them life. Some tombstones, notably in Oriental countries, are equipped with a hollowed-out drinking place for birds:

> For each age is an age that is dying,
> Or one that is coming to birth.

The foregoing thoughts concerning certain aspects of the creative process are advanced as tempting but unproven hypotheses. No claim is offered that the partnership styled "secret sharing" is an unvarying characteristic of creative artists, nor is it suggested that the redistribution of psychic energy that is the *sine qua non* of inspiration is the invariable consequence of object loss. Indeed, even where the latter does seem to be the immediate stimulus for an onrush of the forces of the creative imagination, it is not always clear what psychic mechanisms are at work. In the example of Samuel Johnson, guilt and the need to make amends to a much-neglected mother suggest that an outraged superego goaded him into a condition of literary servitude of a week's duration, not unlike the

---

[11] In a paper published in 1967, Niederland mentioned the restitutive aspects of creativity and gave a number of clinical examples, of which the most dramatic concerned a 25-year-old victim of poliomyelitis whose seemingly lethal course was halted by utilizing what little muscle power remained in one hand in successfully inducing him to draw.

abuse and enslavement that, at a later period in his life, he evidently sought at the hands of another "mother," Hester Thrale (Balderston, 1949). In other instances, grief more than guilt, and fear more than grief, appear to supply the motive power that unleashes the forces of the creative mind.

Here, as in all hypotheses concerning human behavior, and notably in the sphere of artistic creativity, it would appear rash and reckless to seek for general formulas: poems, like babies, are conceived for a variety of motives, and the emotional states that accompany the period of their gestation range from a beatific assurance of God's love and protection to a smoldering fire of fury and hatred. It has been asserted that the creative act serves as a restitution of lost or damaged objects, and there is good evidence that sometimes this is so. Yet, for his depiction of Emma, Bovary, Flaubert was accused of using his pen as though it were a scalpel, recalling the assertion of Degas that the artist must approach his work in the same frame of mind in which the criminal commits his deed, and this is also evidently true—sometimes. Yet it would seem quite unlikely that so universal an activity as painting, for example, or one like storytelling, which is begun so early in the course of each individual life, could possess a single psychic significance. It would appear more plausible to view the creative impulse as comparable to a biological function, like breathing or urinating, which under certain circumstances may become the vehicle for a host of psychological meanings, and consequently subject to wide fluctuations of functioning.

Seen in this light, it may be profitable to inquire into the peculiar circumstances that have surrounded the birth of a given creative work, and while it may be quite appropriate to conclude that the writing of the D Minor Requiem was indeed fostered by Mozart's awareness of his impending death, it surely does not follow that the vast and endless stream that gushed from this magical source—from the age of five years on—represented a sublimated expression of either a drive to effect the restoration of persons destroyed in fantasy, or a wish to destroy them once more. On the contrary, when one surveys this seeming inexhaustible flood of wondrous beauty, or the endless flow of deathless riches poured forth by the Bachs, the Titians, the Verdis, and by all those who, in the words of Cyril Connolly, feel "too old to die" and hence attain a fruitful senescence, one gains the impression that, rather than dealing with drive and defense, the process has the inherent quality of an autonomous ego function, uncontaminated by conflict. Courbet's paintings, it was asserted, dropped from his palette as naturally and abundantly as applies from a tree.

It is not enough to know the past, wrote Paul Claudel; it is necessary to understand it. Surely this is no less true of individual human history, and psychoanalysis can often serve as an indispensable instrument for understanding it.

In the foregoing pages, I have sought to explore its scope in the field of biography and to show how, in the interest of precision, it may aid in sifting myth from fact; how, in seeking to explore the mysteries of human motivation, it can aid in distinguishing *good* reasons from *real* ones; and how, in the study of creative genius, it may aid in discovering those subtle influences that facilitate or hinder its expression. Employed with a serious regard for its value and at the same time with a modest respect for its limitations, psychoanalysis may contribute greatly to the recreation of what Conrad called a "coherent and justifiable personality," and to the historian's goal of making sense out of the vast deal that we know.

REFERENCES

Arvin, N. (1957). *Herman Melville.* New York: Viking.

Baines, J. (1960). *Joseph Conrad, A Critical Biography.* London: Weidenfeld and Nicolson.

Balderston, K. C. (1949). Johnson's Vile Melancholy. In: *Essays Presented to Chauncey B. Tinker.* New Haven: Yale University Press.

Beres, D. (1951). A Dream, a Vision and a Poem. *International Journal of Psycho-Analysis,* 32:97–116.

Binion, R. (1968). *Frau Lou. Nietzsche's Wayward Disciple.* Princeton: Princeton University Press.

Cate, C. (1970). *Antoine de Saint-Exupéry.* New York: Putnam.

Chevrier, P. (1949). *Antoine de Saint-Exupéry.* Paris: Gallimard.

Conrad, Jessie (1935). *Joseph Conrad and His Circle.* New York: Dutton.

Copeland, T. W. (1949). Boswell's Portrait of Burke. In: *Essays Presented to Chauncey B. Tinker.* New Haven: Yale University Press.

Fadiman, C. (1932). The Fetish of Duty. *The Nation,* Sept. 7. pp. 215–216.

Fassett, A. (1958). *The Naked Face of Genius.* Boston: Houghton Mifflin.

Freud, S. (1910). Leonardo Da Vinci and a Memory of His Childhood. *Standard Edition,* 21:59–137. London: Hogarth Press, 1957.

––––––– (1911). Psycho-Analytic Notes on an Autobiographical Account of a Case of Paranoia (Dementia Paranoides). *Standard Edition,* 12:3–82. London: Hogarth Press, 1958.

––––––– (1928). Dostoevsky and Parricide. *Standard Edition,* 21:175–196. London: Hogarth Press, 1961.

––––––– (1933). Preface to Marie Bonaparte's *The Life and Works of Edgar Allan Poe. Standard Edition,* 22:254. London: Hogarth Press, 1964.

––––––– (1936). Letter to Arnold Zweig, May 31 (Letter #285). In: *Letters of Sigmund Freud,* ed. Ernest L. Freud. New York: Basic Books, 1960.

Heiman, M. (1959). Rip Van Winkle: A Psychoanalytic Note on the Story and Its Author. *American Imago,* 16:1–47.

Hitschmann, E. (1956). *Great Men.* New York: International Universities Press.

Hueffer, F. M. (1932). *Return to Yesterday.* New York: Horace Liveright.

Kohut, H. (1960). Beyond the Bounds of the Basic Rule. *Journal of the American Psychoanalytic Association,* 8:567–86.

Krutch, J. W. (1944). *Samuel Johnson.* New York: Henry Holt.

Mencken, H. L. (1925). The Conrad Wake. *American Mercury,* 4:505.

Meyer, B. C., and Blacher, R. S. (1960). The Creative Impulse—Biologic and Artistic Aspects. In: *The Psychoanalytic Study of Society,* Vol. 1, ed. W. Muensterberger and S. Axelrad. New York: International Universities Press, pp. 251–271.

Muller, H. (1952). *The Uses of the Past.* New York: Oxford University Press.

Niederland, W. G. (1967). Clinical Aspects of Creativity. *American Imago,* 24 (1 & 2):6–34.

Reich, W. (1944). Alban Berg. In: *Grove's Dictionary of Music and Musicians—Supplementary Volume.* New York: Macmillan, pp. 38–42.

––––––– (1963). *Alban Berg.* New York: Harcourt, Brace and World.

Robinson, F. The Barber: Neat but Unshaven. In: *RCA–Victor* recording of The Barber of Seville, #LM6143.

Roy, J. (1964). *Passion et Mort de Saint-Exupéry*. Paris: René Julliard.

Serly, T. Quoted on jacket of recording by Columbia of *Concerto* #3 of Bartok, #LM 4239.

Steegmuller, F. (1949). *Maupassant: A Lion in the Path*. New York: Grosset and Dunlap.

Sterba, E., and Sterba, R. (1954). *Beethoven and His Nephew*. New York: Pantheon.

Symons, A. J. A. (1966). *The Quest for Corvo*. Baltimore: Penguin.

Symons, J. (1966). The Author and the Quest. In: *The Quest for Corvo*, A. J. A. Symons. Baltimore: Penguin, pp. 9–12.

Vincent, H. P. (1949). *The Trying-Out of Moby Dick*. Boston: Houghton Mifflin.

Williams, S. J. (1935). *The Life of Washington Irving*, Vol. 1. New York: Oxford University Press.

Zeligs, M. (1967). *Fraternity and Fratricide: An Analysis of Whittaker Chambers and Alger Hiss*. New York: Viking.

NAME INDEX